hand**book**

KEY NOTES | TERMS
DEFINITIONS | FORMULAE

Chemistry

Highly Useful for Class XI & XII Students, Engineering
& Medical Entrances and Other Competitions

hand**book**

KEY NOTES | TERMS
DEFINITIONS | FORMULAE

Chemistry

Highly Useful for Class XI & XII Students, Engineering
& Medical Entrances and Other Competitions

Preeti Gupta
Supported by
Saleha Khan
Shahana Ansari

ARIHANT PRAKASHAN, (SERIES) MEERUT

✿ arihant
Arihant Prakashan (Series), Meerut
All Rights Reserved

ꖷ **Administrative & Production Offices**

Regd. Office
'Ramchhaya' 4577/15, Agarwal Road, Darya Ganj, New Delhi -110002
Tele: 011- 47630600, 43518550; Fax: 011- 23280316

Head Office
Kalindi, TP Nagar, Meerut (UP) - 250002
Tele: 0121-2401479, 2512970, 4004199; Fax: 0121-2401648

ꖷ **Sales & Support Offices**

Agra, Ahmedabad, Bengaluru, Bareilly, Chennai, Delhi, Guwahati, Hyderabad, Jaipur, Jhansi, Kolkata, Lucknow, Meerut, Nagpur & Pune

ꖷ **ISBN** : 978-93-13196-49-5

ꖷ **Price** : ₹ 295.00

PO No. : TXT-59-T050687-12-22

Published by Arihant Publications (India) Ltd.

For further information about the books published by Arihant
log on to **www.arihantbooks.com** or email to **info@arihantbooks.com**

❶/arihantpub 🄴/@arihantpub ▶ Arihant Publications ◉ /arihantpub

PREFACE

Handbook means reference book listing brief facts on a subject. So, to facilitate the students in this we have released this **Handbook of Chemistry** this book has been prepared to serve the special purpose of the students, to rectify any query or any concern point of a particular subject.

This book will be of highly use whether students are looking for a quick revision before the board exams or just before other examinations like Engineering Entrances, Medical Entrances or any similar examination, they will find that this handbook will answer their needs admirably.

This handbook can even be used for revision of a subject in the time between two shift of the exams, even this handbook can be used while travelling to Examination Centre or whenever you have time, less sufficient or more.

The format of this handbook has been developed particularly so that it can be carried around by the students conveniently.

The objectives of publishing this handbook are :

- To support students in their revision of a subject just before an examination.
- To provide a focus to students to clear up their doubts about particular concepts which were not clear to them earlier.
- To give confidence to the students just before they attempt important examinations.

However, we have put our best efforts in preparing this book, but if any error or what so ever has been skipped out, we will by heart welcome your suggestions. A part from all those who helped in the compilation of this book a special note of thanks goes to Ms. Shivani of Arihant Publications.

Author

CONTENTS

1

Basic Concepts of Chemistry

Chemistry

It is the branch of science which deals with the composition, structure and properties of matter.

Antoine Laurent Lavoisier is called the father of chemistry.

Branches of Chemistry

```
Chemistry ─┬─ Inorganic chemistry is concerned with the study of
           │  elements (other than carbon) and their compounds.
           │
           ├─ Organic chemistry is the branch of chemistry which is
           │  concerned with organic compounds or substances
           │  produced by living organisms.
           │
           ├─ Physical chemistry is concerned with the explanation of
           │  fundamental principles.
           │
           └─ Analytical chemistry is the branch of chemistry which is
              concerned with qualitative and quantitative analysis of
              chemical substances.
```

In addition to these, biochemistry, war chemistry, nuclear chemistry, forensic chemistry, earth chemistry etc., are other branches of chemistry.

Matter

Anything which occupies some space and has some mass is called matter. It is made up of small particles which have space between them. The matter particles attract each other and are in a state of continuous motion.

Classification of Matter

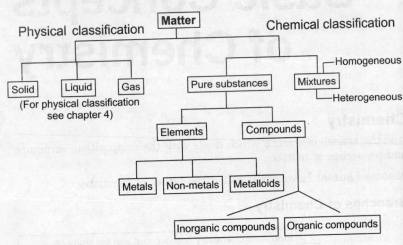

Pure Substances

They have characteristics different from the mixtures. They have fixed composition, whereas mixtures may contain the components in any ratio and their composition is variable.

Elements

It is the simplest form of pure substance, which can neither be decomposed nor be built from simpler substances by ordinary physical and chemical methods. It contains only one kind of atoms. The number of elements known till date is 118.

An element can be a metal, a non-metal or a metalloid.

Hydrogen is the most abundant element in the universe.
Oxygen (46.6%), a non-metal, is the most abundant element in the earth crust.
Al is the most abundant metal in the earth crust.

Compounds

It is also the form of matter which can be formed by combining two or more elements in a definite ratio by mass. It can be decomposed into its constituent elements by suitable chemical methods, e.g. water (H_2O) is made of hydrogen and oxygen in the ratio 1 : 8 by mass.

Compounds can be of two types :

(i) **Inorganic compounds** Previously, it was believed that these compounds are derived from non-living sources, like rocks and minerals. But these are infact the compounds of all the elements except hydrides of carbon (hydrocarbons) and their derivatives.

(ii) **Organic compounds** According to earlier scientists, these compounds are derived from living sources like plants and animals, or these remain buried under the earth; (e.g. petroleum). According to modern concept, these are the hydrides of carbon and their derivatives.

Mixtures

These are made up of two or more pure substances. They can possess variable composition and can be separated into their components by some physical methods.

Mixtures may be **homogeneous** (when composition is uniform throughout) or **heterogeneous** (when composition is not uniform throughout).

Mixture Separation Methods

Common methods for the separation of mixtures are:

(a) **Filtration** Filtration is the process of separating solids that are suspended in liquids by pouring the mixture into a filter funnel. As the liquid passes through the filter, the solid particles are held on the filter.

(b) **Distillation** Distillation is the process of heating a liquid to form vapours and then cooling the vapours to get back the liquid. This is a method by which a mixture containing volatile substances can be separated into its components.

(c) **Sublimation** This is the process of conversion of a solid directly into vapours on heating. Substances showing this property are called sublimate, e.g. iodine, naphthalene, camphor. This method is used to separate a sublimate from non-sublimate substances.

(d) **Crystallisation**   It is a process of separating solids having different solubilities in a particular solvent.

(e) **Magnetic separation**   This process is based upon the fact that a magnet attracts magnetic components of a mixture of magnetic and non-magnetic substances. The non-magnetic substance remains unaffected. Thus, it can be used to separate magnetic components from non-magnetic components.

(f) **Atmolysis**   This method is based upon rates of diffusion of gases and used for their separation from a gaseous mixture.

Atoms and Molecules

Atom is the smallest particle of an element which can take part in a chemical reaction. It may or may not be capable of independent existence.

Molecule is the simplest particle of matter that has independent existence. It may be homoatomic, e.g. H_2, Cl_2, N_2 (diatomic), O_3 (triatomic) or heteroatomic, e.g. HCl, NH_3, CH_4 etc.

Physical Quantities and Their Measurements

Physical quantity is a physical property of a material that can be quantified by measurement and their measurement does not involve any chemical reaction.

To express the measurement of any physical quantity, two things are considered:

(i) Its unit,

(ii) The numerical value.

Magnitude of a physical quantity = numerical value × unit

Unit

It is defined as "some fixed standard against which the comparison of a physical quantity can be done during measurement."

Units are of two types:

(i) Basic units   (ii) Derived units

(i) The **basic or fundamental units** are length (m), mass (kg), time (s), electric current (A), thermodynamic temperature (K), amount of substance (mol) and luminous intensity (Cd).

(ii) Derived units are basically derived from the fundamental units, e.g. unit of density is derived from units of mass and volume.

Different systems used for describing measurements of various physical quantities are:

(a) **CGS system** It is based on centimetre, gram and second as the units of length, mass and time respectively.

(b) **FPS system** A British system which used foot (ft), pound (lb) and second (s) as the fundamental units of length, mass and time respectively.

(c) **MKS system** It is the system which uses metre (m), kilogram (kg) and second (s) respectively for length, mass and time; ampere (A) was added later on for electric current.

(d) **SI system** (1960) International system of units or SI units contains following seven basic and two supplementary units:

Basic Physical Quantities and Their Corresponding SI Units

Physical quantity	Name of SI unit	Symbol for SI unit
Length (l)	metre	m
Mass (m)	kilogram	kg
Time (t)	second	s
Electric current (I)	ampere	A
Thermodynamic temperature (T)	kelvin	K
Amount of substance (n)	mole	mol
Luminous intensity (I_v)	candela	Cd

Supplementary units It includes plane angle in radian and solid angle in steradian.

Prefixes

The SI units of some physical quantities are either too small or too large. To change the order of magnitude, these are expressed by using prefixes before the name of base units. The various prefixes are listed as:

Multiple	Prefix	Symbol	Multiple	Prefix	Symbol
10^{24}	yotta	Y	10^{-1}	deci	d
10^{21}	zeta	Z	10^{-2}	centi	c
10^{18}	exa	E	10^{-3}	milli	m
10^{15}	peta	P	10^{-6}	micro	μ
10^{12}	tera	T	10^{-9}	nano	n
10^{9}	giga	G	10^{-12}	pico	p
10^{6}	mega	M	10^{-15}	femto	f
10^{3}	kilo	K	10^{-18}	atto	a
10^{2}	hecto	h	10^{-21}	zepto	z
10	deca	da	10^{-24}	yocto	y

Some Physical Quantities

(i) **Mass** It is the amount of matter present in a substance. It remains constant for a substance at all the places. Its unit is kg but in laboratories usually gram is used.

(ii) **Weight** It is the force exerted by gravity on an object. It varies from place to place due to change in gravity. Its unit is Newton (N)

(iii) **Temperature** There are three common scale to measure temperature °C (degree celsius), °F (degree fahrenheit) and K (kelvin). K is the SI unit. The temperature on two scales (°C and °F) are related to each other by the following relationship:

$$°F = \frac{9}{5}(°C) + 32$$

The kelvin scale is related to celsius scale as follows:

$$K = °C + 273.15$$

(iv) **Volume** The space occupied by matter (usually by liquid or a gas) is called its volume. Its unit is m^3.

(v) **Density** It is defined as the amount or mass per unit volume and has units $kg\ m^{-3}$ or $g\ cm^{-3}$.

Scientific Notation

In such notation, all measurements (how so ever large or small) are expressed as a number between 1.000 and 9.999 multiplied or divided by 10.

> In general it can be given as = $N \times 10^n$

Here, N is called digit term (1.000–9.999) and n is known as exponent. e.g. 138.42 cm can be written as 1.3842×10^2 and 0.0002 can be written as 2.0×10^{-4}.

Precision and Accuracy

Precision refers to the closeness of the set of values obtained from identical measurements of a quantity. Precision is simply a measure of reproducibility of an experiment.

Precision = individual value – arithmetic mean value

Accuracy is a measure of the difference between the experimental value or the mean value of a set of measurements and the true value.

Accuracy = mean value – true value

In physical measurements, accurate results are generally precise but precise results need not be accurate.

Significant Figures

Significant figures are the meaningful digits in a measured or calculated quantity. It includes all those digits that are known with certainty plus one more which is uncertain or estimated.

Greater the number of significant figures in a measurement, smaller the uncertainty.

Rules for determining the number of significant figures are:
1. All digits are significant except zeros in the beginning of a number.
2. Zeros to the right of the decimal point are significant.
   e.g. 0.132, 0.0132 and 15.0, all have three significant figures.
3. Exact numbers have infinite significant figures.

Calculations Involving Significant Figures
1. **In addition or subtraction**, the final result should be reported to the same number of decimal places as that of the term with the least number of decimal places,

   e.g.   2.512 (4 significant figures)

   2.2 (2 significant figures)

   5.23 (3 significant figures)

   $\overline{9.942} \Rightarrow 9.9$

   (Reported sum should have only one decimal point.)

2. **In multiplication and division**, the result is reported to the same number of significant figures as least precise term or the term with least number of significant figures, e.g.

$$15.724 \div 0.41 = 38.3512195121 \,(38.35)$$

Rounding Off the Numerical Results

When a number is rounded off, the number of significant figures is reduced, the last digit retained is increased by 1 only if the following digit is ≥ 5 and is left as such if the following digit is ≤ 4, e.g.

12.696 can be written as 12.7

18.35 can be written as 18.4

13.93 can be written as 13.9

Dimensional Analysis

Often while calculating, there is a need to convert units from one system to other. The method used to accomplish this is called factor label method or unit factor method or dimensional analysis.

In this,

Information sought = Information given × Conversion factor

Important Conversion Factors

$1 \, dyne = 10^{-5} \, N$	$1 \, L = 1000 \, mL$
$1 \, atm = 101325 \, Nm^{-2}$	$= 1000 \, cm^3$
$= 101325 \, Pa \, (pascal)$	$= 10^{-3} \, m^3$
$1 \, bar = 1 \times 10^5 \, Nm^{-2}$	$= 1 \, dm^3$
$= 1 \times 10^5 \, (pascal)$	
$1 \, L \, atm = 101.325 \, J = 24.21 \, cal$	$1 \, gallon = 3.7854 \, L$
$1 \, cal = 4.184 \, J = 2.613 \times 10^{19} \, eV$	$1 \, eV/atom = 96.485 \, kJ \, mol^{-1}$
$1 \, eV = 1.602189 \times 10^{-19} \, J$	$1 \, amu \, or \, u = 1.66 \times 10^{-27} \, kg$
$1 \, J = 10^7 \, erg$	$= 931.5 \, MeV$
$1 \, \text{Å} = 10^{-10} \, m$	$1 \, esu = 3.3356 \times 10^{-10} \, C$

Laws of Chemical Combinations

The combination of elements to form compounds is governed by the following six basic laws:

Law of conservation of mass (Lavoisier, 1789)

This law states that during any physical or chemical change, the total mass of the products is equal to the total mass of reactants. It does not hold good for nuclear reactions.

Law of definite proportions (Proust, 1799)

According to this law, a chemical compound obtained by different sources always contains same percentage of each constituent element.

Law of multiple proportions (Dalton, 1803)

According to this law, if two elements can combine to form more than one compound, the masses of one element that combine with a fixed mass of the other element, are in the ratio of small whole numbers, e.g. in NH_3 and N_2H_4, fixed mass of nitrogen requires hydrogen in the ratio 3 : 2.

Law of reciprocal proportions (Richter, 1792)

According to this law, when two elements (say A and B) combine separately with the same weight of a third element (say C), the ratio in which they do so is the same or simple multiple of the ratio in which they (A and B) combine with each other. Law of definite proportions, law of multiple proportions and law of reciprocal proportions do not hold good when same compound is obtained by using different isotopes of the same element, e.g. H_2O and D_2O.

Gay Lussac's law of gaseous volumes (In 1808)

It states that under similar conditions of temperature and pressure, whenever gases react together, the volumes of the reacting gases as well as products (if gases) bear a simple whole number ratio.

Avogadro's hypothesis

It states that equal volumes of all gases under the same conditions of temperature and pressure contain the same number of molecules.

Dalton's Atomic Theory (1803)

This theory was based on laws of chemical combinations. It's basic postulates are :

1. All substances are made up of tiny, indivisible particles, called atoms.

2. In each element, the atoms are all alike and have the same mass. The atoms of different elements differ in mass.

3. Atoms can neither be created nor destroyed during any physical or chemical change.

4. Compounds or molecules result from combination of atoms in some simple numerical ratio.

Limitations

(i) It failed to explain how atoms combine to form molecules.

(ii) It does not explain the difference in masses, sizes and valencies of the atoms of different elements.

Atomic Mass

It is the average relative atomic mass of an atom. It indicates that how many times an atom of that element is heavier as compared with $\frac{1}{12}$th part of the mass of one atom of carbon-12.

$$\text{Average atomic mass} = \frac{\text{average mass of an atom}}{\frac{1}{12} \times \text{mass of an atom of } C^{12}}$$

The word average has been used in the above definition and is very significant because elements occur in nature as mixture of several isotopes. So, atomic mass can be computed as

● Average atomic mass $= \dfrac{\text{RA (1)} \times \text{at. mass (1)} + \text{RA (2)} \times \text{at. mass (2)}}{\text{RA(1)} + \text{RA(2)}}$

Here, RA is relative abundance of different isotopes.

● In case of volatile chlorides, the atomic weight is calculated as

$$\text{At. wt.} = \text{Eq. wt.} \times \text{valency}$$

and $\quad \text{valency} = \dfrac{2 \times \text{vapour density of chloride}}{\text{eq. wt. of metal} + 35.5}$

● According to Dulong and Petit's rule,

$$\text{Atomic weight} \times \text{specific heat} = 6.4$$

Gram Atomic Mass (GAM)

Atomic mass of an element expressed in gram is called its gram atomic mass or gram-atom or mole-atom.

Molecular Mass

It is the mass of a molecule, i.e. number of times a molecule is heavier than $\frac{1}{12}$th mass of C-12 atom. Molecular mass of a substance is an additive property and can be calculated by taking algebraic sum of atomic masses of all the atoms of different elements present in one molecule.

$$\text{Molecular mass} = \frac{\text{average relative mass of one molecule}}{\frac{1}{12} \times \text{mass of C-12 atom}}$$

Gram molecular mass or molar mass is molecular mass of a substance expressed in gram.

$$\text{Molecular mass} = 2 \times \text{VD (Vapour density)}$$

Formula Mass

Some substances such as sodium chloride do not contain discrete molecules as their constituent units. The formula such as NaCl is used to calculate the formula mass instead of molecular mass as in the solid state sodium chloride does not exist as a single entity. e.g. formula mass of sodium chloride is 58.5 u.

Equivalent Mass

It is the mass of an element or a compound which would combine with or displaces (by weight) 1 part of hydrogen or 8 parts of oxygen or 35.5 parts of chlorine.

$$\text{Eq. wt. of metal} = \frac{\text{wt. of metal}}{\text{wt. of } H_2 \text{ displaced}} \times 1.008$$

$$\text{or} \qquad = \frac{\text{wt. of metal}}{\text{wt. of oxygen combined}} \times 8$$

$$\text{or} \qquad = \frac{\text{wt. of metal}}{\text{wt. of chlorine combined}} \times 35.5$$

$$\text{Eq. wt. of metal} = \frac{\text{wt. of metal}}{\text{volume of } H_2 \text{ (in mL) displaced at STP}} \times 11200$$

In general,

$$\frac{\text{Wt. of substance } A}{\text{Wt. of substance } B} = \frac{\text{Eq. wt. of substance } A}{\text{Eq. wt. of substance } B}$$

or for a compound (I) being converted into another compound (II) of same metal,

$$\frac{\text{Wt. of compound I}}{\text{Wt. of compound II}}$$

$$= \frac{\text{eq. wt. of metal + eq. wt. of anion of compound I}}{\text{eq. wt. of metal + eq. wt. of anion of compound II}}$$

$$\text{Eq. mass of a salt} = \frac{\text{formula mass}}{\text{total positive or negative charge}}$$

$$\text{Equivalent mass} = \frac{\text{atomic mass or molecular mass}}{n \text{ factor}}$$

n factor for various compounds can be obtained as

   (i) n factor for acids i.e. basicity

   (Number of ionisable H^+ per molecule is the basicity of acid.)

Acid	HCl	H_2SO_4	H_3PO_3	H_3PO_4	$H_2C_2O_4$
Basicity	1	2	2	3	2

   (ii) n factor for bases, i.e. acidity.

   (Number of ionisable OH^- per molecule is the acidity of a base.)

Base	NaOH	$Mg(OH)_2$	$Al(OH)_3$
Acidity	1	2	3

   (iii) In case of ions, n factor is equal to charge of that ion.

   (iv) In redox titrations, n factor is equal to change in oxidation number.

$$Cr_2O_7^{2-} + 6e^- + 14H^+ \longrightarrow 2Cr^{3+} + 2H_2O$$

$$n \text{ factor} = 6$$

$$MnO_4^- + 8H^+ + 5e^- \longrightarrow Mn^{2+} + 4H_2O$$

$$n \text{ factor} = 5$$

Equivalent mass of organic acid ($RCOOH$) is calculated by the following formula

$$\frac{\text{Eq. wt. of silver salt of acid }(RCOOAg)}{\text{Eq. wt. of Ag (or 108)}} = \frac{\text{Wt. of silver salt}}{\text{Wt. of silver}}$$

Mole Concept

Term **mole** was suggested by Ostwald (Latin word mole = heap)

A mole is defined as the amount of substance which contains same number of elementary particles (atoms, molecules or ions) as the number of atoms present in 12 g of carbon (C-12).

$1 \text{ mol} = 6.023 \times 10^{23}$ atoms = one gram-atom = gram atomic mass

$1 \text{ mol} = 6.023 \times 10^{23}$ molecules = gram molecular mass

In gaseous state at STP ($T = 273$ K, $p = 1$ atm)

Gram molecular mass = 1 mol = 22.4 L = 6.022×10^{23} molecules

Standard number 6.023×10^{23} is called **Avogadro number** in honour of Avogadro (he did not give this number) and is denoted by N_A.

The volume occupied by one mole molecules of a gaseous substance is called molar volume or gram molecular volume.

$$\text{Number of moles } = \frac{\text{amount of substance (in gram)}}{\text{molar mass}}$$

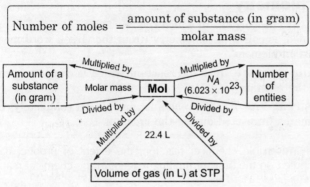

Number of molecules = number of moles $\times N_A$

Number of molecules in 1g compound $= \dfrac{N_A}{\text{g-molar mass}}$

Number of molecules in 1 cm^3 (1 mL) of an ideal gas at STP is called **Loschmidt number** (2.69×10^{19}).

One amu or u (unified mass) is equal to exactly the $\frac{1}{12}$th of the mass of ^{12}C atom, i.e. 1 amu or u $= \dfrac{1}{12} \times$ mass of one carbon (C^{12}) atom

$$1 \text{ amu} = \frac{1}{N_A} = 1 \text{ Avogram} = 1 \text{ Aston}$$

$$= 1 \text{ Dalton} = 1.66 \times 10^{-24} \text{ g}$$

One mole of electrons weighs 0.55 mg (5.5×10^{-4} g).

Empirical and Molecular Formulae

Empirical formula is the simplest formula of a compound giving simplest whole number ratio of atoms present in one molecule, e.g. CH is empirical formula of benzene (C_6H_6).

Molecular formula is the actual formula of a compound showing the total number of atoms of constituent elements present in a molecule of compound, e.g. C_6H_6 is molecular formula of benzene.

$$\text{Molecular formula} = (\text{Empirical formula})_n$$

where, n is simple whole number having values 1, 2, 3, ..., etc., and can be calculated as

$$n = \frac{\text{molecular formula mass}}{\text{empirical formula mass}}$$

Stoichiometry

The relative proportions in which the reactants react and the products are formed, is called stoichiometry (from the Greek word meaning 'to measure an element'.)

Limiting reagent It is the reactant which is completely consumed during the reaction.

Excess reagent It is the reactant which is not completely consumed and remains unreacted during the reaction.

In a irreversible chemical reaction, the extent of product can be computed on the basis of limiting reagent in the chemical reaction.

Per cent Yield

The actual yield of a product in any reaction is usually less than the theoretical yield because of the occurrence of certain side reactions.

$$\text{Per cent yield} = \frac{\text{actual yield}}{\text{theoretical yield}} \times 100$$

2

Atomic Structure

Atom

John Dalton proposed (in 1808) that atom is the smallest indivisible particle of matter. Atomic radii are of the order of 10^{-8} cm. It contains three subatomic particles namely electrons, protons and neutrons.

Electron

Electron was discovered as a result of study of cathode rays by JJ Thomson. It was named by Stony.

It carries a unit negative charge (-1.6×10^{-19} C).

Mass of electron is 9.11×10^{-31} kg and mass of one mole of electron is 0.55 mg. Some of the characteristics of cathode rays are:

(i) These travel in straight line away from cathode and produce fluorescence when strike the glass wall of discharge tube.

(ii) These cause mechanical motion in a small pin wheel placed in their path.

(iii) These produce X-rays when strike with metal and are deflected by electric and magnetic field.

Charge to Mass Ratio of Electron

In 1897, British physicist JJ Thomson measured the ratio of electrical charge (e) to the mass of electron (m_e) by using cathode ray tube and applying electrical and magnetic field perpendicular to each other as well as to the path of electrons. Thomson argued that the amount of deviation of the particles from their path in the presence of electrical or magnetic field may vary as follows:

(i) If greater the magnitude of the charge on the particles, greater is the deflection.

(ii) The mass of the particle, lighter the particle, greater the deflection.

(iii) The deflection of electrons from its original path increase with the increase in the voltage. By this Thomson determined the value e/m_e as 1.758820×10^{11} C kg^{-1}.

Proton

Rutherford discovered proton on the basis of anode ray experiment. It carries a unit positive charge ($+1.6 \times 10^{-19}$ C).

The mass of proton is 1.007276 u.

The $\dfrac{e}{m}$ ratio of proton is 9.58×10^{-4} C /g. ($\dfrac{e}{m}$ ratio is maximum for hydrogen gas.)

Some of the characteristics of anode rays are:

(i) These travel in straight line and possess mass many times heavier than the mass of an electron.

(ii) These are not originated from anode but are produced in the space between the anode and the cathode.

(iii) These also cause mechanical motion and are deflected by electric and magnetic field.

(iv) Specific charge $\left(\dfrac{e}{m}\right)$ for these rays depends upon the nature of the gas taken and is maximum for H_2.

Neutron

Neutrons are neutral particles. It was discovered by Chadwick (1932). The mass of neutron is 1.675×10^{-24} g or 1.008665 amu or u.

$$^{9}_{4}\text{Be} + {}^{4}_{2}\text{He} \longrightarrow {}^{12}_{6}\text{C} + {}^{1}_{0}n$$
$$(\alpha' - \text{particles}) \qquad\qquad (\text{Neutron})$$

Some Other Subatomic Particles

(a) **Positron** Positive electron ($^{0}_{+1}e$), discovered by Dirac (1930) and Anderson (1932).

(b) **Neutrino and antineutrino** Particles of small mass and no charge as stated by Fermi (1934).

(c) **Meson** Discovered by Yukawa (1935) and Kemmer. They are unstable particles and include pi ions [π^+, π^- or π^0].

(d) **Anti-proton** It is negative proton produced by Segre and Weigland (1955).

Thomson's Atomic Model

Atom is a positive sphere with a number of electrons distributed within the sphere. It is also known as plum pudding model. It explains the neutrality of an atom. This model could not explain the results of Rutherford scattering experiment.

Rutherford's Nuclear Model of Atom

It is based upon α-particle scattering experiment. Rutherford presented that

(i) most part of the atom is empty.

(ii) atom possesses a highly dense, positively charged centre, called **nucleus** of the order 10^{-13} cm.

(iii) entire mass of the atom is concentrated inside the nucleus.

(iv) electrons revolve around the nucleus in circular orbits.

(v) electrons and the nucleus are held together by electrostatic forces of attraction.

Drawbacks of Rutherford's Model

(i) According to electromagnetic theory, when charged particles are accelerated, they emit electromagnetic radiations, which comes by electronic motion and thus orbit continue to shrink, so atom is unstable. It doesn't explain the stability of atom.

(ii) It doesn't say anything about the electronic distribution around nucleus.

Atomic Number (Z)

Atomic number of an element corresponds to the total number of protons present in the nucleus or total number of electrons present in the neutral atom.

Mass Number (A)

The mass of the nucleus is due to protons and neutrons, thus they are collectively called **nucleons.** The total number of nucleons is termed as mass number of the atom.

Mass number of an element = number of protons + number of neutrons

Representation of an Atom

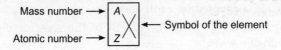

Mass number ⟶ A
Atomic number ⟶ Z X ⟵ Symbol of the element

Different Types of Atomic Species

(a) **Isotopes** Species with same atomic number but different mass number are called isotopes, e.g. $_1H^1$, $_1H^2$.

(b) **Isobars** Species with same mass number but different atomic number are called isobars, e.g. $_{18}Ar^{40}$, $_{19}K^{40}$.

(c) **Isotones** Species having same number of neutrons are called isotones, e.g. $_1H^3$ and $_2He^4$ are isotones.

(d) **Isodiaphers** Species with same isotopic number are called isodiaphers, e.g. $_{19}K^{39}$, $_9F^{19}$.

Isotopic number = mass number − [2 × atomic number]

(e) **Isoelectronic** Species with same number of electrons are called isoelectronic speices, e.g. Na^+, Mg^{2+}.

(f) **Isosters** Species having same number of atoms and same number of electrons, are called isosters, e.g. N_2 and CO.

Developments Leading to the Bohr's Model of Atom

Two developments played a major role in the formulation of Bohr's model:

(i) Dual character of the electromagnetic radiation which means that radiation possess wave like and particle like properties.

(ii) Atomic spectra explained by electronic energy level in atoms.

Electromagnetic Wave Theory (Maxwell)

The energy is emitted from source continuously in the form of radiations and magnetic fields. All electromagnetic waves travel with the velocity of light (3×10^8 m/s) and do not require any medium for their propagation.

An electromagnetic wave has the following characteristics:

(i) **Wavelength** It is the distance between two successive crests or troughs of a wave. It is denoted by the Greek letter λ (lambda).

(ii) **Frequency** It represents the number of waves which pass through a given point in one second. It is denoted by ν (nu).

(iii) **Velocity (v)** It is defined as the distance covered in one second by the waves. Velocity of light is 3×10^{10} cms^{-1}.

(iv) **Wave number** It is the reciprocal of wavelength and has units cm^{-1}. It is denoted by $\bar{\nu}$ (nu bar).

(v) **Amplitude (a)** It is the height of the crest or depth of the trough of a wave.

Wavelength (λ), frequency (v) and velocity (v) of any electromagnetic radiations are related to each other as $v = v\lambda$.

Electromagnetic wave theory was successful in explaining the properties of light such as interference, diffraction etc., but it could not explain the

1. Black body radiation
2. Photoelectric effect

These phenomena could be explained only if electromagnetic waves are supposed to have particle nature. Max Planck provided an explanation for the behaviour of black body and photoelectric effect.

Particle Nature of Electromagnetic Radiation : Planck's Quantum Theory

Planck explain the distribution of intensity of the radiation from black body as a function of frequency or wavelength at different temperatures.

$$E = hv = \frac{hc}{\lambda} \qquad\qquad (\because c = v\lambda)$$

where, h = Planck's constant = 6.63×10^{-34} J-s

E = energy of photon or quantum

v = frequency of emitted radiation

If n is the number of quanta of a particular frequency and E_T be total energy then

$$E_T = nhv$$

Black Body Radiation

If the substance being heated is a black body, the radiation emitted is called black body radiation.

Photoelectric Effect

It is the phenomenon in which beam of light of certain frequency falls on the surface of metal and electrons are ejected from it.

This phenomenon is known as photoelectric effect. It was first observed by Hertz.

$$W_0 = hv_0$$

$$W_0 = \frac{hc}{\lambda_{max}}$$

hv \ $\frac{1}{2} mv^2$

Metal hv_0 [work function]

Threshold frequency (v_0) = minimum frequency of the radiation

Work function (W_0) = required minimum energy of the radiation

$$E = \text{KE} + W_0$$

$\therefore \quad \dfrac{1}{2} mv^2 = h(v - v_0)$ [Kinetic energy of ejected electron $= h(v - v_0)$]

where, $\quad v$ = frequency of incident radiation

v_0 = threshold frequency

Electromagnetic Spectrum

The different types of electromagnetic radiations differ only in their wavelengths and hence, frequencies. When these electromagnetic radiations are arranged in order of their increasing wavelengths or decreasing frequencies, the complete spectrum obtained is called electromagnetic spectrum.

Different Types of Radiations and Their Sources

Type of radiation	Wavelength (in Å)	Generation source
Gamma rays	0.01 to 0.1	Radioactive disintegration
X-rays	0.1 to 150	From metal when an electron strikes on it
UV-rays	150 to 3800	Sun rays
Visible rays	3800 to 7600	Stars, arc lamps
Infrared rays	7600 to 6×10^6	Incandescent objects
Micro waves	6×10^6 to 3×10^9	Klystron tube
Radio waves	3×10^{14}	From an alternating current of high frequency

Electromagnetic spectra may be emission or absorption spectrum on the basis of energy absorbed or emitted. An **emission spectrum** is obtained when a substance emits radiation after absorbing energy. An **absorption spectra** is obtained when a substance absorbs certain wavelengths and leave dark spaces in bright continuous spectrum.

A spectrum can be further classified into two categories such as

(i) **Continuous or band spectrum** A spectrum in which there is no sharp boundary between two different radiations.

(ii) **Discontinuous or line spectrum** A spectrum in which radiations of a particular wavelength are separated from each other through sharp boundaries.

Bohr's Model

Neils Bohr proposed his model in 1931. Bohr's model is applicable only for one electron system like H, He^+, Li^{2+} etc.

Assumptions of Bohr's model are

1. Electrons keep revolving around the nucleus in certain fixed permissible orbits where it doesn't gain or lose energy. These orbits are known as **stationary orbits.**

   $$\text{Number of waves in an orbit} = \frac{\text{circumference of orbit}}{\text{wavelength}}$$

2. The electrons can move only in those orbits for which the angular momentum is an integral multiple of $\frac{h}{2\pi}$, i.e.

   $$mvr = \frac{nh}{2\pi} \qquad (n = 1, 2, 3.....)$$

   where, m = mass of electron; v = velocity of electron;

   r = radius of orbit

   n = number of orbit in which electrons are present

3. Energy is emitted or absorbed only when an electron jumps from higher energy level to lower energy level and *vice-versa*.

   $$\Delta E = E_2 - E_1 = h\nu = \frac{hc}{\lambda}$$

4. The most stable state of an atom is its ground state or normal state.

   From Bohr's model, energy, velocity and radius of an electron in nth Bohr orbit are

   (i) Velocity of an electron in nth Bohr orbit

   $$(v_n) = 2.165 \times 10^6 \frac{Z}{n} \text{ m/s}$$

   (ii) Radius of nth Bohr orbit

   $$(r_n) = 0.53 \times 10^{-10} \frac{n^2}{Z} \text{ m} = 0.53 \frac{n^2}{Z} \text{ Å}$$

   (iii) $E_n = -2.178 \times 10^{-18} \frac{Z^2}{n^2}$ J/atom

   $$= -1312 \frac{Z^2}{n^2} \text{ kJ/ mol}$$

   $$= -13.6 \frac{Z^2}{n^2} \text{ eV/atom}$$

$$\Delta E = -2.178 \times 10^{-18} \left(\frac{1}{n_1^2} - \frac{1}{n_2^2} \right) Z^2 \text{ J/atom}$$

where, n = number of shell; Z = atomic number

As we go away from the nucleus, the energy levels come closer, i.e. with the increase in the value of n, the difference of energy between successive orbits decreases.

Thus, $E_2 - E_1 > E_3 - E_2 > E_4 - E_3 > E_5 - E_4$, etc.

Emission Spectrum of Hydrogen

According to Bohr's theory, when an electron jumps from ground state to excited state, it emits a radiation of definite frequency (or wavelength). Corresponding to the wavelength of each photon of light emitted, a bright line appears in the spectrum.

The number of spectral lines in the spectrum when the electron comes from nth level to the ground level $= \dfrac{n(n-1)}{2}$

Hydrogen spectrum consist of line spectrum.

Series	Region	n_1	n_2
(i) Lyman	UV	1	2, 3, 4, ...
(ii) Balmer	Visible	2	3, 4, 5, ...
(iii) Paschen	IR	3	4, 5, 6, ...
(iv) Brackett	IR	4	5, 6, 7, ...
(v) Pfund	far IR	5	6, 7, ...
(vi) Humphery	far IR	6	7, 8, 9, ...

Wave number ($\bar{v}$) is defined as reciprocal of the wavelength.

$$\bar{v} = \frac{1}{\lambda} \Rightarrow \bar{v} = RZ^2 \left(\frac{1}{n_1^2} - \frac{1}{n_2^2} \right)$$

where,
$$n_1 = 1, 2 \ldots\ldots$$
$$n_2 = n_1 + 1, n_1 + 2 \ldots\ldots$$

Here, λ = wavelength

R = Rydberg constant = 109677.8 cm^{-1}

First line of a series is called line of longest wavelength (shortest energy) and last line of a series is the line of shortest wavelength (highest energy, $n_2 = \infty$).

Sommerfeld Extension to Bohr's Model

According to this theory, the angular momentum of revolving electron in an elliptical orbit is an integral multiple of $\dfrac{h}{2\pi}$, i.e.

$$mvr = \frac{kh}{2\pi}$$

From Bohr model, $\quad mvr = \dfrac{nh}{2\pi}$

For K shell, $n = 1, k = 1$ Circular shape
$\quad\;$ L shell, $n = 2, k = 1, 2$ Circular
$\quad\;$ M shell, $n = 3, k = 1, 2, 3$ Elliptical
$\quad\;$ N shell, $n = 4, k = 1, 2, 3, 4$ Elliptical

Limitations of Bohr's Theory

(i) It is unable to explain the spectrum of atom other than hydrogen like doublets or multielectron atoms.

(ii) It could not explain the ability of atom to form molecules by chemical bonds. Hence, it could not predict the shape of molecules.

(iii) It is not in accordance with the Heisenberg uncertainty principle and could not explain the concept of dual character of matter.

(iv) It is unable to explain the splitting of spectral lines in the presence of magnetic field (**Zeeman effect**) and electric field (**Stark effect**).

Towards Quantum Mechanical Model of the Atom

Two important developments which contributed significantly in the formulation of such a model were given below

1. de-Broglie Principle (Dual Nature)

de-Broglie explains the dual nature of electron, i.e. both particle as well as wave nature.

$$\lambda = \frac{h}{mv} \quad \text{or} \quad \frac{h}{p} = \lambda \qquad [p = mv \text{ (momentum)}]$$

where, λ = wavelength; v = velocity of particle; m = mass of particle

$$\lambda = \frac{h}{\sqrt{2m \times KE}}$$

where, KE = kinetic energy.

2. Heisenberg's Uncertainty Principle

According to this principle, "it is impossible to specify at any given instant both the momentum and the position of subatomic particles simultaneously like electron."

$$\Delta x \cdot \Delta p \geq \frac{h}{4\pi}$$

where, Δx = uncertainty in position; Δp = uncertainty in momentum

Quantum Mechanical Model of Atom

It is the branch of chemistry which deals with dual behaviour of matter. It is given by Werner Heisenberg and Erwin Schrodinger.

Schrodinger wave equation is

$$\frac{\partial^2 \psi}{\partial x^2} + \frac{\partial^2 \psi}{\partial y^2} + \frac{\partial^2 \psi}{\partial z^2} + \frac{8\pi^2 m}{h^2}(E - U)\psi = 0$$

where, x, y, z = cartesian coordinates

m = mass of electron, E = total energy of electron

U = potential energy of electron, h = Planck's constant

ψ (Psi) = wave function which gives the amplitude of wave

ψ^2 = probability function

For H-atom, the equation is solved as

$$\hat{H}\psi = E\psi$$

where, $\hat{H}$ is the total energy operator, called Hamiltonian. If the sum of kinetic energy operator (T) and potential energy operator (U) is the total energy, E of the system,

$$H = T + U$$
$$(T + U)\psi = E\psi$$

The atomic orbitals can be represented by the product of two wave functions (i) radial wave function (ii) angular wave function.

The orbital wave function, ψ has no significance, but ψ^2 has significance, it measures the electron probability density at a point in an atom. ψ can be positive or negative but ψ^2 is always positive.

Difference between Orbit and Orbital

	Orbit	Orbital
1.	An orbit is a well defined circular path around the nucleus in which the electron revolves.	An orbital is the three dimensional space around the nucleus within which the probability of finding an electron is maximum.
2.	The maximum number of electrons in any orbit is given by $2n^2$ where n is the number of the orbit.	The maximum number of electrons present in any orbital is two.

Shapes of Atomic Orbitals

The shapes of the orbitals are

s-spherical, p-dumb bell, d-double-dumb-bell, f-Diffused

These orbitals combine to form subshell.

   (i) s-subshell will have only one spherical orbital.

   (ii) p-subshell has three orbitals (p_x, p_y, p_z).

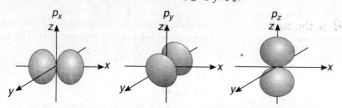

   (iii) d-subshell has five orbitals ($d_{xy}, d_{yz}, d_{zx}, d_{x^2-y^2}$ and d_{z^2}).

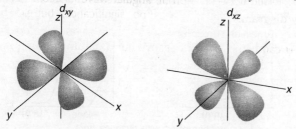

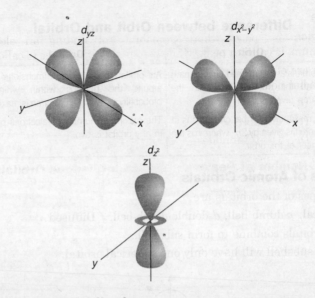

Wave function distribution

The orbital wave function (ψ) for an electron in an atom has no physical meaning. It is a mathematical function of the coordinates of the electron.

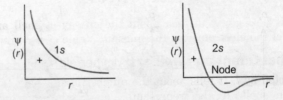

Probability Diagrams

The graph plotted between ψ^2 and distance from nucleus is called probability diagram.

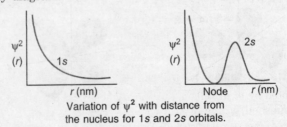

Variation of ψ^2 with distance from the nucleus for $1s$ and $2s$ orbitals.

Node

A region or space, where probability of finding an electron is maximum, is called a peak, while zero probability space is called **node.**

Nodes are of two types :

(a) Radial nodes
(b) Angular nodes

    (i) $(n - l - 1)$ = radial node

    (ii) (l) = angular node

    (iii) $(n - 1)$ = total nodes

Number of Peaks and Nodes for Various Orbitals

S. No.	Type of orbital	Number of peaks	Number of nodes
1.	s	n	$n - 1$
2.	p	$n - 1$	$n - 2$
3.	d	$n - 2$	$n - 3$
4.	f	$n - 3$	$n - 4$

Quantum Numbers

Each electron in an atom is identified in terms of four quantum numbers.

Principal Quantum Number (Neils Bohr)

It is denoted by n. It tells us about the main shell in which electron resides. It also gives an idea about the energy of shell and average distance of the electron from the nucleus. Value of n = any integer.

Azimuthal Quantum Number (Sommerfeld)

It is denoted by l. It tells about the number of subshells (s, p, d, f) in any main shell. It also represents the angular momentum of an electron and shapes of subshells. The orbital angular momentum of an electron $= \sqrt{l(l+1)}\ \dfrac{h}{2\pi}$

Value of $l = 0$ to $n - 1$.

$$l = 0 \text{ for } s, \quad l = 2 \text{ for } d$$
$$l = 1 \text{ for } p, \ l = 3 \text{ for } f$$

Number of subshells in main energy level = n.

Magnetic Quantum Number (Lande)

It is denoted by m. It tells about the number of orbitals and orientation of each subshell. Value of $m = -l$ to $+l$ including zero.

Number of orbitals in each subshell $= (2l + 1)$.

S. No.	Subshell	Orbital
1.	s	1
2.	p	3
3.	d	5
4.	f	7

Number of orbitals in main energy level = n^2.

Maximum number of electrons in nth shell = $2n^2$

Spin Quantum Number (Ublenbeck and Goldsmith)

It is denoted by m_s or s. It indicates the direction of spinning of electron, i.e. clockwise or anti-clockwise.

Maximum number of electrons in main energy level = $2n^2$

Electronic Configuration

Arrangement of electrons in various shells, subshells and orbitals in an atom is known as electronic configuration.

Filling of Orbitals in Atom

Aufbau Principle

According to this principle, in the ground state of an atom, the electrons occupy the lowest energy orbitals available to them, i.e. the orbitals are filled in order of increasing value of $n + l$. For the orbitals having the same value of $n + l$, the orbtial having lower value of n is filled up first.

The general order of increasing energies of the orbital is

$$1s < 2s < 2p < 3s < 3p < 4s < 3d < 4p < 5s < 4d < 5p < 6s < 4f < 5d$$
$$< 6p < 7s < 5f < 6d < 7p$$

Thus, the filling of electrons in various subshells within the atom can be summerised through following figure.

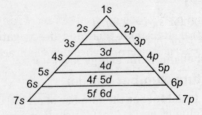

The energy of atomic orbitals for H-atom varies as

$$1s < 2s = 2p < 3s = 3p = 3d < 4s = 4p = 4d = 4f$$

Pauli Exclusion Principle

It states, no two electrons in an atom can have identical set of four quantum numbers.

The maximum number of electrons in s subshell is 2, p subshell is 6, d subshell is 10 and f subshell is 14.

Hund's Rule of Maximum Multiplicity

It states,

(i) In an atom no electron pairing takes place in the p, d or f-orbitals until each orbital of the given subshell contains one electron.

(ii) The unpaired electrons present in the various orbitals of the same subshell should have parallel spins.

Methods of Writing Electronic Configuration

(i) **Orbital method** In this, the electrons present in respective orbitals are denoted. e.g. $Cl(17) = 1s^2, 2s^2, 2p^6, 3s^2, 3p^5$.

(ii) **Shell method** In this, the number of electrons in each shell is continuously written. e.g. $Cl\,(17) = 1s^2, 2s^2, 2p^6, 3s^2, 3p^5$

$$\underbrace{\qquad}_{K} \quad \underbrace{\qquad}_{L} \quad \underbrace{\qquad}_{M}$$

2, 8, 7

(iii) **Box method** In this method, each orbital is denoted by a box and electrons are represented by half-headed (↿) or full-headed (↑) arrows. An orbital can occupy a maximum of two electrons. e.g.

$$Cl(17) = \boxed{\text{↿⇂}}_{1s^2} \quad \boxed{\text{↿⇂}}_{2s^2} \quad \boxed{\text{↿⇂}|\text{↿⇂}|\text{↿⇂}}_{2p^6} \quad \boxed{\text{↿⇂}}_{3s^2} \quad \boxed{\text{↿⇂}|\text{↿⇂}|\text{↑}}_{3p^5}$$

Half-filled and completely filled electronic configurations are more stable. Hence, outer configuration of Cr is $3d^5 4s^1$ and Cu is $3d^{10} 4s^1$.

Electronic Configuration of Ions

To write the electronic configuration of ions, first write the electronic configuration of neutral atom and then add (for negative charge) or remove (for positive charge) electrons in outer shell according to the nature and magnitude of charge present on the ion. e.g.

$$O(8) = 1s^2, 2s^2 2p^4, \quad O^{2-}\,(10) = 1s^2, 2s^2 2p^6$$

3

Classification of Elements and Periodicity in Properties

Classification of Elements

With the discovery of a large number of elements, it became difficult to study the elements individually, so classification of elements was done to make the study easier.

Earlier Attempts to Classify Elements

Many attempts were made to classify the known elements from time to time. The earlier attempts are as follows:

Prout's Hypothesis (1815)

According to this theory, hydrogen atom was considered as the fundamental unit from which all other atoms were made. It is also known as unitary theory.

Dobereiner's Triads (1829)

Dobereiner classified the elements into groups of three elements with similar properties in such a manner so that the atomic weight of the middle element was the arithmetic mean of the other two, e.g.

Element	Li	Na	K
Atomic weight	7	23	39

$$\text{Mean of atomic masses} = \frac{7 + 39}{2} = 23$$

Similarly Cl, Br, I; Ca, Sr, Ba are two more examples of such triads.

Limitations

Dobereiner could not arrange all the elements known at that time into triads. He could identify only three such triads that have been mentioned.

Newland's Octaves (1864) (Law of Octaves)

Newland states that when elements are arranged in order of increasing atomic masses, every eighth element has properties similar to the first just like in the musical note [Every eighth musical note is the same as the first mentioned note]. This can be illustrated as given below

sa	re	ga	ma	pa	dha	ni
Li	Be	B	C	N	O	F
Na	Mg	Al	Si	P	S	Cl

Limitations

1. This classification was successful up to the element calcium.
2. When noble gas elements were discovered at a later stage, their inclusion in these octaves disturbed the entire arrangement.

Lother Meyer's Atomic Volume Curve (1869)

Meyer presented the classification of elements in the form of a curve between atomic volume and atomic masses and stated that the properties of the elements are the periodic functions of their atomic volumes.

$$\left[\text{Here, atomic volume} = \frac{\text{Molecular mass}}{\text{Density}} \right]$$

He concluded that the elements with similar properties occupy similar position in the curve.

Mendeleev's Periodic Table

Mendeleev's periodic table is based upon Mendeleev's periodic law which states "The physical and chemical properties of the elements are a periodic function of their atomic masses."

At the time of Mendeleev, only 63 elements were known.

This periodic table is divided into seven horizontal rows (**periods**) and eight vertical columns (**groups**). Zero group was added later on in the modified Mendeleev's periodic table.

Importance of Mendeleev's Periodic Table

Few important achievements of periodic table are

(i) Systematic study of the elements.

(ii) Prediction of new elements and their properties, he left space for the elements yet to be discovered, e.g. he left spaces for Ga and Ge and named these elements as **EKa-aluminium** (Ga) and **EKa-silicon** (Ge) respectively.

(iii) Atomic mass correction of doubtful elements on the basis of their expected positions and properties.

Modified Form of Mendeleev's Periodic Table

Group →	I A	I B	II A	II B	III A	III B	IV A	IV B	V A	V B	VI A	VI B	VII A	VII B	VIII	VIII	VIII	0 Zero
1	H 1.008																	He 4.003
2	Li 6.94		Be 9.01		B 10.82		C 12.01		N 14.008		O 16		F 19					Ne 20.183
3	Na 22.99		Mg 24.32		Al 26.98		Si 28.09		P 30.975		S 32.06		Cl 35.46					Ar 39.944
4	K 39.10	Cu 63.54	Ca 40.08	Zn 65.38	Sc 44.96	Ga 69.72	Ti 47.90	Ge 72.60	V 50.95	As 74.91	Cr 52.01	Se 78.96	Mn 54.94	Br 79.91	Fe 55.85	Co 58.94	Ni 58.69	Kr 83.80
5	Rb 85.48	Ag 107.88	Sr 87.63	Cd 112.41	Y 88.92	In 114.76	Zr 91.22	Sn 118.70	Nb 92.91	Sb 121.76	Mo 95.95	Te 127.61	Tc 99	I 126.9	Ru 101.1	Rh 102.91	Pd 106.7	Xe 131.3
6	Cs 132.91	Au 197.0	Ba 137.36	Hg 200.61	La 138.92	Tl 204.39	Hf 178.6	Pb 207.21	Ta 180.92	Bi 209	W 183.92	Po 210	Re 186.31	At [210]	Os 190.2	Ir 192.2	Pt 195.23	Rn 222
7	Fr 223		Ra 226.05		Ac 227													

Defects in the Mendeleev's Periodic Table

(i) **Position of hydrogen** Hydrogen has been placed in group IA (alkali metals), but it also resembles with halogens of group VIIA. Thus, its position in the Mendeleev's periodic table is controversial.

(ii) **Position of isotopes** As Mendeleev's classification is based on atomic weight, isotopes would have to be placed in different positions due to their different atomic weights, e.g. $_1^1H$, $_1^2H$, $_1^3H$ would occupy different positions.

(iii) **Anomalous positions of some elements** Without any proper justification, in some cases the element with higher atomic mass precedes the element with lower atomic mass.

For example, Ar (atomic weight = 39.9) precedes K (atomic weight = 39.1) and similarly Co (atomic weight = 58.9) has been placed ahead of Ni (atomic weight = 58.7).

(iv) **Position of lanthanoids and actinoids** Lanthanoids and actinoids were not placed in the main periodic table.

Modern Periodic Table (1913)

Moseley modified Mendeleev's periodic law. He stated "Physical and chemical properties of elements are the periodic function of their atomic numbers." It is known as modern periodic law and considered as the basis of Modern Periodic Table.

When the elements were arranged in increasing order of atomic numbers, it was observed that the properties of elements were repeated after certain regular intervals of **2, 8, 8, 18, 18** and **32**. These numbers are called **magic numbers** and cause of periodicity in properties due to repetition of similar electronic configuration.

Structural Features of Long Form of Periodic Table

(i) Long form of periodic table is called **Bohr's periodic table**. There are 18 groups and seven periods in this periodic table.

(ii) The horizontal rows are called **periods**.

First period ($_1$H —$_2$He) contains 2 elements. It is the shortest period.

Second period ($_3$Li —$_{10}$Ne) and **third period** ($_{11}$Na—$_{18}$Ar) contain 8 elements each. These are short periods.

Fourth period ($_{19}$K —$_{36}$Kr) and **fifth period** ($_{37}$Rb —$_{54}$Xe) contain 18 elements each. These are long periods.

Sixth period ($_{55}$Cs —$_{86}$Rn) consists of 32 elements and is the longest period.

Seventh period starting with $_{87}$Fr is incomplete and consists of 19 elements.

(iii) The 18 vertical columns are known as **groups**.

Elements of group 1 are called **alkali metals**.

Elements of group 2 are called **alkaline earth metals**.

Elements of group 16 are called **chalcogens** [ore forming elements].

Elements of group 17 are called **halogens**. [sea salt forming elements]

Elements of group 18 are called **noble gases**.

Anomalous behaviour of the first element of a group. The first element of a group differs considerably from its congeners (i.e. the rest of the elements of its group).

This is due to (i) small size (ii) high electronegativity and (iii) non availability of d-orbitals for bonding. Anomalous behaviour is observed among the second row elements (i.e. Li to F).

(iv) The periodic table is divided into four main blocks (s, p, d and f) depending upon the subshell to which the valence electron enters into.

   (a) **s-block elements** Ist and IInd group elements belong to this block and the last electron enters in s-subshell.

   General electronic configuration $= ns^{1-2}$.

   (b) **p-block elements** Group 13th to 18th belong to this block in which last electron enters in p-orbital.

   Their general electronic configuration is $ns^2 np^{1-6}$.

   This is the only block which contains metal, non-metal and metalloids. Examples of metalloids are B, Si, Ge, As, Sb, Te and At.

   The elements of s-and p-block elements are collectively called representative elements.

   (c) **d-block elements** Group 3rd to 12th belong to this block, in which last electron enters in d-orbital.

   They have inner incomplete shell, so known as transition elements.

   General electronic configuration is $ns^{1-2}(n-1)d^{1-10}$.

   d-block elements are generally coloured, paramagnetic and exhibit variable valency.

   (d) **f-block elements** They constitute two series $4f$ (lanthanoids) and $5f$ (actinoids) in which last electron is in $4f$ and $5f$ subshell respectively.

   General electronic configuration

   $$(n-2)f^{1-14}(n-1)d^{0-1}ns^2$$

The f-block elements are also called as **inner-transition elements**.

Elements with atomic number greater than 92 (U_{92}) are called the **transuranic** or **transuranium elements.** All these elements are man-made through artificial nuclear reactions.

Very recently, on August 16, 2003, IUPAC approved the name for the element of atomic number 110, as **Darmstadtium**, with symbol Ds.

Limitations of Long Form of Periodic Table

In the long form of the periodic table:

(i) The position of hydrogen still remains uncertain.

(ii) The inner-transition elements do not find a place in the main body of the table. They are placed separately.

Predicting the Position of an Element in the Periodic Table

First of all write the complete electronic configuration. The principle quantum number of the valence shell represents the period of the element.

The subshell in which the last electron is filled corresponds to the block of the element.

Group of the element is predicted from the electrons present in the outermost (n) or penultimate ($n-1$) shell as follows :

For s-block elements,

group number = number of ns-electrons

(Number of valence electrons)

For p-block elements,

group number = 10 + number of ns and np electrons

For d-block elements,

group number = the sum of the number of $(n-1)\,d$ and ns electrons.

For f-block elements, group number is always 3.

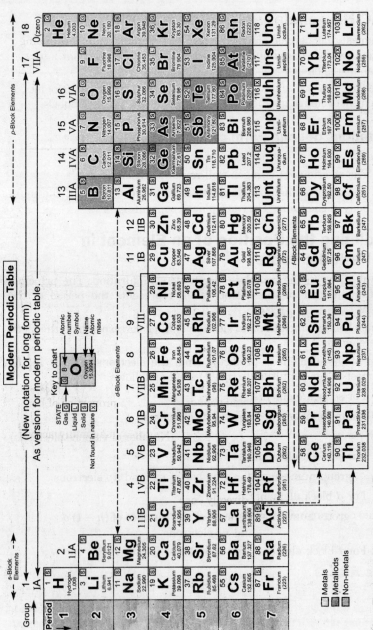

Modern Periodic Table

--- (New notation for long form)
--- As version for modern periodic table.

Note The International Union of Pure and Applied Chemistry has approved the name and symbols of four newly discovered elements : Nihonium (Nh), Moscovium (Mc), Tennessine (Ts) and Oganesson (Og) respectively for element 113, 115, 117 and 118.

IUPAC Nomenclature of Elements With $Z > 100$

The names are derived directly from the atomic numbers using numerical roots for 0 and numbers from 1-9 and adding the suffix *ium*.

Digit	0	1	2	3	4	5	6	7	8	9
Root	nil	un	bi	tri	quad	pent	hex	sept	oct	enn
Abbreviation	*n*	*u*	*b*	*t*	*q*	*p*	*h*	*s*	*o*	*e*

The IUPAC names and symbols of elements with $Z > 100$ are

Z	101	102	103	104	105	106	107	108	109	110
IUPAC name	Unnilu nium	Unnilb ium	Unniltr ium	Unnilq uadium	Unnilp entium	Unnilh exium	Unnils eptium	Unnilo ctium	Unnil enneium	Ununn ilium
Symbol	Unu	Unb	Unt	Unq	Unp	Unh	Uns	Uno	Une	Uun

Metals, Non-metals and Metalloids

- **Metals** comprise more than 78% of all known elements and appears on the left side of the periodic table.
- In contrast, **non-metals** are located at the top right handside of the periodic table.
- Within the non-metals, some elements show the properties of both metals and non-metals, i.e. metalloids. These elements border the *zig-zag* line beginning from boron and running diagonally across the *p*-block.

Periodic Properties

The properties which are directly or indirectly related to their electronic configuration and show gradual change when we move from left to right in a period or from top to bottom in a group are called periodic properties.

Atomic Radius

It is the distance from the centre of the nucleus to the outermost shell containing of electrons. It is an hypothetical definition because in a single atom, it is almost impossible to measure this distance. Hence, practically, atomic radius is defined in the following four ways :

Covalent radius

If the combining atoms are non-metals (except noble gases) and the bond between them is the single covalent bond then their radius is called the covalent radius. It is measured as the half of their internuclear distance, i.e. For an atom A in a molecule A_2.

$$r_A = \frac{r_A + r_A}{2} = \frac{d_{A-A}}{2}$$

$$[\text{Distance}_{A-A} = \text{Radius of } A + \text{Radius of } A]$$

For heterodiatomic molecule AB,

$$d_{A-B} = r_A + r_B + 0.09(X_A - X_B)$$

Where, X_A and X_B are electronegativities of A and B.

van der Waals' Radius

It is defined as one-half of the distance between the nuclei of two non-bonded isolated atoms or two adjacent atoms belonging to two neighbouring molecules of an element in the solid state.

Metallic Radius

It is defined as one-half of the internuclear distance between the centres of nuclei of the two adjacent atoms in the metallic crystal.

Ionic Radius

An atom can be changed to a cation by loss of electrons and to an anion by gain of electrons. A cation is always smaller than the parent atom because during its formation effective nuclear charge increases and sometimes a shell may also decrease. On the other hand, the size of an anion is always larger than the parent atom because during its formation effective nuclear charge decreases.

In case of iso-electronic ions, the higher the nuclear charge, smaller is the size, e.g. $Al^{3+} < Mg^{2+} < Na^{+} < F^{-} < O^{2-} < N^{3-}$

The order of radii is :

covalent radius < metallic radius < van der Waals' radius

In general, the atomic size decreases on moving from left to right in a period due to increase in effective nuclear charge and increases on moving from top to bottom in a group due to addition of new shells.

The concept of effective nuclear charge is discussed below :

Effective Nuclear Charge

In a multielectron atom, the electron of the inner-shell decrease the force of attraction exerted by the nucleus on the valence electrons. This is called shielding effect. Due to this, the nuclear charge (Z) actually present on the nucleus, reduces and is called effective nuclear charge (Z_{eff}).

It is calculated by using the formula
$$Z_{eff} = Z - \sigma$$
where, σ = screening constant

The magnitude of σ is determined by Slater's rules.

Slater Rules

(i) Write the electronic configuration in the following order and groups.
$(1s)\,(2s, 2p)\,(3s, 3p)\,(3d),(4s, 4p)\,(4d)\,(4f)\,(5s, 5p)$ etc.

(ii) Electrons of $(n + 1)$ shell (shell higher than considering electrons) do not contribute in shielding, i.e. $\sigma = 0$

(iii) All other electrons in (ns, np) group contribute $\sigma = 0.35$ each.

(iv) All electrons of $(n - 1)s$ and p shell contribute $\sigma = 0.85$ each.

(v) All electrons of $(n - 2)s$ and p shell or lower shell contribute $\sigma = 1.00$ each

(vi) All electrons of nd and nf orbital contribute $\sigma = 0.35$ and those of $(n - 1)$ and f or lower orbital contribute $\sigma = 1.00$ each.

e.g. $\qquad$ Be $(4) = 1s^2, 2s^2$

(for $2s$) $\qquad$ for $1s$
$$\sigma = 0.35 \;+\; 2 \times 0.85 = 2.05$$
$$Z_{eff} = Z - \sigma = 4 - 2.05 = 1.95$$

Ionisation Enthalpy (IE)

It is the amount of energy required to remove the loosely bound electron from the isolated gaseous atom.
$$A(g) + IE \longrightarrow A^+(g) + e^-$$
Various factors with which IE varies are :

(i) Atomic size : varies inversely

(ii) Screening effect : varies inversely

(iii) Nuclear charge : varies directly

Generally left to right in periods, ionisation enthalpy increases; down the group, it decreases.

IE values of inert gases are exceptionally higher due to their stable configurations. Successive ionisation enthalpies
$$IE_3 > IE_2 > IE_1$$
IE_1. of N is exceptionally greater than that of oxygen due to stable half-filled $2p$-orbitals.

Among transition elements of $3d$-series, $_{24}Cr$ and $_{29}Cu$ have higher IE_2 due to half-filled and fully-filled stable d-orbitals.

Electron Gain Enthalpy $(\Delta e_g H)$

It is the amount of energy released when an electron is added in an isolated gaseous atom. First electron gain enthalpy is negative while the other successive electron gain enthalpy will be positive due to repulsion between the electrons already present in the anion and the electron being added.

$$O(g) + e^- \longrightarrow O^-(g); \qquad \Delta e_g H = -141 \text{ kJ mol}^{-1}$$

$$O^-(g) + e^- \longrightarrow O^{2-}(g); \qquad \Delta e_g H = +780 \text{ kJ mol}^{-1}$$

Various factors with which electron gain enthalpy varies are :

(i) Atomic size : varies directly

(ii) Nuclear charge : varies directly

Along a period, electron gain enthalpy becomes more and more negative while on moving down the group, it becomes less negative.

Noble gases have positive electron gain enthalpies.

Halogens have maximum value of $\Delta e_g H$ within a period due to smallest atomic size.

F and O atom have small size and high charge density, therefore they have lower values of electron gain enthalpy, than Cl and S respectively.

$$Cl > F; \; S > O$$

Elements having half-filled and fully-filled orbitals exhibit more stability, therefore, electron gain enthalpy will be low for such elements.

Electron gain enthalpy can be measured by Born-Haber cycle and elements with high $\Delta e_g H$, are good oxidising agent.

Electronegativity (EN)

It is defined as the tendency of an atom to attract the shared electron pair towards itself in a polar covalent bond. Various factors with which electronegativity varies are :

(i) Atomic size : varies inversely

(ii) Charge on the ion : varies directly, e.g. $Li < Li^+$, $Fe^{2+} < Fe^{3+}$

(iii) Hybridisation : (Electronegativity $\propto$ % age s-character in the hybrid orbital)

Electronegativity of carbon atom $= C_2H_6 < C_2H_4 < C_2H_2$

In periods as we move from left to right electronegativity increases, while in the groups electronegativity decreases down the group.

For noble gases, its value is taken as zero.

Electronegativity helps to predict the polarity of bonds and dipole moment of molecules.

Electronegativity order of some elements (on Pauling scale) is

$$\underset{(4.0)}{F} > \underset{(3.5)}{O} > \underset{(3.0)}{N} \approx \underset{(3.0)}{Cl} > \underset{(2.8)}{Br}$$

(i) **Mulliken scale**

$$\text{Electronegativity } (x) = \frac{IE + \Delta e_g H}{2}$$

(ii) **Pauling scale** The difference in electronegativity of two atoms A and B is given by the relationship

$$x_B - x_A = 0.208\sqrt{\Delta}$$

where, $\Delta = E_{A-B} - \sqrt{E_{A-A} \times E_{B-B}}$

(Δ is known as resonance energy.)

E_{A-B}, E_{A-A} and E_{B-B} represent bond dissociation energies of the bonds $A-B, A-A$ and $B-B$ respectively.

(iii) **Allred and Rochow's scale**

$$\text{Electronegativity} = 0.744 + \frac{0.359\, Z_{eff}}{r^2}$$

Where, Z_{eff} is the effective nuclear charge = $Z - \sigma$

Where, σ is screening constant. It's value can be determined by Slater's rule.

Valency

It is defined as the combining capacity of the element. The valency of an element is related to the electronic configuration of its atom and usually determined by electrons present in the valence shell.

On moving along a period from left to right, valency increases from 1 to 4 and then decreases to zero (for noble gases) while on moving down a group the valency remains the same.

Transition metals exhibit variable valency because they can use electron from outer as well as penultimate shell.

Chemical Reactivity

Reactivity of metal increases with decrease in IE, electronegativity and increase in atomic size as well as electropositive character.

Reactivity of non-metals increases with increase in electronegativity as well as electron gain enthalpy and decrease in atomic radii.

Melting and Boiling Points

On moving down the group, the melting point and boiling point for metallic elements go on decreasing due to the decreasing forces of attraction. However, for non-metals, melting point and boiling point generally increase down the group.

⌈ Along a period from left to right, melting point and boiling point increases and reaches a maximum value in the middle of the period and then start decreasing. ⌋

Tungsten (W) has highest melting point (3683 K) among metals, carbon (diamond) has the highest melting point among non-metals. Helium has lowest melting point (−270° C) among all elements,

Electropositivity or Metallic Character

The tendency of an atom of the element to lose valence electrons and form positive ion is called electropositivity.

Greater the electropositive character, greater is the metallic character.

Electropositive character decreases on moving across the period and increases on moving down the group.

Alkali metals are the most electropositive and halogens are the least electropositive element in their respective period.

Basic nature of oxides ∝ metallic character, i.e. it also decreases along a period and increases down the group.

Density

Li metal has minimum density while osmium (Os) metal has maximum density.

Diagonal Relationship

Certain elements of 2nd period show similarity in properties with their diagonal elements in the 3rd period as shown below :

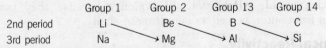

Thus, Li resembles Mg, Be resembles Al and B resembles Si. This is called diagonal relationship and this is due to the reason that these pairs of elements have almost identical ionic radii and polarizing power (i.e. charge/size ratio). Elements of third period, i.e. Mg, Al and Si are known as **bridge elements.**

4

Chemical Bonding and Molecular Structure

Chemical Bond

It is defined as the attractive force which hold the various chemical constituents (atoms, ions, etc.) together in different chemical species. Bond forms to get the stability, with a release of energy.

Kossel-Lewis Approach to Chemical Bonding

According to this theory, atoms take part in the bond formation to complete their octet or to acquire the electronic configuration of the nearest inert gas atoms (octet rule). This can be achieved by gaining, losing or sharing the electrons.

Lewis Symbols

Valence electrons are reported by dots around the chemical symbol of element, e.g.

$$\text{Li} \quad \cdot \text{B} \cdot \quad \cdot \overset{\displaystyle\cdot}{\text{C}} \cdot \quad :\overset{\displaystyle\cdot\cdot}{\text{F}}: \quad :\overset{\displaystyle\cdot\cdot}{\underset{\displaystyle\cdot\cdot}{\text{Ne}}}:$$

Octet Rule

According to Octet rule during the formation of a covalent bond, the atoms attain an inert gas electronic configuration (valence shell contains $8e^-$ or shell is completely filled). An atom may attain this configuration by gaining, losing or sharing electrons with other atoms.

Exceptions to the Octet Rule

(i) Incomplete octet of the central atom, e.g. LiCl, BeH_2 and BCl_3

$$\text{Li} : \text{Cl} \; ; \; \text{H} : \text{Be} : \text{H} \; ; \; \overset{\text{Cl}}{\underset{}{\text{Cl} : \text{B} : \text{Cl}}}$$

(ii) Odd-electron molecules

$$\overset{\bullet\bullet}{\underset{\bullet}{N}} = \overset{\bullet\bullet}{O} \; ; \; \overset{\bullet\bullet}{O} = \overset{+}{N} - \overset{\bullet\bullet}{\underset{\bullet\bullet}{O}}\overset{-}{:} \; ; \; ClO_2^-, He_2^+$$

(iii) Expanded octet of central atoms

PCl_5	SF_6	H_2SO_4
[10 electrons around the P atom]	[12 electrons around the S atom]	[12 electrons around the S atom]

Ionic Bond

A chemical bond formed by complete transference of electrons from one atom (metal) to another (non-metal) and hence, each atom acquires the stable nearest noble gas configuration, is called ionic bond or **electrovalent bond**, e.g. formation of sodium chloride

$$\text{Na}^\bullet \; + \; {}^\bullet\overset{\bullet\bullet}{\underset{\bullet\bullet}{\text{Cl}}}{:} \longrightarrow [\text{Na}^+ \; {:}\overset{\bullet\bullet}{\underset{\bullet\bullet}{\text{Cl}}}{:}^-]$$

(2,8,1)   (2, 8, 7)   (2, 8)   (2, 8, 8)

Favourable factors for the formation of ionic bonds

(i) Metal should have low ionisation enthalpy.

(ii) Non-metal must have high electron gain enthalpy.

(iii) The energy released during the formation of 1 mole of crystal lattice, i.e. lattice enthalpy must be high.

⌐ Some elements exhibit variable electrovalency. The reason for this is unstable configuration of penultimate orbit and inert pair effect. ⌐

Ions

Species carrying either positive or negative charge are termed as ions. Species carrying positive charge are called **cations** and those carrying negative charge are called **anions**. Metals usually form cation while non-metals (except H) usually form anions.

General Characteristics of Ionic Compounds

(i) Ionic compounds are usually solid in nature.

(ii) Ionic compounds have high melting and boiling points.

(iii) Ionic compounds are soluble in polar solvents like water but insoluble in non-polar solvents like benzene, CCl_4 etc.

(iv) Ionic compounds are good conductor in molten state and in aqueous solution.

(v) Ionic compounds have crystal structure.

Method of Writing Formula of Ionic Compound

(i) Write the symbol of cation at the left and anion at the right.

(ii) Write their electrovalencies in figures on the top of each symbol as $A^x B^y$.

(iii) Divide their valencies by HCF.

(iv) Now apply criss-cross rule as $\underset{A \quad B}{\overset{x \quad y}{\times}}$, i.e. formula is $A_y B_x$.

e.g. formula of aluminium sulphate $\underset{Al \quad SO_4}{\overset{3+ \quad 2-}{\times}}$ is $Al_2(SO_4)_3$.

Born Haber Cycle

This cycle is based upon the fact that the formation of an ionic compound may occur either by direct combination of the elements or by an alternate process in which :

(i) The reactants (metal) are vaporised to convert into gaseous state.

(ii) The gaseous atoms are converted into ion.

(iii) The gaseous ions are combined to form ionic lattice of molecules.

e.g. formation of NaCl can be shown as

$$Na(s) + \frac{1}{2}Cl_2(g) \xrightarrow{Q} Na^+Cl^-$$

$$\downarrow S \qquad \downarrow \frac{1}{2}D$$

$$Na(g) \qquad Cl$$

$$\downarrow I \qquad \downarrow -E$$

$$Na^+ + \qquad Cl^- \xrightarrow{-U}$$

Thus, $\qquad Q = S + I + \frac{1}{2}D - E - U$

where, S = enthalpy of sublimation, I = ionisation enthalpy

D = enthalpy of dissociation, E = electron gain enthalpy

U = lattice enthalpy

Q = total enthalpy change.

Covalent Bond

A chemical bond formed between two atoms by mutual sharing of electrons between them so as to complete their octets or duplets, is known as **covalent bond** and the number of electrons contributed by each atom is known as **covalency**, e.g. formation of Cl_2.

$$:\overset{..}{\underset{..}{Cl}}\cdot \ + \ \cdot\overset{..}{\underset{..}{Cl}}: \ \longrightarrow \ (:\overset{..}{Cl}(\cdot\cdot)\overset{..}{Cl}:)$$

$$\underset{2,8,7}{\qquad} \quad \underset{2,8,7}{\qquad} \qquad\qquad \text{or}$$

$$Cl\text{—}Cl$$

In covalent bonding, the shared pairs of electrons present between the atoms are called **bond pairs** while unshared or non-bonding electron pairs are known as **lone pairs**.

Types of Covalent Bonds

(a) Non-polar Covalent Bond

If the covalent bond is formed between two homonuclear atoms, i.e. between atoms of exactly equal electronegativity, e.g. H_2, Cl_2 etc.

(b) Polar Covalent Bond

If a covalent bond is formed between the different atoms, the shared pair is displaced towards the more electronegative atom causing greater concentration of electron density around the more electronegative atom. Such a covalent bond develops some ionic character and is called **polar covalent bond**, (e.g. H—Cl).

Properties of Covalent Compounds

(i) In general, covalent compounds exist in the liquid or gaseous state at room temperature due to magnitude of intermolecular forces.

(ii) Covalent compounds have low melting and boiling points.

(iii) Covalent compounds are generally poor conductors of electricity because they do not contain free electrons or ions to conduct electricity.

(iv) They are soluble in non-polar solvents like benzene but usually insoluble in water.

Formal Charge on an Atom in a Molecule/Ion

Formal charge (F.C.) on an atom in a Lewis structure

= [total number of valence electrons in the free atom]

− [total number of non-bonding (lone pair) electrons]

$$-\frac{1}{2} \text{ [total number of bonding (shared) electrons]}$$

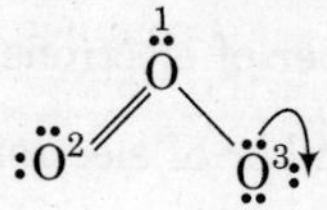

F.C. on $O^2 = 6 - 2 - \frac{1}{2}(6) = +1$

F.C. on $O^2 = 6 - \left[4 + \frac{1}{2} \times 4\right] = 6 - 6 = 0$

F.C. on $O^3 = 6 - \left[6 + \frac{1}{2} \times 2\right] = 6 - 7 = -1$

Hence, O_3 along with the formal charges can be represented as follows:

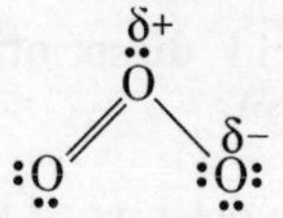

Bond Characteristics

Bond Length

In a covalently bonded molecule, distance between the nuclei of the two atoms is known as bond length. Bond length increases with increase in the size of bonded atoms and decreases with an increase in the number of bonds between bonded atoms.

Bond type	Covalent bond length (in pm)
C—H	107 pm
C—C	154 pm
C=C	133 pm
C≡C	120 pm

Bond length is determined by X-ray diffraction or electron diffraction methods.

Bond Angle

In a covalently bonded molecule having more than two atoms, the bonds form an angle with each other, which is known as bond angle. In general an increase in the size of central atom decreases the bond angle.

Factors affecting bond angle (i) Lone pair repulsion (ii) hybridisation of central atom. It is determined by X-rays diffraction method.

Bond Order

It is defined as the number of covalent bonds present in a molecule.

$$\text{Bond order} = \frac{1}{2} \text{ [Number of electrons in bonding orbitals}$$
$$- \text{ Number of electrons in anti-bonding orbitals]}$$
$$\text{Bond order} \propto \frac{1}{\text{bond length}}$$

If bond order comes out to be zero, the molecule does not exist.

Bond Enthalpy

It is the amount of energy released when one mole of covalent bonds is formed while the bond dissociation enthalpy is the amount of energy required to break one mole of bonds of the same kind so as to separate the bonded atoms in the gaseous state.

The bond enthalpy and bond dissociation enthalpy are equal in magnitude and opposite in sign.

⌈ Bond dissociation enthalpy is determined by thermal or spectroscopic ⌉
methods.

As the bond order increases, bond enthalpy also increases and bond length decreases.

Factors affecting bond enthalpy
(i) atomic size
(ii) electronegativity
(iii) extent of overlapping
(iv) bond order

Fajan's Rule

The partial covalent character of ionic bonds was discussed by Fajan's in terms of following rules:

The smaller the size of cation and the larger the size of the anion, the greater the covalent character of an ionic bond.

The greater the charge on the cation or anion, the greater the covalent character of the ionic bond.

Resonance

According to the concept of resonance, a single Lewis structure cannot explain all the properties of the molecules. The molecule is then supposed to have many structures, each of which can explain most of the properties.

The actual structure lies in between of all these contributing structures and is called resonance hybrid and the different individual structures are called resonating structures or canonical structures. This phenomenon is known as resonance.

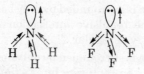

Resonance in ozone molecule

Resonance stabilises the molecule as the energy of the resonance hybrid is less than the energy of any single canonical structure.

Resonance averages the bond characteristics as a whole.

The difference in the energy of the resonance hybrid and the most stable contributing structure (having least energy) is called resonance energy. Greater the resonance energy, greater is the stability of the molecule.

⌜ Calculation of bond order for molecules showing resonance :
Bond order
$$= \frac{\text{total number of bonds between two atoms in all the structures}}{\text{total number of resonating structures}}$$ ⌟

Dipole Moment (μ)

It is defined as the product of the magnitude of the charge and the distance between the centres of positive and negative charges.

$$\mu = \text{charge } (Q) \times \text{distance of separation } (r)$$

Dipole moment is expressed in Debye (D).

$$1\,D = 1 \times 10^{-18} \text{ esu-cm} = 3.33564 \times 10^{-30} \text{ C-m}$$

where, C is coulomb and m is meter.

(The shift in electron density is symbolised by broken arrow)

In chemistry, presence of dipole moment is represented by the crossed arrow ($+\!\!\longrightarrow$) put on Lewis structure of molecule. The cross is on positive end and arrow head is on negative end.

NH_3 has higher dipole moment than NF_3.

Resultant dipole moment,

$$\mu = \sqrt{\mu_1^2 + \mu_2^2 + 2\mu_1\mu_2 \cos\theta}$$

Applications of Dipole Moment

1. Dipole moment is helpful in predicting the geometry of the molecule.
2. Dipole moment helps in determining the polarity.

   Hannay-Smith equation

   Per cent ionic character = $16 [X_A - X_B] + 3.5 [X_A - X_B]^2$

   where, X_A and X_B are the electronegativities of atoms.

   Per cent ionic character can also be calculated by dipole moment as

   Per cent ionic character = $\dfrac{\text{observed dipole moment}}{\text{calculated dipole moment}} \times 100$

3. Non-polar molecule has zero dipole moment like BF_3, CCl_4, etc.

$\mu = 0$ $\mu = 0$

4. *cis* and *trans* isomers can be distinguished by dipole moments usually *cis* isomer have higher dipole moment and hence, higher polarity.
5. Dipole moment is greatest for *ortho* isomer; zero for *para* isomer; and less than that of *ortho,* for *meta* isomer.

The Valence Shell Electron Pair Repulsion (VSEPR) Theory

According to this theory,

1. The geometry of a molecule or ion depends on the number of electron pairs in the valence shell of its central atom.
2. To attain minimum repulsive state, electron pairs try to stay as far away as possible.
3. If the central atom is surrounded by only bonded electron pairs of similar atoms, the repulsive interactions are similar and the molecular geometry is regular.
4. If the central atom is surrounded by only bonded electron pairs of dissimilar atoms, the repulsive interactions are not equivalent and hence, the geometry of molecule will not be regular.

5. If the central atom is surrounded by both bonded pairs (*bp*) as well as lone pairs (*lp*) of electrons, repulsive interactions are not equivalent and hence, geometry of the molecule will be irregular. The repulsive interactions decrease in the order

$$lp - lp > lp - bp > bp - bp$$

Shapes (Geometry) of Molecules Containing Bond Pairs Only or Bond Pairs and Lone Pairs

Total number of electron pairs	Number of bond pairs	Number of Lone pairs	Geometry (shape) of the molecule	Illustrative examples
2	2	0	B—A—B Linear	BeF_2, CO_2, $BeCl_2$
3	3	0	Triangular planar	BF_3, $AlCl_3$, SO_3
	2	1	Bent (V-shape)	SO_2, O_3, NO_2
4	4	0	Tetrahedral	CH_4, SiF_4, NH_4^+
	3	1	Trigonal pyramidal	NH_3, PCl_3, NCl_3, PH_3
	2	2	Bent	H_2O, H_2S

Contd....

Total number of electron pairs	Number of bond pairs	Number of Lone pairs	Geometry (shape) of the molecule	Illustrative examples
5	5	0	Trigonal bipyramidal	PCl_5
	4	1	See saw	SF_4
	3	2	T-shaped	ClF_3, BrF_3
	2	3	Linear	XeF_2, I_3^-, ICl_2^-
6	6	0	Octahedral	SF_6
	5	1	Square pyramidal	BrF_5, ClF_5

Contd...

Total number of electron pairs	Number of bond pairs	Number of Lone pairs	Geometry (shape) of the molecule	Illustrative examples
	4	2	 Square planar	XeF_4

Valence Bond Theory of Covalent Bond

According to this theory, a covalent bond is formed by the overlapping of two half-filled atomic orbitals having electrons with opposite spins. It is based on wave nature of electron.

(i) Sigma Bond (σ bond)

This type of covalent bond is formed by head-on overlap, i.e. end to end overlap along the internuclear axis. Sigma bond can be formed by any one of the following types of combinations of atomic orbitals :

   (a) s-s overlapping   (b) s-p overlapping   (c) p-p overlapping (axial)

The strength of σ bond depends upon the extent of overlapping between atomic orbitals. The greater the extent of overlapping, the stronger is the σ bond.

(ii) Pi Bond (π bond)

It is formed by the sidewise or lateral overlapping between p-atomic orbitals [p-p side by side or lateral overlapping]

π bond is a weaker bond than σ bond.

Comparison of Sigma and Pi Bonds

Sigma bond	Pi bond
1. This bond is formed by overlapping of orbitals along their internuclear axis. 	This bond is formed by sideway overlapping of atomic orbitals.
2. Free rotation along a σ bond is possible.	Free rotation about a π bond is not possible.
3. Sigma bond consist of only one electron cloud symmetrical about the internuclear axis.	Pi (π) bond consists of two electron clouds, one above the plane of atomic nuclei and the other below it.

Limitations of VBT

It fails to explain

1. The magnetic properties of some molecules.
2. Bonding in electron deficient compounds.

Hybridisation

It is defined as the mixing of the atomic orbitals belonging to the same atom but having slightly different energies so that a redistribution of energy takes place between them resulting in the formation of new orbitals of equal energies and identical shapes. The new orbitals thus formed are known as hybrid orbitals and are more stable.

Method for Finding the Hybridisation

Apply the following formula to find the hybridisation of central atom.

$$Z = \frac{1}{2} \begin{pmatrix} \text{number of valence electrons of central atom} \\ + \text{ number of monovalent atoms attached to it} \\ + \text{ negative charge if any } - \text{ positive charge if any} \end{pmatrix}$$

Value of Z	2	3	4	5	6	7
Hybridisation	sp	sp^2	sp^3	sp^3d	sp^3d^2	sp^3d^3

Examples

Hybridisation of N in $NH_3 = \frac{1}{2}[5 + 3 + 0 - 0] = 4 \Rightarrow sp^3$

Hybridisation of S in $SO_4^{2-} = \frac{1}{2}[6 + 0 + 2 - 0] = 4 \Rightarrow sp^3$

Some Common Types of Hybridisation with Shapes and Examples

Types of hybridisation	Atomic orbitals involved	Representing directions of hybrid orbitals formed alongwith bond angles	Examples
sp	one s + one p	180° Linear	$BeCl_2$, BeH_2, C_2H_2
sp^2	one s + two p	120° Triangular planar	BF_3, BCl_3, C_2H_4, CO_3^{2-}

Types of hybridisation	Atomic orbitals involved	Representing directions of hybrid orbitals formed alongwith bond angles	Examples
sp^3	one s + three p	109°28′ Tetrahedral	CH_4, CCl_4, $SnCl_4$, NH_4^+
dsp^2	one d + one s + two p	90° Square planar	XeF_4
sp^3d	one s + three p + one d	90° 120° Trigonal bipyramidal	PCl_5, PF_5
sp^3d^2	one s + three p + two d	90° Octahedral	SF_6, $[CrF_6]^{3-}$

Coordinate or Dative Bond

It is a type of covalent bond in which the electron pair (lone pair) is donated by one atom but shared by both the atoms so as to complete their octets, e.g.

(i) $NH_3 \rightarrow BF_3$
donor   acceptor

(ii) $:\!O\!=\!O \rightarrow \ddot{O}\!:$

Molecular Orbital Theory

According to this theory, the atomic orbitals combine to form the molecular orbitals. The number of molecular orbitals formed is equal to the number of atomic orbitals involved. Molecular orbital of lower energy is known as **bonding molecular orbital** and that of higher energy is known as **anti-bonding molecular orbital**. Aufbau rule, Pauli's exclusion principle and Hund's rule are all applicable for molecular orbitals.

Formation of Molecular Orbtials :
Linear Combination of Atomic Orbitals (LCAO)

1. The molecular orbitals are formed by LCAO (Linear combination of atomic orbitals) method, i.e. by addition or subtraction of wave functions of individual atoms, thus

$$\Psi_{MO} = \Psi_A \pm \Psi_B$$
$$\Psi_b = \Psi_A + \Psi_B \qquad \text{[constructive interference]}$$
$$\Psi_a = \Psi_A - \Psi_B \qquad \text{[destructive interference]}$$

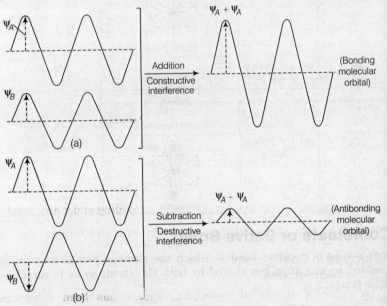

2. The shape of molecular orbitals is governed by the shape o atomic orbitals, e.g. s-s and p-p overlapping.

(i) Combination between $1s$ and $1s$ atomic orbitals gives $\sigma 1s$ an $\overset{*}{\sigma}1s$ orbitals.

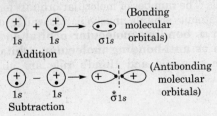

(ii) Combination between $2s$ and $2s$ orbitals gives $\sigma 2s$ and $\overset{*}{\sigma} 2s$ orbitals.

(iii) Combination between $2p_z$ and $2p_z$ atomic orbitals gives $\sigma 2p_z$ and $\sigma * 2p_z$ orbitals

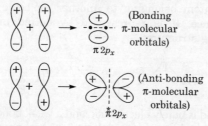

$2p_y$ atomic orbitals will also overlap in the same way and thus, resulting molecular orbitals are $\pi 2p_y$ and $\overset{*}{\pi} 2p_y$.

If molecular orbital has symmetry with respect to centre, it is called **gerade (g)** otherwise **ungerade (u)**. All σ bonding and $\overset{*}{\pi}$ anti-bonding MO are g while all π bonding and $\overset{*}{\sigma}$ anti-bonding MO are u.

Electronic Configuration and Bond Order (BO) of Molecules

The order of energy of molecular orbitals has been determined experimentally by spectroscopy for the elements of the second period. The increasing order of energies of the molecular orbitals in homonuclear diatomic molecules is

$$\sigma 1s < \overset{*}{\sigma} 1s < \sigma 2s < \overset{*}{\sigma} 2s < \sigma 2p_z < (\pi 2p_x \approx \pi 2p_y) < (\overset{*}{\pi} 2p_x \approx \overset{*}{\pi} 2p_y) < \overset{*}{\sigma} 2p_z$$

[For O_2, F_2, Ne_2 more than 14 electrons]

$$\sigma 1s < \overset{*}{\sigma} 1s < \sigma 2s < \overset{*}{\sigma} 2s < (\pi 2p_x \approx \pi 2p_y) < \sigma 2p_z < (\overset{*}{\pi} 2p_x \approx \overset{*}{\pi} 2p_y) < \overset{*}{\sigma} 2p_z$$

[For B_2, C_2, N_2 upto 14 electrons]

$$\text{Bond order (BO)} = \frac{N_b - N_a^*}{2}$$

A positive bond order, (i.e. $N_b > N_a^*$) means a stable molecule while a negative (i.e. $N_b < N_a^*$) or zero, (i.e. $N_b = N_a^*$) bond order means unstable molecule.

> Molecular species having unpaired electrons are paramagnetic, while if all the electrons in the orbitals are paired then the molecule is diamagnetic.

Hydrogen Bond

It is defined as the force of attraction existing between hydrogen atom covalently bonded to highly electronegative atom (N, O or F) and the electronegative atom belonging to another molecule of the same or different substance. It is represented by dotted lines. The chains possess a *zig-zag* structure.

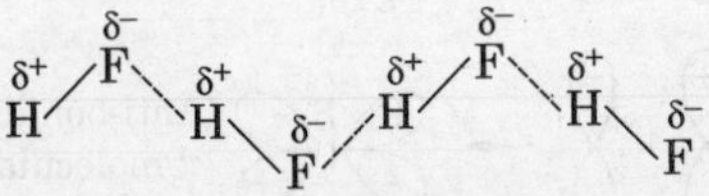

> Hydrogen bond is purely electrostatic and a weak bond. The strength of the strongest hydrogen bond is about 5-10 kcal per mol. The more the electronegativity of atom involved in H-bonding, the more is the bond strength, e.g.
>
> H--F > H--O > H--N
>
> 10 kcal/mol > 7 kcal/mol > 2.0 kcal/mol

Types of hydrogen bonds are:

Intermolecular H-bonding

H-bonding involving two or more different molecules. e.g. o-nitrophenol.

Intramolecular H-bonding

H-bonding within a same molecule. e.g., p-nitrophenol

Applications of Intermolecular H-bonding

(i) **Melting point and boiling point of water** Water has the lowest molecular weight among the hydrides of group 16 elements yet it has the highest melting and boiling points. It is due to intermolecular H-bonding in H_2O.

(ii) **Ice has less density than water** In crystal structure of ice, every water molecule is associated with four other water molecules by H-bonding in a cage like tetrahedral structure. On melting the ice, H-bonds are broken and space between water molecules decreases and density of water increases up to 4°C. Above 4°C, more H-bonds are broken, the water molecules get apart from each other and the density again decreases. Thus, water has maximum density at 4°C.

(iii) **Melting point and boiling point of alcohols** The marked difference between the melting and boiling points of alcohols is also due to H-bonding.

Applications of Intramolecular H-bonding

Volatile character of nitrophenols *o*-nitrophenol is more volatile (b.p. 214°C) as compared to *meta* (b.p. 290°C) and *para* (b.p. 279°C). It is due to chelation (ring like structure).

In *meta* and *para* isomer, chelation is not possible due to the formation of desired size of ring.

Metallic Bond

The attractive force that binds the metal ions to the mobile electrons is called metallic bond. The positive metal ions are called positive cores or kernels and mobile electrons are electron pool or electron gas. **Electron-sea theory of metallic bond** explains number of the properties of the metal.

Strength of bonds

Ionic bond > covalent bond > metallic bond > H-bond

5

States of Matter

Five states of matter are known, *viz*, solid, liquid, gas, plasma and Bose-Einstein condensate. Out of these, solid, liquid and gas are commonly found while remaining two are found only under specific conditions.

Interconversion of States of Matter

These states are interconvertible.

(i) **Melting point** This is the temperature at which a matter converts from its solid state to liquid state. It decreases in the presence of impurity.

(ii) **Boiling point** This is the temperature at which the vapour pressure of a liquid becomes equal to the atmospheric pressure.

It increases in the presence of impurity and with rise in pressure. Boiling point of water is 100°C.

(iii) **Freezing point** At this temperature, a matter converts from its liquid state into solid state.

Freezing point of water is 0°C.

(iv) **Evaporation** It is the process of conversion of a liquid into vapours at any temperature.

Due to evaporation,

(a) water droplets appear on the outer surface of a glass containing ice-cold water.

(b) water kept in earthen pot becomes cool during summer.

(c) desert cooler cool better on a hot dry day.

In short,

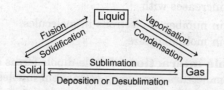

The temperature and pressure at which all the three states of a substance can exist together in equilibrium is called **triple point**, e.g. ice, liquid water and water vapours can coexist i.e. ice $\rightleftharpoons$ water $\rightleftharpoons$ vapour at 0.0098°C and 4.58 mm of Hg.

Plasma

It is a state of matter similar to gas in which a certain portion of the gaseous particles are ionised. Because of the average strength of the electrical forces, the plasma is neutral. It is commonly found in the universe.

On earth, plasma is naturally occurring in flames, lightnings and the auroras.

Bose-Einstein Condensate

A Bose-Einstein condensate is a gaseous superfluid phase formed by atoms cooled to temperature very near to absolute zero.

This state was first predicted by Satyendra Nath Bose and Albert Einstein in 1924-25. Such first condensate was produced by Eric Cornell and Carl Wiemann in 1995. It can be thought of as the opposite of a plasma.

Intermolecular Forces

The forces of attraction existing among the molecules of a substance (gaseous, liquid or solid) are called intermolecular forces.

Greater the intermolecular forces, higher is the melting and boiling point. Attractive intermolecular forces are known as van der Waals' forces.

The different types of intermolecular forces are briefly explained below:

(i) **Dispersion forces or London forces** Dispersion forces or London forces are present among non-polar atoms and molecules, e.g. among the atoms or chlorine molecules. These are the weakest intermolecular forces.

These forces increases with

(i) increase in number of electrons in molecules,

(ii) increase in molecular size.

(ii) **Dipole-dipole interactions** Dipole-dipole forces act between the molecules possessing permanent dipoles.

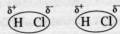

The interaction is stronger than London forces and weaker than ion-ion interaction. The intensity of these forces is generally hampered by increase in temperature.

(iii) **Dipole-induced dipole forces** Dipole-induced dipole forces act between the polar molecules having permanent dipole and the molecules lacking permanent dipole.

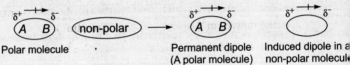

(iv) **Hydrogen bond** It is a special case of dipole-dipole interaction. This is found in the molecules in which highly polar N—H, O—H or H—F bonds are present. The strength of H-bond is determined by the coulombic interaction between the lone-pair electrons of the electronegative atom of one molecule and H-atom of other molecule.

Thermal Energy

Thermal energy is the energy of a body arising from motion of its atoms or molecules.

So, Thermal energy ∝ Temperature of the substances

Factors Deciding Physical State of a Substance

For gaseous state,

$$\text{Forces of attraction} \ll \text{Thermal energy}$$

For liquid state,

$$\text{Forces of attraction} > \text{Thermal energy}$$

For solid state,

$$\text{Forces of attraction} \gg \text{Thermal energy}$$

The Gaseous State

It is the most disordered state of matter. Characteristics of this state of matter are:

(i) In gases, the intermolecular forces are weakest.

(ii) Gases are highly compressible.

(iii) Gases exert pressure equally in all directions.

(iv) Gases have much lower density than the solids and liquids.

(v) The volume and the shape of gases are not fixed.

(vi) Gases mix evenly and completely in all proportions without any mechanical aid.

Measurable Properties of Gases

(i) **Mass** It is expressed in gram or kg.

(ii) **Volume** It is equal to the volume of the container and is expressed in terms of litre (L), millilitre (mL), cubic centimetre (cm^3), cubic metre (m^3) or cubic decimetre (dm^3).

$$1\ L = 1000\ mL = 1000\ cm^3 = 1\ dm^3$$
$$1\ m^3 = 10^3\ dm^3 = 10^6\ cm^3 = 10^6\ mL = 10^3 L$$

(iii) **Pressure** Gas pressure is measured with manometer and atmospheric pressure is measured by barometer.

$$1\ atm = 76\ cm\ of\ Hg = 760\ mm\ of\ Hg = 760\ torr$$
$$1\ atm = 101.325\ kPa = 101325\ Pa = 101.325\ Nm^{-2}$$
$$= 1.01325\ bar$$
$$1\ bar = 10^5\ Pa = 0.987\ atm$$

Measurement of pressure of gas

(a) Open end manometer, $p_{gas} = p_{atom} - h$

(b) Closed end manometer, $p_{gas} = h$

where h is difference in the mercury levels in the two columns of density (d) (of a gas).

(iv) **Temperature** It is measured in celsius scale (°C) or in Kelvin scale (K). SI unit of temperature is kelvin (K).

$$T\ (K) = t°\ (C) + 273$$

Standard temperature and pressure (STP or NTP) means 273.15 (0°C) temperature and 1 bar (i.e. exactly 10^5 pascal) pressure. At NTP, molar volume of an ideal gas is 22.71098 L mol^{-1}.

Gas Laws

Boyle's Law (1662)

The volume of a given mass of a gas is inversely proportional to its pressure at constant temperature.

$$V \propto \frac{1}{p} \text{ or } Vp = K$$

K is a constant and its value depends on mass, temperature and nature of gas.

$$\therefore \qquad p_1 V_1 = p_2 V_2$$

Graphical Representation of Boyle's Law

Graphs of p vs V or p vs $\frac{1}{V}$ or pV vs p at constant temperature are known as **isotherms**.

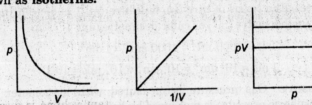

Air is dense at the sea level because it is compressed by the mass of air above it.

Charles' Law (1787)

The volume of the given mass of a gas increases or decreases by $\frac{1}{273}$ its volume for each degree rise or fall of temperature respectively at constant pressure.

$$V_t = V_0 \left(1 + \frac{t}{273}\right) \text{ at constant } p$$

Or

The volume of a given mass of a gas is directly proportional to the absolute temperature at constant pressure.

$$V \propto T \text{ (at constant } p), \frac{V}{T} = \text{constant or } \frac{V_1}{T_1} = \frac{V_2}{T_2}$$

Absolute zero is the theoretically possible temperature at which the volume of the gas becomes zero. It is equal to 0°C or 273.15 K.

Graphical Representation of Charles' Law

A graph of V *vs* T at constant pressure is known as **isobar**.

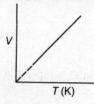 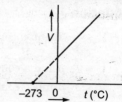

Charles' law explains that gases expand on heating, so hot air is less dense than cold air.

Gay Lussac's Law (1802)

The pressure of a given mass of gas increases or decreases by $\frac{1}{273}$ of its

pressure for each degree rise or fall of temperature respectively at constant volume.

$$p_t = p_0\left(1 + \frac{t}{273}\right) \text{ at constant } V \text{ and } n$$

Or

The pressure of a given mass of a gas at constant volume is **directly proportional** to absolute temperature.

$$p \propto T \text{ or } p = KT \text{ or } \frac{p}{T} = K \text{ at constant } V \text{ and } n \text{ or } \frac{p_1}{T_1} = \frac{p_2}{T_2}$$

Graphical Representation of Gay Lussac's Law

A graph of p *vs* T at constant volume is known as **isochore**.

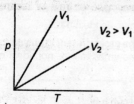

Avogadro's Law

It states that equal volumes of all gases under the same conditions of temperature and pressure contain equal number of molecules.

Mathematically

$$V \propto n \qquad \text{(at constant } T \text{ and } p\text{)}$$

$$\frac{V}{n} = K \qquad \left[n = \text{number of moles, } n = \frac{m}{M}\right]$$

Molar gas volume The volume of one mole of a gas, i.e. 22.4 L at STP (0°C, 1 atm) is known as molar gas volume.

Ideal Gas Equation

$$V \propto \frac{1}{p}, T \text{ and } n \text{ constant} \qquad \text{(Boyle's law)}$$

$$V \propto T, p \text{ and } n \text{ constant} \qquad \text{(Charles' law)}$$

$$V \propto n, p \text{ and } T \text{ constant} \qquad \text{(Avogadro's law)}$$

$$\Rightarrow \qquad V \propto \frac{nT}{p}$$

or $\qquad pV \propto nT$

or $\qquad pV = nRT.$

This is known as **ideal gas equation**. R is known as universal gas constant.

From the ideal gas equation, density,

$$d = \frac{pM}{RT} \qquad \text{(where, } M = \text{molecular mass)}$$

Numerical Values of R

(i) $R = 0.0821$ L atm $mol^{-1}K^{-1}$

(ii) $R = 0.083$ L bar $mol^{-1}K^{-1}$

(iii) $R = 8.314$ $JK^{-1}mol^{-1}$

(iv) $R = 8.314 \times 10^7$ erg $K^{-1}mol^{-1}$

(v) $R = 1.987$ or 2 cal $K^{-1}mol^{-1}$

Ideal gas The gas which obeys the equation $pV = nRT$ at every temperature and pressure range strictly is known as ideal gas.

Real gases Since none of the gases present in universe strictly obey the equation $pV = nRT$, hence they are known as real or non-ideal gases. Real gases behave ideally at low p and high T.

Graham's Law of Diffusion

Under similar conditions of temperature and pressure, the rates of diffusion of gases are inversely proportional to the square root of their densities.

Mathematically, $\qquad \dfrac{r_1}{r_2} = \sqrt{\dfrac{d_2}{d_1}} = \sqrt{\dfrac{M_2}{M_1}}$

Diffusion is the tendency of gases to distribute itself uniformly throughout the available space while **effusion** is the movement of gas through a small hole when it is subjected to pressure.

Dalton's Law of Partial Pressure

At constant temperature, the total pressure exerted by a mixture of non-reacting gases is the sum of partial pressures of different gases present in the mixture.

$$p = p_1 + p_2 + p_3 + \ldots$$

Partial pressure of a gas = mole fraction of the gas × total pressure.

If n_1, n_2 and n_3 are moles of non-reacting gases filled in a vessel of volume V at temperature T, the total pressure, p is given by

$$p = (n_1 + n_2 + n_3)RT/V$$

This is the equation of state of a gaseous mixture.

Pressure of a dry gas can be determined by Dalton's law. When a gas is collected over water, its observed pressure is equal to the sum of the pressure of dry gas and the pressure of water vapour (aqueous tension) then pressure of moist gas = pressure of dry gas + aqueous tension.

Aqueous tension It is the pressure exerted by water vapours at a particular temperature. It depends upon temperature.

Kinetic Theory of Gases

Main assumptions of this theory are:

1. A gas consists of large number of small particles, called **molecules**.
2. Volume occupied by gas molecules is negligible as compared to the total volume of the gas.
3. There is continuous rapid random motion of gas molecules. The molecules collide with each other and with the walls of container.
4. The molecules are perfect elastic bodies and there is no loss of kinetic energy during collisions.
5. There are no attractive forces between the gaseous molecules.
6. The pressure exerted by a gas is due to the bombardment of gas molecules against the walls of the container.
7. The different molecules possess different velocities and hence, different energies. The avearge KE is directly proportional to absolute temperature.

$$KE = \frac{3}{2} RT$$

$\therefore$ Average kinetic energy per molecule = $\dfrac{3}{2}kT$

Here, k is Boltzmann constant, it is gas constant per molecule.

$$k = \dfrac{R}{N_A} = 1.38 \times 10^{-23} \text{ JK}^{-1} \text{ mol}^{-1}$$

From the above postulates, the kinetic gas equation derived is

$$pV = \dfrac{1}{3}mnU^2$$

where, U = root mean square velocity = $\sqrt{\dfrac{3RT}{M}}$

Velocities of Gas Molecules

The different velocities possessed by gas molecules are :

(i) **Most probable velocity** (α) It is the velocity possessed b maximum fraction of gas molecules at a particular temperature.

$$\alpha = \sqrt{\dfrac{2RT}{M}}$$

(ii) **Average velocity** ($\bar{v}$) This is the average of the differer velocities of all the molecules.

$$\bar{v} = \sqrt{\dfrac{8RT}{\pi M}}$$

(iii) **Root mean square velocity** (U_{rms}) It is the square root the mean of the square of the different velocities of the molecule

$$U_{rms} = \sqrt{\dfrac{n_1 c_1^2 + n_2 c_2^2 + n_3 c_3^2 + \ldots}{n_1 + n_2 + n_3 + \ldots}}$$

Mathematically, $U = \sqrt{\dfrac{3RT}{M}} = \sqrt{\dfrac{3pV}{M}} = \sqrt{\dfrac{3p}{d}}$ $\left[\sqrt{\dfrac{3p}{d}} = \sqrt{\dfrac{3RT}{M}} \right.$

$$\alpha : \bar{v} : U = 1 : 1.128 : 1.224$$

Deviation from Ideal Behaviour

At high pressure and low temperature, the gases deviate considerably from the ideal behaviour. Deviation can be expressed in terms of compressibility factor (Z), expressed as

$$Z = \frac{pV}{nRT}$$

In case of ideal gas, $pV = nRT, Z = 1$

In case of real gas, $pV \neq nRT, Z \neq 1$

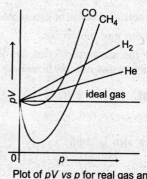

Plot of pV vs p for real gas and ideal gas.

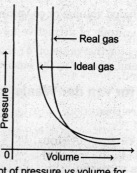

Plot of pressure vs volume for real gas and ideal gas.

It can be seen easily that at constant temperature, pV vs p plot for real gas is not a straight line.

Negative deviation In such case, $Z < 1$, gas is more compressible.

Positive deviation In such case, $Z > 1$, gas is less compressible.

The factors affecting the deviation are:

(i) **Nature of the gas** In general, the most easily liquefiable and highly soluble gases show larger deviation.

(ii) **Pressure** The deviation is more at high pressure. CO_2 and N_2 show negative deviation at low pressure and positive deviation at high pressure.

(iii) **Temperature** The deviation is more at low temperature. H_2 and He always show positive deviations at 0°C

Cause of deviation from the ideal behaviour It is due to two faulty assumptions of kinetic theory of gases, particularly not valid at high pressure and low temperature.

1. Volume occupied by the gas molecules is negligible as compared to the total volume of the gas.
2. There are no attractive forces between the gas molecules.

van der Waals' Equation

After volume and pressure correction, van der Waals' obtained the following equation for n moles of a gas.

$$\left(p + \frac{n^2a}{V^2}\right)(V - nb) = nRT$$

$$\left(p + \frac{a}{V^2}\right)(V - b) = RT, \qquad \text{(for one mole)}$$

where,

b = excluded volume or co-volume = 4 × actual volume of gas molecules

a = magnitude of attractive forces between gas molecules.

The greater the value of 'a', the greater the strength of van der Waals forces and greater is the ease with which a gas can be liquefied.

Units for van der Waals' constant

Pressure correction,

$$p = \frac{n^2a}{V^2} \quad \text{or} \quad a = \frac{pV^2}{n^2} = \text{atm L}^2 \text{ mol}^{-2}$$

Volume correction,

$$V = nb \quad \text{or} \quad b = \frac{V}{n} = \text{L mol}^{-1}$$

Limitation of van der Waals' Equation

There is specific range of temperature and pressure, to apply th equation. It deviates at very high pressure and very low temperature.

Liquefaction of Gases and Critical Points

The phenomenon of conversion of a gas into liquid is known a liquefaction. The liquefaction of a gas takes place when th intermolecular forces of attraction becomes so high that it exist in th liquid. A gas can be liquefied by

(i) increasing pressure

(ii) decreasing temperature.

The critical points are as follows

(i) **Critical temperature** (T_C) It may be defined as th temperature above which no gas can be liquefied. Critica temperature of CO_2 is 30.98°C.

Critical temperature (T_C) of some gases are He (5.4), H_2(33.2), N_2(126.0), CO(134.4), O_2 (154.3), CO_2(304.1), NH_4(405.5),

$$T_C = \frac{8a}{27Rb}$$

(ii) **Critical pressure** (p_C) At critical temperature, the pressure needed to liquefy a gas is known as critical pressure.

$$p_C = \frac{a}{27b^2}$$

(iii) **Critical volume** (V_C) The volume occupied by one mole of a gas at critical temperature and critical pressure is known as critical volume.

$$V_C = 3b$$

(iv) **Boyle's temperature** (T_b) Temperature at which a real gas exhibits ideal behaviour for considerable range of pressure is called Boyle's temperature.

$$T_b = \frac{a}{bR}$$

Liquid State

If a substance is having melting point below room temperature and boiling point above room temperature, the substance is known as liquid. In liquid state, matter has definite shape and molecular motion is in between solids and gases.

Properties of Liquids

(i) **Vapour pressure** The pressure exerted by the vapours above the liquid surface when these are in equilibrium with the liquid at a given temperature is known as vapour pressure of liquid.

The vapour pressure of a liquid depends on :

(i) Nature of liquid

(ii) Temperature : Vapour pressure increases with increasing temperature.

(ii) **Boiling point** The temperature at which vapour pressure of liquids becomes equal to the atmospheric pressure, is called boiling point.

At 1 atm pressure, boiling point is known as normal boiling point.

At 1 bar pressure, boiling point is known as standard boiling point.

Boiling point varies linearly with external pressure.

(iii) **Surface tension** It is the force acting per unit length perpendicular to the imaginary line drawn on the surface of liquid. It is denoted by γ (gamma).

$$\text{SI unit : Nm}^{-1} \qquad \gamma = \frac{\text{Force } (F)}{\text{Length } (L)}$$

Dimensions : kgs^{-2}

The magnitude of surface tension of a liquid depends on the attractive forces between the molecules. It is measured with the help of an apparatus, called stalgmometer.

Surface tension decreases as the temperature increases.

Rise or fall of liquid in a capillary tube is due to surface tension.

(iv) **Viscosity** Viscosity is a measure of resistance to flow which arises due to internal friction between layers of fluid as they slip past one another while liquid flows.

When there is a regular gradation of velocity, in passing from one layer to the next, it is called laminar flow.

$$F = \eta \frac{A dv}{dz}$$

where, F = forces required to maintain the flow of layers.

A = area of contact

dv/dz = velocity gradient; (the change in velocity with distance.)

'η' is proportionality constant and is called **coefficient of viscosity**. **Viscosity coefficient** is the force when velocity gradiant is unity and the area of contact is unit area. CGS unit of coefficient of viscosity is poise. S.I. unit of coefficient of viscosity is Nsm^{-2}.

6

The Solid State

Solids are the chemical substances which are characterised by definite shape and volume, rigidity, high density, low compressibility. The constituent particles (atoms, molecules or ions) are closely packed and held together by strong interparticle forces.

Types of Solids

The solids are of two types : Crystalline solids and amorphous solids.

Distinction Between Crystalline and Amorphous Solids

S.No.	Crystalline solids	Amorphous solids
1.	These have definite and regular arrangement of the constituent particles in space.	These doesn't have any regular arrangement of the constituent particles in space.
2.	These are true solids.	These are super cooled liquids or pseudo solids.
3.	These have long order in arrangement of the particles.	These have short order in arrangement of particles.
4.	These are anisotropic in nature, i.e. their physical properties are different in different directions.	These are isotropic in nature i.e. their physical properties are same in all the directions.
5.	They have sharp melting points.	They melt over a certain range of temperature.
6.	They undergo a clean cleavage when cut.	They undergo irregular cleavage when cut.
7.	They have a definite and characteristic heat of fusion.	They do not have definite heat of fusion.

Types of Crystalline Solids

Character	Ionic solids	Covalent or network solids	Molecular solids	Metallic solids
Constituent particles	Positive and negative ions	Atoms	Molecules	Positive metal ions (kernels) and free electrons
Bonding forces	Electrostatic or coulombic attraction	Covalent	van der Waals' Dipole-dipole	Metallic bonding
Melting point	High melting point	Very high melting point	Low melting point	Moderate to high melting point
Physical nature	Hard and brittle	Very hard	Very soft	Hard but malleable and ductile
Conductance	Conductors in aqueous solution or in molten state but insulators in solid state	Non-conductor	Insulator	Good conductor
Examples	NaCl, CaF_2, MgO, ZnS	Diamond, Silica, SiC	H_2O, CO_2, CCl_4, HCl, SO_2	Cu, Fe, Ag, Mg.

Note Molecular solids are further subdivided into non-polar molecular solids, polar molecular solids and hydrogen bonded molecular solids.

Structure Determination by X-ray Diffraction (Bragg's Equation)

When a beam of X-rays falls on a crystal plane composed of regularly arranged atoms or ions, the X-rays are diffracted. If the waves are in phase after reflection, the difference in distance travelled by the two rays (i.e. path difference) must be equal to an integral number of wavelength, $n\lambda$ for constructive interference.

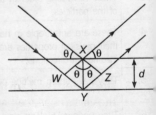

Thus, path difference $= WY + YZ$

$$= XY \sin\theta + XY \sin\theta$$

$$= 2 XY \sin\theta = 2d \sin\theta$$

$$\therefore \qquad n\lambda = 2d \sin\theta$$

This equation is called Bragg's equation.

where, $n = 1, 2, 3 \ldots$ (diffraction order),

λ = wavelength of X-rays incident on crystal and

d = distance between atomic planes

θ = angle at which interference occurs.

Crystal Lattices

In three dimensional space, a regular arrangement and repeating pattern of the constituent particles of a crystal in which each particle is depicted as a point is known as **crystal lattice** or **space lattice**.

Unit Cell

The smallest geometrical portion of the crystal lattice which can be used as repetitive unit to build up the whole crystal is called unit cell.

Types of Unit Cell

1. **Simple or primitive unit cell** In which the particles are present at the corners of unit cell only.

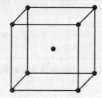

2. **Face centred unit cell** In which the particles are present at the corners as well as at the centre of each of six faces of unit cell.

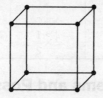

3. **Body centred unit cell** In which the particles are present at the corners as well as at the centre of unit cell.

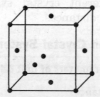

4. **End centred unit cell** In which the particles are present at the corners and at the centre of two opposite faces of unit cell.

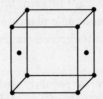

Number of Particles Per Unit Cell

Unit cell	No. of particles and their contribution			Total
	Corner	Face	Centre	
Simple cubic	$8 \times \dfrac{1}{8}$	—	—	1
Face centred	$8 \times \dfrac{1}{8}$	$6 \times \dfrac{1}{2}$	—	4
Body centred	$8 \times \dfrac{1}{8}$	—	1	2
End centred	$8 \times \dfrac{1}{8}$	$2 \times \dfrac{1}{2}$	—	2

Seven Crystal Systems and Possible Variations

There are about 230 crystal forms, which have been grouped into 14 types of space lattices, called **Bravais Lattices**, on the basis of their symmetry and seven different crystal systems on the basis of interfacial angles and axial distances.

Seven Crystal Systems

	Crystal system	Parameters of unit cell		Possible variation
		Axial distances or edge lengths	Angles	
1.	Cubic	$a = b = c$	$\alpha = \beta = \gamma = 90°$	Primitive, body centred, face centred.
2.	Tetragonal	$a = b \neq c$	$\alpha = \beta = \gamma = 90°$	Primitive, body centred
3.	Rhombohedral or trigonal	$a = b = c$	$\alpha = \beta = \gamma \neq 90°$	Primitive

	Crystal system	Parameters of unit cell		Possible variation
		Axial distances or edge lengths	Angles	
1.	Cubic	$a = b = c$	$\alpha = \beta = \gamma = 90°$	Primitive, body centred, face centred.
4.	Orthorhombic	$a \neq b \neq c$	$\alpha = \beta = \gamma = 90°$	Primitive, body, face and end centred.
5.	Monoclinic	$a \neq b \neq c$	$\alpha = \gamma = 90°, \beta \neq 90°$	Primitive and end centred.
6.	Triclinic	$a \neq b \neq c$	$\alpha \neq \beta \neq \gamma \neq 90°$	Primitive
7.	Hexagonal	$a = b \neq c$	$\alpha = \beta = 90°, \gamma = 120°$	Primitive

Coordination Number (CN)

It is defined as the number of particles immediately adjacent to each particle in the crystal lattice. In simple cubic lattice, CN is 6, in body centred lattice, CN is 8 and in face centred cubic lattice, CN is 12.

High pressure increases CN and high temperature decreases the CN.

Close Packing in Crystals

Packing in solids may be divided into the following categories :

One Dimensional packing of constituent particles

In one dimensional close packing arrangement, the coordination number is 2.

Two Dimensional Packing of Constituent Particles

(i) **Square Close Packing** When atoms arranged in a row is stacked with atoms arranged in another row exactly one over another is known as square close packing. Coordination number in square close packing is 4. This is also known as *AAA*...type arrangement space occupied by spheres is 52.4%.

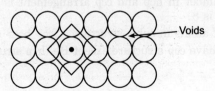
Voids

(ii) **Hexagonal Close Packing** This is generated by placing spheres of the second row in the depressions of first row. Coordination number in hexagonal closed packing is 6. This is also known as *ABAB*...type arrangement space occupied by spheres is 60.4%. Hence, it is more efficient.

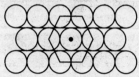

Three Dimensional Packing of Constituent Particles

(a) **Three dimensional closed packing from two dimensional square close packed layers** When two dimensional square close packed layers are arranged exactly one over the other they constitute a three dimensional close packing. The arrangement is known as *AAA* arrangement.

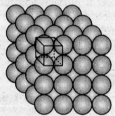

(b) **Three dimensional close packing from two dimensional hexagonal close packed layers** When hexagonal close packed layers are stacked kone over another, they form three dimensional close packing.

   (i) **Hexagonal close packing** When third layer is placed over second layer in such a way that they constitute tetrahedral void. The arrangement is called *ABAB* pattern.

   (ii) **Cubic close packing** When the third layer is placed over second layer in such a way that sphere covers octahedral voids. The arrangement is called *ABABC* pattern.

In both these arrangements 74% space is occupied.

Coordination number in hcp and ccp arrangement is 12 while in bcc arrangement, it is 8.

Close packing of atoms in cubic structure = fcc > bcc > scc

All noble gases have ccp structure except He (hcp structure).

Void or Space or Holes

Empty or vacant space present between spheres of a unit cell, is called void or space or hole or interstitial void. When particles are close packed resulting in either ccp or hcp structure, three types of voids are generated:

Trigonal voids exist in two dimensional arrangement.

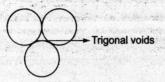

Trigonal voids

Tetrahedral voids are holes or voids surrounded by four spheres present at the corner of a tetrahedron. Coordination number of a tetrahedral void is 4.

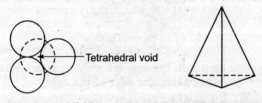

Tetrahedral void

$$r_{\text{void}} = 0.225 \times r_{\text{sphere}}$$ (for tetrahedral voids)

Octahedral voids are holes surrounded by six spheres located on a regular tetrahedron. Coordination number of octahedral void is 6.

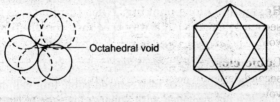

Octahedral void

$$r_{\text{void}} = 0.414 \times r_{\text{sphere}}$$ (for octahedral voids)

The number of octahedral voids present in a lattice is equal to the number of close packed particles.

The number of tetrahedral voids present in a lattice is twice to the number of close packed particles.

Packing Efficiency or Packing Fraction

The percentage of total space filled by the particles.

(i) **Primitive cubic unit cell** Atoms touch each other along edges.

Hence, $d = a$ or $r = \dfrac{a}{2}$ ($r =$ radius of atom and $a =$ edge length)

Therefore,

$$PF = \frac{\text{Volume of one atom}}{\text{Volume of cubic unit cell}} = \frac{\dfrac{4}{3}\pi r^3}{(2r)^3} = 0.524 \text{ or } 52.4\%$$

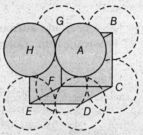

Simple cubic unit cell, the spheres are in contact with each other along the edge of the cube

(ii) **Face centred cubic unit cell** Atoms touch each other along the face diagonal.

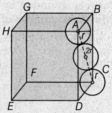

Cubic close packing, or face centred cubic unit cell other sides are not provided with spheres for sake of clarity

Hence, $d = a/\sqrt{2}$

or $r = \sqrt{2}a/4$ ($\because$ Length of face diagonal $= \sqrt{2}a$)

Therefore, $PF = \dfrac{4 \times \dfrac{4}{3}\pi r^3}{\left(\dfrac{4r}{\sqrt{2}}\right)^3} = 0.74 \text{ or } 74\%$

The packing efficiency of hcp and ccp structures is also 74%.

(iii) **Body centred cubic unit cell** Atoms touch each other along the body diagonal.

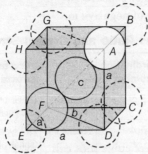

Body-centred cubic unit cell (sphere along the body diagonal are shown with solid boundaries)

Hence, $\qquad d = \sqrt{3}a/2$

or $\qquad r = \sqrt{3}a/4 \quad$ ($\because$ Length of body diagonal $= \sqrt{3}a$)

Therefore, $\qquad PF = \dfrac{2 \times \dfrac{4}{3}\pi r^3}{\left(\dfrac{4r}{\sqrt{3}}\right)^3} = 0.68$ or 68%

The packing efficiency of hcp and ccp structure is also 74%.

Density of Unit Cell (d)

$$\text{Density of unit cell} = \frac{\text{mass of unit cell}}{\text{volume of unit cell}}$$

$$d = \frac{Z \cdot m}{a^3} = \frac{ZM}{a^3 \times N_A} \text{ kg/cm}^3$$

$$\left[\text{Mass of an atom } (m) = \frac{M}{N_A}\right]$$

(The density of the unit cell is same as the density of the substance.)

where, d = density of unit cell, M = molecular weight

Z = number of atoms per unit cell, N_A = Avogadro number

a = edge length of unit cell.

The Structure of Ionic Crystals

The **ionic radius ratio** of cation and anion play a very important role in giving a clue to the nature of the crystal structure of ionic substance.

The ratio r_+ to r_- is called radius ratio.

$$\text{Radius ratio} = \frac{\text{radius of positive ion}}{\text{radius of negative ion}} = \frac{r_+}{r_-}$$

Radius Ratio and Crystal Structure

S. No.	Radius ratio (r_+ / r_-)	Coordination number	Shape	Crystal structure	Example
1.	< 0.225	2 or 3	Linear or triangular	Linear or triangular	B_2O_3
2.	0.225–0.414	4	Tetrahedral	ZnS type (sphalerite)	CuCl, CuBr, HgS, BaS
3.	0.414–0.732	4 or 6	Squar planar or octahedral	NaCl type	MgO, NaBr, CaS, KBr, CaO, AgCl
4.	0.732 or more	8	Cube	CsCl type	CsI, CsBr, NH_4Br, TlBr

Ionic crystals may be of two types:

(i) *AB* type and   (ii) A_2B or AB_2

Structure of Ionic Crystals

Ionic crystal type	Cation occupy	Anion form	Coordination number
NaCl (Rock salt structure) type	All octahedral voids	fcc unit cell	6 : 6
CsCl type	Body centre	simple cubic unit cell	8 : 8
ZnS (Sphalerite structure) type	Alternate tetrahedral voids	fcc unit cell	4 : 4
CaF_2 (Fluorite structure) type	Alternate body centre	simple cubic unit cell	8 : 4
Na_2O (Antifluorite structure) type	All tetrahedral sites	fcc unit cell	4 : 8

On applying pressure, NaCl structure (6 : 6 coordination) changes into CsCl structure (8 : 8 coordination) and reverse of this occur at high temperature (760 K).

Imperfections Defects in Solids

In a crystalline solid, the atoms, ions and molecules are arranged in a definite repeating pattern, but some defects may occur in the pattern. Deviations from perfect arrangement may occur due to rapid cooling or presence of additional particles.

The defects are of two types, namely **point defects** and **line defects**.

The irregularities or deviations from ideal arrangement in entire rows of lattice points is called **line defects.**

Point defects are the irregularities or deviations from ideal arrangement around a point or an atom in a crystalline substance.

Point defects can be classified into three types :

(1) stoichiometric defects   (2) impurity defects

(3) non-stoichiometric defects.

1. Stoichiometric Defect

These are point defects that do not disturb the stoichiometry of the solid. They are also called **intrinsic** or **thermodynamic defects**.

(a) **In non ionic solids,** two types of defects are present:

Vacancy Defect When some of the lattice sites are vacant, crystal is said to have vacancy defect and results in decrease in density of substance.

Interstitial Defect When some constituent particles occupy an interstitial site, the crystal is said to have interstitial defect and results in increase in density of substances.

(b) **In ionic solids,** basically these are of two types, Frenkel defect and Schottky defect.

	Schottky defect	Frenkel defect
1.	It is due to equal number of cations and anions missing from the lattice sites.	It is due to the dislocation of ions (usually cations) from the lattice sites to occupy the interstitial sites.
2.	This results in the decrease in density of crystal.	It has no effect on the density of crystal.
3.	This type of defect is found in highly ionic compounds with high coordination number, e.g. NaCl, CsCl, etc.	This type of defect is found in crystal where the difference in the size of cations and anions is very large, e.g. AgCl, ZnS, etc.

AgBr has both Schottky and Frenkel defects. Frenkel defects are not found in pure alkali metal halides because cations are of large size.

2. Impurity Defect

It arises when foreign atoms or ions are present in the lattice. In case of ionic compounds, the impurity is also ionic in nature. When the impurity has the same charge as the host ion, it just substitutes some of the host ions. Impurity defects can also be introduced by adding

impurity has the same charge as the host ion, it just substitutes some of the host ions. Impurity defects can also be introduced by adding impurity ions having different charge than host ions, e.g. molten NaCl containing a little amount of $SrCl_2$ is crystallised. In such cases,

cationic vacancies produced = [number of cations of higher valence × difference in valence of the host cation and cation of higher valence]

3. Non-Stoichiometric Defect

Non-stoichiometric crystals are those which do not obey the law of constant proportions. The number of positive and negative ions present in such compounds are different from those expected from their ideal chemical formulae. However, the crystal as a whole is neutral.

Types of non-stoichiometric defects are as follows:

(i) **Metal excess defect due to anionic vacancies** Alkali halides like NaCl and KCl show this type of defect. F-centres are the sites from where anions are missing and the vacant sites are occupied by electrons. F-centres contribute colour and paramagnetic nature of the crystal [F stands for German word *Farbe* meaning colour].

Metal excess defect due to presence of extra cations at interstitial sites, e.g. zinc oxide is white in colour at room temperature. On heating, it loses oxygen and turns yellow.

$$ZnO \xrightarrow{\text{Heating}} Zn^{2+} + \frac{1}{2}O_2 + 2e^-$$

(ii) **Metal deficiency defect due to cation vacancy** It is due to the absence of a metal ion from its lattice site and charge is balanced by ion having higher positive charge. Transition metals exhibit this defect, e.g. FeO, which is found in the composition range from $Fe_{0.93}O$ to $Fe_{0.96}O$.

In crystal of FeO, some Fe^{2+} cations are missing and the loss of positive charge is made up by the presence of required number of Fe^{3+} ions.

Electrical Properties of Solids

Solids can be classified into three types on the basis of their conductivities.

Classification of Solids on the Basis of Electrical Conductivity

Type of solid	Conductivity (ohm^{-1} m^{-1})	Reason of conductivity	Examples
Conductors	$10^4 - 10^7$ (Very high)	Motion of electrons	Metals like Ag, Al
Insulators	10^{-20} to 10^{-10} (Very low)	Do not permit electricity to pass	Wood, rubber, bakelite
Semiconductors	$10^{-6} - 10^4$ (Moderate)	Motion of interstitial electrons or holes or both	Si, Ge, etc.

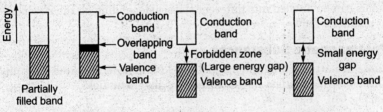

Conductors   Insulator   Semiconductor

The electricity produced on heating a polar crystal is called **'pyroelectricity'**. When mechanical stress is applied on polar crystals, electricity produced due to displacement of ions is called **'piezoelectricity'**.

Semiconductors

Electronic conductors having electrical conductivity in the range of $10^4 - 10^{-6}$ Ω^{-1} m^{-1} are known as semiconductors, e.g. Si, Ge, Sn (grey), Cu_2O, SiC and GaAs.

Intrinsic Semiconductors

Pure substances that are semiconductors are known as intrinsic (undoped) semiconductors, e.g. Si, Ge.

Extrinsic Semiconductors

Their conductivity is due to the presence of impurities. They are formed by doping. It is defined as addition of impurities to a semiconductor to increase the conductivity. Doping of Si or Ge is carried out with P, As, Sb, B, Al or Ga.

(i) ***n*-type semiconductors** Silicon or germanium doped with 15 group elements like phosphorus is called *n*-type semiconductor. The conductivity is due to the presence of negative charge (electrons).

(ii) ***p*-type semiconductors** Silicon or germanium doped with 13 group element like gallium is called *p*-type semiconductor. The conductivity is due to the presence of positive holes.

Some typical 13-15 compounds are InSb, AlP and GaAs and some typical 12-16 compounds are ZnS, CdS, CdSe and HgTe.

These exhibit electrical and optical properties of great use in electronic industry.

Magnetic Properties of Solids

Solids can be divided into different classes depending on their response to magnetic field.

Paramagnetic Substances

These are attracted by the magnetic field and have unpaired electrons. These lose magnetism in the absence of magnetic field, e.g. O_2, Cu^{2+}, Fe^{3+}, etc.

Diamagnetic Substances

These are weakly repelled by the magnetic field and do not have any unpaired electron, e.g. $TiO_2, V_2O_5, C_6H_6, NaCl$, etc.

Ferromagnetic Substances

These are attracted by the magnetic field and show permanent magnetism even in the absence of magnetic field, e.g. Fe, Co, CrO_2 and Ni.

Anti-ferromagnetic Substances

These substances have net magnetic moment zero due to compensatory alignment of magnetic moments, e.g. MnO, MnO_2, FeO, NiO, Cr_2O_3 etc.

Ferrimagnetic Substances

These substances have a net dipole moment due to unequal parallel and anti-parallel alignment of magnetic moments, e.g. Fe_3O_4, ferrites ($M^{2+}Fe_2O_4$), where M = Mg, Cu, Zn etc.

7

Thermodynamics

The branch of science which deals with the quantitative relationship between heat and other forms of energies is called **thermodynamics.**

Thermodynamic Terms

  (i) **System** It refers to the part of universe in which observations are carried out.

 (ii) **Surroundings** The part of universe other than the system is known as surroundings.

(iii) **Boundary** The wall that separates the system from the surroundings is called boundary.

(iv) **Thermodynamic equilibrium** A system in which the macroscopic properties do not undergo any change with time is called thermodynamic equilibrium.

 (v) **Thermal equilibrium** If there is no flow of heat from one portion of the system to another, the system is said to be in thermal equilibrium.

(vi) **Mechanical equilibrium** If no mechanical work is done by one part of the system on another part of the system, it is said to be in mechanical equilibrium. Such a condition exists when pressure remains constant.

Types of Systems

  (i) **Open system** The system in which energy and matter both can be exchanged with the surroundings.

 (ii) **Closed system** The system in which only energy can be exchanged with the surroundings.

(iii) **Isolated system** The system in which neither energy nor matter can be exchanged with the surroundings.

State of System

When microscopic properties have definite value, the conditions of existence of the system is known as state of system.

State functions (State variables) When values of a system are independent of path followed and depend only on initial and final state, it is known as state function, e.g. $\Delta U, \Delta H, \Delta G$ etc.

Path functions These depend upon the path followed, e.g. work, heat, etc.

Thermodynamic Properties

Intensive Properties

Properties of the system which depend only on the nature of matter but not on the quantity of matter are called intensive properties, e.g. pressure, temperature, specific heat, etc.

Extensive Properties

Properties of the system which are dependent on the quantity of matter are called extensive properties, e.g. internal energy, volume, enthalpy, etc.

Thermodynamic Process

It is the operation which brings change in the state of the system. Thermodynamic processes are

(i) **Isothermal process** In which temperature remains constant, i.e. $(dT = 0, \ \Delta U = 0)$.

(ii) **Isochoric process** In which volume remains constant, i.e. $(\Delta V = 0)$.

(iii) **Isobaric process** In which pressure remains constant, i.e. $(\Delta p = 0)$.

(iv) **Adiabatic process** In which heat is not exchanged by system with the surroundings, i.e. $(\Delta q = 0)$.

(v) **Cyclic process** It is a process in which system returns to its original state after undergoing a series of change, i.e. $\Delta U_{\text{cyclic}} = 0$; $\Delta H_{\text{cyclic}} = 0$.

(iv) **Reversible process** A process that follows the reversible path, i.e. the process which occurs in infinite number of steps in a way that the equilibrium conditions are maintained at each step, and the process can be reversed by infinitesimal change in the state of functions.

(vii) **Irreversible process** The process which cannot be reversed and amount of energy increases. All natural processes are irreversible.

Internal Energy (E or U)

It is the total energy within the substance. It is the sum of many types of energies like vibrational energy, translational energy, etc. It is an extensive property and state function.

Its absolute value cannot be determined but experimentally change in internal energy (ΔU) can be determined by

$$\Delta U = U_2 - U_1 \quad \text{or} \quad \Sigma U_P - \Sigma U_R$$

For exothermic process, $\Delta U = -$ ve, whereas for endothermic process $\Delta U = +$ve.

U depends on temperature, pressure, volume and quantity of matter and is independent of the method by which state has been attained.

Zeroth Law of Thermodynamics or Law of Thermal Equilibrium

The law states that if the two systems are in thermal equilibrium with a third system then they are also in thermal equilibrium with each other. Temperature is used here to know whether the system is in thermal equilibrium or not.

First Law of Thermodynamics

Energy can neither be created nor destroyed although it can be converted from one form to the other.

Mathematically, $\Delta U = q + W$

where, ΔU = internal energy change

q = heat added to system

W = work added to system

Sign convention

(i) q is $+$ ve $=$ heat is supplied to the system

(ii) q is $-$ ve $=$ heat is lost by the system

(iii) W is $+$ve $=$ work done on the system

(iv) W is $-$ve $=$ work done by the system

Modes of Transference of Energy

Work (W)

If the system involves gaseous substances and there is a difference of pressure between system and surroundings, work is referred as pressure-volume work (W_{pV}).

Expression for Pressure-Volume Work

(i) Work done in irreversible expansion against constant pressure p under isothermal conditions

$$q = -W_{pV} = p_{ext} \Delta V$$

(ii) Work done in reversible expansion under isothermal conditions

$$q = -W_{rev} = 2.303 \, nRT \log \left(\frac{V_2}{V_1} \right)$$

or $$q = -W_{rev} = 2.303 \, nRT \log \frac{p_1}{p_2}$$

(iii) Work done in reversible expansion under adiabatic conditions

$$W_{rev} = \frac{nR}{\gamma - 1} (T_2 - T_1)$$

where, $\gamma = $ Poisson's ratio

(Under adiabatic conditions $T V^{\gamma - 1} = $ constant)

(iv) Work done in irreversible expansion under adiabatic conditions

$$W_{irrev} = -p_{ext} \times nR \left[\frac{p_1 T_2 - p_2 T_1}{p_1 p_2} \right]$$

(v) When an ideal gas expands in vacuum then

$$p_{ext} = 0$$

Work done is maximum in reversible conditions.

Units CGS system – erg

SI system – joule

⌐Work and heat both appear only at the boundary of the system during a change in state. ⌐

Heat (q)

It occurs when there is a difference of temperature between system and surroundings. It is a random form of energy and path dependent.

Its units are **joule** or **calorie**.

Heat Capacity of a System

Heat capacity (C) of a system is defined as the amount of heat required to raise the temperature of a system by 1°C.

Molar Heat Capacity

It is the heat capacity of 1 mole of substance of the system.

Specific Heat Capacity

It is the heat capacity of 1 g of substance of the system.

$$q = mc\,\Delta T,$$

where, m = mass of substance, c = specific heat or specific heat capacity

Molar heat capacity, at constant pressure, $C_p = c_p \times M$

Molar heat capacity, at constant volume, $C_V = c_V \times M$

(c_p and c_V are specific heats at constant pressure and constant volume respectively and M is molecular weight of gas)

$$c_p - c_V = R \qquad (R = \text{Molar gas constant})$$
$$C_p - C_V = \frac{R}{M}$$

The molar heat capacity at constant volume, $C_V = \left(\frac{3}{2}\right)R$

The molar heat capacity at constant pressure,

$$C_p = \left(\frac{3}{2}\right)R + R = \left(\frac{5}{2}\right)R$$

Poisson's ratio, $\quad \gamma = \dfrac{C_p}{C_V} = \left(\dfrac{5}{3}\right) = 1.66$

$\gamma = 1.66$ for monoatomic gas

$\gamma = 1.40$ for diatomic gas

$\gamma = 1.33$ for triatomic gas

Measurement of ΔH and ΔU : Calorimetry

(a) **For gaseous reactions** Reactions involving gases are carried out in a bomb calorimeter at constant volume.

$\Delta U = -$ (Heat absorbed by bomb calorimeter)

(b) **For reaction in solution** Reactions involving solution are carried out at constant pressure inside a coffee-cup calorimeter.

$\Delta_r H = (mc\,\Delta T)_{\text{calorimeter}} + (mc\,\Delta T)_{\text{solution}}.$

Enthalpy (H)

It is the sum of internal energy and pV-energy of the system. It is a state function and extensive property. Mathematically,

$$H = U + pV$$

Like U, absolute value of H also cannot be known, ΔH is determined experimentally.

$$\Delta H = H_2 - H_1 \quad \text{or} \quad \Delta H = \Sigma H_P - \Sigma H_R$$

For exothermic reaction (the reaction in which heat is evolved), $\Delta H = -\text{ve}$, whereas for endothermic reaction (the reaction in which heat is absorbed), $\Delta H = +\text{ve}$.

Relationship between ΔH and ΔU

$$\Delta H = \Delta U + p\,\Delta V \quad \text{or} \quad \Delta H = \Delta U + \Delta n_{(g)}RT$$

Here, Δn_g = change in the number of gas moles.

Enthalpy Change or Reaction Enthalpy ($\Delta_r H$)

It is the change in enthalpy that accompanies a chemical reaction represented by a balanced chemical equation.

$$\Delta_r H = \Sigma H_{(P)} - \Sigma H_{(R)}$$

Enthalpy of reaction expressed at the standard state conditions is called standard enthalpy of reaction ($\Delta H^{\ominus}$).

Factors affecting enthalpy of reaction are

(i) Physical state of reactants and products.

(ii) Allotropic forms of elements involved.

(iii) Chemical composition of reactants and products.

(iv) Amount of reactants.

(v) Temperature.

Various Forms of Enthalpy of Reaction

Enthalpy of Formation ($\Delta_f H^{\circ}$)

It is the heat change when one mole of compound is obtained from its constituent elements. Enthalpy of formation at standard state is known as **standard enthalpy of formation** ($\Delta_f H^{\circ}$) and is taken as zero by convention.

Enthalpy of Combustion ($\Delta_C H^{\circ}$)

It is the enthalpy change taking place when one mole of a compound undergoes complete combustion in the presence of oxygen ($\Delta_C H$).

$\Delta_C H$ is always negative, because process of combustion is exothermic.

Enthalpy of Solution ($\Delta_{sol} H°$)

It is the enthalpy change when one mole of a substance is dissolved in large excess of solvent, so that on further dilution no appreciable heat change occur.

So, $$\Delta_{sol} H° = \Delta_{lattice}\ H° + \Delta_{hyd}\ H°$$

Enthalpy of Hydration ($\Delta_{hyd}\ H°$)

It is the enthalpy change when one mole of anhydrous or partially hydrated salt combines with required number of moles of water to form a specific hydrate undergoes complete combustion. It is an exothermic process.

Enthalpy of Fusion ($\Delta_{fus}\ H°$)

It is the enthalpy change that accompanies melting of one mole of solid substance.

Enthalpy of Vaporisation ($\Delta_{vap}\ H°$)

It is the enthalpy change that accompanies conversion of one mole of liquid substance completely into vapours.

Enthalpy of Neutralisation ($\Delta_n\ H°$)

It is the enthalpy change that takes place when 1 g-equivalent of an acid (or base) is neutralised by 1 g-equivalent of a base (or acid) in dilute solution.

Enthalpy of neutralisation of strong acid and strong base is always constant, i.e. 57.1 kJ.

⌈Enthalpy of neutralisation of strong acid and weak base or weak acid and strong base is not constant and numerically less than 57.1 kJ due to the fact that here the heat is used up in ionisation of weak acid or weak base. This is known as **enthalpy of ionisation of weak acid/or base**.⌋

Enthalpy of Transition ($\Delta_t H°$)

It is the enthalpy change when one mole of the substance undergoes transition from one allotropic form to another.

Enthalpy of Atomisation ($\Delta_a H°$)

It is the enthalpy change occurring when one mole of the molecule breaks into its atoms.

Enthalpy of Dilution

It is the enthalpy change, when one mole of a substance is diluted from one concentration to another.

Enthalpy of Sublimation ($\Delta_{sub}H^{\circ}$)

It is the enthalpy change, when one mole of a solid substance sublimes.

Lattice Enthalpy

It is the enthalpy change, when one mole of an ionic compound dissociates into its ions in gaseous state.

Bond Enthalpy ($\Delta_{bond}H^{\circ}$)

Enthalpy is required to break a bond and energy is released when bond is formed. For this, two different terms are used in thermodynamics.

(a) **Bond dissociation enthalpy** The enthalpy change is the change in enthalpy when one mole of covalent bonds of a gaseous covalent compound is broken to form product in the gas phase.

(b) **Mean bond enthalpy** The average value of dissociation energies of polyatomic molecule.

Some factors affecting the bond enthalpy:

(i) Size of atoms   (ii) Electronegativity

(iii) Bond length   (iv) Number of bonding electrons

Joule-Thomson Effect

The phenomenon of cooling of a gas when it is made to expand adiabatically from a region of high pressure to a region of extremely low pressure is known as **Joule-Thomson effect**. This effect is zero when an ideal gas expands in vacuum.

When an ideal gas undergoes expansion under adiabatic condition in vacuum, no change takes place in its internal energy, i.e. $\left(\dfrac{\partial E}{\partial V}\right)_T = 0$

where, $\left(\dfrac{\partial E}{\partial V}\right)_T$ is called the internal pressure.

Joule-Thomson Coefficient

The number of degrees of temperature change produced per atmospheric drop in pressure at constant enthalpy when a gas is allowed to expand through a porous plug is called Joule-Thomson coefficient. It is given as

$$\mu = \frac{dT}{dp}$$

where, μ = Joule-Thomson coefficient, dT = change in temperature

dp = change in pressure.

Inversion Temperature

The temperature below which a gas becomes cooler on expansion is known as the inversion temperature. It is given as

$$T_i = \frac{2a}{Rb}$$

where, a and b = van der Waals' constant.

At inversion temperature T_i, the Joule Thomson coefficient $\mu = 0$, i.e. the gas is neither heated nor cooled.

Laws of Thermochemistry

Lavoisier Laplace Law

The enthalpy change during a reaction is equal in magnitude to the enthalpy change in the reverse process but it is opposite in sign.

Hess's Law of Constant Heat Summation

The standard enthalpy of a reaction, which takes place in several steps, is the sum of the standard enthalpies of the intermediate reactions into which the overall reactions may be divided at the same temperature.

According to Hess's law

$$\Delta H = \Delta H_1 + \Delta H_2 + \Delta H_3$$

Applications of Hess's law are

(a) In determination of heat of formation.

(b) In determination of heat of transition.

(c) In determination of heat of hydration.

(d) To calculate bond energies.

Trouton's Rule

According to this rule, "The ratio of enthalpy of vaporisation and normal boiling point of a liquid is approximately equal to 88 J per mol per kelvin, i.e.

$$\frac{\Delta H_{vap}}{T} \approx 88 \text{ J/mol/K}$$

Dulong and Petit Law

This law states "The product of specific heat and molar mass of any metallic element is equal to 6.4 cal/mol/°C, i.e.

Specific heat × molar mass = 6.4 cal/mol/°C

Kirchhoff's Equation

$$\Delta C_p = \frac{\Delta H_2 - \Delta H_1}{T_2 - T_1} \text{ and } \Delta C_V = \frac{\Delta E_2 - \Delta E_1}{T_2 - T_1}$$

Clausius-Clapeyron Equation

$$-2.303 \log \frac{p_2}{p_1} = \frac{\Delta H_V}{R} \left(\frac{T_2 - T_1}{T_1 T_2} \right)$$

where, ΔH_V = molar heat of vaporisation.

Spontaneous Process

The physical or chemical process which proceeds by its own in a particular direction under given set of conditions without outside help is called spontaneous process. It cannot be reversed.

All natural processes are spontaneous process.

Spontaneous process where no initiation is needed

(i) Sugar dissolves in water.

(ii) Evaporation of water.

(iii) Nitric oxide (NO) reacts with oxygen.

Spontaneous process where some initiation is required

(i) Coal keeps on burning once initiated.

(ii) Heating of $CaCO_3$ to give calcium oxide and CO_2 is initiated by heat.

$$CaCO_3(s) \xrightarrow{\Delta} CaO(s) + CO_2(g)$$

Entropy (S)

It is the measure of degree of randomness or disorder of the molecules. It is a state function and extensive property.

Units : $JK^{-1} mol^{-1}$

The change in entropy during a process is mathematically given as

$$\Delta_r S° = \Sigma S° \text{(products)} - \Sigma S° \text{(reactants)} = \frac{q_{rev}}{T} = \frac{\Delta H}{T}$$

where, q_{rev} = heat absorbed by the system in reversible manner

T = temperature

$\Delta S > 0$, Increase in randomness, heat is absorbed.

$\Delta S < 0$, Decrease in randomness, heat is evolved.

Entropy of even elementary substances are not zero.

Entropy change of an ideal gas is given by

$$\Delta S = nC_V \ln\left(\frac{T_2}{T_1}\right) + nR \ln\left(\frac{V_2}{V_1}\right)$$

Entropy Change During Phase Transition

The change of matter from one state to another state is called **phase transition**.

The entropy changes at the time of phase transition:

$$\Delta S_{\text{melting}} = \frac{\Delta H_{\text{fusion}}}{T_m}$$

$$T_m = \text{melting point of substance}$$

$$\Delta S_{\text{vaporisation}} = \frac{\Delta H_{\text{vaporisation}}}{T_b}$$

$$T_b = \text{boiling point of substance}$$

$$\Delta S_{\text{sublimation}} = \frac{\Delta H_{\text{sublimation}}}{T_{\text{sub}}}$$

$$T_{\text{sub}} = \text{sublimation temperature}$$

Enthalpy Criterion of Spontaneous Process

All the processes which are accompanied by decrease of energy (exothermic reactions, having negative value of ΔH) occur spontaneously. It fails when some endothermic reactions occur spontaneously.

Entropy Criterion of Spontaneous Process

A process is spontaneous if and only if the entropy of the universe increases.

For a process to be spontaneous

$$(\Delta S_{\text{universe}} > 0 \text{ or } \Delta S_{\text{syst}} + \Delta S_{\text{surr}} > 0)$$

At equilibrium state, $\Delta S = 0$.

Limitations of ΔS criterion and need for another term We cannot find entropy change of surroundings during chemical changes. So we need another parameter for spontaneity *viz* Gibbs' energy of system (G).

Second Law of Thermodynamics

The entropy of the universe is always increasing in the course of every spontaneous or natural change.

Or

All spontaneous processes or natural changes are thermodynamically irreversible without the help of an external work, i.e., heat cannot flow itself from a colder to hotter body.

Gibbs Energy or Gibbs Free Energy

It is the energy available for a system at some conditions and by which useful work can be done. It is a state function and extensive property.
Mathematically, $G = H - TS$

Change in Gibbs energy during the process is given by Gibbs Helmholtz equation.

$$(\Delta G = G_2 - G_1 = \Delta H - T\Delta S)$$

where, ΔG = Gibbs free energy, H = enthalpy of system

TS = random energy,

$\Delta G_{system} = -T\Delta S_{total}$ [In hypothetical system where $\Delta H = 0$]

The Gibbs energy criterion of spontaneity

$\Delta G > 0$, process is non-spontaneous

$\Delta G < 0$, process is spontaneous

$\Delta G = 0$, process is in equilibrium state.

Effect of Temperature on Spontaneity

S.No.	Sign of ΔH	Sign of ΔS	$\Delta G = \Delta H - T\Delta S$	Remarks
1.	Negative	Positive	Always negative	Spontaneous at all temperatures
2.	Positive	Negative	Always positive	Non-spontaneous at all temperatures
3.	Positive	Positive	Positive at low temperature	Non-spontaneous at low temperature
			Negative at high temperature	Spontaneous at high temperature
4.	Negative	Negative	Negative at low temperature	Spontaneous at low temperature
			Positive at high temperature	Non-spontaneous at high temperatures

Now an exothermic reaction which is non-spontaneous at high temperature may become spontaneous at low temperature. Similarly, endothermic reactions which are non-spontaneous at low temperature may become spontaneous at high temperature.

Standard Free Energy Change (ΔG°)

It is the change in free energy which takes places when the reactants are converted into products at the standard states, i.e. (1 atm and 298 K)

$$\Delta G^\circ = \Delta H^\circ - T\Delta S^\circ$$

$$\Delta G^\circ = \Sigma \Delta G^\circ_{f \,(\text{Products})} - \Sigma \Delta G^\circ_{f \,(\text{Reactant})}$$

where, ΔG°_f = standard energy of formation

Standard energy of formation of all free elements is zero.

Gibbs Energy Change and Equilibrium

Criterion for equilibrium,

$$A + B \rightleftharpoons C + D$$

$$\Delta G = 0$$

Now, relation

$$\Delta G = \Delta G^\circ + RT \ln Q$$

$$0 = \Delta G^\circ + RT \ln K$$

or

$$\Delta G^\circ = - RT \ln K$$

or

$$\Delta G^\circ = - 2.303 \, RT \log K$$

$\Rightarrow$ We also know that

$$\Delta G^\circ = \Delta H^\circ - T\Delta S^\circ = - RT \ln K$$

Relation between ΔG° and EMF of the Cell

$$\Delta G^\circ = - nFE^\circ_{\text{cell}}$$

where, n = number of electrons lost or gained

F = Faraday or 96500 C

E°_{cell} = standard electrode potential

Third Law of Thermodynamics

This law was formulated by Nernst in 1906. According to this law, "The entropy of a perfectly crystalline substance at zero K or absolute zero is taken to be zero".

We can find absolute entropies of pure substances at different temperature.

$$\Delta S = \int_0^T C_p d \ln T = 2.303 \int_0^T C_P \, d \log T$$

where, C_p = heat capacities

T = temperature between 0 K and T K.

This law is only applicable for perfectly crystalline substances. If there is imperfection at 0 K, the entropy will be larger than zero.

Carnot Cycle

It is an imaginary cycle which demonstrates the maximum conversion of heat into work. It involves four processes

(i) isothermal reversible expansion;

(ii) adiabatic reversible expansion;

(iii) isothermal reversible compression;

(iv) adiabatic reversible compression.

The efficiency of a heat engine in a Carnot cycle,

$$\eta = \frac{T_2 - T_1}{T_2} = \frac{q_2 - q_1}{q_2} = \frac{w}{q_2}$$

8
Chemical Equilibrium

On carrying a chemical reaction in a closed vessel at a particular temperature, initially the reactant concentration keep on decreasing and product concentration keep on increasing. After sometime, a stage is reached at which there is no net reaction, this stage is called **state of equilibrium**.

Physical and Chemical Processes

Physical processes involve such changes, which only affect the physical properties of the substance undergoing changes but have no effect on the **chemical composition** and properties.

Chemical processes involve changes in chemical composition and properties. Whenever a chemical change occurs, we can say that a **chemical reaction** has taken place.

Types of Chemical Reactions

1. Decomposition Reactions

In these reactions, a compound decomposes to produce two or more different substances.
e.g.

$$PCl_5(g) \rightleftharpoons PCl_3(g) + Cl_2(g)$$

Digestion of food is also a decomposition reaction.

⌐ Decomposition by heat is called thermal decomposition and decomposition by sunlight is called photochemical decomposition. ⌐

2. Displacement Reactions

These reactions involve displacement of one element or group by another. These are infact redox reactions, e.g.

$$Zn(s) + H_2SO_4(aq) \longrightarrow ZnSO_4(aq) + H_2(g)$$

3. Double Displacement or Metathesis Reactions

In these, reactions two compounds react to form two new compounds and no change in oxidation state takes place, e.g. precipitation reactions, neutralisation reactions.

$$AgNO_3(aq) + NaCl(aq) \longrightarrow AgCl(s) + NaNO_3(aq)$$

4. Reversible and Irreversible Reactions

	Irreversible reactions	Reversible reactions
1.	Chemical reactions which always proceed to completion in only forward direction, e.g. $AgNO_3(aq) + NaCl(aq) \longrightarrow AgCl(aq)$ $+ NaNO_3(aq)$	Reactions which do not proceed to completion in forward direction and also proceed in the backward direction under suitable conditions, e.g. $N_2(g) + 3H_2(g) \rightleftharpoons 2NH_3$
2.	These reactions never attain an equilibrium.	These reactions attain an equilibrium.

Equilibrium can be established for both physical processes and chemical reactions. When no change in the concentration of either of the reactants or products takes place, this stage of the system is the dynamic equilibrium.

Equilibrium can be classified as :

(a) Physical Equilibrium

Equilibrium set up in physical processes like evaporation of water, melting of solids, dissolution of solutes, etc., is called physical equilibrium, e.g. Ice $\rightleftharpoons$ Water

At equilibrium,

Rate of melting of ice = Rate of freezing of water

(b) Chemical Equilibrium

If a reversible reaction is carried out in a closed vessel, a stage is attained where the speed of the forward reaction equals to the speed of the backward reaction. It corresponds to chemical equilibrium. At equilibrium,

Rate of forward reaction (R_f) = Rate of backward reaction (R_b)

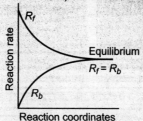

Characteristics of Chemical Equilibrium

1. Equilibrium can be attained from either side.
2. Equilibrium is dynamic in nature, i.e. at equilibrium, reaction does not stop.
3. At equilibrium, there is no change in the concentration of various species.
4. The equilibrium state remains unaffected by the presence of catalyst. Catalyst helps to attain the equilibrium state rapidly.
5. Equilibrium can be achieved in a closed container only.
6. The observable physical properties of the process become constant.

Types of Equilibrium

Homogeneous Equilibrium

In homogeneous equilibrium, the reactants and products are present in the same phase or physical state (gaseous or liquid).

$$2SO_2(g) + O_2(g) \rightleftharpoons 2SO_3(g)$$

Heterogeneous Equilibrium

In heterogeneous equilibrium, the reactants and products are present in two or more physical states or phases.

$$3Fe(s) + 4H_2O(g) \rightleftharpoons Fe_3O_4(s) + 4H_2(g)$$

Law of Mass Action

Guldberg and **Waage** states that the rate of a chemical reaction is directly proportional to the product of the active masses of the reacting substances. For a general reaction,

$$aA + bB \rightleftharpoons cC + dD$$

Rate of forward reaction $\propto [A]^a [B]^b = k_f [A]^a [B]^b$

Rate of backward reaction $\propto [C]^c [D]^d = k_b [C]^c [D]^d$

where, k_f and k_b are rate constants.

In heterogeneous equilibrium, the active mass of pure solids and liquids are taken as

At equilibrium,

Rate of forward reaction = Rate of backward reaction

$$k_f [A]^a [B]^b = k_b [C]^c [D]^d$$

$$\frac{k_f}{k_b} = K_c = \frac{[C]^c [D]^d}{[A]^a [B]^b}$$

where, K_c is called the **equilibrium constant**.

Use of Partial Pressures Instead of Concentration

For gaseous reactions, partial pressures are convenientaly used since at any fixed temperature partial pressure is directly proportional to concentration. For a general gaseous reaction,

$$aA + bB \rightleftharpoons cC + dD$$

$$K_p = \frac{p_C^c \times p_D^d}{p_A^a \times p_B^b}$$

Relation between K_c and K_p

$$K_p = K_c [RT]^{\Delta n_g}$$

where, Δn_g = moles of products − moles of reactants (gaseous only)

Relation between K_c and K_p for different types of reactions

(i) When $\Delta n_g = 0$, $K_p = K_c$

(ii) When $\Delta n_g = +ve$, $K_p > K_c$

(iii) When $\Delta n_g = -ve$, $K_p < K_c$

Units of K_p and K_c

(i) Unit of $K_p = (atm)^{\Delta n_g}$　　　(ii) Unit of $K_c = (mol\ L^{-1})^{\Delta n_g}$

Characteristics of Equilibrium Constant $(K_p$ or $K_c)$

1. It has definite value for every chemical reaction at a particular temperature.

2. The more is the value of K_c or K_p, the more is the extent of completion of reaction, i.e. $K_c < 1$ indicates lesser concentration of products than reactants.

   $K \geq 10^3$ shows completion of reaction and $K \leq 10^{-3}$ shows that the reaction does not proceed at all.

3. When the reaction can be expressed as sum of two other reactions, the K_c of overall reaction is equal to the product of equilibrium constants of individual reactions.

4. The equilibrium constant is independent of initial concentrations of reactants.

5. Equilibrium constant is independent of presence of catalyst.

6. K_c for backward reaction is inverse of K_c for forward reaction.

7. If an equation is multiplied by n, the K becomes K^n, and if it is divided by m, the k becomes $\sqrt[m]{k}$.

8. In equilibrium constant expression if activities are used in place of molar concentration, k becomes dimensionless.

Reaction Quotient

For any reversible reaction at any stage other than equilibrium, the ratio of the molar concentrations of the products to that of the reactants, where each concentration term is raised to the power equal to the stoichiometric coefficient to the substance concerned, is called the reaction quotient, Q_c.

For a general reaction,

$$a\,A + bB \rightleftharpoons cC + dD$$

which is not at equilibrium,

$$Q_c = \frac{[C]^c\,[D]^d}{[A]^a\,[B]^b}$$

If

(i) $Q_c > K_c$, the value of Q_c will tend to decrease to reach the value of K_c (towards equilibrium) and the reaction will proceed in the backward direction.

(ii) $Q_c < K_c$, Q_c will tend to increase and the reaction will proceed in the forward direction.

(iii) $Q_c = K_c$, the reaction is at equilibrium.

Relationship between *K* and Standard Gibbs Free Energy Change

Gibbs free energy change and reaction quotient are related as

$$\Delta G = \Delta G^\circ + 2.303RT \log Q_c$$

At equilibrium, $\Delta G = 0$ and $Q_c = K_c$

$$\therefore \qquad \Delta G^\circ = -2.303\, RT \log K_c$$
or
$$\Delta G^\circ = -2.303\, RT\, K_p \qquad \text{(for ideal gases)}$$

Le-Chatelier's Principle

There are three main factors which affect the state of equilibrium. They are (i) **concentration** (ii) **temperature** and (iii) **pressure.**

Le-Chatelier's principle states that if a system at equilibrium is subjected to a change in concentration, pressure or temperature, the equilibrium shifts in the direction that tends to nulify the effect of the change.

Effect of Change of Concentration

If at equilibrium the concentration of one of the reactants is increased, the equilibrium will shift in the forward direction and *vice-versa.*

Effect of Change in Pressure

No effect of pressure on equilibria having same moles of reactants and products, e.g. $N_2 + O_2 \rightleftharpoons 2NO$.

When there is change in the number of moles, the equilibrium will shift in the direction having smaller number of moles when the pressure is increased and *vice-versa*, e.g.

$$N_2 + 3H_2 \rightleftharpoons 2NH_3 \qquad \text{[High } p\text{, high yield of NH}_3\text{]}$$

Effect of Temperature

When process is exothermic, low temperature favours the forward reaction. When process is endothermic, high temperature favours the formation of products.

Effect of Addition of Inert Gas

(i) **Addition of inert gas at constant pressure** At constant pressure, if an inert gas is added, it will increase the volume of the system. Therefore, the equilibrium will shift in a direction in which there is an increase in the number of moles of gases.

(ii) **Addition of inert gas at constant volume** If keeping volume of the system constant, an inert gas is added, the relative molar concentration of the substance will not change. Hence, the equilibrium position of the reaction remains unaffected.

Effect of Catalyst

The presence of catalyst does not change the position of equilibrium. It simply fastens the attainment of equilibrium.

Le-Chatelier's Principle Applicable to Physical Equilibrium

(i) **Effect of pressure on solubility** The increased pressure, will increase the solubility of gas and *vice-versa*.

(ii) **Effect of temperature on solubility** Solubility of such substances will increase with increase of temperature and *vice-versa*, e.g. dissolution of NH_4Cl, KCl, KNO_3, etc. The dissolution of calcium acetate and calcium hydroxide is exothermic, so their solubility is lowered at higher temperature.

(iii) **Effect of pressure on the melting point of ice**

$$Ice \rightleftharpoons liquid\ water$$

The ice occupy the more volume than liquid water, so increased pressure will result in melting of ice according to Le-Chatelier principle.

Favourable conditions for some chemical equilibria to get higher yield of product.

Chemical equilibria	Favourable condition for forward direction
$N_2 + 3H_2 \rightleftharpoons 2NH_3$	High pressure, low temperature and isolation of NH_3 by liquefaction.
$N_2 + O_2 \rightleftharpoons 2NO$	High temperature and isolation of NO.
$PCl_5 \rightleftharpoons PCl_3 + Cl_2$	Low pressure, high temperature and isolation of PCl_3 and Cl_2.

9

Ionic Equilibrium

The equilibrium established between the unionised molecules and the ions in the solution of weak electrolytes is called ionic equilibrium.

e.g. $$CH_3COOH \rightleftharpoons CH_3COO^- + H^+$$

Non-electrolytes

A solution of solute like urea, glucose, etc. does not contain any ion, hence the solution is bad conductor of electricity. Such solutes are termed as non-electrolytes.

Electrolytes

Chemical substances which can conduct electricity in their aqueous state or in molten state are called electrolytes. The conduction of current through electrolyte is due to the movement of ions.

1. Strong Electrolytes

Electrolytes which dissociate almost completely into constituent ions in aqueous solution are known as strong electrolytes, e.g. all salts (except $HgCl_2, CdBr_2$), mineral acids like HCl, H_2SO_4, HNO_3, etc., and bases like NaOH, KOH, etc.

2. Weak Electrolytes

Electrolytes which dissociate to a lesser extent in aqueous solution are called weak electrolyte. All organic acids (except sulphonic acids), and bases like NH_3, NH_4OH, amines, H_3BO_3, HCN etc.

Degree of Ionisation or Degree of Dissociation (α)

It is the fraction of the total number of molecules which ionise (dissociate) into constituent ions.

$$\alpha = \frac{\text{number of molecules ionised or dissociated}}{\text{total number of molecules taken}}$$

For strong electrolytes,
$$\alpha = 1$$
For weak electrolytes $\alpha < 1$

Values of the degree of dissociation (α) depends upon the following factors:

- (i) nature of solute
- (ii) nature of solvent
- (iii) concentration
- (iv) temperature
- (v) addition of other species.

Calculation of the Degree of Dissociation (α) from Density Measurement

$$\alpha = \frac{D - d}{d(y - 1)}$$

where, y = number of moles of product from one mole of reactant,

D = theoretical vapour density and

d = observed vapour density

Now, molecular mass = $2 \times VD$

$\therefore$ $$\alpha = \frac{M_c - M_o}{M_o}$$

where, M_c = calculated molecular weight and

M_o = observed molecular weight.

Ostwald's Dilution Law

According to Ostwald, the degree of dissociation (α) of weak electrolyte is inversely proportional to the square root of the molar concentration of the solution.

$$K = \frac{C\alpha^2}{1 - \alpha}$$

If α is very small $1 - \alpha \approx 1$ $\Rightarrow$ $K = C\alpha^2$

or $$\alpha = \sqrt{\frac{K}{C}} \Rightarrow \alpha \propto \frac{1}{\sqrt{C}}$$

Here, K is dissociation constant and C is molar concentration of the solution.

Acids and Bases

Earlier definitions of acids and bases was given by Robert Boyle, who classified them on the basis of their properties. According to him, acids are the substances, which have sour taste, turns blue litmus red, liberate hydrogen with metals, conduct electricity in aqueous solution and neutralise bases.

Bases are the substance which have bitter taste, turns red litmus blue, soapy to touch, conduct electricity in aqueous solution and neutralise acids.

Arrhenius Concept of Acids and Bases

Acid is a chemical substance which dissociates in aqueous solution to give hydrogen ions (H^+) or hydronium ions (H_3O^+).

Base is a chemical substance which dissociates in aqueous solution to give hydroxyl ions (OH^-).

Arrhenius theory fails to explain the acidic and basic behaviour in non-aqueous solutions. It cannot explain the acidic character of $AlCl_3$, BF_3 and basic character of NH_3, PH_3 and free H^+ and OH^- ions do not exist in water.

Bronsted Concept of Acids and Bases

Acid is a chemical substance that can donate a proton (H^+) to some other substance and a base is a chemical substance that can accept a proton from other substance. Thus, an acid is a proton donor (protogenic) and a base is proton acceptor (protophilic).

$$\underset{\text{Base}_2}{NH_3} + \underset{\text{Acid}_1}{H_2O} \rightleftharpoons \underset{\text{Acid}_2}{NH_4^+} + \underset{\text{Base}_1}{OH^-}$$

Conjugate pair

Conjugate pair

> Strong acid has weak conjugate base and weak acid has strong conjugate base. Strong base has weak conjugate acid and weak base has strong conjugate acid.
> $HClO_4$ is the strongest while HCN is the weakest hydracid known. CsOH is the strongest base known.

Amphoteric or amphiprotic substance or ampholytes are the substances which act as an acid as well as a base, e.g. water acts as an acid with NH_3 and a base with acetic acid.

The order of acidic strength of some acids is

$$HClO_4 > HI > HBr > H_2SO_4 > HCl > HNO_3$$

Relative Strength of Acids and Bases

Greater the K_a value of an acid (or lesser the pK_a), stronger is the acid. Similarly, greater the K_b (or lesser the pK_b) of a base, stronger is the base.

$$\frac{\alpha_1}{\alpha_2} = \sqrt{\frac{K_{a_1}}{K_{a_2}}} = \frac{\text{strength of acid } (HA)_1}{\text{strength of acid } (HA)_2}$$

$$\frac{\alpha_1}{\alpha_2} = \sqrt{\frac{K_{b_1}}{K_{b_2}}} = \frac{\text{strength of base } (BOH)_1}{\text{strength of base } (BOH)_2}$$

Leveling effect The acids like $HClO_4$, H_2SO_4, HNO_3, etc. react with water almost completely to form H_3O^+ ions. Therefore, all the strong acids in aqueous solutions appear equally strong and their relative strengths in aqueous solution cannot be compared. Since, H_3O^+ is the strongest acid in water, the strength of above acids come down to the level of H_3O^+ strength in water. Similarly, strong bases like NaOH, KOH, $Ba(OH)_2$ come down to the strength of OH^- ion in water. This is called levelling effect.

Bronsted concept fails to explain acidic nature of BF_3 and $AlCl_3$.

Lewis Concept of Acids and Bases

Lewis acid is a chemical substance which can accept a pair of electrons, e.g.

  (i) Molecules with incomplete octet of central atom like BF_3, $AlCl_3$, $BeCl_2$, $MgCl_2$ etc.

 (ii) Simple cations like Ag^+, Na^+ etc.

(iii) Molecules in which the central atom has vacant d-orbital, e.g. SF_4, $SnCl_4$, PF_3, etc.

Lewis base is a chemical substance which can donate a pair of electrons, e.g.

  (i) Neutral molecules containing lone pairs like $\overset{\cdot\cdot}{N}H_3$, $R\overset{\cdot\cdot}{N}H_2$, $R\overset{\cdot\cdot}{O}H$, etc.

 (ii) Negatively charged species like $C\overset{\cdot\cdot}{N}$, $\overset{\cdot\cdot}{C}l$, $O\overset{\cdot\cdot}{H}$, etc.

(iii) In coordination complexes, the ligands act as Lewis base.

Limitations of Lewis Concept

(i) It does not explain the behaviour of protonic acids such as HCl, H_2SO_4, HNO_3 etc.

(ii) It does not predict the magnitude of relative strength of acids and bases.

All Bronsted-Lowry's acids are Lewis acids while all Lewis acids need not be Bronsted-Lowry's acids.

The Ionisation Constant of Water

Ionic product is the product of the concentration of hydronium ions and hydroxyl ion in pure water, which remains constant at a particular temperature. It is symbolized by K_w. At 298 K, ionic product of water (K_w) is given as $K_w = [H_3O^+][OH^-] = 1 \times 10^{-14}$ mol^2L^{-2}.

The value of K_w increases with increase in temperature.

We can distinguish acidic, neutral and basic aqueous solutions by the relative value of the H_3O^+ and OH^- concentration.

$$\text{Acidic} : [H_3O^+] > [OH^-]$$

$$\text{Neutral} : [H_3O^+] = [OH^-]$$

$$\text{Basic} : [H_3O^+] < [OH^-]$$

The pH Scale

pH is defined as the negative logarithm of hydrogen ion concentration.
$$pH = -\log[H^+] \quad \text{and} \quad [H^+] = 10^{-pH}$$

Total $[H^+]$ or $[OH^-]$ in a mixture of two strong acids or bases $= \dfrac{\Sigma NV}{\Sigma V}$.

Similarly, negative logarithm of hydroxyl ion concentration is pOH.
$$pOH = -\log[OH^-]$$

As we know $K_w = [H^+][OH^-] = 1 \times 10^{-14}$ (at 298 K)

$$-\log K_w = -\log[H^+] - \log[OH^-] = 14$$

$\Rightarrow \qquad pK_w = pH + pOH = 14$ (at 298 K)

The pH scale (at 25°C)

H_3O^+	1	10^{-1}	10^{-2}	10^{-3}	10^{-4}	10^{-5}	10^{-6}	10^{-7}	10^{-8}	10^{-9}	10^{-10}	10^{-11}	10^{-12}	10^{-13}	10^{-14}
pH	0	1	2	3	4	5	6	7	8	9	10	11	12	13	14

← Acidic character increases   Neutral   Basic character increases →

pH value of an acid having H^+ concentration less than 10^{-7}, is always in between 6 and 7. For 10^{-8} N HCl solution, it is 6.958. Similarly, for 10^{-8} NaOH solution, the pH is 7.04 (because basic solutions always have pH greater than 7.)

pH of solution is accurately measured by pH meter or emf method or roughly by pH paper or indicator paper.

⌐pH can be zero in 1N HCl solution or it can be negative for more
 concentrated solution like 2N, 3N, 10 N etc.   ⌐

pH range for some important substances are:
> Gastric juice = 1 – 3
> Vinegar = 2.4 – 3.4
> Tears = 7.4
> Human urine = 4.8 – 8.4
> Blood plasma = 7.3 – 7.4
> Boiled water = 6.5625

Dissociation Constant of Weak Acid and Weak Base

Let us consider the dissociation of weak acid (HA) as

$$HA \;\rightleftharpoons\; H^+ \;+\; A^-$$

Initially	C	0	0
At equilibrium	$C(1-\alpha)$	$C\alpha$	$C\alpha$

∵ Dissociation constant of an acid,

$$K_a = \frac{[H^+][A^-]}{[HA]} = \frac{C\alpha^2}{(1-\alpha)}$$

Similarly, for the dissociation of a weak base BOH as

$$BOH \;\rightleftharpoons\; B^+ + OH^-$$

Dissociation constant of the base

$$K_b = \frac{[B^+][OH^-]}{[BOH]} = \frac{C\alpha^2}{(1-\alpha)}$$

Relation between Acid Dissociation (K_a) and Base Dissociation (K_b) Constants

K_a and K_b are related to each other by the following formula,

$$K_a \times K_b = K_w$$

Dissociation Constant for Polyprotic Acids and Bases

For a tribasic acid,

$$H_3PO_4 \underset{K_{a_1}}{\rightleftharpoons} H^+ + H_2PO_4^-$$

$$H_2PO_4^- \underset{K_{a_2}}{\rightleftharpoons} H^+ + HPO_4^{2-}$$

$$HPO_4^{2-} \underset{K_{a_3}}{\rightleftharpoons} H^+ + PO_4^{3-}$$

The overall dissociation constant (K) is given as

$$K = K_1 \times K_2 \times K_3$$

where, $K_1 > K_2 > K_3$

$$\text{pH of } H_2PO_4^- \text{ in aqueous medium} = \frac{pK_{a_1} + pK_{a_2}}{2}$$

$$\text{pH of } HPO_4^{2-} \text{ in aqueous medium} = \frac{pK_{a_2} + pK_{a_3}}{2}$$

Similarly, for a dibasic acid like H_2CO_3, $pH = \dfrac{pK_{a_1} + pK_{a_2}}{2}$

Similarly, in case of a conjugate acid-base pair,

$K_w = K_a \times K_b$ by taking negative logarithm of both sides of the equation, then pK values of conjugate acid and base are related to each other by the equation

$$pK_a + pK_b = pK_w = 14 \text{ (at 298 K)}$$

The extent of dissociation of an acid depends on the **strength** and **polarity** of the H-A bond.

(a) As the size of A increases down the group, H-A bond strength decreases and so the acid strength increases.

$$\xrightarrow{\hspace{4cm}} \text{Size increases}$$
e.g., $HF \ll HCl \ll HBr \ll HI$
$$\xrightarrow{\hspace{4cm}} \text{Acid strength increases}$$

(b) As the electronegativity of A increases, the strength of the acid also increases.

$$\xrightarrow{\hspace{4cm}} \text{Electronegativity of } A \text{ increases}$$
e.g., $CH_4 < NH_3 < H_2O < HF$
$$\xrightarrow{\hspace{4cm}} \text{Acid strength increases}$$

Common Ion Effect

It is defined as the suppression of the dissociation of a weak electrolyte by the addition of a strong electrolyte having some common ion, e.g. degree of dissociation of ammonium hydroxide decreases in the presence of ammonium chloride.

$$NH_4OH \rightleftharpoons NH_4^+ + OH^-$$

$$NH_4Cl \longrightarrow \underset{\text{Common ion}}{NH_4^+} + Cl^-$$

According to Le-Chatelier principle, because of the presence of common ion, degree of dissociation of NH_4OH decreases.

Common ion effect is used in

(i) purification of common salt.

(ii) salting out of soap.

(iii) qualitative analysis.

Group II radicals are precipitated out in the presence of HCl which suppress the S^{2-} ion concentration, which is just sufficient to precipitate only group II radicals. Similarly in group III, NH_4OH is added in presence of NH_4Cl to avoid the precipitation of group V radicals.

Isohydric Solutions

If the concentration of the common ions in the solution of two electrolytes, e.g. OH^- ion concentration in $Ca(OH)_2$ and $Ba(OH)_2$ solutions, is same then on mixing them there is no change in degree of dissociation of either of the electrolytes. Such solution are called isohydric solutions.

Salts

These are the product of reaction between an acid and a base.

This reaction is called neutralisation reaction.

Types of Salts

(a) **Normal salts** These are obtained by complete neutralisation of an acid with a base, e.g. $NaCl$, K_2SO_4 etc.

(b) **Acidic salts** These are formed by incomplete neutralisation of polybasic acids. e.g. $NaHCO_3$, Na_2HPO_4 etc.

(c) **Basic salts** These are formed by incomplete neutralisation of polyacidic base, e.g. $Mg(OH)Cl$, $Bi(OH)_2Cl$, etc.

(d) **Double salts** These are formed by the combination of two simple salts and exist only in solid state, e.g. Mohr salt or ferrous ammonium sulphate [$FeSO_4 \cdot (NH_4)_2SO_4 \cdot 6H_2O$], alum etc.

(e) **Complex salts** These are formed by the combination of simple salts or molecular compounds. These are stable in solid state as well as in solutions.

The properties of their solutions are different from the properties of substances from which they have been constituted.

(f) **Mixed salts**   These salts furnish more than one cation or more than one anion when dissolved in water, e.g. $Ca(OCl)Cl$, $NaKSO_4$, etc.

Salt Hydrolysis

Salts are strong electrolytes and on dissolution in water split up into ions which react with H^+ or OH^- ions furnished by water yielding acidic or basic solution. The process is known as salt hydrolysis.

Salt of	Example	K_h (hydrolysis constant)	h (degree of hydrolysis)	pH of solution
Weak acid and strong base	CH_3COONa	$\dfrac{K_w}{K_a}$	$\sqrt{\dfrac{K_w}{K_a \cdot C}}$	$\dfrac{1}{2}pK_w + \dfrac{1}{2}pK_a + \dfrac{1}{2}\log C$
Strong acid and weak base	NH_4Cl	$\dfrac{K_w}{K_b}$	$\sqrt{\dfrac{K_w}{K_b \cdot C}}$	$\dfrac{1}{2}pK_w - \dfrac{1}{2}pK_b - \dfrac{1}{2}\log C$
Weak acid and weak base	CH_3COONH_4	$\dfrac{K_w}{K_a \cdot K_b}$	$\sqrt{\dfrac{K_w}{K_a \cdot K_b}}$	$\dfrac{1}{2}pK_w + \dfrac{1}{2}pK_a - \dfrac{1}{2}pK_b$
Strong acid and strong base	NaCl	Does not undergo hydrolysis		

Aqueous solution of salt of strong acid and strong base is neutral. Aqueous solution of salt of a weak acid and a strong base is alkaline due to anionic hydrolysis, and aqueous solution of salt of strong acid and a weak base is acidic due to cationic hydrolysis.

With dilution degree of hydrolysis increases. Hydrolysis is a reverse process of neutralisation.

Buffer Solution

Solution which resists the change in its pH value by addition of a small amount of acid or a base, is called buffer solution.

(a) **Acidic buffer**   They have pH value < 7,

    e.g. CH_3COOH/CH_3COONa, boric acid/borax.

(b) **Basic buffer**   They have pH value > 7

    e.g. NH_4OH / NH_4Cl

Buffer system present in blood is $H_2CO_3 + NaHCO_3$.

Henderson-Hesselbalch Equation

This equation is used to calculate the pH of a buffer solution.

(i) For acidic buffer,

$$pH = pK_a + \log \frac{[salt]}{[acid]}$$

(ii) For basic buffer,

$$pOH = pK_b + \log \frac{[salt]}{[base]}$$

and $pH = 14 - pOH$

Here, $pK_a = -\log K_a$, $pK_b = -\log K_b$ and K_a and K_b are dissociation constants of acid and base.

[salt], [acid] and [base] represent molar concentrations of salt, acid and base respectively.

If addition of a strong acid or base changes the pH of a buffer by/unit, the buffer solution is assumed to be destroyed, i.e.

$$New\ pH = pK_a \pm 1$$

This means the ratio,

$$\frac{[salt]}{[acid]}\ or\ \frac{[salt]}{[base]} = 10\ or\ \frac{1}{10}$$

Buffer Capacity

It is defined as the number of moles of acid or base added in 1 L of solution to change the pH by unity.

Buffer capacity (ϕ)

$$= \frac{\text{number of moles of acids or base added to 1 L of buffer}}{\text{change in pH}}$$

Solubility Product

It is defined as the product of the concentrations of the ions of the salt in its saturated solution at a given temperature raised to the power of the ions produced by the dissociation of one mole of the salt. It is denoted by K_{sp}. Consider the dissociation of an electrolyte A_xB_y

$$A_xB_y \rightleftharpoons x A^{y+} + y B^{x-}$$

$$K_{sp} = [A^{y+}]^x [B^{x-}]^y$$

Application of Solubility Product

1. The concept of K_{sp} helps in predicting the formation of precipitate. In general if
   (i) Ionic product $< K_{sp}$, no ppt is formed.
   (ii) Ionic product $> K_{sp}$, ppt is formed.
   (iii) Ionic product $= K_{sp}$, the reaction is at equilibrium.
2. In predicting the solubility of a sparingly soluble salt

$$\underset{s \text{ mol/L}}{A_xB_y} \rightleftharpoons \underset{xs}{x A^{y+}} + \underset{ys}{y B^{x-}}$$

$$K_{sp} = x^x \cdot y^y \cdot s^{x+y}$$

Knowing the values of K_{sp}, x and y, the solubility of the salt can be computed.

For salts of the type AB : $K_{sp} = s^2$ or $s = K_{sp}$

For salts of the type AB_2 : $K_{sp} = 4s^3$ or $s = \left(\dfrac{K_{sp}}{4}\right)^{\frac{1}{3}}$

For salts of the type AB_3 : $K_{sp} = 27s^4$ or $s = \left(\dfrac{K_{sp}}{27}\right)^{\frac{1}{4}}$

K_{sp} of AgI is lower than that of AgCl. So, the former gets precipitated in preference to later.

Distinction Between Solubility Product and Ionic Product

	Solubility product	Ionic product
1.	It is the product of the ionic concentration in the saturated solution.	It is the product of the ionic concentration at any concentration of the solution.
2.	It is applicable only to the saturated solutions.	It is applicable to all types of solutions.

Acid-Base Indicator

An acid-base indicator is a substance which possesses one colour in acid solution and altogether different colour in alkaline medium or the substance which shows colour change with change in pH. The point where the indicator shows a sudden change in colour during the titration is called end point. End point is the point at which the reaction is observed to be complete.

Theory of indicators

(i) Ostwald theory (ii) Quinonoid theory

Titration Curves and Indicator Used

(a) **Titration curve for the neutralisation of strong acid *vs* strong base** pH curve of strong acid (say HCl) and strong base (say NaOH) is vertical over almost the pH range 4–10. So, the indicators phenolphthalein (pH range 8.3 to 10.5), methyl red (pH range 4.4–6.5 and methyl orange (pH range 3.2–4.5) are suitable for such a titration.

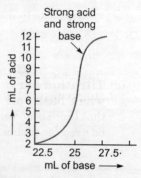

(b) **Titration curve for the neutralisation of strong acid *vs* weak base** pH curve of strong acid (say HCl or H_2SO_4 or HNO_3) with a weak base (say NH_4OH) is vertical over the pH range of 4 to 7. So the indicators methyl red and methyl orange are suitable for such a titration.

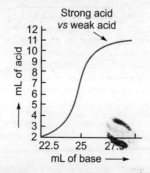

(c) **Titration curve for the neutralisation of weak acid *vs* strong base** pH curve of weak acid (say CH_3COOH or oxalic acid) and strong base (say NaOH) is vertical over the approximate pH range 7 to 11. So, phenolphthalein is the suitable indicator for such a titration.

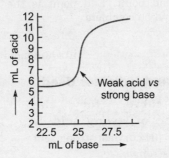

(d) **Titration curve for the neutralisation of weak acid *vs* weak base** pH curve of weak acid and weak base indicates that there is no vertical part and hence, no suitable indicator can be used for such a titration.

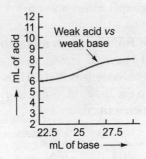

10

Solutions

Solution is a homogeneous mixture of two or more substances in same or different physical phases. The substances forming the solution are called components of the solution. On the basis of number of components a solution of two components is called **binary solution.**

Solute and Solvent

In a binary solution, solvent is the component which is present in large quantity while the other component present in small quantity is known as solute.

Classification of Solutions

(A) Following types of solutions are seen on the basis of physical state of solute and solvent.

S.No.	Solute	Solvent	Examples
Solid solutions			
1.	Solid	Solid	Alloys (Copper dissolved in gold)
2.	Liquid	Solid	Hydrated salts, Amalgam of Hg with Na
3.	Gas	Solid	Solution of hydrogen in palladium
Liquid solutions			
4.	Solid	Liquid	Salt/sugar solution in water
5.	Liquid	Liquid	Alcohol in water
6.	Gas	Liquid	Aerated drinks, O_2 in water
Gaseous solutions			
7.	Solid	Gas	Iodine vapour in air
8.	Liquid	Gas	Water vapour in air
9.	Gas	Gas	Air $(O_2 + N_2)$

If water is used as a solvent, the solution is called **aqueous solution** and if not, the solution is called **non-aqueous solution.**

(B) Depending upon the amount of solute dissolved in a solvent we have the following types of solutions:

(i) **Unsaturated solution** A solution in which more solute can be dissolved without raising temperature is called an unsaturated solution.

(ii) **Saturated solution** A solution in which no more solute can be dissolved further at a given temperature is called a saturated solution.

(iii) **Supersaturated solution** A solution which contains more solute than that would be necessary to saturate it at a given temperature is called a supersaturated solution.

Concentration of Solutions

The concentration of a solution is defined as the relative amount of solute present in a solution. On the basis of concentration of solution, there are two types of solutions:

(i) **Dilute solution** Solution containing relatively very small quantity of solute.

(ii) **Concentrated solution** Solution containing relatively very large quantity of solute.

Methods of Expressing Concentration of Solutions

Various expression for the concentrations of solutions can be summarised as

(i) **Percentage by weight** ($w/w\,\%$) It is defined as the amount of solute present in 100 g of solution.

$$\frac{w}{w}\% = \frac{\text{weight of solute}}{\text{weight of solution}} \times 100$$

(ii) **Percentage by volume** ($v/V\,\%$) It is defined as the volume of solute present in 100 mL of solution,

$$\frac{v}{V}\% = \frac{\text{volume of solute}}{\text{volume of solution}} \times 100$$

(iii) **Percentage of mass by volume** ($w/V\,\%$) It is defined as the weight of solute present in 100 mL of solution.

$$\frac{w}{V}\% = \frac{\text{weight of solute}}{\text{volume of solution}} \times 100$$

(iii) **Mole fraction** (χ)   It is defined as the ratio of the number of moles of a component to the total number of moles of all the components in solution. For a binary solution, if the number of moles of A and B are n_A and n_B respectively, the mole fraction of A will be

$$\chi_A = \frac{n_A}{n_A + n_B}$$

Similarly, $$\chi_B = \frac{n_B}{n_A + n_B}$$ $[\because\ \chi_A + \chi_B = 1]$

(iv) **Parts per million** (ppm)   It is defined as the parts of a component per million parts (10^6) of the solution. It is widely used when a solute is present in trace quantities.

$$\text{ppm} = \frac{\text{number of parts of the component}}{\text{total number of parts of all the components}} \times 10^6$$
$$\text{of the solution}$$

(v) **Molarity** (M)   It is the number of moles of solute present in 1L (dm^3) of the solution.

$$M = \frac{\text{number of moles of solute}}{\text{volume of solution (L)}}$$

$$M = \frac{\text{mass of solute (in gram)} \times 1000}{\text{mol. wt. of solute} \times \text{volume of solution (in mL)}}$$

Molarity varies with temperature due to change in volume of solution. Its unit is g-mol/L.

When molarity of a solution is 1 M, it is called a molar solution. 0.1 M solution is called a decimolar solution while 0.5 M solution is known as semimolar solution.

$$\text{Molarity} = \frac{\text{per cent by mass} \times \text{density} \times 10}{\text{molecular weight}}$$

- Dilution law, $M_1V_1 = M_2V_2$ (for dilution from volume V_1 to V_2)
- For reaction between two reactants, $\dfrac{M_1V_1}{n_1} = \dfrac{M_2V_2}{n_2}$

  where, n_1 and n_2 are stoichiometric coefficients of reactants in balanced equation.

- If two solutions of the same solute are mixed ten molarity of the existing solution.

$$M = \frac{M_1V_1 + M_2V_2}{V_1 + V_2}$$

• Volume of water to be added to set a solution of molarity M_2 from V_1 mL of molarity M_1 is

$$V_2 - V_1 = \left(\frac{M_1 - M_2}{M_2}\right) V_1$$

(vi) **Molality** (m)   It is the number of moles of solute per kilogram of the solvent.

$$\text{Molality} = \frac{\text{mass of solute in gram} \times 1000}{\text{mol. wt. of solute} \times \text{mass of solvent (in g)}}$$

Molality is independent of temperature. Its unit is g-mol/kg.

⌜ When solvent used is water, a molar (1 M) solution is more concentrated than a molal (1 M) solution. ⌟

(vii) **Normality** (N)   The number of gram equivalents of solute present in 1 L of solution.

$$\text{Normality} = \frac{\text{number of gram} - \text{equivalents of solute}}{\text{volume of solution (in L)}}$$

$$\text{Number of gram-equivalents of solute} = \frac{\text{mass of solute in gram}}{\text{equivalent weight}}$$

⌜ Relationship between normality and molarity

$$N \times \text{eq. weight} = M \times \text{mol. weight}$$ ⌟

If two solutions of the same solute having volumes and molarities V_1, M_1 and V_2, M_2 are mixed, the molarity of the resulting solution is

$$M = \frac{V_1 M_1 + V_2 M_2}{V_1 + V_2}$$

Similarly,   Normality (N) = $\dfrac{N_1 V_1 + N_2 V_2}{V_1 + V_2}$

To dilute V_1 mL of a solution having molarity M_1 to molarity M_2 up to the final volume V_2 mL, the volume of water added is

$$V_2 - V_1 = \left(\frac{M_1 - M_2}{M_2}\right) V_1.$$

Similarly, $V_2 - V_1 = \left(\dfrac{N_1 - N_2}{N_2}\right) V_1$

(viii) **Formality** (F)   It is the number of formula weights of solute present per litre of the solution.

$$\text{Formality} = \frac{\text{moles of substance added to solution}}{\text{volume of solution (in L)}}$$

(ix) **Mass fraction** Mass fraction of any component in the solution is the mass of that component divided by the total mass of the solution.

Mass % of a component = $\dfrac{\text{mass of the component in the solution}}{\text{total mass of the solution}} \times 100$

Molality, mole fraction and mass fraction are preferred over molarity, normality, etc., because former involve weights which do not change with temperature.

(x) **Demal** (*D*) It represents one mole of solute present in 1L of solution at 0°C.

Solubility

The maximum amount of a solute that can be dissolved in a given amount of solvent (generally 100 g) at a given temperature is termed as its solubility at that temperature.

The solute can be either solid or gas. Likewise, solubility is defined as the one of solid in liquid or the solubility of gas in liquid.

The solubility of a solute in a liquid depends upon the following factors:

Solubility of gases in liquids

All gases are soluble in water as well as in other liquids to a greater or smaller extent.

Factors affecting solubility of gases

(i) **Nature of the gas** The gases which can be easily liquified, are more soluble in common solvents.

(ii) **Nature of the solvent** The gases which are capable of forming ions in aqueous solutions are much more soluble in water than in other solvents.

(iii) **Temperature** The solubility of most gases in liquids decreases with increase of temperature.

(iv) **Pressure** The solubility of a gases increase with increase in pressure.

Henry's Law

The most commonly used form of Henry's law states "the partial pressure (*p*) of the gas in vapour phase is proportional to the mole fraction (*x*) of the gas in the solution" and is expressed as

$$p = K_H \cdot x$$

Higher the value of K_H at given pressure, the lower is the solubility of the gas in the liquid. The value of K_H decreases with increase in the temperature. Thus, aquatic species are more confortable in cold water [more dissolved O_2] rather than warm water.

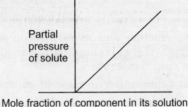

Mole fraction of component in its solution

Applications

1. In manufacture of soft drinks and soda water, CO_2 is passed at high pressure to increase its solubility.

2. To minimise the painful effects (bends) accompanying the decompression of deep sea divers, O_2 diluted with less soluble He gas is used as breathing gas.

3. At high altitudes, the partial pressure of O_2 is less than that at the ground level. This leads to low concentrations of O_2 in the blood of climbers which causes 'anoxia'.

Vapour Pressure

The pressure exerted by the vapour molecules above the liquid surface in equilibrium with the liquid at a given temperature is called vapour pressure.

Factors affecting vapour pressure

Vapour pressure gets affected by following factors.

(i) **Purity of the liquid** Pure liquid always has a vapour pressure higher than its solution.

(ii) **Nature of the liquid** Liquids which have weak intermolecular forces are volatile and have greater vapour pressure.

(iii) **Temperature** The vapour pressure of a liquid increases with increase in temperature.

(iv) **Effect of adding solute** When a liquid contains a solute, some of the solvent molecules are replaced by the solute particles on the liquid surface and therefore, the available surface area for the escape of solvent molecule decreases. Therefore, rate of evaporation as well as rate of condensation both decrease.

Raoult's Law

The Raoult's law states "For a solution of two volatile liquids, the vapour pressure of each liquid in the solution is less than the respective vapour pressure of the pure liquids and the equilibrium partial vapour pressure of the liquid is directly proportional to its mole fraction.

For a solution containing two liquids A and B, the partial vapour pressure of liquid A is

$$p_A \propto \chi_A$$

or $$p_A = k\chi_A$$

where, $$\chi_A = \frac{n_A}{(n_A + n_B)}$$

= mole fraction of liquid A

The proportionality constant is obtained by considering the pure liquid when, $\chi_A = 1$ then $k = p_A^\circ$, the vapour pressure of pure liquid, hence,

$$p_A = p_A^\circ \chi_A$$

Similarly, $$p_B = p_B^\circ \chi_B$$

The total vapour pressure of the solution,

$$p_T = p_A + p_B$$
$$= p_A^\circ \chi_A + p_B^\circ \chi_B$$
$$= p_A^\circ + (p_B^\circ - p_A^\circ) \chi_B$$

Rault's Law as a Special Case of Henry's Law

According to Raoult's law, the vapour pressure of a volatile component in a given solution is given by $p_1 = x_1 \, p_1^0$. In the solution of a gas in a liquid, one of the components is so volatile that it exists a a gas and we have already seen that its solubility is given by Henry's law which states that

$$p = K_H \, x.$$

If we compare the equations for Raoult's law and Henry's law and Henry's law, it can be seen that the partial pressure of the volatile component of gas is directly proportional to its mole fraction in solution. Only the proportionality constant K_H differs from p_1^0. Thus, law becomes a special case of Henry's law in which K_H becomes equal to p_1^0.

Ideal Solutions

Those solutions in which solute-solute (B—B) and solvent-solvent (A—A) interactions are almost similar to solvent-solute (A—B) interactions are called ideal solutions. These solutions satisfy the following conditions :

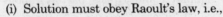

(i) Solution must obey Raoult's law, i.e.,

$$p_A = p_A^\circ \chi_A, \ p_B = p_B^\circ \chi_B$$

(ii) $\Delta H_{mix} = 0$ (No energy evolved or absorbed)

(iii) $\Delta V_{mix} = 0$ (No expansion or contraction on mixing)

Some solutions behave like nearly ideal solutions, e.g., benzene + toluene, n-hexane + n-heptane, ethyl iodide + ethyl bromide, chlorobenzene + bromobenzene.

Non-ideal Solutions

Those solutions which shows deviation from Raoult's law are called non-ideal solutions.

For such solutions,

$$\Delta H_{mix} \neq 0$$
$$\Delta V_{mix} \neq 0$$

(a) **Non-ideal solutions showing positive deviation** In such a case, the $A - B$ interactions are weaker than $A - A$ or $B - B$ interactions and the observed vapour pressure of each component and the total vapour pressure are greater than that predicted by Raoult's law.

$$p_A > p_A^\circ \chi_A; \ p_B > p_B^\circ \chi_B$$
$$p_{total} > p_A^\circ \chi_A + p_B^\circ \chi_B$$

For such solutions

$$\Delta H_{mix} > 0, \ \Delta V_{mix} > 0$$

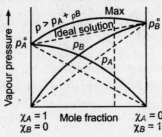

Non-ideal solution showing positive deviation

Examples : Ethanol + water, CS_2 + acetone, CCl_4 + C_6H_6, CCl_4 + $C_6H_5CH_3$, ethanol + cyclohexane, CCl_4 + $CHCl_3$.

(b) **Non-ideal solution showing negative deviation** In such a case, the $A - B$ interactions are stronger than $A - A$ or $B - B$ interactions and the observed vapour pressure of each component and the total vapour pressure are lesser than that predicted by Raoult's law.

$$p_A < p_A^\circ \chi_A \, , \, p_B < p_B^\circ \chi_B$$

$$p_{\text{total}} < p_A^\circ \chi_A + p_B^\circ \chi_B$$

For such solutions,

$$\Delta H_{\text{mix}} < 0, \ \Delta V_{\text{mix}} < 0$$

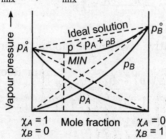

Non-ideal solution showng negative deviation

Examples : $CHCl_3$ + CH_3COCH_3, $CHCl_3$ + C_6H_6, H_2O + HCl, H_2O + HNO_3, methanol + acetic acid.

Azeotropic Mixture

A mixture of two liquids which boils at a particular temperature like a pure liquid and distils over in the same composition is known as constant boiling mixtures. These are formed by non-ideal solutions.

(i) **Minimum boiling azeotropes** are formed by those liquid pairs which show positive deviation from ideal behaviour. Such azeotropes have boiling points lower than either of the components, e.g. C_2H_5OH (95.57%) + H_2O (4.43%) (by mass).

(ii) **Maximum boiling azeotropes** are formed by those liquid pairs which show negative deviation from ideal behaviour. Such azeotropes have boiling points higher than either of the components, e.g. H_2O(20.22%) + HCl [79.78%] by mass.

Colligative Properties

[*Colligative : from Latin = Co means 'together'; ligate means 'to bind'*]

Colligative properties are those properties which depend only upon the number of solute particles in a solution irrespective of their nature.

Relative Lowering of Vapour Pressure

When a non-volatile solute is added to a solvent, to vapour pressure is solvent. Relative lowering in vapour pressure is the ratio of lowering in vapour pressure to vapour pressure of pure solvent. The relative lowering in vapour pressure of solution containing a non-volatile solute is equal to the mole fraction of solute in the solution.

$$\frac{p_A^\circ - p_A}{p_A^\circ} = \chi_B$$

where, $\dfrac{p_A^\circ - p_A}{p_A^\circ}$ = relative lowering of vapour pressure of pure solvent

$$\frac{p_A^\circ - p_A}{p_A^\circ} = \frac{n_B}{n_A + n_B}$$

for dilute solutions, $n_B \ll n_A$.
Hence,

$$\frac{p_A^\circ - p_A}{p_A^\circ} = \frac{n_B}{n_A}$$

or
$$\frac{p_A^\circ - p_A}{p_A^\circ} = \frac{W_B \times M_A}{M_B \times W_A}$$

$$M_B = \frac{W_B}{W_A} \times M_A \times \frac{p_A}{(p_A^\circ - p_A)}$$

Above expression is used to find the molecular weight of an unknown solute dissolved in a given solvent. where, W_B and W_A = mass of solute and solvent respectively, M_B and M_A = molecular weight of solute and solvent respectively.

Ostwald and Walker method is used to determine the relative lowering of vapour pressure.

Elevation in Boiling Point (ΔT_b)

Boiling point of a liquid is the temperature at which its vapour pressure becomes equal to the atmospheric pressure. As the vapour pressure of a solution containing a non-volatile solute is lower than that of the pure solvent, then it's boiling point will be higher than that of the pure solvent as shown in figure. The increase in boiling point is known as elevation in boiling point, ΔT_b

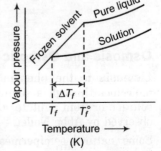

$$\Delta T_b = T_b - T_b^{\circ}$$

$$\Delta T_b = K_b \, m \qquad \text{(where, } m = \text{molality)}$$

K_b is molal elevation constant or ebullioscopic constant. Molecular mass of solute can be calculated as

$$\Delta T_b = \frac{K_b \cdot W_B \times 1000}{M_B \times W_A}$$

$$M_B = K_b \cdot \frac{W_B}{W_A} \times \frac{1000}{\Delta T_b}$$

where, W_B and W_A = mass of solute and solvent respectively.
K_b has units of K/m or K kg mol^{-1}, for water, $K_b = 0.52$ K kg mol^{-1}.

Depression in Freezing Point (ΔT_f)

Freezing point of a liquid is the temperature at which vapour pressure of the solvent in its liquid and solid phase become equal. As we know that vapour pressure of solution containing non-volatile solute is lower than that of pure solvent, solid form gets separated out at a lower temperature as shown in the figure.

This decrease in freezing point of a liquid is known as depression in freezing point.

Depression in freezing point $(\Delta T_f) = T_f^{\circ} - T_f$

$$\Delta T_f = K_f \cdot m = K_f \frac{W_B}{M_B} \times \frac{1000}{W_A}$$

To find molecular mass of solute,

$$M_B = \frac{K_f \cdot W_B \times 1000}{\Delta T_f \cdot W_A}$$

where, K_f is molal depression constant or cryoscopic constant.
K_f has units of K/m or K kg mol^{-1}.

Ethylene glycol is usually added to water in the radiator to lower its freezing point. It is called antifreeze solution.

⌈ Common salt (NaCl) and anhydrous $CaCl_2$ are used to clear snow on the roads because they depress the freezing point of water. The freezing point depression is determined by Beckmann method or Rast method. ⌋

Calculations of molal elevation constant (K_b) and molal depression constant (K_f)

$$K_b = \frac{M_A R(T_b^\circ)^2}{1000 \times \Delta H_v}$$

$$K_f = \frac{M_A \cdot R(T_f^\circ)^2}{\Delta H_f \times 1000}$$

T_b° = boiling point of solvent

T_f° = freezing point of solvent

ΔH_f = molar enthalpy of fusion

ΔH_v = molar enthalpy of vaporisation

where, M_A is molar mass of solvent in kg mol^{-1}, R = gas constant.

$$\frac{K_b}{K_f} = \frac{\Delta T_b}{\Delta T_f}$$

Osmosis and Osmotic Pressure

Osmosis is the phenomenon of spontaneous flow of the solvent molecules through a semipermeable membrane from pure solvent to solution or from a dilute solution to concentrated solution. It was first observed by Abbe Nollet.

Some natural semipermeable membranes are animal bladder, cell membrane etc.

$Cu_2[Fe(CN)_6]$ is an artificial semipermeable membrane which does not work in non-aqueous solutions as it dissolves in them.

Osmosis may be

(i) **Exosmosis** It is outward flow of water or solvent from a cell through semipermeable membrane.

(ii) **Endosmosis** It is inward flow of water or solvent from a cell through a semipermeable membrane.

The hydrostatic pressure developed on the solution which just prevents the osmosis of pure solvent into the solution through a semipermeable membrane is called **osmotic pressure**.

$$\text{Osmotic pressure } (\pi) = RCT; \qquad \left(C = \frac{n_B}{V} = \frac{W_B}{M_B V} \right)$$

$$\Rightarrow \qquad M_B = \frac{W_B RT}{\pi V}$$

$$\pi = \frac{dRT}{M_B}; \qquad \left(d = \frac{W_B}{V} \right)$$

where, d = density, R = solution contant,

T = temperature, M_B = molar mass of solute

Osmotic pressure can be determined by any one of the method listed below

(i) Pfeffer's method

(ii) Berkeley and Hartley's method (very good method)

(iii) Morse and Frazer's method

On the basis of osmotic pressure, the solution can be

(i) **Hypertonic solution** A solution is called hypertonic if its osmotic pressure is higher than that of the solution from which it is separated by a semipermeable membrane.

When a plant cell is placed in a hypertonic solution, the fluid from the plant cell comes out and cell shrinks, this phenomenon is called plasmolysis.

(ii) **Hypotonic solution** A solution is called hypotonic if its osmotic pressure is lower than that of the solution from which it is separated by a semipermeable membrane.

(iii) **Isotonic solution** Two solutions are called isotonic if they exert the same osmotic pressure. These solutions have same molar concentration. 0.91% solution of pure NaCl is isotonic with human RBC's.

Two solutions are isotonic if they have the same molar concentration, e.g. if $x\%$ solution of X is isotonic with $y\%$ solution of Y, this means molar concentration of X = Molar concentration of Y

$$\frac{x}{100} \times \frac{1000}{M_X} = \frac{y \times 1000}{100 \times M_Y} \quad \Rightarrow \quad \frac{x}{M_X} = \frac{y}{M_Y}$$

Osmotic pressure method is the best method for determining the molecular masses of polymers since observed value of any other colligative property is too small to be measured with reasonable accuracy.

Reverse osmosis When the external pressure applied on the solution is more than osmotic pressure, the solvent flows from the solution to the pure solvent, which is called reverse osmosis. Desalination of sea water is done by reverse osmosis.

Abnormal Molecular Masses

In some cases, observed colligative properties deviate from their normal calculated values due to association or dissociation of molecules. As we know,

$$\text{Colligative property} \propto \frac{1}{M_B}$$

Hence, higher and lower values of molar mass is observed in case of association and dissociation respectively, e.g. in benzene, acetic acid gets associated, so, its observed molecular mass is 120. Similarly KCl undergoes dissociation in aqueous solution, so its observed molecular mass is 37.25.

These observed values are corrected by multiplying with van't Hoff factor (i).

van't Hoff Factor (i)

It is the ratio of observed value of colligative property to the calculated value of colligative property.

$$i = \frac{\text{observed value of colligative property}}{\text{calculated value of colligative property}}$$

or $\quad i = \dfrac{\text{normal molecular mass}}{\text{observed molecular mass}}$

or $\quad i = \dfrac{\text{number of particles after association or dissociation}}{\text{number of particles initially}}$

So to correct the observed value of molar mass, van't Hoff factor (i) must be included in different expressions for colligative properties.

$$\Delta T_b = i \, K_b \cdot m$$
$$\Delta T_f = i K_f \cdot m$$

$$\pi = i\,CRT$$

$$\frac{\Delta p}{p_A^\circ} = i x_B$$

i for several strong electrolytes (Complete dissociation)

For KCl, NaCl and $MgSO_4$, *i* approaches 2 as the solution becomes very dilute. As expected, the value of *i* gets close to 3 for K_2SO_4.

Degree of Dissociation (α) and van't Hoff Factor (*i*)

If one molecule of a substance gets dissociated into *n* particles or molecules and α is the degree of dissociation then

$$A \longrightarrow nP$$

Initially	1 mol	0
At eq.	$1 - \alpha$	$n\alpha$

Total number of moles at equilibrium

$$= 1 - \alpha + n\alpha$$

$$\therefore \qquad i = \frac{1 - \alpha + n\alpha}{1}$$

$$\Rightarrow \qquad \alpha = \frac{i-1}{n-1}$$

Degree of Association (α) and van't Hoff Factor (*i*)

If *n* molecules of a substance *A* associate to form A_n and α is the degree of association then

$$nA \longrightarrow A_n$$

Initially	1 mol	0
At equilibrium	$1 - \alpha$	$\dfrac{\alpha}{n}$

Total number of moles at equilibrium

$$= 1 - \alpha + \frac{\alpha}{n}$$

$$i = \frac{1 - \alpha + \dfrac{\alpha}{n}}{1}$$

$$\Rightarrow \qquad \alpha = \frac{i-1}{\dfrac{1}{n} - 1}$$

van't Hoff factor (*i*) > 1 for solutes undergoing dissociation and it is < 1 for solutes undergoing association.

11

Redox Reactions

Chemical reactions which involves both oxidation as well as reduction process simultaneously, are known as redox reactions ('red' from reduction and 'ox' from oxidation). All these reactions are always accompanied by energy change in the form of heat, light or electricity.

Oxidation and Reduction

Oxidation	Reduction
It involves	It involves
(i) Addition of oxygen to an element or compound, or the removal of hydrogen from a compound. e.g. $2Mg + O_2 \longrightarrow 2MgO$ $2H_2S + O_2 \longrightarrow 2H_2O + 2S$	Addition of hydrogen to an element or compound, or the removal of oxygen from a compound. e.g. $H_2S + Cl_2 \longrightarrow 2HCl + S$ $Fe_2O_3 + 3CO \longrightarrow 2Fe + 3CO_2$
(ii) Addition of electronegative element or removal of any other electropositive element. $Zn + S \longrightarrow ZnS$ $2KI + Cl_2 \longrightarrow 2KCl + I_2$	Addition of electropositive element or removal of any other electronegative element. $2HgCl_2 + SnCl_4 \longrightarrow Hg_2Cl_2 + SnCl_4$ $SiCl_4 + 4Na \longrightarrow Si + 4NaCl$
(iii) Oxidation is the loss of electrons by an atom, ion or molecule. It is also known as de-electronation. $Zn \longrightarrow Zn^{2+} + 2e^-$	Reduction is the gain of electrons by an atom, ion or molecule. This process is known as electronation. $Cu^{2+} + 2e^- \longrightarrow Cu$
(iv) Oxidation involves increase in oxidation number.	Reduction involves decrease in oxidation number.
(v) Oxidation is caused by an oxidising agent.	Reduction is caused by a reducing agent.

Reductants and Oxidants

Oxidant or oxidising agent is a chemical substance which can accept one or more electrons and causes oxidation of some other species. In other words, the oxidation number of oxidant decreases in a redox reaction.

Important Oxidants

Molecules of most electronegative elements such as O_2, O_3, halogens.

Compounds having element in its highest oxidation state, e.g. $K_2Cr_2O_7, KMnO_4, HClO_4, H_2SO_4, KClO_3, Ce(SO_4)_2$.

Oxides of metals and non-metals such as MgO, CrO_3, CO_2, etc.

Reductant or reducing agent is a chemical substance which can give one or more electrons and causes reduction of some other species. In other words, the oxidation number of reductant increases in a redox reaction.

Important Reductants

All metals such as Na, Al, Zn, etc., and some non-metals, e.g. C, S, P, H_2, etc.

Metallic hydrides like NaH, LiH, KH, CaH_2, etc.

The compounds having an element in its lowest oxidation state such as $H_2C_2O_4, FeSO_4, Hg_2Cl_2 SnCl_2, H_2S, SO_2, Na_2S_2O_3$, etc.

SO_2, HNO_2 and H_2O_2 can act both as oxidant as well as reductant.

$$\text{Eq. wt. of oxidant/reductant} = \frac{\text{molar mass}}{\text{change in oxidation number}}$$

For disproportionation reaction,

Eq. wt. of oxidant/reductant = sum of eq. wt. of two half reactions

e.g.

$$4H_3PO_3 \longrightarrow 3H_3PO_4 + PH_3$$

$$\text{Eq. wt. of } H_3PO_3 = \frac{M}{2} + \frac{M}{6} = \frac{2M}{3}$$

Oxidation Number

The oxidation number is defined as the charge which an atom appears to have when all other atoms are removed from it as ions. It may have + or − sign.

An element may have different values of oxidation number depending upon the nature of compound in which it is present.

Oxidation number of an element may be a whole number (Positive or negative) or fractional or zero.

Important Points for Determining Oxidation Number

(i) The algebraic sum of the oxidation numbers of all the atoms in an uncharged (neutral) compound is zero. In an ion, the algebraic sum is equal to the charge on the ion.

(ii) All elements in the elementary state have oxidation number zero, e.g. He, Cl_2, S_8, P_4, etc.

(iii) As fluorine is the most electronegative element, it always has an oxidation number of -1 in all of its compounds.

(iv) In compounds containing oxygen, the oxidation number of oxygen is -2 except in peroxides (-1) such as Na_2O_2, in OF_2 and in $O_2 F_2$ ($+2$ and $+1$ respectively).

(v) In all compounds, except ionic metallic hydrides, the oxidation number of hydrogen is $+1$. In metal hydrides like NaH, MgH_2, CaH_2, LiH, etc., the oxidation number of hydrogen is -1.

(vi) Oxidation number for alkali metals is $+1$ and for alkaline earth metals is $+2$.

(vii) Oxidation number of metal in amalgams is zero.

(viii) In case of coordinate bond, it gives $+2$ value of oxidation number to less electronegative atom and -2 value to more electronegative atom when coordinate bond is directed from less electronegative atom to more electronegative atom.

(ix) If coordinate bond is directed from more electronegative to less electronegative atom then its contribution be zero for both the atoms.

(x) For p-block elements [Except F and O], the highest oxidation number is equal to their group number and lowest oxidation number is equal to the group number minus eight.

(xi) In transition elements the lowest oxidation number is equal to the number of ns electrons and highest oxidation number is equal to number of 'ns' and $(n-1)d$ unpaired electrons.

Determination of Oxidation Number of Underlined Element

(i) $K_2\underline{Cr}_2O_7$

Solution

$$\underset{(2 \times 1)}{K_2} \quad \underset{(2 \times x)}{Cr_2} \quad \underset{(-2 \times 7)}{O_7}$$

$$2 + 2x - 14 = 0 \; ; \quad x = +6$$

(ii) $[\underline{Fe}(CN)_6]^{4-}$

Solution

$$[\underset{\underset{x}{\downarrow}}{Fe} \; \underset{\underset{-1}{\downarrow}}{(CN)_6}]^{4-}$$

$$x - 6 = -4 \quad \Rightarrow \quad x = 2$$

(iii) $Na_2\underline{S}_4O_6$

Solution

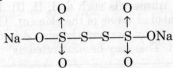

Oxidation number of $Na = +1$

Oxidation number of $O = -2$

$\therefore \quad 2(1) + 4x + 6 \times -2 = 0$

$x = 5/2$, this is average oxidation number, because the compound has two types of sulphur atom.

ON of sulphur bonded with coordinate bond $= 5$

ON of sulphur which have S—S bond $= 0$

$\therefore$ Average oxidation number $= \dfrac{5+5+0+0}{4} = \dfrac{5}{2}$

(iv) Caro's acid ($H_2\underline{S}O_5$)

$$\underset{+1}{H}\!-\!\overset{-2}{O}\!-\!\overset{\overset{\displaystyle O^{-2}}{\uparrow}}{\underset{\underset{\displaystyle O_{-2}}{\downarrow}}{S}}\!-\!\overset{-1}{O}\!-\!\overset{-1}{O}\!-\!\underset{+1}{H}$$

$2 + x - 6 - 2 = 0 \quad \Rightarrow \quad x = 6$

(v) $\underline{Cr}O_5$

$$\overset{-2}{\underset{\overset{-1}{O}\diagdown\ \diagup\overset{-1}{O}}{\underset{\overset{-1}{O}\diagup\ \diagdown\overset{-1}{O}}{\overset{\displaystyle O}{\underset{\displaystyle \|}{Cr}}}}}$$

$x + 4(-1) + (-2)(1) = 0 \Rightarrow x = 6$

(vi) $\underline{C}_3O_2$ (carbon suboxide)

$$\overset{-2}{O}\!=\!\overset{2+}{C}\!=\!\overset{0}{C}\!=\!\overset{2+}{C}\!=\!\overset{-2}{O}$$

(vii) $\underline{N}H_4\underline{N}O_3$

There are two types of nitrogen atoms. Therefore, evaluation should be made separately as

Oxidation number of N in NH_4^+

$x + 4(+1) = +1 \Rightarrow x = -3$

Oxidation number of N in NO_3^-

$y + 3 \times (-2) = -1 \Rightarrow y = 5$

Stock Notations

The oxidation states of elements exhibiting variable oxidation states are specified by **Roman numerals** such as I, II, III, IV, etc., within parenthesis after the symbol or name of the element. This system was introduced for the first time by German chemist, Alfred **Stock** and is known as **Stock** notation. This may be illustrated as

Formula of the compound	Chemical name	Stock notation'
Cu_2O	Cuprous oxide	Copper (I) oxide; $Cu_2(I)O$
Fe_2O_3	Ferric oxide	Iron (III) oxide; $Fe_2(III)O_3$
$HgCl_2$	Mercuric chloride	Mercury (II) chloride; $Hg(II) Cl_2$
$SnCl_2$	Stannous chloride	Stannous (II) chloride, $Sn(II) Cl_2$

Types of Redox Reactions

(i) **Combination reactions** The reactions in which two atoms or molecules combine together to form a third molecule are **combination reactions.**

e.g. $2\overset{0}{Mg}(s) + \overset{0}{O_2}(g) \longrightarrow 2\overset{+2\ -2}{MgO}(s)$

(ii) **Decomposition reactions** The reactions in which molecule breaks down to form two or more components are called **decomposition reactions.**

e.g. $2KClO_3(s) \overset{\Delta}{\longrightarrow} 2KCl(s) + 3O_2(g)$

(iii) **Displacement reactions** The reactions in which an atom (or ion) of a compound is replaced by another ion (or atom) of same nature are called displacement reactions.

These are of the following two types :

(a) **Metal displacement reactions** When a metal in the compound is displaced by some other metal in the elemental state.

e.g. $CuSO_4(aq.) + Zn(s) \longrightarrow Cu(s) + ZnSO_4(aq.)$

(b) **Non-metal displacement reactions** In these reactions, a metal or a non-metal displaces another non-metal from its compound.

e.g. $Mg(s) + 2H_2O(g) \longrightarrow Mg(OH)_2(aq.) + H_2(g)$

(iv) **Intermolecular redox reactions** In such reactions, oxidation and reduction take place separately in two compounds.

e.g. $SnCl_2 + 2FeCl_3 \longrightarrow SnCl_4 + 2FeCl_2$

$$Sn^{2+} \longrightarrow Sn^{4+} \qquad \text{(oxidation)}$$

$$Fe^{3+} \longrightarrow Fe^{2+} \qquad \text{(reduction)}$$

(v) **Intramolecular redox reactions** In these reactions, oxidation and reduction take place in a single compound. e.g.

$$2\overset{+5}{K}\overset{-2}{C}l_3 \longrightarrow 2\overset{-1}{K}Cl + 3\overset{0}{O_2}$$

(vi) **Disproportionation reactions** These reactions involve reduction and oxidation of same element of a compound. e.g.

$$\overset{0}{Cl_2} + 2OH^- \longrightarrow \overset{+1}{Cl}O^- + Cl^- + H_2O$$

This reaction is also known as **autoredox reaction.**

$$2\overset{+1}{H_2}\overset{-1}{O_2}(aq) \longrightarrow 2\overset{+1}{H_2}\overset{-2}{O}(l) + \overset{0}{O_2}(g)$$

Classification of Redox Reactions

Direct Redox Reactions

Chemical reaction in which oxidation as well as reduction is carried out simultaneously in the same container, is known as direct redox reaction. In such reactions, energy is generally liberated in the form of heat energy.

Indirect Redox Reactions

A reaction in which oxidation and reduction are carried out separately in two separate half-cells, is known as indirect redox reaction. In such reactions, energy is generally liberated in the form of electrical energy.

Balancing of Redox Chemical Equations

Every chemical equation must be balanced according to law of conservation of mass. In a balanced chemical equation, the atoms of various species involved in the reactants and products must be equal in number. Redox reaction can be balanced through

(i) Ion electron method   (ii) Oxidation number method.

Ion Electron Method (Half Reaction Method)

This method of balancing was developed by Jette and Lamer in 1927. For example, balance the equation

$$Cu + HNO_3 \longrightarrow Cu(NO_3)_2 + NO + H_2O$$

It involves the following steps.

Step I Write the redox reaction in ionic form.

$$Cu + H^+ + NO_3^- \longrightarrow Cu^{2+} + NO + H_2O$$

Step II Split the redox reaction into its oxidation-half and reduction half-reaction.

$$Cu \xrightarrow{\text{oxidation}} Cu^{2+}$$

and

$$NO_3^- \xrightarrow[\text{(Removal of O)}]{\text{Reduction}} NO$$

Step III Balance atoms of each half-reaction (except H and O) by using simple multiples.

$$Cu \longrightarrow Cu^{2+} \text{ and } NO_3^- \longrightarrow NO$$

(Except H and O, all atoms are balanced)

Step IV Balance H and O as

(i) **For acidic and neutral solutions** Add H_2O molecule to the side deficient in oxygen and H^+ to the side deficient in hydrogen.

$$Cu \longrightarrow Cu^{2+} \text{ and } \boxed{4H^+} + NO_3^- \longrightarrow NO + \boxed{2H_2O}$$

$$\uparrow \text{to balance H} \qquad \uparrow \text{to balance O}$$

(ii) **For alkaline solutions** For each excess of oxygen, add one water molecule to the same side and OH^- ion to the other side to balance H.

Step V Add electrons to the side deficient in electrons.

$$Cu \longrightarrow Cu^{2+} + 2e^-$$

$$3e^- + 4H^+ + NO_3^- \longrightarrow NO + 2H_2O$$

Step VI Equalise the number of electrons in both the reactions by multiplying a suitable number.

$$[Cu \longrightarrow Cu^{2+} + 2e^-] \times 3$$

$$[NO_3^- + 4H^+ + 3e^- \longrightarrow NO + 2H_2O] \times 2$$

Step VII Add the two balanced half reactions and cancel common terms of opposite sides.

$$3Cu \longrightarrow 3Cu^{2+} + 6e^-$$

$$2NO_3^- + 8H^+ + 6e^- \longrightarrow 2NO + 4H_2O$$

$$3Cu + 2NO_3^- + 8H^+ \longrightarrow 3Cu^{2+} + 2NO + 4H_2O$$

Step VIII *Convert the ionic reaction into molecular form by adding spectator ions.*

$$3Cu + 2NO_3^- + 8H^+ + 6NO_3^- \longrightarrow 3Cu^{2+} + 2NO + \underset{\text{spectator ion}}{6NO_3^-} + 4H_2O$$

or
$$3Cu + 8HNO_3 \longrightarrow 3Cu(NO_3)_2 + 2NO + 4H_2O$$

(Ions which are present in solution but do not take part in the redox reaction, are omitted while writing the net ionic equation of a reaction and are known as spectator ions.)

Oxidation Number Method

For example, balance the equation
$$Mg + HNO_3 \longrightarrow Mg(NO_3)_2 + N_2O + H_2O$$
It involves the following steps.

Step I   Write the skeleton equation (if not given)

Step II   Assign oxidation number of each atom

$$\overset{0}{Mg} + \overset{+1 +5 -2}{HNO_3} \longrightarrow \overset{+2}{Mg}\ \overset{+5-2}{(NO_3)_2} + \overset{+1-2}{N_2O},$$

with Reduction arrow from top (+2 ... +1-2) and oxidation arrow below Mg → Mg.

Step III   Balance atoms other than H and O in two processes.

change in OS = 10 - 2 = 8
$$Mg + 2HNO_3 \longrightarrow Mg(NO_3)_2 + N_2O$$
change in OS = 2 - (0) = 2

Step IV   Equalize the total increase or decrease in oxidation number.
$$4Mg + 2HNO_3 \longrightarrow 4Mg(NO_3)_2 + N_2O$$

Step V   Balance H and O
$$8H^+ + 4Mg + 2HNO_3 + 8NO_3^- \longrightarrow 4Mg(NO_3)_2 + N_2O + 5H_2O$$
$$4Mg + 10HNO_3 \longrightarrow 4Mg(NO_3)_2 + N_2O + 5H_2O$$

Redox Reactions in Daily Life

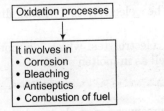

Oxidation processes

It involves in
• Corrosion
• Bleaching
• Antiseptics
• Combustion of fuel

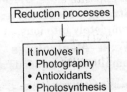

Reduction processes

It involves in
• Photography
• Antioxidants
• Photosynthesis
• Metallurgy

12

Electrochemistry

Electrochemistry is that branch of chemistry which deals with the study of production of electricity from energy released during spontaneous chemical reactions and the use of electrical energy to bring about non-spontaneous chemical transformations.

Conductors

Substances that allow electric current to pass through them are known as conductors. Certain materials called superconductors by definition have zero resistivity or infinite conductivity. e.g. ceramic materials and mixed oxides also show superconductivity at temperature as high as 150 K.

Metallic Conductors or Electronic Conductors

Substances which allow the electric current to pass through them by the movement of electrons are called metallic conductors, e.g. metals.

Electrolytic Conductors or Electrolytes

Substances which allow the passage of electricity through their fused state or aqueous solution and undergo chemical decomposition are called electrolytic conductors, e.g. aqueous solution of acids, bases and salts.

Electrolytes are of two types:

(i) **Strong electrolytes** The electrolytes which dissociate completely into ions.

(ii) **Weak electrolytes** The electrolytes which do not ionise completely in aqueous as well as in molten state.

Cell

Cells are the devices in which interconversion of electrical energy and chemical energy takes place.

A cell is made up of various components i.e. electrolytic solution (already discussed), salt-bridge and electrodes.

Salt-bridge

It is a U-shaped glass tube which contains agar-agar paste with NH_4NO_3, KNO_3 or KCl as conducting electrolytes. **KCl is not used when electrode is made of Ag**. This salt-bridge is only used in electrochemical cell.

Electrodes

These are the materials that conduct electricity to or from the cell due to movement of electrons. It may be taken in any form like wire, rod, sheet etc.

Types of cell

Cells are of two basic types as discussed below

(i) **Electrochemical cell** In this cell chemical reaction (redox reactions) are carried out that result in production of electricity. It is also called voltaic or galvanic cell. One of the important example of this type of cells is Daniell cell.

(ii) **Electrolytic cell** In this cell electricity is used to produce non-spontaneous chemical changes. As there occurs, breaking down of a molecule with the help of electricity, the process is called **electrolysis**.

Electrochemical Cell and Electrolytic Cell

Characteristics	Electrochemical cell (Galvanic cell)	Electrolytic cell
	Salt bridge	
	Anode $M \longrightarrow M^{n+} + ne^-$ Cathode $M^{n+} + ne^- \longrightarrow M$	
1. Definition	A device used to convert chemical energy into electrical energy.	A device used to carry out non-spontaneous chemical reactions by electrical energy.

Characteristics	Electrochemical cell (Galvanic cell)	Electrolytic cell
2. Assembly	It is combination of two half-cells, containing the same or different electrodes in the same or different electrolytes.	It is a single cell containing the same electrodes present in the same electrolyte.
3. Nature of electrodes	Anode is negative, cathode is positive.	Anode is positive, cathode is negative.
4. Movement of electrons	From anode to cathode in external circuit.	Electrons enter through cathode and leave by anode.
5. Spontaneity	Cell reaction is spontaneous	Cell reaction is non-spontaneous.
6. Salt bridge	Salt bridge is required	Salt bridge is not required.

A cell of almost constant emf is called **standard cell**. The most common is Weston standard cell.

General Representation of an Electrochemical Cell

$$M_1(s)\,|\,M_1^{n+}(aq) \qquad || \qquad M_2^{n+}(aq)\,|\,M_2(s)$$

| Anode oxidation half-cell | Salt bridge | Cathode reduction half-cell |

	Cathode	Anode
Sign	Positive due to consumption of electrons	Negative due to release of electrons
Reaction	Reduction	Oxidation
Movement of electrons	Into the cell	Out of cell

Other features of the electrochemical cell are

1. There is no evolution of heat.
2. The solution remains neutral on both sides.
3. The reaction and flow of electrons stops after sometime.

Daniell Cell

An electrochemical cell of zinc and copper metals is known as Daniell cell. This cell converts the chemical energy liberated during the redox reaction to electrical energy and has an electrical potential equal to 1.1 V.

$$Zn(s) + Cu^{2+}(aq) \longrightarrow Zn^{2+}(aq) + Cu(s)$$

When concentration of Zn^{2+} and Cu^{2+} ion has unity ($1 \ mol \ dm^{-3}$) such a device is called galvanic or voltaic cell.

It is represented as :

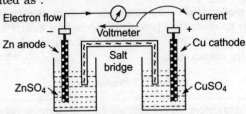

Cell representation,

$$Zn(s) \mid Zn^{2+}(aq) \parallel Cu^{2+}(aq) \mid Cu(s)$$

LHS oxidation, $\qquad Zn \longrightarrow Zn^{2+} + 2e^-$

RHS reduction, $\qquad Cu^{2+} + 2e^- \longrightarrow Cu$

Overall reaction, $\ Zn + Cu^{2+}(aq) \longrightarrow Zn^{2+}(aq) + Cu$

By convention cathode is represented on the RHS and anode on the LHS.

Function of salt bridge

1. It completes the circuit and allows the flow of current.

2. It maintains the electrical neutrality on both sides. Salt-bridge generally contains solution of strong electrolyte such as KNO_3, KCl, etc. KCl is preferred because the transport numbers of K^+ and Cl^- are almost same.

Transport number or transference number The current flowing through an electrolytic solution is carried by the ions. The fraction of the current carried by an ion is called its transport number or transference number. Thus,

$$\text{Transport number of cation, } n_c = \frac{\text{current carried by cation}}{\text{total current}}$$

$$\text{Transport number of anion, } n_a = \frac{\text{current carried by anion}}{\text{total current}}$$

$$\text{Evidently } n_c + n_a = 1$$

Electrode Potential

When an electrode is in contact with the solution of its ions in a half-cell, it has a tendency to lose or gain electrons which is known as electrode potential. It is expressed in volts. It is an intensive property, *i.e.* independent of the amount of species in the reaction.

Oxidation potential The tendency to lose electrons in the above case is known as oxidation potential. Oxidation potential of a half-cell is inversely proportional to the concentration of ions in the solution.

Reduction potential The tendency to gain electrons in the above case is known as reduction potential. According to IUPAC convention, the reduction potential alone be called as the electrode potential unless it is specifically mentioned.

$$E^{\circ}_{\text{red}} = -E^{\circ}_{\text{oxidation}}$$

> It is not possible to determine the absolute value of electrode potential. For this a reference electrode [NHE or SHE] is required. The electrode potential is only the difference of potentials between two electrodes that we can measure by combining them to give a complete cell.

Standard electrode potential The potential difference developed between metal electrode and solution of ions of unit molarity (1M) at 1 atm pressure and 25°C (298 K) temperature is called standard electrode potential. It is denoted by E°.

Reference Electrode

The electrode of known potential is called reference electrode. It may be primary reference electrode like hydrogen electrode or secondary reference electrode like calomel electrode.

Standard hydrogen electrode (SHE)
Standard hydrogen electrode (SHE), also known as normal hydrogen electrode (NHE), consists of platinum wire, carrying platinum foil coated with finely divided platinum black. The wire is sealed into a glass tube, placed in beaker containing 1 M HCl. The hydrogen gas at 1 atm pressure is bubbled through the solution at 298K. Half-cell is Pt H_2 (1 atm) | H^+ (1 M)

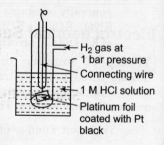

H₂ gas at 1 bar pressure
Connecting wire
1 M HCl solution
Platinum foil coated with Pt black

In SHE, at the surface of plantinum, either of the following reaction can take place

$$2H^+(aq) + 2e^- \longrightarrow H_2(g) \qquad \text{(Reduction)}$$

$$H_2(g) \longrightarrow 2H^+(aq) + 2e^- \qquad \text{(Oxidation)}$$

The electrode potential of SHE has been fixed as zero at all temperatures.

Its main drawbacks are

1. It is difficult to maintain 1 atm pressure of H_2 gas.

2. It is difficult to maintain H^+ ion concentration 1 M.

3. The platinum electrode is easily poisoned by traces of impurities.

Hence, calomel electrodes are conveniently used as reference electrodes. It consists of mercury in contact with Hg_2Cl_2 (calomel) paste in a solution of KCl.

Electromotive Force (emf) of a Cell

It is the difference between the electrode potentials of two half-cells and cause flow of current from electrode at higher potential to electrode at lower potential. It is also the measure of free energy change. Standard emf of a cell,

$$E^\circ_{cell} = E^\circ_{cathode} - E^\circ_{anode} = E^\circ_{right} - E^\circ_{left} = E^\circ_{red} + E^\circ_{oxi}$$

Emf and Cell Potential

S.No.	Emf	Cell potential
1.	Potential difference between two electrodes when no current is flowing in the circuit is called emf.	The potential difference of the two half-cells when electric current flows through the cells is called cell potential.
2.	Emf is the maximum voltage which can be obtained from the cell.	It is always less than the maximum voltage obtainable from the cell.
3.	Emf is measured by a potentiometer.	It is measured by a voltmeter.

Electrochemical Series

It is the arrangement of electrodes in the increasing order of their standard reduction potentials.

Standard Electrode Potential at 298 K

Reaction (Oxidised form) + ne^-	$\rightarrow$	Reduced form	E°/V
$F_2(g) + 2e^-$	$\rightarrow$	$2F^-$	2.87
$Co^{3+} + e^-$	$\rightarrow$	Co^{2+}	1.81
$H_2O_2 + 2H^+ + 2e^-$	$\rightarrow$	$2H_2O$	1.78
$MnO_4^- + 8H^+ + 5e^-$	$\rightarrow$	$Mn^{2+} + 4H_2O$	1.51
$Au^{3+} + 3e^-$	$\rightarrow$	$Au(s)$	1.40
$Cl_2(g) + 2e^-$	$\rightarrow$	$2Cl^-$	1.36
$Cr_2O_7^{2-} + 14H^+ + 6e^-$	$\rightarrow$	$2Cr^{3+} + 7H_2O$	1.33
$O_2(g) + 4H^+ + 4e^-$	$\rightarrow$	$2H_2O$	1.23

Reaction (Oxidised form) + ne^-	$\rightarrow$	Reduced form	E°/V
$MnO_2(s) + 4H^+ + 2e^-$	$\rightarrow$	$Mn^{2+} + 2H_2O$	1.23
$Br_2 + 2e^-$	$\rightarrow$	$2Br^-$	1.09
$NO_3^- + 4H^+ + 3e^-$	$\rightarrow$	$NO(g) + 2H_2O$	0.97
$2Hg^{2+} + 2e^-$	$\rightarrow$	Hg_2^{2+}	0.92
$Ag^+ + e^-$	$\rightarrow$	$Ag(s)$	0.80
$Fe^{3+} + e^-$	$\rightarrow$	Fe^{2+}	0.77
$O_2(g) + 2H^+ + 2e^-$	$\rightarrow$	H_2O_2	0.68
$I_2 + 2e^-$	$\rightarrow$	$2I^-$	0.54
$Cu^+ + e^-$	$\rightarrow$	$Cu(s)$	0.52
$Cu^{2+} + 2e^-$	$\rightarrow$	$Cu(s)$	0.34
$AgCl(s) + e^-$	$\rightarrow$	$Ag(s) + Cl^-$	0.22
$AgBr(s) + e^-$	$\rightarrow$	$Ag(s) + Br^-$	0.10
$2H^+ + 2e^-$	$\rightarrow$	$H_2(g)$	0.00
$Pb^{2+} + 2e^-$	$\rightarrow$	$Pb(s)$	-0.13
$Sn^{2+} + 2e^-$	$\rightarrow$	$Sn(s)$	-0.14
$Ni^{2+} + 2e^-$	$\rightarrow$	$Ni(s)$	-0.25
$Fe^{2+} + 2e^-$	$\rightarrow$	$Fe(s)$	-0.44
$Cr^{3+} + 3e^-$	$\rightarrow$	$Cr(s)$	-0.74
$Zn^{2+} + 2e^-$	$\rightarrow$	$Zn(s)$	-0.76
$2H_2O + 2e^-$	$\rightarrow$	$H_2(g) + 2OH^-(aq)$	-0.83
$Al^{3+} + 3e^-$	$\rightarrow$	$Al(s)$	-1.66
$Mg^{2+} + 2e^-$	$\rightarrow$	$Mg(s)$	-2.36
$Na^+ + e^-$	$\rightarrow$	$Na(s)$	-2.71
$Ca^{2+} + 2e^-$	$\rightarrow$	$Ca(s)$	-2.87
$K^+ + e^-$	$\rightarrow$	$K(s)$	-2.93
$Li^+ + e^-$	$\rightarrow$	$Li(s)$	-3.05

Applications of Electrochemical Series (ECS)

1. The lower the value of E°, the greater the tendency to form cation.

$$M \longrightarrow M^{n+} + ne^-$$

2. Metals placed below hydrogen in ECS replace hydrogen from dil acids but metals placed above hydrogen cannot replace hydrogen from dil acids.

$$Ca + dil. H_2SO_4 \longrightarrow CaSO_4 + H_2 \uparrow$$

possible, $\qquad (Ca + 2H^+ \longrightarrow Ca^{2+} + H_2)$

$$Cu + dil. H_2SO_4 \longrightarrow CuSO_4 + H_2 \uparrow$$

not possible, $\qquad (Cu + 2H^+ \longrightarrow Cu^{2+} + H_2)$

3. Oxides of metals placed below hydrogen are not reduced by H_2 but oxides of iron and metals placed above iron are reduced by H_2.

    (a) SnO, PbO, CuO are reduced by H_2.

    (b) CaO, K_2O are not reduced by H_2.

4. Reducing character increases down the series.

5. Reactivity increases down the series.

6. Determination of emf; emf is the difference of reduction potentials of two half-cells.

$$E_{emf} = E_{RHS} - E_{LHS}$$

    If the value of emf is positive, the reaction takes place spontaneously, otherwise not.

7. Greater the reduction potential of a substance, higher is its oxidising power. (e.g. $F_2 > Cl_2 > Br_2 > I_2$)

8. A negative value of standard reduction potential shows that it is the site of oxidation.

9. Oxides of metals having $E_{red}^\circ \geq 0.79$ will be decomposed by heating to form O_2 and metal.

$$HgO\,(s) \rightarrow Hg\,(l) + \frac{1}{2}O_2\,(g)$$

$$(E_{Hg^{2+}/Hg}^\circ = 0.79\,V)$$

Nernst Equation

The relationship between the concentration of ions and electrode potential is given by Nernst equation.

$$M^{n+} + ne^- \longrightarrow M$$

$$E_{M^{n+}/M} = E_{M^{n+}/M}^\circ - \frac{2.303\,RT}{nF} \log \frac{1}{[M^{n+}]}$$

or
$$E_{M^{n+}/M} = E^\circ_{M^{n+}/M} - \frac{0.0591}{n} \log\left[\frac{1}{M^{n+}}\right] \text{ (at 298 K)}$$

For a electrochemical cell,

$$aA + bB \longrightarrow cC + dD$$

$$E_{\text{cell}} = E^\circ_{\text{cell}} - \frac{2.303RT}{nF} \log \frac{[C]^c[D]^d}{[A]^a[B]^b}$$

Concentration of pure solids and liquids is taken as unity.

Nernst equation and K_c

$\because$ At equilibrium, $E_{\text{cell}} = 0$

$$E^\circ_{\text{cell}} = \frac{0.0591}{n} \log K_c \text{ at 298K}$$

$$\Delta G^\circ = -nFE^\circ_{\text{cell}}$$

Here, ΔG° is the standard **Gibbs free energy change.**

Type of reaction	ΔG°	E°_{cell}	Type of cell
Spontaneous	−ve	+ve	Galvanic
Non-spontaneous	+ve	−ve	Electrolytic
Equilibrium	0	0	Dead battery

Relationship between free energy change and equilibrium constant

$$\Delta G^\circ = -2.303RT \log K_c$$

Concentration Cells

The cells in which both the electrodes are of the same type but the electrolytic solution have different concentration, are called concentration cells.

(i) **Electrode concentration cells** Two hydrogen electrodes of different pressures are dipped in the same solution of electrolyte, e.g.

$$\text{Pt, } H_2(p_1)\,|\,H^+\,|\,H_2(p_2)\text{Pt, } p_1 > p_2$$

$$E_{\text{cell}} = \frac{2.303RT}{nF} \log \frac{p_2}{p_1}$$

(ii) **Electrolyte concentration cells** Electrodes are the same but electrolyte solutions have different concentrations, e.g.

$$\text{Zn}\,|\,\text{Zn}^{2+}(C_1)\,||\,\text{Zn}^{2+}(C_2)\,|\,\text{Zn}, C_2 > C_1$$

$$E_{\text{cell}} = \frac{2.303RT}{nF} \log \frac{C_2}{C_1} = \frac{0.0591}{n} \log \frac{C_2}{C_1}$$

Conductance (G)

It is the ease of flow of electric current through the conductor. It is reciprocal of resistance (R).

$$G = \frac{1}{R}, \text{ Units ohm}^{-1}, \text{ mhos or } \Omega^{-1}$$

Specific Conductivity (κ)

It is the reciprocal of specific resistance.

$$\kappa = \frac{1}{\rho} = \frac{l}{R.a} = G \times \frac{l}{a} = G \times \text{cell constant } (G^*) \quad \left(\frac{l}{a} = \text{cell constant} \right)$$

Units of $\kappa = \Omega^{-1} \text{cm}^{-1} = \text{S cm}^{-1} (\Omega^{-1} = \text{S i.e. Siemens})$

Unit of cell constant is cm^{-1} or m^{-1}.

⌈Specific conductivity decreases on dilution. This is because concentration of ions per cc decreases upon dilution.⌋

Molar Conductivity (Λ_m)

The conductivity of all the ions produced when 1 mole of an electrolyte is dissolved in V mL of solution is known as molar conductivity.

It is related to specific conductance as

$$\Lambda_m = \frac{\kappa \times 1000}{M} \qquad \text{where, } M = \text{molarity.}$$

Its units are $\Omega^{-1} \text{cm}^2 \text{mol}^{-1}$ or $\text{S cm}^2 \text{ mol}^{-1}$.

Equivalent Conductivity (Λ_{eq})

The conducting power of all the ions produced when 1 g-equivalent of an electrolyte is dissolved in V mL of solution, is called equivalent conductivity. It is related to specific conductance as

$$\Lambda_{eq} = \frac{\kappa \times 1000}{N}$$

where, $N =$ normality.

Its units are $\text{ohm}^{-1} \text{ cm}^2 \text{ (equiv}^{-1})$ or $\text{mho cm}^2 \text{ (equiv}^{-1})$ or S cm^2 (g-equiv^{-1}).

Debye-Huckel Onsagar equation It gives a relation between molar conductivity, Λ_m at a particular concentration and molar conductivity, Λ_m at infinite dilution.

$$\Lambda_m = \Lambda_m^0 - A\sqrt{C}$$

where, A is a constant. It depends upon the nature of solvent, temperature and on the type of electrolyte, i.e. the charge on the cation and anion produced on the dissociation of the electrolyte in the solution. Thus, $NaCl, CaCl_2, MgSO_4$ are known as 1-1, 2-1 and 2-2 electrolytes respectively. All electrolytes of a particular type have the same value for A.

Factors Affecting Conductivity

(i) **Nature of electrolyte** The strong electrolytes like $KNO_3, KCl, NaOH$, etc. are completely ionised in aqueous solution and have high values of conductivity (molar as well as equivalent). The weak electrolytes are ionised to a lesser extent in aqueous solution and have lower values of conductivity (molar as well as equivalent).

(ii) **Concentration of the solution** The concentrated solutions of strong electrolytes have significant interionic attractions, which reduce the speed of ions and lower the value of Λ_m and Λ_{eq}. The dilution decreases such attractions and increases the value of Λ_m and Λ_{eq}. The limiting value, Λ_m^0 or Λ_m^∞ (the molar conductivity at zero concentration or at infinite dilution) can be obtained by extrapolating the graph.

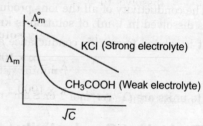

In case of **weak electrolytes**, the degree of ionisation increases on dilution which increases the value of Λ_m and Λ_{eq}. The limiting value Λ_m^0 cannot be obtained by extrapolating the graph. The limiting value, Λ_{m}^0, for weak electrolytes is obtained by Kohlrausch law.

(iii) **Temperature** The increase of temperature decreases inter-ionic attractions and increases kinetic energy of ions and their speed. Thus, Λ_m and Λ_{eq} increase with temperature.

Kohlrausch's Law

At infinite dilution, the molar conductivity of an electrolyte is the sum of the ionic conductivities of the cations and anions, e.g. for $A_x B_y$.

$$\Lambda_m^0 (A_x B_y) = x\Lambda_{A^+}^0 + y\Lambda_{B^-}^0 \quad \text{or} \quad \Lambda_{eq}^0 = \Lambda_{A^+}^0 + \Lambda_{B^-}^0$$

(where, $\Lambda_{A^+}^0$ and $\Lambda_{B^-}^0$ are the limiting molar conductivity of the cation and anion respectively).

Applications

(i) Determination of equivalent/molar conductivities of weak electrolytes at infinite dilution, e.g.

$$\Lambda^{\infty}_{CH_3COOH} = \Lambda^{\infty}_{CH_3COONa} + \Lambda^{\infty}_{HCl} - \Lambda^{\infty}_{NaCl}$$

$$\Lambda^{\infty}_{NH_4OH} = \Lambda^{\infty}_{NH_4Cl} + \Lambda^{\infty}_{NaOH} - \Lambda^{\infty}_{NaCl}$$

(ii) Determination of degree of dissociation (α) of an electrolyte at a given dilution,

$$\alpha = \frac{\text{molar conductance at concentration `C'}}{\text{molar conductance at infinite dilution}} = \frac{\Lambda^C_m}{\Lambda^{\infty}_m}$$

The **dissociation constant** (K) of the weak electrolyte at concentration C of the solution can be calculated by using the formula

$$K_c = \frac{C\alpha^2}{1 - \alpha}$$

where, α is the degree of dissociation of the electrolyte.

(iii) Salts like $BaSO_4, PbSO_4, AgCl, AgBr$ and AgI which do not dissolve to a large extent in water are called **sparingly soluble salts**.

The **solubility of a sparingly soluble salt can be calculated as**

$$\Lambda^{\circ}_m = \frac{\kappa \times 1000}{\text{solubility (in mol L}^{-1})}$$

$$\text{Solubility (in mol L}^{-1}) = \frac{\kappa \times 1000}{\Lambda^{\circ}_m}$$

Electrolysis

It is the process of decomposition of an electrolyte when electric current is passed through either its aqueous solution or molten state.

(i) In electrolytic cell both oxidation and reduction takes place in the same cell.

(ii) Anode is positively charged and cathode is negatively charged, in electrolytic cell.

(iii) During electrolysis of molten electrolyte, cations are liberated at cathode, while anions at the anode.

(iv) When two or more ions compete at the electrodes, the ion with higher reduction potential gets liberated at the cathode while the ion with lower reduction potential at the anode.

For metals to be deposited on the cathode during electrolysis, the voltage required is almost the same as the standard electrode potential. However for liberation of gases, some extra voltage is required than the theoretical value of the standard electrode potential. The extra voltage thus required is called **over voltage** or **bubble voltage**.

How to Predict the Products of Electrolysis?

When an aqueous solution of an electrolyte is electrolysed, if the cation has higher reduction potential than water (–0.83 V), cation is liberated at the cathode (e.g. in the electrolysis of copper and silver salts) otherwise H_2 gas is liberated due to reduction of water (e.g. in the electrolysis of K, Na, Ca salts, etc.) Similarly if anion has higher oxidation potential than water (– 1.23 V), anion is liberated at anode (e.g. Br^-) otherwise O_2 gas is liberated due to oxidation of water (e.g. in case of F^-, aqueous solution of Na_2SO_4 as oxidation potential of SO_4^{2-} is – 0.2 V).

Discharge potential is defined as the minimum potential that must be applied across the electrodes to bring about the electrolysis and subsequent discharge of the ion on the electrode.

Faraday's Laws of Electrolysis

1. First law

The amount of the substance deposited or liberated at cathode is directly proportional to the quantity of electricity passed through an electrolyte.

$$W \propto I \times t = I \times t \times Z = Q \times Z$$

I = current in amp, t = time in sec,

Q = quantity of charge (coulomb)

Z is a constant known as electrochemical equivalent.

When I = 1 amp, t = 1 sec and then Q = 1 coulomb, then $w = Z$.

Thus, electrochemical equivalent is the amount of the substance deposited or liberated by passing 1A current for 1 sec (i.e. 1 coulomb, $I \times t = Q$)

2. Second law

When the same quantity of electricity is passed through different electrolytes, the amounts of the substance deposited or liberated at the electrodes are directly proportional to their equivalent weights. Thus,

$$\frac{\text{Mass of } A}{\text{Mass of } B} = \frac{\text{eq. wt. of } A}{\text{eq. wt. of } B} \quad \text{or} \quad \frac{\omega_1}{\omega_2} = \frac{E_1}{E_2} \Rightarrow \frac{Z_1 Q}{Z_2 Q} = \frac{E_1}{E_2}$$

Hence, electrochemical equivalent $\propto$ equivalent weight.

Batteries

These are source of electrical energy which may have one or more cells connected in series. For a good quality battery, it should be reasonably light, compact and its voltage should not vary appreciably during its use.

Primary Batteries

In the primary batteries, the reaction occurs only once and after use over a period of time, battery becomes dead and cannot be reused again.

(i) **Dry cell or Leclanche cell**

Anode-Zinc container

Cathode-Graphite rod surrounded by MnO_2 powder

Electrolyte-Paste of $NH_4Cl + ZnCl_2$

Cathode reaction,

$$2MnO_2(s) + 2NH_4^+(aq) + 2e^- \longrightarrow Mn_2O_3(s) + 2NH_3(g) + H_2O(l)$$

Anode reaction, $Zn(s) \longrightarrow Zn^{2+}(aq) + 2e^-$

Cell potential 1.25 V to 1.5 V

(ii) **Mercury cell**

Anode-Zn-Hg amalgam

Cathode-Paste of $(HgO + C)$

Electrolyte-Moist paste of KOH-ZnO

Cathode reaction, $HgO(s) + H_2O(l) + 2e^- \longrightarrow Hg(l) + 2OH^-$

Anode reaction, $Zn(Hg) + 2OH^-\, aq \longrightarrow ZnO(s) + H_2O(l) + 2e^-$

Net reaction, $Zn(Hg) + HgO(s) \longrightarrow ZnO(s) + Hg(l)$

Cell potential 1.35 V and remains constant during its life as the net reaction does not involve any ion in solution whose concentration can change during its life time.

Secondary Batteries

These cells can be recharged and can be used again and again, e.g.

(i) **Lead Storage battery**

Anode-Spongy lead

Cathode-Grid of lead packed with PbO_2

Electrolyte-38% H_2SO_4 by mass

Anode reaction, $Pb(s) + SO_4^{2-}(aq) \longrightarrow PbSO_4(s) + 2e^-$

Cathode reaction,
$$\underline{PbO_2(s) + SO_4^{2-}(aq) + 4H^+(aq) + 2e^- \longrightarrow PbSO_4(s) + 2H_2O(l)}$$

Net reaction,
$$Pb(s) + PbO_2(s) + 4H^+(aq) + 2SO_4^{2-}(aq) \longrightarrow 2PbSO_4(s) + 2H_2O(l)$$

When recharged the cell reactions are reversed.

(ii) **Nickel-Cadmium storage cell**

Anode-Cadmium

Cathode-Metal grid containing NiO_2

Electrolyte-KOH solution

Anode reaction,
$$Cd(s) + 2OH^-(aq) \longrightarrow Cd(OH)_2(s) + 2e^-$$

Cathode reaction,
$$\underline{NiO_2(s) + 2H_2O(l) + 2e^- \longrightarrow Ni(OH)_2(s) + 2OH^-(aq)}$$

Net reaction,
$$Cd(s) + NiO_2(s) + 2H_2O(l) \longrightarrow Cd(OH)_2(s) + Ni(OH)_2(s)$$
$$\text{Cell potential} = 1.4 \text{ V}$$

Nickle-cadmium cell has longer life than the lead storage cell.

Fuel Cells

Galvanic cells which use energy of combustion of fuels like H_2, CH_4, CH_3OH, etc., as the source to produce electrical energy are called fuel cells. The fuel cells are pollution free and have high efficiency. Fuel cell produces electricity with an efficiency of about 70% as compared to thermal plants whose efficiency is about 40%.

Hydrogen-Oxygen Fuel Cell

Electrodes-Made of porous graphite impregnated with catalyst (Pt, Ag or a metal oxide).

Electrolyte-Aqueous solution of KOH or NaOH

Oxygen and hydrogen are continuously fed into the cell.

Oxidation Half-cell reaction,
$$2H_2(g) + 4OH^-(aq) \longrightarrow 4H_2O(l) + 4e^- \qquad \text{(at anode)}$$

Reduction half-cell reaction,
$$O_2(g) + 2H_2O(l) + 4e^- \longrightarrow 4OH^-(aq) \qquad \text{(at cathode)}$$

Net reaction,
$$2H_2(g) + O_2(g) \longrightarrow 2H_2O(l)$$

EMF of the cell 1 V.

Thermodynamic efficiency of a fuel cell,

$$\eta = \frac{\Delta G}{\Delta H} \times 100 = \frac{-nF\, E_{cell}}{\Delta H}$$

Corrosion

Slow formation of undesirable compounds such as oxides, sulphides or carbonates at the surface of metals by reaction with moisture and other atmospheric gases is known as corrosion.

Factors Affecting Corrosion

(i) Reactivity of metals

(ii) Presence of moisture and atmospheric gases like CO_2, SO_2, etc.

(iii) Presence of impurities

(iv) Strains in the metal

(v) Presence of electrolyte

Rusting of Iron-Electrochemical Theory

An electrochemical cell, also known as corrosion cell, is developed at the surface of iron.

Anode-Pure iron

Cathode-Impure surface

Electrolyte,
$$CO_2 + H_2O \longrightarrow H_2CO_3 \rightleftharpoons 2H^+ + CO_3^{2-}$$

Anode reaction, $\quad 2Fe(s) \longrightarrow 2Fe^{2+}(aq) + 4e^-$

Cathode reaction, $\underline{\quad O_2(g) + 4H^+(aq) + 4e^-(l) \longrightarrow 2H_2O(l)}$

Net reaction, $\quad 2Fe(s) + 4H^+(aq) + O_2(g) \longrightarrow 2Fe^{2+}(aq) + 2H_2O(l)$

At surface,
$$4Fe^{2+}(aq) + O_2(g) + 4H_2O(l) \longrightarrow 2Fe_2O_3(s) + 8H^+(aq)$$
$$Fe_2O_3(s) + xH_2O(l) \longrightarrow Fe_2O_3 \cdot xH_2O \text{ (Rust)}$$

Rusting of iron can be prevented by the following methods:

(i) Barrier protection through coating of paints or electroplating.

(ii) Through galvanisation or coating of surface with tin metal.

(iii) By the use of antirust solutions (bis phenol).

(iv) By cathodic protection in which a metal is protected from corrosion by connecting it to another metal which is more easily oxidised.

13

Chemical Kinetics

The branch of chemistry, which deals with the rate of chemical reactions, the factors affecting the rate of reactions and the mechanism of the reaction, is called chemical kinetics.

Chemical Reactions on the Basis of Rate of Reaction

(i) **Fast/Instantaneous reactions** Chemical reactions which complete in less than $1ps\,(10^{-12}\,s)$ time, are known as fast reaction. It is practically impossible to measure the speed of such reactions, e.g. ionic reactions, organic substitution reactions.

(ii) **Slow reactions** Chemical reactions which completes in a long time from some minutes to some years are called slow reactions. e.g. rusting of iron, transformation of diamond etc.

(iii) **Moderately slow reactions** Chemical reactions which are intermediate between slow and fast reactions are called moderately slow reactions.

Rate of Reaction

Rate of a chemical reaction is the change in the concentration of any one of the reactants or products per unit time. It is expressed in $mol\,L^{-1}\,s^{-1}$ or Ms^{-1} or atm time^{-1} units.

Rate of reaction

$$= \frac{\text{decrease/increase in the concentration of reactant/product}}{\text{time taken}}$$

This rate of reaction is known as **average rate of reaction** (r_{av}). $(r_{av}$ can be calculated by dividing the concentration difference by the time interval).

For a chemical reaction,

$$aA + bB \longrightarrow cC + dD$$

$$\text{Average rate of reaction } (r_{av}) = -\frac{1}{a}\frac{\Delta[A]}{\Delta t} = -\frac{1}{b}\frac{\Delta[B]}{\Delta t}$$

$$= \frac{1}{c}\frac{\Delta[C]}{\Delta t} = \frac{1}{d}\frac{\Delta[D]}{\Delta t}$$

Rate of disappearance of $A = -\dfrac{\Delta[A]}{\Delta t}$

Rate of disappearance of $B = -\dfrac{\Delta[B]}{\Delta t}$

Rate of appearance of $C = \dfrac{\Delta[C]}{\Delta t}$

Rate of appearance of $D = \dfrac{\Delta[D]}{\Delta t}$

Instantaneous Rate of Reaction

Rate of a chemical reaction at a particular moment of time, is known as instantaneous rate of reaction.

For reaction, $\qquad R \longrightarrow P$

$$r_{inst} = -\frac{\Delta[R]}{\Delta t} \text{ or } \frac{\Delta[P]}{\Delta t} \text{ as } \Delta \to d$$

$$\Rightarrow \qquad r_{inst} = -\frac{d[R]}{dt} = \frac{d[P]}{dt}$$

Methods for measuring reaction rate (i) pH measurement, (ii) change in optical activity, (iii) change in pressure, (iv) change in conductance.

Slowest step of a reaction was called rate determining step by van't Hoff.

Factors Affecting Rate of Reaction

(i) Nature and concentration of reactant

(ii) Temperature

(iii) Surface area of reactant

(iv) Radiations and catalyst

(v) Pressure of gas

Rate Law Expressions

It is defined as a mathematical expression in which reaction rate is given in terms of molar concentration of reactants with each term raised to some power.

For a chemical reaction,

$$aA + bB \longrightarrow \text{Products}$$

According to the law of mass action,

$$\text{Rate} \propto [A]^a \, [B]^b = k[A]^a \, [B]^b$$

But experimentally, it is observed that the rate of reaction is found to depend upon 'α' concentration terms of A and 'β' concentration terms of B. Then,

$$\text{Rate} \propto [A]^\alpha \, [B]^\beta = k \, [A]^\alpha \, [B]^\beta$$

where, $[A]$ and $[B]$ molar concentrations of A and B respectively and k is the velocity constant or rate constant. The above expression is known as **rate law**.

Rate Constant or Specific Reaction Rate

In the above expression, k is called rate constant or velocity constant.

Rate constant may be defined as the specific rate of reaction when the molar concentrations of the reactants is taken to be unity, i.e.

$$\text{Rate} = k, \text{ if } [A] = [B] = 1$$

Units of rate constant or specific reaction rate for a nth order reaction is given as

$$k = \frac{1}{\text{Time}} \times \frac{1}{[\text{Conc.}]^{n-1}}$$

Characteristics of rate constant

(i) Greater the value of rate constant, faster is the reaction.

(2) Each reaction has a particular value of rate constant at a particular temperature.

(iii) The value of rate constant for the same reaction changes with temperature.

(iv) The value of rate constant for a reaction doesn't depend upon the concentration of the reactants.

Order and Molecularity of a Reaction

Find of plain order and molecularity separately given comparison differences

Order of reaction	Molecularity of reaction
1. Order of reaction is the sum of the concentration terms on which rate of reaction actually depends. Or It is also defined as sum of the exponents of the molar concentrations in the rate law equation.	Molecularity of a reaction is the number of atoms, ions or molecules that must collide with one another to form products in a chemical reaction.
2. It can be fractional as well as zero.	It cannot be zero or fractional.
3. It is an experimentally determined term.	It is theoretically determined term.
4. Order of reaction is applicable to elementary as well as complex reactions.	Molecularity is applicable only to elementary reactions.
5. Negative order reaction is also possible, e.g. $2O_3 \longrightarrow 3O_2$ Rate = $k[O_3]^2[O_2]^{-1}$ Order w.r.t O_2 is -1.	Molecularity can never be negative.

6. Types of reactions depending upon orders
 	
(i) Zero order reaction
 	
   (I) $H_2(g) + Cl_2(g) \xrightarrow{hv} 2HCl$
 	
   (II) $2NH_3 \xrightarrow{Pt} N_2 + 3H_2$
 	
(ii) First order reaction
 	
   (I) $H_2O_2 \longrightarrow H_2O + \frac{1}{2}O_2$
 	
   (II) Radioactive disintegration
 	
   (III) Inversion of cane sugar.
 	
(iii) Second order reaction
 	
   (I) $2HI \longrightarrow H_2 + I_2$
 	
   (II) Alkaline hydrolysis of ester (saponification)
 	
(iv) Third order reaction
   $2NO + O_2 \longrightarrow 2NO_2$
	Types of reactions depending upon molecularity
	
	(i) Unimolecular reaction,
	   $N_2O_4(g) \longrightarrow 2NO_2(g)$
	
	(ii) Bimolecular reactions,
	   $2HI(g) \longrightarrow H_2(g) + I_2(g)$
	
	(iii) Trimolecular reactions,
	   $2NO(g) + O_2(g) \longrightarrow 2NO_2(g)$

Integrated Rate Equation for Zero Order Reactions

Zero order reaction means that the rate of the reaction is proportional to zero power of the concentration of reactants.

$$k_0 = \frac{1}{t}\{[A]_0 - [A]\}$$

[where, $[A]_0$ is initial concentration and $[A]$ is final concentration]

$$t = t_{1/2} \text{ when } [A] = \frac{[A]_0}{2}$$

Half-life period, $t_{1/2} = \dfrac{[A]_0}{2k_0}$

Units of rate constant, $k_0 = \text{mol L}^{-1}\text{s}^{-1} = $ unit of rate

For zero order gaseous reactions,

$$k_0 = \frac{1}{t}[p_0 - p] \quad \text{and} \quad t_{1/2} = \frac{p_0}{2k_0}$$

Integrated Rate Equation for First Order Reactions

First order reaction means that the rate of the reaction is proportional to the first power of the concentration of the reactnat.

$$k_1 = \frac{2.303}{t}\log\frac{[A]_0}{[A]} \Rightarrow [A] = [A]_0 e^{-k_1 t}$$

Half-life period $(t_{1/2})$ It is concentration independent term.

$$t = t_{1/2}, [A] = \frac{[A]_0}{2}$$

Amount of a substance after n half-lives $= \dfrac{[A]_0}{2^n} \Rightarrow t_{1/2} = \dfrac{0.693}{k_1}$

For such reactions, $t_{75\%} = 2 \times t_{50\%} \Rightarrow t_{99.9\%} = 10 \times t_{1/2}$

All radioactive changes follow the first order kinetics.

Integrated rate equation for first order gaseous reactions,

$$A(g) \longrightarrow B(g) + C(g)$$

Initial pressure $(t = 0)$ p_0 atm   0   0

Pressure at t $[p_0 - p]$ atm p atm p atm

$$k_1 = \frac{2.303}{t}\log\frac{p_0}{(2p_0 - p_t)}$$

For first order chemical reactions,

$$CH_3COOC_2H_5 + H_2O \xrightarrow{H^+} CH_3COOH + C_2H_5OH$$

$$k_1 = \frac{2.303}{t} \log\left(\frac{V_\infty - V_0}{V_\infty - V_t}\right)$$

(V_0, V_t and V_∞ are the volumes of NaOH solution used for the titration of same volume of the reaction mixture after times 0, t and ∞ respectively.)

Pseudo First Order Reaction

Chemical reactions which appear to be of higher order but actually are of the lower order are called pseudo first order reactions. In case of pseudo first order reaction, chemical reaction between two substances takes place and one of the reactant is present in excess, e.g. hydrolysis of ester.

$$CH_3COOC_2H_5 + H_2O \longrightarrow CH_3COOH + C_2H_5OH$$

So, in this reaction,

$$\text{Rate} = k\,[CH_3COOC_2H_5]$$

For chemical reaction,

$$C_{12}H_{22}O_{11} + H_2O \xrightarrow{H^+} \underset{\text{glucose}}{C_6H_{12}O_6} + \underset{\text{fructose}}{C_6H_{12}O_6}$$

$$k = \frac{2.303}{t} \log\left(\frac{r_0 - r_\infty}{r_t - r_\infty}\right)$$

[r_0, r_t and r_∞ are the polarimetric readings at $t = 0$, t and ∞ respectively.]

Methods to Determine Order of Reaction

(i) **Graphical method** In this method, rate of reaction is plotted against the concentration.

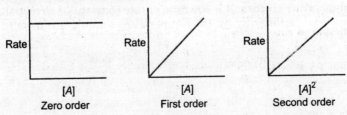

Zero order   First order   Second order

(ii) **Initial rate method** In this method, the order of a reaction is determined by varying the concentration of one of the reactants while others are kept constant.

(iii) **Integrated rate law method** In this method out of different integrated rate equation which gives the most constant value for the rate constant corresponds to a specific order of reaction.

(iv) **Half-life period ($t_{1/2}$) method** In general half-life period ($t_{1/2}$) of a reaction of nth order is related to initial concentration of the reactant as

$$t_{1/2} \propto \frac{1}{[A]_0^{n-1}}$$

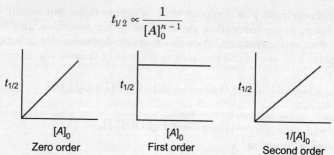

Zero order	First order	Second order
$t_{1/2}$ vs $[A]_0$	$t_{1/2}$ vs $[A]_0$	$t_{1/2}$ vs $1/[A]_0$

This method is employed only when the rate law involved only one concentration term.

(v) **Ostwald's isolation method** This method is employed in determining the order of complicated reactions by isolating one of the reactants so far as its influence on the reaction rate is concerned.

Temperature Dependence of Rate of a Reaction

For every 10°C rise in temperature, the rate of reaction becomes double, but only 16% collisions increases. It can be explained by Arrhenius equation.

Temperature coefficient is the ratio of rate constant of a reaction at two temperature differing by 10. Temperature selected are usually 298 K and 308 K.

$$\text{Temperature coefficient} = \frac{k_{t+10}}{k_t} \approx 2 \text{ to } 3$$

Arrhenius Equation

Arrhenius equation is a mathematical expression to give a quantitative relationship between rate constant and temperature, and the expression is

$$k = Ae^{-E_a/RT}$$

or 　　$$\ln k = \ln A - \frac{E_a}{RT}$$

or 　　$$\log_{10} k = \log_{10} A - \frac{E_a}{2.303RT}$$

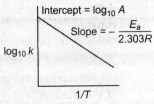

where, A = frequency or Arrhenius factor. It is also called
　　　　pre-exponential factor

　　R = gas constant

　　E_a = activation energy

Activated Complex (or Transition State)

Activated complex is the highest energy unstable intermediate between the reactants and products and gets decomposed immediately (having very short life), to give the products. In this state, bonds of reactant are not completely broken while the bonds of products are not completely formed.

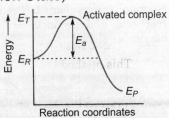

Threshold energy (E_T)　The minimum amount of energy which the reactant must possess in order to convert into products is known as threshold energy.

Activation energy (E_a)　The additional amount of energy, required by the reactant so that their energy becomes equal to the threshold value is known as activation energy.

$\Rightarrow$ 　　　　　$$E_a = E_T - E_R$$

Lower the activation energy, faster is the reaction.

Different reactions have different rates because their activation energies are different. Larger the value of E_a, smaller the value of rate constant and greater is the effect of a given temperature rise on K.

Important points about Arrhenius equation

(i) If k_2 and k_1 are rate constant at temperature T_2 and T_1 then

$$\log \frac{k_2}{k_1} = \frac{E_a}{2.303\,R} \left(\frac{T_2 - T_1}{T_1 T_2} \right)$$

(ii) Fraction of molecules with energy equal to or greater than the activation energy is called Boltzmann factor and is given by

$$x = \frac{n}{N} = e^{-E_a/RT} \quad \text{and} \quad \log_e x = \frac{-E_a}{2.303\,RT}$$

(iii) E_a is constant for a particular reaction.

(iv) E_a doesn't depend on temperature, volume, pressure, etc., but gets affected by catalyst.

In the Arrhenius equation, when $T \to \infty$ then $k = A e^0 = A$ when $E_a = 0$, $k = A$ and the rate of reaction becomes independent of temperature.

Role of Catalyst in a Chemical Reaction

A catalyst is a chemical substance which alters the rate of a reaction without itself undergoing any permanent chemical change.

In the chemical reactions, catalyst provides an alternate pathway or reaction mechanism by reducing the activation energy between reactants and products and hence, lowering the potential energy barrier as shown.

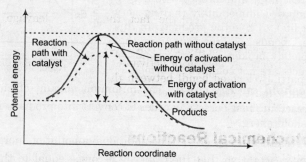

In the presence of catalyst, activation energy decreases and hence,

$$\frac{k_P}{k_a} = e^{(E_a - E_P)/RT} = e^{\Delta E/RT}$$

where, P denotes presence of catalyst and a denotes absence of catalyst.

Theory of Reaction Rates

Collision Theory

According to this theory, the reactant molecules are assumed to be hard spheres and the reaction is postulated to occur, when molecules collide with each other.

The number of collisions between the reacting molecules taking place per second per unit volume is known as **collision frequency** (Z_{AB}).

But only those collisions in which the colliding species are associated with certain minimum amount of energy and collide in proper orientation result in the product formation, such collisions are called **fruitful collisions** or **effective collision**.

Here, rate $= -\dfrac{dv}{dt}$ = collision frequency × fraction of effective collision

$$= Z_{AB} \times f = Z_{AB} \times e^{-E_a/RT}$$

where, Z_{AB} represents the collision frequency of reactants, A and B $e^{-E_a/RT}$ represents the fraction of molecules with energies equal to or greater than E_a.

So, to account for effective collisions, another factor, P called the probability or steric factor is introduced.

So, $\qquad\qquad$ rate $= PZ_{AB}\, e^{-E_a/RT}$

The Activated Complex Theory or Transition State Theory

$$\text{Reactants} \rightleftharpoons \text{Activated complex} \longrightarrow \text{Products}$$

This theory is based on the fact that bond cleavage and bond formation, involved in a chemical reaction, must occur simultaneously. Hence, the reactants are not converted directly into the products. There is an energy barrier or activated complex [intermediate product with partially formed bond] between the reactants and products. The reactants must cross this energy barrier before converting into products. The height of the barrier determines the threshold energy.

Photochemical Reactions

Chemical reactions, that occur on exposure to visible radiation are called photochemical reactions.

(i) The rate of a photochemical reactions is affected by the intensity of light.

(ii) Temperature has little effect on photochemical reactions.

Quantum yield or quantum efficiency of a photochemical reaction,

$$\phi = \dfrac{\text{number of reactant molecules reacting in a given time}}{\text{number of photons (quanta) of light absorbed in the same time}}$$

14

Surface Chemistry

Surface chemistry is the branch of chemistry which deals with the phenomenon that occurs on the surfaces or interfaces, such phenomenon includes corrosion, catalysis, crystallisation, etc.

Adsorption

The phenomena of accumulation of a substance at the surface of other substance rather than in its bulk is called adsorption.

Due to unbalanced attractive forces, accumulation of molecular species at the surface rather than in the bulk of a solid or liquid takes place. The molecular species accumulates at the surface is termed as **adsorbate** and the material on the surface of which the adsorption takes place is called **adsorbent**, e.g.

(i) O_2, H_2, Cl_2, NH_3 gases are adsorbed on the surface of charcoal.

(ii) Silica gels adsorb water molecules from air.

Charcoal, silica gel, metals such as Ni, Cu, Ag, Pt and colloids are some adsorbents.

Causes of Adsorption

In case of solids or liquids the particles present in their bulk are surrounded by same kind of species (atoms, molecules etc.) from all the sides. Thus, all are surrounded by the same environment. But this fact is not true for the particles present at their surface. These particles are not surrounded by species (atoms, molecules etc.) of same kind from all the sides and hence, they possess some unbalanced or residual attractive forces. These forces are responsible for attracting particles of another substance at its surface of solids or liquids.

Important Characteristics of Adsorption

1. It is specific and selective in nature.
2. Adsorption is spontaneous process, therefore change in free energy (ΔG) is negative.

$$\Delta G = \Delta H - T\Delta S,$$

   For the negative value of ΔG, in a system, in which randomness decreases, ΔH must be negative. Hence, adsorption is always exothermic.

   Adsorption of gases over the surface of metal is called **occlusion**.

Desorption

It is a process of removing an adsorbed substance from a surface on which it is adsorbed, is known as desorption.

Distinction between Adsorption and Absorption

	Adsorption	Absorption
1.	It involves unequal distribution of the molecular species in bulk and at the surface.	It involves uniform distribution of the molecular species throughout the bulk.
2.	It is a surface phenomenon.	It occurs throughout the body of material.
3.	It is rapid in the beginning.	It occurs at a uniform rate.

Sorption

It is a process in which both adsorption and absorption take place simultaneously.

Positive and Negative Adsorption

When the concentration of the adsorbate is more on the surface of the adsorbent than in the bulk, it is called positive adsorption.

On the other hand, if the concentration of the adsorbate is less relative to its concentration in the bulk, it is called negative adsorption, e.g. when a dilute solution of KCl is shaken with blood charcoal, it shows negative adsorption.

Find define Physisorption and Chemisorption then diffrences are to be given

Distinction between Physisorption and Chemisorption

	Physisorption	Chemisorption
1.	It arises when the adsorbate molecules accumulate on the surface of adsorbent on account of weak van der Waals' forces.	It arises when the adsorbate molecules accumulate on the surface of adsorbent on account of strong chemical bonds.
2.	It occurs at low temperature.	It occurs at high temperature.
3.	Heat of adsorption is low and it is in the range of 20-40 kJ/mol.	Heat of adsorption is high and it is in the range of 80-240 kJ/mol.
4.	It is reversible process.	It is an irreversible process.
5.	Multilayer adsorption and thus, adsorbed layer is several molecules thick.	Monolayer adsorption. Thus, adsorbed layer is only unimolecular in thickness.

Factors Affecting Adsorption

(a) **Nature of adsorbent** Same gas may be adsorbed to different extents on different adsorbents.

(b) **Surface area of the adsorbent** Greater the surface area, greater is the extent of adsorption.

(c) **Nature of the gas being adsorbed** Greater is the critical temperature of a gas, greater are the van der Waals' forces of attraction and thus, greater is the adsorption.

Gas	H_2	N_2	CO	CH_4	CO_2	HCl	NH_3	SO_2
Critical temp. (K)	33	126	134	190	304	324	406	430

(d) **Temperature** Adsorption is an exothermic process involving the equilibrium :

Gas (adsorbate) + Solid (adsorbent) $\rightleftharpoons$ Gas adsorbed on solid + Heat

Applying Le-Chatelier principle, increase of temperature decreases the adsorption and *vice-versa*.

(e) **Pressure** Adsorption increases with pressure at constant temperature. The effect is large if temperature is kept constant at low value.

(f) **Activation of the solid adsorbent** Activation means increasing the adsorbing power of the solid adsorbent. This can be done by subdividing the solid adsorbent or by removing the gases already adsorbed by passing superheated steam.

Adsorption Isotherms

It is the plot of the mass of gas adsorbed per gram of adsorbent (x/m) *versus* equilibrium pressure at constant temperature.

Freundlich Adsorption Isotherm

It gave an empirical relationship between the quantity of gas adsorbed by unit mass of solid adsorbent and pressure at a particular temperature. It can be expressed by the equation,

$$\frac{x}{m} = kp^{1/n} \ (n > 1) \qquad \qquad ...(i)$$

Where, x is the mass of the gas adsorbed on mass m of the adsorbent at pressure p, k and n are constants which depend on the nature of the adsorbent and the gas at a particular temperature.

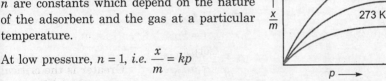

At low pressure, $n = 1$, *i.e.* $\frac{x}{m} = kp$

At high pressure, $n > 1$, *i.e.* $\frac{x}{m} = k$

(independent of p)

At moderate pressure,

$$\frac{x}{m} = kp^{1/n}$$

where, $\frac{1}{n} = 0$ to 1.

Taking logarithm of Eq. (i)

$$\log \frac{x}{m} = \log k + \frac{1}{n} \log p$$

Plot of $\log \frac{x}{m}$ *vs* $\log p$ is a straight line with slope $\frac{1}{n}$ and intercept on y-axis $= \log k$.

The factor $\frac{1}{n}$ can have values between 0 and 1 (Probable range 0.1 to 00.5).

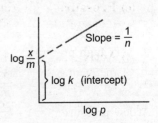

Freundlich Adsorption Equation for Solutions

$$\frac{x}{m} = kC^{1/n}$$

where, C is the equilibrium concentration. On taking logarithm of the above equation, we have

$$\log \frac{x}{m} = \log k + \frac{1}{n} \log C$$

Langmuir Adsorption Isotherm

According to Langmuir, the degree of adsorption is directly proportional to θ, i.e. the fraction of surface area occupied.

$$\frac{x}{m} \propto \theta = k'\theta$$

As,

$$\theta = \frac{kp}{1 + kp}$$

$\therefore$

$$\frac{x}{m} = \frac{k' \cdot kp}{1 + kp}$$

$$\frac{1}{x/m} = \frac{1 + kp}{kk' \cdot p}$$

Multiply by P on both sides

$$\frac{p}{x/m} = \frac{1}{kk'} + \frac{p}{k'}$$

If $\dfrac{p}{x/m}$ is plotted against p, it will give a straight line

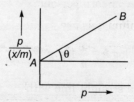

At very high pressure, $\quad 1 + kp \approx kp$

$$\frac{x}{m} = \frac{k' \cdot kp}{kp} = \text{constant} \ (k')$$

At low pressure, $\quad 1 + kp \approx 1$

$$\frac{x}{m} = k' \cdot kp$$

Adsorption Isobars

These are plots of $\dfrac{x}{m}$ *vs* temperature t at constant pressure. For physical and chemical adsorption, they are shown below.

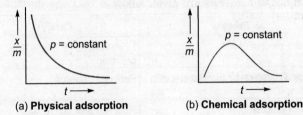

(a) **Physical adsorption**   (b) **Chemical adsorption**

Adsorption Isostere

These are the plot of temperature *versus* pressure for a given amount of adsorption.

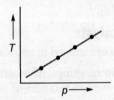

Applications of Adsorption

  (i) For production of high vacuum.

 (ii) Gas masks containing activated charcoal are used for breathing in coalmines. They adsorb poisonous gases.

(iii) Silica and aluminium gels are used as adsorbents for controlling humidity.

(iv) Removal of colouring matter from solutions.

 (v) It is used in heterogeneous catalysis.

(vi) In separation of inert gas.

(vii) As adsorption indicators.

(viii) In chromatographic analysis.

(ix) Qualitative analysis, e.g. lake test for Al^{3+}.

 (x) In curing diseses

Catalysis

Catalyst is a chemical substance which can change the rate of reaction without being used up in that reaction and this process is known as catalysis.

Some examples of catalysis are given below

S.No.	Process	Catalyst
1.	Haber's process of NH_3	Finely divided Fe (Mo acts as promoter)
2.	Ostwald's process for manufacture of nitric acid	Platinised asbestos
3.	Contact process for H_2SO_4	Platinised asbestos or V_2O_5
4.	Lead chamber process for H_2SO_4	Nitric oxide
5.	Decon's process	$CuCl_2$

A catalyst may be positive (i.e. increases rate of reaction) or negative (i.e. decreases rate of reaction).

Characteristics of Catalysts

1. The catalyst remains unchanged in mass and chemical composition.

2. In case of reversible reactions, the catalyst does not influence the composition of reaction mixture at equilibrium. It only helps to attain the equilibrium quickly.

3. A catalyst does not alter Gibb's energy (ΔG) of a reaction.

4. A catalyst catalyses the spontaneous reactions but does not catalyse non-spontaneous reactions.

Promoters and Poisons

Promoters are chemical substances that enhance the activity of a catalyst while poisons decreases the activity of a catalyst.

Types of Catalysis

(a) **Homogeneous catalysis** In this catalysis, the catalyst and reactants are in the same physical state [phase], e.g.

$$2SO_2(g) + O_2(g) \xrightarrow{NO(g)} 2SO_3(g)$$

(b) **Heterogeneous catalysis** In heterogeneous catalysis, the catalyst is present in a different phase than that of reactants, e.g.

$$N_2(g) + 3H_2(g) \xrightarrow{Fe(s)} 2NH_3(g)$$

(c) **Autocatalysis** When one of the product of a reaction acts as catalyst, the process is called autocatalysis.

Adsorption Theory of Heterogeneous Catalysis

The mechanism involves five steps :

(i) Diffusion of reactants to the surface of the catalyst.

(ii) Adsorption of reactant molecules on the surface of the catalyst.

(iii) Occurrence of chemical reaction on the catalyst's surface through formation of an intermediate.

(iv) Desorption of reaction products from the catalyst surface.

(v) Diffusion of reaction products away from the catalyst's surface.

Important Features of Solid Catalysts

(i) **Activity** The activity of a catalyst depends upon the strength of chemisorption to a large extent. The adsorption should be reasonably strong but not so strong that they become immobile and no space is available for other reactants to get adsorbed.

(ii) **Selectivity** The selectivity of a catalyst is its ability to direct a reaction to yield a particular product, e.g. starting with H_2 and CO using different catalysts, we get different products.

$$CO(g) + 3H_2(g) \xrightarrow{\text{Ni}} CH_4(g) + H_2O(g)$$

$$CO(g) + 2H_2(g) \xrightarrow{\text{Cu, ZnO-Cr}_2\text{O}_3} CH_3OH(g)$$

$$CO(g) + H_2(g) \xrightarrow{\text{Cu}} HCHO(g)$$

Shape-selective catalysis The catalytic reaction that depends upon the pore structure of the catalyst and the size of the reactant and product molecules is called shape-selective catalysis. Cracking/isomerisation of hydrocarbons in the presence of zeolites is an example of shape-selective catalysis.

An important zeolite catalyst used in the petroleum industry is ZSM-5. It converts alcohols directly into gasoline.

Enzyme Catalysis

Enzymes are complex nitrogenous organic compounds which are produced by living plants and animals. They are actually protein molecules of high molecular mass and form colloidal solutions in water. The enzymes are also known as biochemical catalysts and the phenomenon is known as biochemical catalysis.

Mechanism of Enzyme Catalysis

$$Step\ I \qquad E + S \longrightarrow ES$$

$$Step\ II \qquad ES \longrightarrow E + P$$

Mechanism of enzyme catalysed reaction

Some examples of enzyme catalysed reactions are:

(i) $\underset{\text{Sucrose}}{C_{12}H_{22}O_{11}} + H_2O \xrightarrow{\text{Invertase}} \underset{\text{Glucose}}{C_6H_{12}O_6} + \underset{\text{Fructose}}{C_6H_{12}O_6}$

(ii) $\underset{\text{Glucose}}{C_6H_{12}O_6} \xrightarrow{\text{Zymase}} \underset{\text{Ethanol}}{2C_2H_5OH} + 2CO_2$

(iii) $\underset{\text{Starch}}{n(C_6H_{10}O_5)_n} + nH_2O \xrightarrow{\text{Diastase}} \underset{\text{Maltose}}{nC_{12}H_{22}O_{11}} \xrightarrow[+ H_2O]{\text{Maltase}} \text{Glucose}$

(iv) $\underset{\text{Urea}}{NH_2CONH_2} + H_2O \xrightarrow{\text{Urease}} 2NH_3 + CO_2$

(Source of invertase, zymase and maltase is yeast and that of diastase is malt. Soyabean is the source of urease.)

(v) In stomach, the pepsin enzyme converts proteins into peptides while in intestine, the pancreatic trypsin converts proteins into amino acids by hydrolysis.

(vi) *Lactobacilli* is used to convert milk into curd.

Characteristics of Enzyme Catalysis

(i) **High efficiency** One molecule of an enzyme may transform one million molecules of reactant per minute.

(ii) **Highly specific nature** Each enzyme catalyst cannot catalyse more than one reaction.

(iii) **Optimum temperature** Enzyme catalyst gives higher yield at optimum temperature, i.e. at 298-310 K. Human body temperature, i.e. at being 310 K is suited for enzyme catalysed reactions.

(iv) **Optimum pH** The rate of an enzyme catalysed reaction is maximum at optimum pH range 5 to 7.

(v) **Activators** Activators like ions such as Na^+, Ca^{2+}, Mn^{2+} help in the activation of enzymes which cannot act on their own strength.

(vi) **Co-enzyme** Co-enzymes are the substances having nature similar to the enzyme and their presence increases the enzyme activity. Mostly vitamins act as co-enzymes.

(vii) **Effect of inhibitors** Inhibitors slow down the rate of enzymatic reaction. The use of many drugs is based on enzyme inhibition action of those drugs in the body.

15

Colloidal State

A **colloid** is a heterogeneous system in which one substance is dispersed (dispersed phase) as very fine particles in another substance called dispersion medium. The study of the colloidal state of matter was started by **Thomas Graham** (1861).

Comparison of True Solution, Colloidal Solution and Suspension

	True solution	**Colloidal solution**	**Suspension**
(i)	Particle size < 10 Å (1 nm)	10 Å – 1000 Å (1 nm – 100 nm)	> 1000 Å (100 nm)
(ii)	Pass through filter paper as well as animal membrane.	Pass through filter paper but not through animal membrane.	Pass through neither of the two.
(iii)	Do not settle.	Do not settle.	Settle on standing.
(iv)	Particles are invisible.	Particles scatter light.	Particles are visible.
(v)	Diffuse quickly.	Diffuse slowly.	Do not diffuse.
(vi)	Clear and transparent.	Translucent.	Opaque.

Classification of Colloids

(A) Types of colloids based on physical state of dispersed phase and dispersion medium

Dispersed phase	Dispersion medium	Type of colloid	Examples
Solid	Solid	Solid sol	Coloured glasses and gem stones.
Solid	Liquid	Sol	Paints, cell fluids, ink, gold sol, proteins.
Solid	Gas	Aerosol	Smoke, dust
Liquid	Solid	Gel	Cheese, butter, jellies, boot polish.

Dispersed phase	Dispersion medium	Type of colloid	Examples
Liquid	Liquid	Emulsion	Milk, hair cream.
Liquid	Gas	Aerosol	Fog, mist, cloud, insecticide sprays.
Gas	Solid	Solid sol	Pumice stone, foam rubber.
Gas	Liquid	Foam	Froth, whipped cream, soap-suds.

Depending on the nature of dispersion medium, the colloids can be named as **hydrosols** or **aquasols** (for water), **alcosols** (for alcohols), **benzosols** (for benzene) and **aerosols** (for gases).

(B) Types of colloids based on nature of interaction between dispersed phase and dispersion medium

S. No.	Property	Lyophilic colloid	Lyophobic colloid
(i)	Formation	Formed easily by direct mixing the two phases.	Special chemical methods are required.
(ii)	Affinity for the medium	Have affinity for the dispersion medium.	Do not have any affinity for the dispersion medium.
(iii)	Stability	Highly stable due to the layers of dispersion medium.	Less stable and are easily coagulated due to the presence of charge.
(iv)	Reversibility	Reversible.	Irreversible.
(v)	Electrophoresis	May or may not show.	Show.
(vi)	Coagulation	Small amounts of electrolyte have no effect.	Small amounts of electrolyte may coagulate the sol.
(vii)	Examples	Sol of gum, gelatin, starch, rubber, etc.	Sol of metals and their sulphides.

(C) Types of colloids based on type of particles of the dispersed phase

Macromolecular colloids	Multimolecular colloids	Associated colloids
The colloids in which the dispersed phase particles are large molecules (usually polymer) having dimensions comparable to those of colloidal particles are called macromolecular colloids, e.g. starch, protein in water, synthetic rubber, polystyrene.	A colloid in which large number of atoms or smaller molecules of a substance aggregate together to form species having size in the colloidal range (1-1000 nm) is called multimolecular colloid, e.g. sulphur sol consists of particles containing a thousand or more of S_8 sulphur molecules.	These are the chemical substances which behave as normal strong electrolytes at low concentration but as colloids at higher concentration and are called micelles. Micelles may contain as many as 100 or more particles. These colloids have both lyophobic and lyophilic parts.

Kraft temperature (T_k) It is the minimum temperature of the colloidal system above which the formation of micelles takes place.

Critical micelle concentration (CMC) The minimum concentration of the surfactant at which the formation of a micelle takes place is called critical micelle concentration, e.g. CMC for soaps is $\sim 10^{-4}$ to 10^{-3} mol L^{-1}.

Preparation of Colloids

Lyophilic sols can be easily prepared by shaking the lyophilic material with the dispersion medium, e.g. preparation of starch sol.

Lyophobic sols can be prepared by following methods.

Condensation/Aggregation Method

These methods involve the joining of a large number of small particles to form particles of colloidal size. Some methods are

(i) **Oxidation**

$$Br_2 + H_2S \longrightarrow 2HBr + \underset{\text{Colloidal sol}}{S}$$

$$SO_2 + 2H_2S \longrightarrow 3S(sol) + 2H_2O$$

(ii) **Reduction**

$$2AuCl_3 + 3SnCl_2 \longrightarrow \underset{\substack{\text{Gold sol or purple} \\ \text{of cassius}}}{2Au(sol)} + 3SnCl_4$$

(iii) **Hydrolysis**

$$FeCl_3 + 3H_2O \longrightarrow \underset{\text{Sol}}{Fe(OH)_3} + 3HCl$$

(iv) **Double decomposition**

$$As_2O_3 + 3H_2S \longrightarrow \underset{\text{Sol}}{As_2S_3} + 3H_2O$$

Dispersion/Disintegration Method

In this method, bigger particles are broken down to colloidal size. Some methods are

(i) **Mechanical disintegration** In this method, suspension is grind well in a colloid mill consisting of two steel discs which rotate in opposite directions at very high speed. The materials to be converted into colloidal sol is fed in between the two discs in the form of a wet slurry. The particles get broken to colloidal dimensions by the operating shearing force.

(ii) **Electrical disintegration/Bredig's Arc method** This process involves dispersion as well as condensation. In this method, electric arc is struck between electrodes of the metal (gold, silver, platinum, etc) immersed in the dispersion medium. The intense heat produced vapourises the metal which then condenses to form particles of colloidal size.

(iii) **Peptization** This method is used to convert fresh precipitate into colloidal state by shaking with dispersion medium in the presence of small amount of electrolyte. The electrolyte used (having an ion in common with the material to be dispersed) this purpose is called **peptizing agent**.

Purification of Colloidal Solutions

The process used for reducing the amount of impurities to a requisite minimum of a colloid, is known as purification of colloidal solutions.

(i) **Dialysis** It is based upon the principle that impurities of true solutions can pass through the parchment paper or cellophane membrane while, colloidal particles cannot.

In this process, dissolved substances are removed from the colloidal solution by means of diffusion through a suitable membrane.

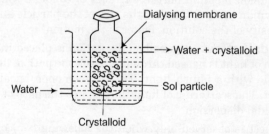

(ii) **Electrodialysis** The process of dialysis is quite slow. So, if the dissolved substance in the impure colloidal solution is only the electrolyte, then electric field is applied. The colloidal solution is placed in a bag of suitable membrane, while pure water is taken outside.

(iii) **Ultrafiltration** Ultrafiltration is the process of separation of colloidal particles from the solvent and soluble solutes present in the colloidal solution by specially prepared filters, called ultrafilters.

Properties of Colloidal Solution

General Properties

(i) **Colligative property** Due to high average molecular masses of colloidal particles, mole fraction of the dispersed phase is very low. So, the values of colligative properties are very small.

(ii) **Colour** The colour of colloidal solution depends on the wavelength of light scattered by the dispersed particles. The wavelength of light further depends on the size and nature of the particles. The colour of colloidal particles also depends on the manner in which the observer receives the light.

(iii) **Visibility** The particles of colloidal solution are not visible to naked eye or under ordinary microscope.

(iv) **Filterability** Colloidal particles can pass through ordinary filter paper, but can't pass through parchment paper or animal membrane.

Optical and Mechanical Properties

(i) **Brownian movement** Sol particles move in a random *zig-zag* manner due to the unequal impacts of the particles of dispersion medium on the particles of colloidal sol. It is called Brownian motion. Smaller the size of the particle and lesser the viscosity of the solution, faster is the motion.

(ii) **Tyndall effect** If a colloidal solution is placed in dark and a beam of light is passed through the sol, the path of light becomes visible with a bluish light. This phenomenon is called Tyndall effect. The scattering of light illuminates the path of beam in the colloidal dispersion.

Tyndall effect is observed only when the following two conditions are satisfied :

(i) The diameter of the dispersed particles is not much smaller than the wavelength of the light used.

(ii) The refractive indices of the dispersed phase and the dispersion medium differ greatly in magnitude.

Tyndall effect is also observed when sunlight enters in a dark room through a slit or when light is thrown from a light projector in a cinema hall. Tale of comets is seen as a Tyndall cone due to scattering of light by the tiny solid particles, left by the comet in its path.

Electrical Properties

(i) **Charge on colloidal particles** Colloidal particles always carry an electric charge. The nature of this charge is the same on all the particles in a given colloidal solution and may be either + ve or –ve. The charge on the particles is due to either of the given reasons:

(a) Due to preferential adsorption of either + ve or – ve ion which is common and present in excess, e.g. when $AgNO_3$ and KI solutions are mixed, the particles of AgI are precipitated. These particles can adsorb Ag^+ or I^- ions. If KI is in excess, I^- ions would be adsorbed giving [AgI] I^- negative sol but if $AgNO_3$ is in excess, a positive sol [AgI] Ag^+ is obtained.

SnO_2 can act as positively charged as well as negatively charged colloid depending upon the nature of medium.

(b) Due to electron capture by sol particles during electro dispersion method.

(c) By frictional electrification.

(d) By the dissociation of molecules followed by aggregation of ions. Two layers are developed on the particle, one is fixed layer and the other is diffused layer. Potential difference across this electric double layer is called **zeta potential** or **electrokinetic potential.**

Positively charged colloids are metal hydroxides, basic dyes like methylene blue sol, protein in acidic medium, oxides like TiO_2 sol. Examples of negatively charged colloids are metals (like Cu, Ag, Au, etc.), metal sulphide, acid dyes like eosin and sols of starch, gum, gelatin, clay, charcoal, etc.

(ii) **Electrophoresis** The phenomenon of movement of colloidal particles towards the oppositely charged electrodes under the influence of applied electric field is called electrophoresis.

(iii) **Coagulation/flocculation** The process of conversion of sol into a suspension is called flocculation or coagulation or precipitation.

It can be brought about by :

(a) addition of suitable electrolyte solution

(b) continuous electrophoresis

(c) prolonged dialysis

(d) mixing two oppositely charged colloidal solution

(e) heating or cooling

Coagulating value is the minimum amount of electrolyte (in millimoles/litres) needed to coagulate the colloidal solution. Smaller the coagulating or flocculating value of an electrolyte, greater is its coagulating power.

$$\text{Coagulating power} \propto \frac{1}{\text{Flocculating value}}$$

Hardy-Schulze rule Greater the valency of the oppositely charged ions of the electrolyte, more will be its coagulating power, i.e. coagulating power ∝ charge of ion, e.g. for As_2O_3 sol the order is, $Sn^{4+} > Al^{3+} > Ca^{2+} > Na^+$

Similarly for TiO_2 sol, the order is, $[Fe(CN)_6]^{4-} > PO_4^{3-} > SO_4^{2-} > Cl^-$

Protective Colloids

In the presence of a lyophilic colloid lyophobic sol gets protected towards the action of electrolyte. This phenomenon is called **protection** and the lyophilic colloid is termed as **protective colloid**.

Gold Number

The protective power of protective colloid is measured in terms of gold number which is defined as the number of mg of the protective colloid which just prevents the coagulation of 10 mL of standard gold sol when 1 mL of 10% solution of NaCl is added to it. Smaller the gold number of a protective colloid, greater is its protective power. Gold number of gelatin is 0.005-0.01 and of starch is 20-25.

Emulsion

It is a colloidal dispersion in which both dispersed phase and dispersion medium are liquid.

Types of Emulsions

(i) Oil in water [oil is dispersed phase and water is dispersion medium], e.g. milk.

(ii) Water in oil [water is dispersed phase and oil is dispersion medium], e.g. cod liver oil.

Dye test and dilution test must be used to distinguish between the two types of emulsions.

Characteristics of emulsion

Emulsions show all the properties of sols. Their important characteristics are as follows

(i) They can be diluted with liquid forming the dispersion medium in the emulsion.

(ii) Their particles size is larger than those of other size. It ranges from 1000 Å to 10 000 Å.

(*iii*) They scatter light and thus, exhibit Tyndall effect.

(*iv*) Brownian motion is also observed in emulsions where size of the particle is too near to the limit of 10^{-6}m.

Emulsifiers

Emulsifying agents or emulsifiers are the substances added in small quantity to stabilize the emulsions of fairly high concentration.

Demulsification The separation of an emulsion into its consituent liquids is called demulsification. It can be carried out by freezing, boiling, centrifugation, etc.

Gels

Gel is a liquid-solid colloidal system in which a liquid is dispersed in a solid. Gels are of two types : elastic gels (e.g. gelatin, agar-agar, starch) and non-elastic gels (e.g. silica, alumina and ferric oxide).

When gels are allowed to stand, they give out small quantity of trapped liquid and the gel shrinks in volume. This phenomenon is called **syneresis** or **weeping of gel**.

Colloids Around Us

Most of the substances we come across in our daily life are colloids. Following are the examples of colloids.

(i) Blue colour of the sky.

(ii) For, mist and rain.

(iii) Food articles like milk, butter, ice-creams, etc.

(iv) Blood which is a colloidal solution of an albuminoid substance.

(v) Fertile soils are colloidal in nature in which humus acts as a protective colloid.

(vi) Formation of delta.

Applications of Colloids

(i) In medicine, e.g. argyrol (a silver sol used as eye lotion).

(ii) In chrome tanning.

(iii) In sewage disposal.

(iv) In purification of drinking water.

(v) In the preparation of nano-materials often use as catalyst.

(vi) In photography.

(vii) In producing artificial rain.

(viii) Blood clotting by ferric chloride or potash alum.

(ix) In smoke precipitation (cottrell precipitator)

16

Principles & Processes of Isolation of Elements

Elements in Nature

Earth crust is the source of many elements. Out of these elements, 70% are metals. Aluminium is the most abundant metal of earth crust and iron comes second. The percentage of different elements in earth crust are O-49%, Si-26%, Al-7.5%, Fe-4.2%, Ca-3.2%, Na-2.4%, K-2.3%, Mg-2.3%, H-1%

Metals occur in two forms in nature (i) in native state (ii) in combined state, depending upon their chemical reactivities.

Native State

Elements which have low chemical reactivity or noble metals having least electropositive character are not attacked by oxygen, moisture and CO_2 of the air. These elements, therefore, occur in the free state or in the native state, e.g. Au, Ag, Pt, S, O, N, noble gases, etc.

Combined State

Highly reactive elements which are readily attacked by moisture, oxygen and carbon dioxide of the air, such as F, Cl, Na, K, etc., occur in nature in combined form as their compounds such as oxides, carbonates, sulphides, halides, etc.

Hydrogen is the only non-metal which exists in oxidised form only.

Minerals and Ores

The naturally occurring substances in the form of which the metals occur in the earth crust along with impurities are called **minerals.**

Every mineral is not suitable for the extraction of the metal. The mineral from which the metal is economically and conveniently extracted is called an **ore.**

Thus, all ores are minerals but all minerals are not ores.

Important Ores/Minerals

Combined state	Element	Ore/mineral
Oxides	Fe	Haematite (Fe_2O_3), Magnetite (Fe_3O_4), Limonite ($Fe_2O_3 \cdot 3H_2O$), Chromite ($FeO \cdot Cr_2O_3$)
	Al	Bauxite ($Al_2O_3 \cdot 2H_2O$), Diaspore ($Al_2O_3 \cdot H_2O$), Corundum (Al_2O_3)
	Mn	Pyrolusite (MnO_2)
	Zn	Zincite (ZnO)
	Ti	Rutile (TiO_2)
	Cu	Cuprite (Cu_2O)
	Sn	Cassiterite or tin stone (SnO_2)
Carbonates	Ca	Calcite ($CaCO_3$)
	Mg	Magnesite ($MgCO_3$)
	Ca, Mg	Dolomite ($CaCO_3 \cdot MgCO_3$)
	Cu	Malachite [$CuCO_3 \cdot Cu(OH)_2$]
	Zn	Calamine ($ZnCO_3$)
	Fe	Siderite or spathic ore ($FeCO_3$)
	Pb	Cerusite ($PbCO_3$)
	Au	Azurite [$2CuCO_3 \cdot Cu(OH)_2$]
Sulphides	Fe	Iron pyrite (FeS_2)
	Cu	Copper glance (Cu_2S)
	Cu, Fe	Copper pyrite or chalcopyrite ($CuFeS_2$)
	Hg	Cinnabar (HgS)
	Zn	Zinc blende (ZnS)
	Pb	Galena (PbS)
	Ag	Argentite or silver glance (Ag_2S)
Halides	Na	Common salt or Rock salt (NaCl)
	Al	Cryolite (Na_3AlF_6)
	K, Mg	Carnallite ($KCl \cdot MgCl_2 \cdot 6H_2O$)
	Ag	Horn silver (AgCl)

Terms Related to Extraction of Elements

(i) **Flux** The substance added to convert infusible mass (impurities) into some fusible mass is called flux.

Infusible mass + flux $\longrightarrow$ fusible mass (slag)

Depending upon the nature of impurity, it may be acidic or basic.

- **Acidic flux** It is used to remove basic impurities. e.g., Silica (SiO_2), boron trioxide (B_2O_3), phosphorus pentaoxide (P_2O_5) etc., are acidic flux.

e.g.
$$\underset{\substack{\text{Basic} \\ \text{impurity} \\ \text{(infusible)}}}{FeO} + \underset{\text{Acidic flux}}{SiO_2} \longrightarrow \underset{\text{Fusible slag}}{FeSiO_3}$$

- **Basic flux** It is used to remove acidic impurities e.g., lime (CaO), lime stone ($CaCO_3$), magnesia (MgO) etc., are basic flux.

e.g.
$$\underset{\text{Acidic impurity}}{SiO_2} + \underset{\text{Basic flux}}{MgO} \longrightarrow \underset{\text{Fusible slag}}{MgSiO_3}$$

(ii) **Slag** The fusible mass obtained by the reaction of flux and infusible mass is called slag and this process is called **slagging operation.**

(iii) **Gangue or Matrix** Impurities associated with ores are called gangue or matrix.

Metallurgy

The entire scientific and technological process used for isolation of the metal from its ores is known as metallurgy.

Types of Metallurgical Processes

(i) **Pyrometallurgy** In this type of metallurgy is used to extract the element. Cu, Fe, Zn, Sn, etc., are extracted by this method.

(ii) **Hydrometallurgical process** In this method, metals are extracted by the use of their aqueous solution. Ag and Au are extracted by this method.

(iii) **Electrometallurgical process** In this method process of electrolysis is used in the extraction of metals. Na, K, Li, Ca, etc., are extracted from their molten salt solution through electrolytic method.

Steps Involved in Metallurgy

Following steps are involved in the metallurgy :

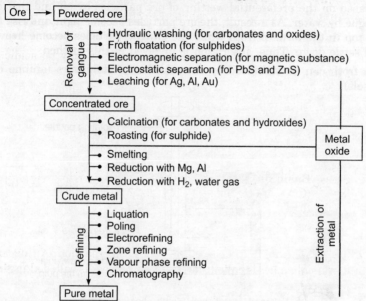

Crushing of the Ore

The big lumps of ore are crushed into smaller pieces with the help of jaw-crushers. The process of grinding the crushed ore into fine powder with the help of the stamp mills is called **pulverisation**.

Concentration of Ores

Removal of unwanted materials (e.g. sand, clays, etc.) from the ore is known as **ore concentration**, ore dressing or ore benefaction. It can be carried out by various ways depending upon the nature of the ore.

Hydraulic Washing/Gravity Separation/Levigation

The process by which lighter earthy impurities are removed from the heavier ore particles by washing with water is called **levigation**. The lighter impurities are washed away. Thus, this method is based on the difference in the densities (specific gravities) of ore and gangue.

This method is commonly used for oxide ores such as haematite, tin stone and native ores of Au, Ag, etc.

Froth Flotation

This method is used for the concentration of sulphide ores. The method is based on the preferential wetting of ore particles by oil and that of gangue by water. As a result, the ore particles become light and rise to the top in the form of froth while the gangue particles become heavy and settle down. Thus, adsorption is involved in this method.

The froth can be stabilised by the addition of stabilisers (aniline or cresols).

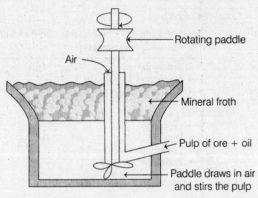

Froth flotation process (schematic)

Activator They activate the floating property of one of the component of the ore and help in the separation of different minerals present in the same ore. $CuSO_4$ is used as activator.

Depressants These are used to prevent certain types of particles from forming the froth with air bubbled, e.g. NaCN can be used as a depressant in the separation of ZnS and PbS ores. KCN is an another depressant.

Collectors It increases the non-wettability of ore particles by water, e.g. pine oils, xanthates and fatty acids.

Electromagnetic Separation

This method of concentration is employed when either the ore or the impurities associated with it are magnetic in nature, e.g. chromite, $FeCr_2O_4$, containing magnetic silicious gangue and wolframite, $FeWO_4$, containing cassiterite, SnO_2 (non-magnetic impurities) can be separated by this method.

Electrostatic Separation

This method is used for the separation of lead sulphide (good conductor of electricity) which is charged immediately in an electrostatic field and is thrown away from the roller from zinc sulphide (poor conductor of electricity) which is not charged and hence, drops vertically from the roller.

Chemical Method-Leaching

Leaching is the process in which the ore is concentrated by chemical reaction with a suitable reagent which dissolves the ore but not the impurities, e.g. bauxite is leached with a hot concentrated solution of NaOH which dissolves aluminium while other oxides (Fe_2O_3, TiO_2, SiO_2), remain undissolved and noble metals (Ag and Au) are leached with a dilute aqueous solution of NaCN or KCN in the presence of air.

$$\underset{\text{bauxite}}{Al_2O_3 \cdot 2H_2O} + 2NaOH \longrightarrow \underset{\text{sod. meta aluminate}}{2NaAlO_2} + 3H_2O$$

and

$$\underset{\text{argentite}}{Ag_2S} + 4NaCN \longrightarrow \underset{\substack{\text{sod. argento} \\ \text{cyanide}}}{2Na[Ag(CN)_2]} + Na_2S$$

Leaching of Ag or Au with NaCN is called cyanide process.

Extraction of Crude Metals from Concentrated Ore

The concentrated ore is usually converted to oxide before reduction, as oxides are easier to reduce. Thus, isolation of crude metal from concentrated ore involves two major steps:

(i) Conversion to oxide.   (ii) Reduction of the oxides to metal.

Conversion to Oxides

(i) **Calcination** It is the process of converting an ore into its oxides by heating it strongly, below its melting point in a limited supply of air or in absence of air.

During calcination, volatile impurities as well as organic matter and moisture are removed.

$$\underset{\text{Bauxite}}{Al_2O_3 \cdot 2H_2O} \xrightarrow{\text{Heat}} Al_2O_3 + 2H_2O$$

$$\underset{\text{limestone}}{CaCO_3} \xrightarrow{\text{Heat}} CaO + CO_2$$

$$\underset{\text{dolomite}}{CaCO_3 \cdot MgCO_3} \xrightarrow{\text{Heat}} CaO + MgO + 2CO_2$$

Calcination is used for metal carbonates and hydroxides and is carried out in reverberatory furnace.

(ii) **Roasting** It is the process of converting an ore into its metallic oxide by heating it strongly, below its melting point in excess of air. This process is commonly used for sulphide ores and is carried out in blast furnace or reverberatory furnace. Roasting helps to remove the non-metallic impurities and moisture.

$$2ZnS + 3O_2 \longrightarrow 2ZnO + 2SO_2\uparrow$$

$$2PbS + 3O_2 \longrightarrow 2PbO + 2SO_2\uparrow$$

The furnaces used in calcination and roasting employ refractory materials which resist high temperature and do not become soft. The SO_2 produced is utilised for manufacturing of H_2SO_4.

Acidic refractories   : SiO_2 and $SiO_2 + Al_2O_3$

Basic refractories   : CaO and MgO

Neutral refractories   : Graphite, chromites, etc.

Heavy metals like Cu, Zn, Fe, Sn, etc., are obtained by roasting and smelting.

Reduction of the Oxides to Metal

The roasted or the calcined ore is then converted to the free metal by reduction. Reduction method depends upon the activity of metal.

Metals which are low in the activity series (like Cu, Hg, Au) are obtained by heating their compounds in air; metals which are in the middle of the activity series (like Fe, Zn, Ni, Sn) are obtained by heating their oxides with carbon while metals which are very high in the activity series, (e.g. Na, K, Ca, Mg, Al) are obtained by electrolytic reduction method.

(i) **Smelting** (reduction with carbon) The process of extracting the metal by fusion of its oxide ore with carbon (C) or CO is called **smelting**. It is carried out in a reverberatory furnace.

e.g.
$$ZnO + C \longrightarrow Zn + CO\uparrow$$

$$Fe_2O_3 + CO \xrightarrow{823\,K} 2FeO + CO_2$$

$$Fe_2O_3 + 3C \longrightarrow 2Fe + 3CO\uparrow$$

During smelting a substance, called **flux** is added which removes the non-fusible impurities as fusible slag. This slag is insoluble in the molten metal and is lighter than the molten metal. So, it floats over the molten metal and is skimmed off.

Acidic flux   For basic impurities, acidic flux is added.

e.g. $CaO + SiO_2 \longrightarrow CaSiO_3$

$$\underset{\text{acidic flux}}{FeO} + SiO_2 \longrightarrow \underset{\text{fusible slag}}{FeSiO_3}$$

Basic flux   For acidic impurities, basic flux is added.

e.g. $SiO_2 + CaCO_3 \longrightarrow CaSiO_3 + CO_2\uparrow$

$$SiO_2 + \underset{\text{basic flux}}{MgCO_3} \longrightarrow \underset{\text{fusible slag}}{MgSiO_3} + CO_2 \uparrow$$

In the extraction of Cu and Fe, the slag obtained are respectively $FeSiO_3$ and $CaSiO_3$.

The obtained slag is used in road making as well as in the manufacturing of cement and fertilizers.

(ii) **Reduction by hydrogen**   It is done for W or Mo oxide.

$$WO_3 + 3H_2 \xrightarrow{\text{Heat}} W + 3H_2O$$

(iii) **Reduction by aluminium**   It is known as alumino thermic reduction or Gold Schmidt thermite process. Aluminium powder is used for this purpose.

e.g. $Cr_2O_3 + 2Al \longrightarrow Al_2O_3 + 2Cr$

Mixture of the oxide and Al in the ratio of 3 : 1 is known as **thermite** and mixture of $BaO_2 + Mg$ powder acts as ignition powder.

(iv) **Auto reduction**   This is used for reduction of sulphide ores of Pb, Hg, Cu, etc. The sulphide ore is heated in a supply of air at 770-970 K when the metal sulphide is partially oxidised to form its oxide or sulphate which then reacts with the remaining sulphide to give the metal.

e.g. $2Cu_2S + 3O_2 \longrightarrow 2Cu_2O + 2SO_2$

$Cu_2S + 2Cu_2O \longrightarrow 6Cu + SO_2$

(v) **Reduction by Mg**

$$TiCl_4 + 2Mg \longrightarrow 2MgCl_2 + Ti \quad \text{(Kroll's process)}$$

(vi) **Electrolytic reduction or electrometallurgy**   It is the process of extracting highly electropositive (active) metals such as Na, K, Ca, Mg, Al, etc by electrolysis of their oxides, hydroxides or chlorides in fused state, e.g. Mg is prepared by the electrolysis of fused salt of $MgCl_2$ (Dow's process).

Thermodynamic Principle in Extraction of Metals

The free energy change (ΔG) occurring during the reduction processes help in deciding the suitable method for reduction.

For the spontaneous reduction of an oxide, halide or sulphide by an element, the essential condition is that there is a decrease in the free energy of the system (i.e., –ve value of ΔG).

More the negative value of ΔG, the higher is the reducing power of an element. ΔG can be given as

$$\Delta G = \Delta H - T\Delta S$$

where, ΔH = enthalpy change; ΔG = Gibbs free energy

T = temperature; ΔS = entropy change

For the reduction of a metal oxide with a reducing agent, the plot of $\Delta G°$ against temperature is studied, which is called **Ellingham diagram.**

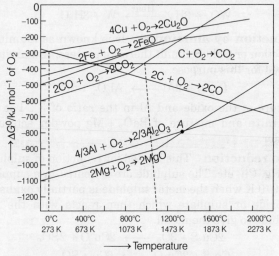

Plot of Gibbs energy ($\Delta G°$) *vs* T (Ellingham diagram)

Characteristics of Ellingham Diagram

1. All the plots slope upwards since $\Delta G°$ becomes more positive when temperature increases, i.e. stability of oxides decreases.

2. A metal will reduce the oxide of other metals which lie above it in Ellingham diagram, i.e. the metals for which the free energy of formation ($\Delta G_f°$) of their oxides is more negative can reduce those metal oxides which has less negative $\Delta G_f°$.

3. The decreasing order of the negative values of ΔG_f° of metal oxides is Ca > Mg (below 1773 K) > Al > Ti > Cr > C > Fe
   $$> Ni > Hg > Ag$$
   Thus, Al reduces FeO, CrO and NiO in thermite reduction but it will not reduce MgO at temperature below 1773 K.
   Mg can reduce Al_2O_3 below 162 K but above 1023 K, Al can reduce MgO.

4. CO is more effective reducing agent below 1073 K and above 1073 K, coke is more effective reducing agent, e.g. CO reduces Fe_2O_3 below 1073 K but above it, coke reduces Fe_2O_3. Coke reduces ZnO above 1270 K.

Electrochemical Principle of Metallurgy

In the reduction of molten metal salt, electrolysis is done. It is based on the electrochemical principle.

$$\Delta G^{\circ} = -nFE^{\circ}$$

where, n = no. of electrons
E° = electrode potential of redox couple formed in the system. Since, more reactive metals have large negative values of the electrode potential, hence their reduction is difficult. If the difference in two values of E° of redox couple is positive, then ΔG° will be negative and less reactive metal can be obtained from its salt by more reactive metal.

Refining or Purification of Crude Metals

Physical Methods

(i) **Liquation** This method is used for refining the metals having low melting points (such as Sn, Pb, Hg, Bi) than the impurities. The impure metal is placed on the sloping hearth and is gently heated. The metal melts and flows down leaving behind the non-fusible impurities.

(ii) **Distillation** This is useful for low boiling metals such as Zn, Hg. The impure liquid metal is evaporated to obtain the pure metal as distillate.

(iii) **Cupellation** This method is used when impure metal contains impurities of other metals which form volatile oxides, e.g. traces of lead ore removed from silver (as volatile PbO) by this process.

Chemical Methods

(i) **Poling** This method is used when the impure metal contains impurities of its own oxide, e.g. Cu_2O in blister copper and SnO_2 in impure Sn. The molten impure metal is stirred with green wood poles. At the high temperature, wood liberates gases such as CH_4 which reduces any oxides present in the metal.

(ii) **Electro-refining** In this method, impure metal forms the anode while the cathode is a rod or sheet of pure metal. The electrolytic solution consists of a soluble salt of the metal.

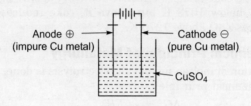

Anode, $$Cu \longrightarrow Cu^{2+} + 2e^-$$

Cathode, $$Cu^{2+} + 2e^- \longrightarrow Cu(s)$$

On passing electricity, the pure metal gets deposited on the cathode while the insoluble impurities settle down below the anode as anode mud or anode sludge. Metals like Cu, Ag, Au, Cr, Zn, Ni, etc are purified by this method.

(iii) **Zone-refining** This method is based upon the principle of fractional crystallisation, i.e. difference in solubilities of impurities in molten and solid state of metal. Semiconductors like silicon, germanium, gallium arsenide and indium antimonide are purified by this method. Elements of very high purity are obtained by this method.

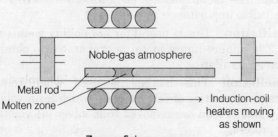

Zone refining process

(iv) **Vapour phase refining** In this method, crude metal is made free from impurities by first converting it into its volatile compound by heating with a chemical reagent at low temperature. After this, the volatile compound is decomposed by heating to some higher temperature to give pure metal.

(a) **van Arkel method** This method is used for preparing ultra-pure metal used in space technology (e.g. Ti, Zr, etc.)

$$\underset{\text{impure}}{Ti(s)} + 2I_2(s) \xrightarrow{523 \text{ K}} TiI_4(g) \xrightarrow{1700 \text{ K}} \underset{\text{pure}}{Ti(s)} + 2I_2(g)$$

$$\underset{\text{impure}}{Zr(s)} + 2I_2 \xrightarrow{870 \text{ K}} ZrI_4(g) \xrightarrow{1800 \text{ K}} \underset{\text{pure}}{Zr(s)} + 2I_2(g)$$

(b) **Mond's process** It is used for refining of nickel.

$$\underset{\text{impure}}{Ni} + 4CO \xrightarrow{330-350 \text{ K}} Ni(CO)_4$$

$$Ni(CO)_4 \xrightarrow{450-470 \text{ K}} \underset{\text{pure}}{Ni} + 4CO$$

(v) **Chromatographic method** This method is based on the principle that different components of a mixture are differently adsorbed on an adsorbent. Adsorption chromatography is generally used. The impure metal is dissolved in a suitable solvent and the solution is allowed to run slowly into an adsorbent column packed with alumina (Al_2O_3). The metal and the impurities present are adsorbed at different rates. These are then eluted with suitable eluent (solvent). In this method, weakly adsorbed component is eluted first and the strongly adsorbed component is eluted afterwards.

Occurrence, Extraction and Uses of Some Metals

1. Aluminium (Al)

Occurrence

(i) Bauxite — $Al_2O_3 \cdot xH_2O$　　(ii) Cryolite — Na_3AlF_6

Common method of extraction Electrolysis of Al_2O_3 dissolved in molten Na_3AlF_6 (neutral flux).

Neutral flux is the neutral compound added to the ore to decrease its melting point and to make it conducting, e.g. CaF_2, cryolite (Na_3AlF_6) etc.

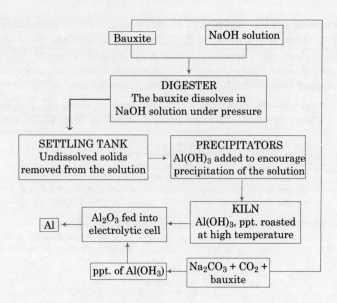

Uses Making electric wires, silver paint, kitchen utensils, food packing, extraction of Mo, Cr, etc.

2. Iron (Fe)

Occurrence

(i) Haematite — Fe_2O_3 (ii) Magnetite — Fe_3O_4

Common method of extraction Reduction of the oxide with CO and coke in blast furnace. The iron obtained from blast furnace contains about 4% carbon and many impurities in smaller amount (e.g. S, P, Si, Mn) and is known as **pig iron.**

Cast iron is different from pig iron and is made by melting pig iron with scrap iron and coke using hot air blast.

It has slightly lower carbon content (about 3%) and is extremely hard and brittle.

Wrought iron or **malleable iron** is the purest form of commercial iron and is prepared from cast iron by oxidising impurities in a reverberatory furnace lined with haematite. This haematite oxidises carbon to carbon monoxide.

$$Fe_2O_3 + 3C \longrightarrow 2Fe + 3CO$$

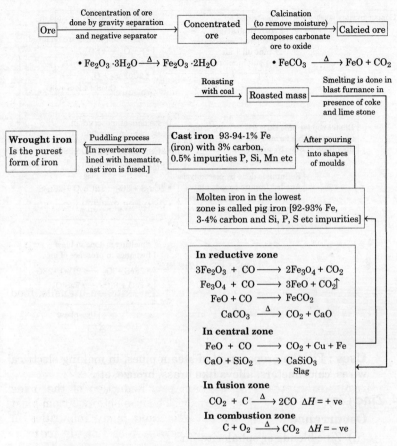

- $Fe_2O_3 \cdot 3H_2O \xrightarrow{\Delta} Fe_2O_3 \cdot 2H_2O$
- $FeCO_3 \xrightarrow{\Delta} FeO + CO_2$

In reductive zone
$$3Fe_2O_3 + CO \longrightarrow 2Fe_3O_4 + CO_2$$
$$Fe_3O_4 + CO \longrightarrow 3FeO + CO_2\uparrow$$
$$FeO + CO \longrightarrow FeCO_2$$
$$CaCO_3 \xrightarrow{\Delta} CO_2 + CaO$$

In central zone
$$FeO + CO \longrightarrow CO_2 + Cu + Fe$$
$$CaO + SiO_2 \longrightarrow CaSiO_3$$
$$\text{Slag}$$

In fusion zone
$$CO_2 + C \xrightarrow{\Delta} 2CO \quad \Delta H = + ve$$

In combustion zone
$$C + O_2 \xrightarrow{\Delta} CO_2 \quad \Delta H = - ve$$

Uses : Making wrought iron and different varieties of steel.

3. Copper (Cu)

Occurrence

(i) Copper pyrites — $CuFeS_2$

(ii) Copper glance — Cu_2S

Common method of extraction Roasting of sulphide partially and reduction.

$Cu_2S + FeS$ is called matte. Blister copper contains 96-98% copper with small amounts of Ag and Au as impurity.

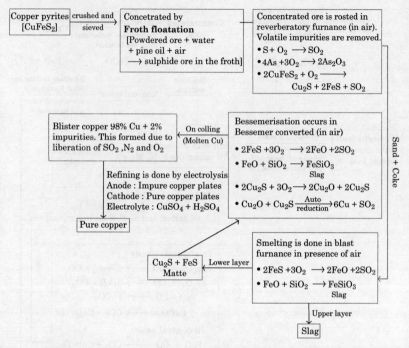

Uses : For the preparation of steam pipes, in making electrical wires, calorimeters, alloys like brass, bronze, etc.

4. Zinc (Zn)

Occurrence

(i) Zinc blende or sphalerite-ZnS

(ii) Calamine — $ZnCO_3$

(iii) Zincite — ZnO

Common method of extraction Roasting followed by reduction with coke.

The metal may be purified by fractional distillation.

97–98% pure zinc is called **spelter.**

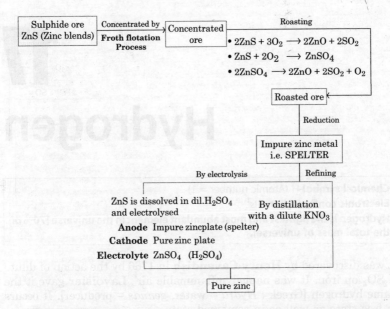

Uses : Making alloys like brass, german silver, for making dry cell, for galvanisation of iron, etc.

17

Hydrogen

Chemical symbol-H (Atomic number = 1)
Electronic configuration $-1s^1$
Hydrogen is the lightest and most abundant element in the universe [70% of the total mass of universe].

It was discovered by **Henry Cavendish** in 1766 by the action of dilute H_2SO_4 on iron. It was named 'inflammable air'. **Lavoisier** gave it the name hydrogen [Greek : *Hydra* = water, *gennas* = producer]. It occurs in free state as well as in combined state.

Position of Hydrogen in the Periodic Table

Hydrogen resembles with alkali metals (group 1) as well as halogens (group 17). At the same time, it differs from both in certain characteristics. That is why hydrogen is called **"rogue element"**. However, it has been placed in group 1 on the basis of its configuration $1s^1$, which is the basis of modern classification of elements.

Isotopes of Hydrogen

Hydrogen exists in the form of three isotopes:

Name	Symbol	Atomic number	Relative atomic mass	Density	Relative abundance	Nature
Protium	^1_1H or H	1	1.0078	0.09	99.98%	Non-radioactive
Deuterium	^2_1H or D	1	2.0141	0.18	0.0156%	Non-radioactive
Tritium	^3_1H or T	1	3.016	0.27	10^{-15}%	Radioactive (emits β-rays, $t_{1/2} = 12.33$ year)

Dihydrogen [H_2]

Methods of Preparation of Dihydrogen

(a) **Lab methods**

(i) $Zn + H_2SO_4(aq) \longrightarrow ZnSO_4(aq) + H_2(g)$
   dilute

Metals which have reduction potential lesser than H, can liberate H_2 from acids.

Pure zinc is not used because it reacts slowly. The presence of some impurities increases the rate of reaction due to the formation of electrochemical couples.

Conc sulphuric acid is also not used because it oxidises, H_2 formed into H_2O.

$Zn + 2H_2SO_4(\text{conc.}) \longrightarrow ZnSO_4 + SO_2 + 2H_2O$

(ii) It can also be prepared by the reaction of zinc with aqueous alkali.

$$Zn + 2NaOH \xrightarrow{\Delta} \underset{\text{sodium zincate}}{Na_2ZnO_2} + H_2$$

(b) **Commercial production of dihydrogen**

(i) By the electrolysis of acidified water

$$H_2O \rightleftharpoons H^+ + OH^- \qquad \text{(Ionisation)}$$

At cathode, $\qquad H^+ + e^- \longrightarrow H^\bullet \qquad$ (Reduction)

$$H^\bullet + H^\bullet \longrightarrow H_2$$

At anode, $\qquad 4OH^- \longrightarrow 4OH + 4e^- \qquad$ (Oxidation)

$$4OH \longrightarrow 2H_2O + O_2$$

(ii) From water gas (Bosch process)

$$\underset{\text{water gas}}{\underbrace{CO + H_2}} + \underset{\text{steam}}{H_2O} \xrightarrow[773K]{Fe_2O_3 + Cr_2O_3} CO_2 \uparrow + 2H_2$$

[water gas shift reaction]

Carbon dioxide is removed by dissolving it in water under pressure (20-25 atm) and hydrogen left behind is collected.

(iii) From steam (Lane's process)-Super heated steam is passed over iron filings heated to about 1023-1073 K when hydrogen is formed.

$$3Fe + 4H_2O \text{ (steam)} \xrightarrow{1023-1073 \text{ K}} Fe_3O_4 + 4H_2$$

(iv) Highly pure (> 99.95%) dihydrogen is obtained by electrolysing warm aqueous barium hydroxide solution between nickel electrodes.

(v) **From hydrocarbons by partial oxidation**

$$\underset{\text{natural gas}}{CH_4} + \underset{\text{steam}}{H_2O} \xrightarrow[\text{1270 K}]{\text{Ni-Cr catalyst}} CO + 3H_2$$

(vi) It is also obtained as a by-product in the manufacture of NaOH and chlorine by the electrolysis of brine solution.

During electrolysis, the reactions that take place are

At anode, $\qquad 2\bar{Cl}(aq) \longrightarrow Cl_2(g) + 2e^-$

At cathode, $2H_2O(l) + 2e^- \longrightarrow H_2(g) + 2OH^-(aq)$

The overall reactions by adding spectator Na^+ ions,

$$2Na^+(aq) + 2\bar{Cl}(aq) + 2H_2O(l) \longrightarrow$$
$$Cl_2(g) + H_2(g) + 2Na^+ + 2\bar{OH}(aq)$$

Physical Properties of Dihydrogen

Dihydrogen is a colourless, odourless, tasteless, combustible gas. It is lighter than air and insoluble in water. It is neutral to litmus.

Chemical Properties of Dihydrogen

(i) **Reactivity** The relative inertness of dihydrogen at room temperature is because of its high enthalpy of H—H bond i.e. high bond dissociation energy. So its reactions take place under specific conditions only (at high temperature).

(ii) **Action with non-metals**

$$2H_2(g) + O_2(g) \xrightarrow[\text{or Electric discharge}]{970 \text{ K}} 2H_2O(l); \Delta H^\circ = -285.9 \text{ kJ mol}^{-1}$$

$$N_2(g) + 3H_2(g) \xrightarrow[\text{Fe (Mo)}]{673 \text{ K}/200 \text{ atm}} 2NH_3(g); \Delta H^\circ = -92.6 \text{ kJ mol}^{-1}$$

$$H_2(g) + X_2(g) \xrightarrow{\text{Dark}} 2HX(g) \text{ (where, } X \text{ represents halogens)}$$

Order of reactivity of halogens:

$$F_2 > Cl_2 > Br_2 > I_2$$

(iii) **Reaction with metals** Here H_2 acts as oxidising agent.

$$2Na + H_2 \xrightarrow{\Delta} 2NaH$$

$$Ca + H_2 \xrightarrow{\Delta} CaH_2 \text{ (Hydrolith)}$$

(iv) **Reducing action of dihydrogen**

$$CuO + H_2 \xrightarrow{\Delta} Cu + H_2O$$

(v) **Reactions with metal ions and metal oxides**

$$H_2(g) + Pd^{2+}(aq) \longrightarrow Pd(s) + 2H^+(aq)$$

$$yH_2(g) + M_xO_y(s) \longrightarrow xM(s) + yH_2O(l)$$

(vi) **Reaction with organic compounds**

(a) Veg. oil $+ H_2 \xrightarrow{Ni/400K}$ Veg. ghee

(b) $R-CH=CH_2 + H_2 + CO \xrightarrow{[Co(CO)_4]_2} RCH_2CH_2CHO$

$$RCH_2CH_2CHO + H_2 \xrightarrow[\Delta]{Ni} RCH_2CH_2CH_2OH$$

Uses of Dihydrogen

1. It is used in the manufacture of CH_3OH.

$$CO(g) + 2H_2(g) \xrightarrow{Co} CH_3OH(l)$$

2. It produces temperature of 2850°C and oxy-atomic hydrogen flame produces a temperature of 4000°C, so it is used in oxy-hydrogen flame.

3. The largest single use of H_2 is in the synthesis of NH_3 which is used in the manufacture of HNO_3 and fertilizers.

4. Liquid hydrogen mixed with liquid oxygen is used as rocket fuel in space research.

5. H_2 is used as a reducing agent in extraction of metals.

6. H_2 is used in fuel cell for generating electrical energy.

7. Hydrogen is used in the manufacture of synthetic petrol. (By heating H_2 with coal and heavy oils under very high pressure in the presence of catalyst.)

8. It is use for the preparation of metal hydrides, hydrogen chloride.

9. It is used in metallurgical processes to reduce heavy metal oxides to metals.

10. Atomic hydrogen and oxy hydrogen torches find use for cutting and welding purposes.

Different Forms of Hydrogen

Atomic Hydrogen

It is obtained from thermal decomposition of molecular hydrogen at high temperature and low pressure.

$$H_2 \xrightarrow{\text{Electric arc}} 2H; \qquad \Delta H = 105.4 \text{ kcal mol}^{-1}$$

It is very reactive and its half-life period is 0.33 s.

Nascent Hydrogen

Freshly prepared hydrogen is known as nascent hydrogen and is more reactive than ordinary hydrogen. It causes the reduction of certain compounds which is not possible with ordinary hydrogen. It can never be isolated.

$$Zn + H_2SO_4 \longrightarrow ZnSO_4 + 2[H]$$

Activity of nascent H depends upon the reaction by which it is obtained.

Adsorbed Hydrogen

Adsorption of hydrogen at the metal surface is called **occlusion**. This hydrogen brings out many chemical changes such as reduction and hydrogenation. Occlusion decreases with rise in temperature.

Ortho and Para Hydrogen

When in hydrogen molecule, the nuclear spins are in the same direction, it is known as ortho hydrogen. On the other hand when the nuclear spins are in the opposite direction, it is known as para hydrogen. At room temperature hydrogen consists of 75% ortho and 25% para hydrogen.

Ortho hydrogen　　　　Para hydrogen

Hydrides

The compounds of hydrogen with metals and non-metals (except noble gases) are called hydrides.

Ionic or Saline Hydrides

These are formed by elements of group I, II, (except Be and Mg) by heating them in hydrogen. These are white colourless solids (crystalline) having high m.p. and b.p. easily decomposed by water, CO_2 or SO_2.

$$CaH_2 + 2H_2O \longrightarrow Ca(OH)_2 + 2H_2$$
$$CaH_2 + 2CO_2 \longrightarrow (HCOO)_2Ca$$

They are strong reducing agents. Alkali metal hydrides are used for making $LiAlH_4$, $NaBH_4$, etc and for removing last traces of water from organic compounds.

Molecular or Covalent Hydrides

These are formed by elements of p-block having higher electronegativity than hydrogen.

(i) **Electron deficient hydrides** These are the hydrides which do not have sufficient number of electrons needed to form normal covalent bonds, e.g. hydrides of group 13 (BH_3, AlH_3, etc.)

(ii) **Electron precise hydrides** These are the hydrides which have exact number of electrons needed to form normal covalent bonds, e.g. hydrides of group 14 (CH_4, SiH_4, etc.)

(iii) **Electron rich hydrides** These are the hydrides which have greater number of electrons than required to form normal covalent bonds, e.g. hydrides of group 15, 16, 17, (NH_3, PH_3, H_2S, HF, HCl, etc). The excess electrons in these hydrides are present as lone pairs of electrons.

Metallic or Interstitial or Non-stoichiometric Hydrides

The transition metals and rare earth metals combine with hydrogen to form interstitial hydrides. They exhibit metallic properties and are powerful reducing agents. They are non-stoichiometric hydrides and their composition varies with temperature and pressure for e.g. $LaH_{2.76}$, $TiH_{1.73}$. Metals of group 7, 8 and 9 do not form hydrides and this region of the Periodic Table is called **hydride gap**.

Polymeric Hydrides and Complex Hydrides

Polymeric hydrides are formed by elements having electronegativity in the range 1.4 to 2.0, e.g. $(BeH_2)_n$, $(AlH_3)_n$, etc. In complex hydrides, H^- acts as ligand and is attached to central metal atom, e.g. $LiAlH_4$, $LiBH_4$, etc.

Water

Water is the most abundant and widely distributed on the earth. Human body has about 65% and some plants have as much as 95% H_2O. It occurs in all the three physical states. H_2O is a covalent molecule in which oxygen is sp^3-hybridised. It has bent structure.

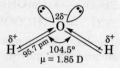

The crystalline form of water is ice. It has a highly ordered three dimensional hydrogen bonded structure. Examination of ice crystals with X-rays shows that each oxygen atom is surrounded tetrahedrally by four oxygen atom.

Physical Properties of Water

1. Water is a colourless, odourless, tasteless liquid. It has abnormally high b.p., f.p., heat of vaporisation due to hydrogen bonding.

2. Pure water is not a good conductor so it is made conductor by adding small amount of acid or alkali.

3. Density of ice (which is mass per unit volume) is lesser than that of water and it floats over water.

4. Water has maximum density at 4°C. This property of maximum density at 277 K helps aquatic animals to survive during winter months.

5. Water is a highly polar solvent with high dielectric constant 78.39. It interacts with polar or ionic substances effectively with the release of considerable amount of energy due to ion dipole interaction. The dissolution of covalent compounds like urea, glucose and C_2H_5OH, etc is due to the tendency of these molecules to form hydrogen bond with water.

Chemical Properties of Water

1. Water is amphoteric in nature.

$$\underset{\text{base}}{H_2O(l)} + \underset{\text{acid}}{HCl(aq)} \rightleftharpoons \underset{\text{acid}}{H_3O^+(aq)} + \underset{\text{base}}{Cl^-(aq)}$$

$$\underset{\text{acid}}{H_2O(l)} + \underset{\text{base}}{NH_3(aq)} \rightleftharpoons \underset{\text{acid}}{NH_4^+(aq)} + \underset{\text{base}}{OH^-(aq)}$$

2. In redox reactions, water reacts with metals and non-metals both.

$$2Na(s) + 2H_2O(l) \longrightarrow 2NaOH(aq) + H_2(g)$$
$$2F_2(g) + 2H_2O(l) \longrightarrow 4H^+(aq) + 4F^-(aq) + O_2(g)$$

3. In **hydrated salts**, water may remain in five types such as coordinated water, hydrogen bonded water, lattice water, clathrate water and zeolite water.

4. A number of compounds such as calcium hydride, calcium phosphide, etc., undergo hydrolysis with water.

Purification of Water

It involves two processes

(i) Removal of suspended impurities

(ii) Destroying the bacteria.

Suspended particles are removed by coagulation with alum followed by filtration. Exposure to sunlight, boiling, chlorination (treatment with liquid Cl_2 or bleaching powder), ozonisation and addition of $CuSO_4$ are some processes which are employed to destroy bacteria.

Soft and Hard Water

The water which produces large amount of lather with soap is known as soft water and which forms a scum with soap is known as hard water.

Types of Hardness of Water

(i) **Temporary hardness** It is due to the presence of bicarbonates of calcium and magnesium.

(ii) **Permanent hardness** It is due to the presence of chlorides and sulphates of calcium and magnesium.

Removal of Temporary Hardness

It can be achieved :

(i) **By boiling** The soluble bicarbonates are converted into insoluble carbonates.

$$Ca(HCO_3)_2 \xrightarrow{\text{Heating}} CaCO_3 \downarrow + H_2O + CO_2 \uparrow$$

$$Mg(HCO_3)_2 \xrightarrow{\text{Heating}} Mg(OH)_2 \downarrow + 2CO_2 \uparrow$$

(ii) **By Clark's process** By adding lime water or milk of lime.

$$M(HCO_3)_2 + 2Ca(OH)_2 \longrightarrow MCO_3 \downarrow + 2H_2O + 2CaCO_3$$

Removal of Permanent Hardness

(i) **By adding washing soda** The calcium or magnesium salts are precipitated as carbonates.

$$MgCl_2 + Na_2CO_3 \longrightarrow MgCO_3 \downarrow + 2NaCl$$

(ii) **By adding caustic soda** The temporary and permanent hardness can be removed by adding caustic soda.

$$CaSO_4 + 2NaOH \longrightarrow Ca(OH)_2 \downarrow + Na_2SO_4$$
$$MgCl_2 + 2NaOH \longrightarrow Mg(OH)_2 \downarrow + 2NaCl$$

(iii) **By adding sodium phosphate** (Na_3PO_4) The phosphates of calcium and magnesium are precipitated.

$$3CaCl_2 + 2Na_3PO_4 \longrightarrow Ca_3(PO_4)_2 \downarrow + 6NaCl$$
$$3CaSO_4 + 2Na_3PO_4 \longrightarrow Ca_3(PO_4)_2 \downarrow + 3Na_2SO_4$$

Similarly, magnesium also precipitate out in the form of magnesium phosphate, $Mg_3(PO_4)_2$.

(iv) **Calgon's process** Calgon is sodium hexa metaphosphate $(Na_6P_6O_{18})$. This calgon when added to hard water form soluble complex.

$$\underset{\text{calgon}}{2CaSO_4 + Na_2[Na_4(PO_3)_6]} \longrightarrow \underset{\text{soluble}}{2Na_2SO_4 + Na_2[Ca_2(PO_3)_6]}$$

Similarly, Mg^{2+} can also precipitate as $Na_2[Mg_2(PO_3)_6]$ and water becomes free from Ca^{2+} and Mg^{2+} ions.

(v) **Permutit process** Permutit is hydrated sodium aluminium silicate $Na_2Al_2Si_2O_8 \cdot xH_2O$. It exchanges its sodium ions for divalent ions Ca^{2+} and Mg^{2+}.

$$Na_2Al_2Si_2O_8 + MCl_2 \longrightarrow MAl_2Si_2O_8 + 2NaCl\,(M = Ca \text{ or } Mg)$$

> Permutit when fully exhausted can be regenerated by treating with 10% solution of sodium chloride. It is most efficient method to get water with zero degree of hardness.

(vi) **By synthetic resins** These are of two types:

(a) **Cation exchange resins** are big molecules containing sulphonic acid group ($-SO_3H$). It is first changed into sodium salt with the general formula $\overset{-}{R}\overset{+}{Na}$. The hard water is passed through it so Ca^{2+} and Mg^{2+} are exchanged and removed.

$$2R^-Na^+ + Ca^{2+} \longrightarrow R_2Ca + 2Na^+$$
$$2R^-Na^+ + Mg^{2+} \longrightarrow R_2Mg + 2Na^+$$

The resins like permutit can be regenerated with a solution of NaCl.

(b) **Anion exchange resins** are also big molecules and can exchange anions. They contain an amino group.

$$R\text{NH}_2 + H_2O \longrightarrow R\overset{+}{\text{NH}}_3\overset{-}{\text{OH}}$$

$$2R\text{NH}_3^+\overset{-}{\text{OH}} + \text{CO}_3^{2-} \rightleftharpoons (R\text{NH}_3^+)_2\text{CO}_3 + 2\text{OH}^-$$

$$2R\text{NH}_3^+\text{OH}^- + \text{Cl}^- \rightleftharpoons R\text{NH}_3^+\text{Cl}^- + \text{OH}^-$$

The water is first passed through cation resins and then through anion resin and pure distilled water is obtained.

Measurement of Degree of Hardness

Degree of hardness is defined as the number of parts of calcium carbonate or equivalent to various calcium and magnesium salts present in one million parts of water by mass. It is expressed in ppm.

$$\text{Degree of hardness (in ppm)} = \frac{\text{wt. of CaCO}_3\text{ (g)}}{\text{wt. of hard water (g)}} \times 10^6$$

The molecular wt. of $Ca(HCO_3)_2$, $Mg(HCO_3)_2$, $CaCl_2$, $MgCl_2$, $CaSO_4$ and $MgSO_4$ is 162, 146, 111, 95, 136 and 120 respectively. The mol. wt. of $CaCO_3$ is 100.

Thus, 162 g $Ca(HCO_3)_2$, 146 g $Mg(HCO_3)_2$, 111 g $CaCl_2$, 95 g $MgCl_2$, 136 g $CaSO_4$ and 120 g $MgSO_4$ are equivalent to 100 g $CaCO_3$.

Hydrogen Peroxide [H_2O_2]

H_2O_2 was discovered by J.L. Thenard in 1818. It is an important compound used in pollution control treatment of domestic and industrial effluents.

Methods of Preparation

(i) $BaO_2 \cdot 8H_2O(s) + H_2SO_4(aq)$

$$\longrightarrow BaSO_4(s) + H_2O_2(aq) + 8H_2O(l)$$

(ii) $2HSO_4^-(aq) \xrightarrow{\text{Electrolysis}} \underset{\text{peroxodisulphate}}{HO_3SOOSO_3H(aq)} \xrightarrow[\text{Hydrolysis}]{H_2O}$

$$2HSO_4^-(aq) + 2H^+(aq) + H_2O_2(aq)$$

(iii) 2-ethylanthraquinol $\underset{H_2/Pd}{\overset{O_2\text{ (air)}}{\rightleftharpoons}}$ H_2O_2 + oxidised product

Physical Properties

(i) In the pure state, H_2O_2 is almost colurless (very pale blue) liquid.

(ii) it is miscible with water in all proportions and forms a hydrate $H_2O_2 \cdot H_2O$.

Strength of Hydrogen Peroxide

The most common method to express the strength of H_2O_2 is in terms of the volume (in mL) of oxygen liberated at NTP by decomposition of 1 mL of that sample of H_2O_2. A solution of H_2O_2 labelled as '10 volume' actually means "1 mL of 3% of a solution of H_2O_2 on decomposition by heat produces 10 mL of oxygen at NTP". Similarly, 1 mL of 20 volume, 30 volume and 100 volume H_2O_2 solution produce 20 mL, 30 mL and 100 mL of oxygen at N.T.P. respectively.

(i) Strength of H_2O_2 in terms of normality

$$\frac{68 \times X}{22.4} = 17 \times N \quad \Rightarrow \quad X = 5.6 \times N$$

where, X is volume strength of H_2O_2.

(ii) % strength $= 17/56 \times$ volume strength

(iii) $X = 11.2 \times$ molarity.

Structure

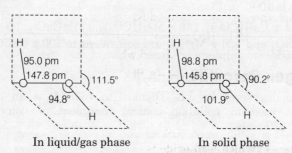

In liquid/gas phase   In solid phase

Chemical Properties of H_2O_2

(i) **Acidic nature** It is weakly acidic in nature and pure hydrogen peroxide turns blue litmus red.

(ii) **Oxidising agent** It acts as a strong oxidising agent in acidic as well as in basic medium.

$$H_2O_2 + 2H^+ + 2e^- \longrightarrow 2H_2O$$

$$H_2O_2 + OH^- + 2e^- \longrightarrow 3OH^-$$

e.g. oxidising action of H_2O_2 is

$$2Cr^{3+} + 3H_2O_2 + 10OH^- \longrightarrow 2CrO_4^{2-} + 8H_2O$$

$$Mn^{2+} + H_2O_2 + 2OH^- \longrightarrow MnO_2 + 2H_2O$$

(iii) **Reducing agent**

(a) In acidic medium

$$2MnO_4^- + 6H^+ + 5H_2O_2 \longrightarrow 2Mn^{2+} + 8H_2O + 5O_2$$

$$Cr_2O_7^{2-} + 8H^+ + 3H_2O_2 \longrightarrow 2Cr^{3+} + 7H_2O + 3O_2$$

(b) In basic medium

$$2K_3[Fe(CN)_6] + 2KOH + H_2O_2 \longrightarrow 2K_4[Fe(CN)_6] + 2H_2O + O_2$$

(iv) **Bleaching properties** Its bleaching action is due to oxidation by atomic oxygen and permanent.

$$H_2O_2 \longrightarrow H_2O + [O]$$

$$dye + [O] \longrightarrow dye \text{ is oxidised and bleached}$$

Storage of Hydrogen Peroxide (H_2O_2)

It is stored in the presence of traces of alcohol, acetanilide or sodium pyrophosphate which slow down the rate of decomposition of hydrogen peroxide.

Test

1. It liberates I_2 from acidified KI.

$$2KI + H_2O_2 \longrightarrow 2KOH + I_2$$

2. Black lead sulphide is turned white by it.

$$PbS + 4H_2O_2 \longrightarrow PbSO_4 + 4H_2O$$

Uses

It is used as a bleaching agent, disinfectant, source of power (90% H_2O_2 as fuel in submarines, rockets and helicopters), in restoration of old paintings in which lead oxide is used as white paint.

30% H_2O_2 is called **perhydrol** which is used as an antiseptic and germicide for washing wounds, teeth and ears. (Volume strength is 100 and molarity is 8.8)

Heavy Water [D_2O]

It was discovered by Urey in 1932. It can be prepared by exhaustive electrolysis of ordinary water using nickel electrodes. It is colourless, odourless, tasteless liquid.

Chemical Reactions of Heavy Water

$$D_2O \longrightarrow
\begin{cases}
\xrightarrow{\text{Na}} \text{NaOD} + \frac{1}{2} D_2 \text{ (sodium deuteroxide)} \\[4pt]
\xrightarrow{\text{SO}_3} D_2SO_4 \text{ (deuterosulphuric acid)} \\[4pt]
\xrightarrow{\text{CaC}_2} Ca(OD)_2 + C_2D_2 \\[4pt]
\xrightarrow{\text{Al}_4C_3} 4Al(OD)_3 + CD_4 \\[4pt]
\xrightarrow{\text{Ca}_3P_2} 3Ca(OD)_2 + 2PD_3
\end{cases}$$

Uses of Heavy Water

It is used

1. in nuclear reactors to slow down the speed of neutrons and is called moderator.
2. as a tracer compound to study the mechanisms of many reactions.

Hydrogen Economy

Hydrogen economy is the use of liquid hydrogen as an alternate source of energy. The technology involves the production, transportation and storage of energy in the form of liquid or gaseous hydrogen. Large scale production of hydrogen can be done by electrolysis of water or by thermochemical reaction cycle. Storage of hydrogen in liquid form can be done in vacuum insulated cryogenic tanks or in a metal or in an alloy like iron-titanium alloy as interstitial hydride. Hydrogen fuel has many advantages over conventional fuels in that it is non-polluting and it liberates large amount of energy on combustion.

Photohydrogen is used to obtain renewable energy from sunlight by using microscopic organism such as bacteria or algae.

18

The s-Block Elements

In the s-block elements, the last electron enters in the s-orbital.

As the s-orbital can accommodate only two electrons, two groups (1 and 2) belong to the s-block.

The general electronic configuration of s-block elements is $ns^{1 \text{ or } 2}$

Alkali Metals [Group-I]

Group-I elements have one electron in their valence shell. They do not occur in the native or free state. These elements are collectively known as alkali metals because their oxides and hydroxides form strong alkalies like NaOH, KOH, etc. Lithium is known as **bridge element**.

General Characteristics of Alkali Metals

(i) **Electronic configuration** [noble gas] ns^1

Element	At. no.	Electronic configuration
Li	3	[He] $2s^1$
Na	11	[Ne] $3s^1$
K	19	[Ar] $4s^1$
Rb	37	[Kr] $5s^1$
Cs	55	[Xe] $6s^1$
Fr	87	[Rn] $7s^1$ (Radioactive)

(ii) **Atomic radii** The alkali metals have the biggest atomic radii in their respective periods.

Atomic radii increases as we go down the group due to the addition of a new shell in each subsequent step.

All of these have bcc lattice with coordination number 8.

(iii) **Ionic radii** Ionic radii of the alkali metals are much smaller than their corresponding metals due to lesser number of shells and contractive effect of the increased nuclear charge.

The ionic radii of all these alkali metal ions go on increasing on moving down the group.

(iv) **Density** These are light metals with low densities. Lithium is the lightest known metal. On moving down the group, density increases from Li to Cs.

This is because, down the group, both the atomic size and atomic mass increases but the effect of increase in atomic mass is more as compared to increase in atomic size.

⌐The density of potassium is lesser than that of sodium because of the ⌐
abnormal increase in size on moving down from Na to K. ⌐

(v) **Melting and boiling points**

(i) The melting and boiling points of alkali metals are quite low and decrease down the group due to weakening of metallic bond.

(ii) Fr is a liquid at room temperature.

(vi) **Softness** These are soft, malleable and ductile solids which can be cut with knife. They possess metallic lustre when freshly cut due to oscillation of electrons.

(vii) **Atomic volume** Atomic volume of alkali metals is the highest in each period and goes on increasing down the group from top to bottom [Li to Cs].

(viii) **Ionisation enthalpy** The first ionisation enthalpy of alkali metals is the lowest amongst the elements in their respective periods and decreases on moving down the group.

The second ionisation enthalpies of all the alkali metals are very high because, by releasing an electron, ions acquire stable noble gas configuration, so removal of second electron is difficult.

(ix) **Electropositive character** Due to low ionisation enthalpies, alkali metals are strongly electropositive or metallic in nature and electropositive nature increases from Li to Cs due to decrease in ionization enthalpy.

(x) **Oxidation state** The alkali metal atoms show only +1 oxidation state, because their unipositive ions attain the stable noble gas configuration.

The alkali metal ions attain noble gas configuration with no unpaired electrons so, they are diamagnetic in nature. Alkali metals however have paramagnetic nature due to one unpaired electron.

(xi) **Hydration of ions** The degree of hydration depends upon the size of the cation. Smaller the size of a cation, greater is its hydration enthalpy. Relative degree of hydration,

$$Li^+ > Na^+ > K^+ > Rb^+ > Cs^+$$

(xii) **Flame colouration** Alkali metals and their salts impart characteristic colours to the flame because the outer electrons get excited to higher energy levels. When the electron return to the original state, it releases visible light of characteristic wavelength which provides a colour to the flame.

Li	Na	K	Rb	Cs
Crimson Red	Yellow	Violet	Red violet	Blue

(xiii)**Photoelectric effect** Due to very low ionisation enthalpy, alkali metals specially 'Cs' exhibit photoelectric effect, (i.e. eject electrons when exposed to light) so it is used in photoelectric cells.

(xiv) **Electrical conductivity** Due to the presence of loosely held valence electrons which are free to move throughout the metal structure, the alkali metals are good conductors of heat and electricity. Electrical conductivity increases from top to bottom in the order

$$Li^+ < Na^+ < K^+ < Rb^+ < Cs^+$$

(xv) **Reducing character** All the alkali metals are good reducing agents due to their low ionisation energies. Their reducing character, follows the order

$$Na < K < Rb < Cs < Li$$

Note : Lithium (Li), exceptionally has highest reducing character in aqueous solution.

Chemical Properties of Alkali Metals

(i) **Action of air** On exposure to moist air, their surface get tarnished due to the formation of their oxides, hydroxides and carbonates.

$$4Na(s) + O_2(g) \longrightarrow 2Na_2O(s)$$
$$Na_2O(g) + H_2O(l) \longrightarrow 2NaOH(s)$$
$$2NaOH(s) + CO_2(g) \longrightarrow Na_2CO_3(s) + H_2O(l)$$

Hence, they are kept under inert liquid like kerosene oil but lithium is kept wrapped in paraffin wax because it floats on the surface of kerosene oil due to its low density.

Note *Fire due to alkali metals is extinguished by* CCl_4.

(ii) **Action of oxygen**

(a) All the alkali metals when heated with oxygen form different types of oxides. e.g. lithium forms lithium oxide (Li_2O), sodium forms sodium peroxide (Na_2O_2), while K, Rb and Cs form superoxides MO_2 (where, M = K, Rb or Cs), along with normal oxides.

⌐The stability of peroxides and superoxides increases as the size of alkali metal increases.⌐

(b) Superoxides are coloured and paramagnetic as these possess three electron bond $\left[\ddot{\overset{\times}{O}} \!\cdot\!\cdot\!\cdot\! \ddot{\overset{..}{O}} \right]^-$ where one unpaired electron is present.

(c) All oxides, peroxides and superoxides are basic in nature.

Basic strength of oxides increases in the order
$$Li_2O < Na_2O < K_2O < Cs_2O$$
Na_2O_2 acquires yellow colour due to the presence of superoxides as an impurity.

KO_2 (potassium superoxide) is used as a source of oxygen in submarines, space shuttles and in emergency breathing apparatus such as oxygen masks.

(iii) **Action of water or compounds containing acidic hydrogen**
$$2M + 2H_2O \longrightarrow 2MOH + H_2$$
(where, M = Li, Na, K, Rb, and Cs)

The reactivity order with water is
$$Li < Na < K < Rb < Cs$$

This is due to increase in electropositive character in the same order. KOH is stronger base than NaOH.

LiOH is used to remove carbon dioxide from exhaled air in confined quarters like submarines and space vehicles.

(iv) **Action of hydrogen** All the alkali metals react with hydrogen at 673 K to form crystalline ionic hydrides of the general formula M^+H^-.

$$2M + H_2 \longrightarrow 2MH \quad (\text{where, } M = \text{Li, Na, K, Rb, Cs})$$

The reactivity of alkali metals towards hydrogen is

$$\text{Li} > \text{Na} > \text{K} > \text{Rb} > \text{Cs}.$$

(v) **Reaction with halogens** Alkali metals combine readily with halogens to form ionic halides M^+X^- (with the exception of some lithium halides).

$$2M + X_2 \longrightarrow 2M^+X^-$$

$$(\text{where, } M = \text{Li, Na, K etc., and } X = \text{F, Cl, Br, I})$$

The reactivity of alkali metals towards a particular halogen increases in the order

$$\text{Li} < \text{Na} < \text{K} < \text{Rb} < \text{Cs}$$

For a given halide, ionic character increases as the size of metal ion increases.

$$\text{Li}X > \text{Na}X < \text{K}X < \text{Rb}X < \text{Cs}X$$

All alkali metal halides except LiF, are freely soluble in water (LiF is soluble in non-polar solvents because it has strong covalent bond).

LiCl is more covalent than KCl due to smaller size of Li.

Bigger the anion, larger is its polarisability. Hence, the covalent character follows the order

$$\text{LiI} > \text{LiBr} > \text{LiCl} > \text{LiF}$$

(vi) **Solubility in liquid ammonia** All alkali metals dissolve in liquid ammonia giving deep blue solution due to formation of ammoniated metal cations and ammoniated electrons in the solution.

$$M + (x + y)\,\text{NH}_3 \longrightarrow \underset{\text{ammoniated cation}}{[M(\text{NH}_3)_x]^+} + \underset{\text{ammoniated electron}}{[e(\text{NH}_3)_y]^-}$$

The blue colour is due to the excitation of ammoniated electron to higher energy levels and the absorption of photons occurs in the red region of the spectrum. This solution is highly conducting and paramagnetic because of the presence of ammoniated electrons and ammoniated cations.

(vii) **Nature of carbonates and bicarbonates** Li_2CO_3 is unstable towards heat.

$$\text{Li}_2\text{CO}_3 \xrightarrow{\Delta} \text{Li}_2\text{O} + \text{CO}_2$$

The thermal stability of carbonates increases on moving down the group as

$$Li_2CO_3 < Na_2CO_3 < K_2CO_3 < Rb_2CO_3 < Cs_2CO_3$$

All the bicarbonates (except $LiHCO_3$ which exists in solution) exist as solids and on heating form carbonates.

$$2NaHCO_3 \xrightarrow{\Delta} Na_2CO_3 + CO_2 + H_2O$$

The solubility of the carbonates and bicarbonates increases on moving down the group due to decrease in lattice enthalpies. Thus, the order is

$$LiHCO_3 < NaHCO_3 < KHCO_3 < RbHCO_3 < CsHCO_3$$

A mixture of Na_2CO_3 and K_2CO_3 is known as **fusion mixture**. K_2CO_3 is known as **pearl ash**.

(viii) **Nature of nitrates** $LiNO_3$ on heating decomposes to give NO_2 and O_2, while the nitrates of the other alkali metals decompose on heating and give nitrites and O_2.

$$4LiNO_3 \xrightarrow{\Delta} 2Li_2O + 4NO_2 + O_2$$

$$2NaNO_3 \xrightarrow{\Delta} 2NaNO_2 + O_2$$

$NaNO_3$ is called **chile saltpeter** and KNO_3 is called **Indian saltpeter**.

(ix) **Nature of sulphates** Li_2SO_4 is insoluble in water whereas the other sulphates, i.e. Na_2SO_4, K_2SO_4 are soluble in water.

$Na_2SO_4 \cdot 10H_2O$ is called **Glauber's salt**.

Uses of Alkali Metals

(i) Lithium is used for making alloys, in thermonuclear reactions, in battaries etc.

(ii) Sodium can be used to make alloys, as coolant in fast-breeder-nuclear reactors as reductant, in sodium vapour lamp etc.

(iii) Potassium play a vital role in biological system and can be used for synthesis of may fertiliser. It is also a good aborbent of CO_2.

Anomalous Behaviour of Lithium

Lithium shows anomalous behaviour due to the following reasons :

1. It has the smallest size in its group.
2. It has very high ionization enthalpy and highest electronegativity in the group.

3. Absence of d-orbitals in its valence shell.

As a result, it differs from the other alkali metals in the following properties :

 (i) Lithium is harder than other alkali metals, due to strong metallic bond.

 (ii) Lithium combines with O_2 to form lithium monoxide, Li_2O whereas other alkali metals form peroxides (M_2O_2) and superoxides (MO_2).

(iii) Lithium, unlike the other alkali metals, reacts with nitrogen to form the nitride.

$$6Li + N_2 \longrightarrow \underset{\text{Lithium nitride}}{2Li_3N}$$

(iv) Li_2CO_3, LiF and lithium phosphate are insoluble in water while the corresponding salts of other alkali metals are soluble in water.

 (v) Li_2CO_3 decomposes on heating to evolve CO_2, whereas other alkali metal carbonates do not.

(vi) Lithium nitrate on heating evolves O_2 and NO_2 and forms Li_2O while other alkali metal nitrates on heating form their respective nitrites.

Diagonal Relationship

Lithium shows diagonal resemblance with magnesium [the element of group 2] and this resemblance is due to similar polarising power, i.e. $\left[\dfrac{\text{ionic charge}}{\text{ionic radius}}\right]$ of both these elements.

	Group 1	Group 2	Group 13	Group 14
2nd period	Li	Be	B	C
3rd period	Na	Mg	Al	Si

Lithium resembles magnesium in the following respects :

1. The atomic radius of lithium is 1.31 Å while that of magnesium is 1.34 Å.

2. The ionic radius of Li^+ ion is 0.60 Å, which is very close to that of Mg^{2+} ion (0.65 Å).

3. Lithium (1.0) and magnesium (1.2) have almost similar electronegativities.

4. Both Li and Mg are hard metals.

5. LiF is partially soluble in water like MgF_2.

6. Both combine with O_2 to form monoxides, e.g. Li_2O and MgO.

7. Both $LiOH$ and $Mg(OH)_2$ are weak bases.

8. Both $LiCl$ and $MgCl_2$ are predominantly covalent.

9. Both Li and Mg combine with N_2 to form their respective nitrides, Li_3N and Mg_3N_2.

10. Both lithium and magnesium nitrates on heating evolve NO_2 and O_2 leaving behind their oxides.

Compounds of Sodium

1. Sodium Chloride, Common Salt or Table Salt [NaCl]

Sea water contains 2.7 to 2.9% by mass of the salt. Sodium chloride is obtained by evaporation of sea water but due to the presence of impurities like $CaCl_2$ and $MgCl_2$, it has deliquescent nature. It is purified by passing HCl gas through the impure saturated solution of NaCl and due to common ion effect, pure NaCl gets precipitated. 28% NaCl solution is called **brine**.

Uses of Sodium Chloride (NaCl)

(i) As enhance of flavour and as preservative for food.

(ii) In preparation of many compounds like Na_2CO_3, NaOH, Na_2O_2, $NaHCO_3$ etc.

(iii) To clear the ice on high-ways, which blocks the roads during winter.

(iv) As physiological solution (0.9% NaCl in water), as it is iso-osmotic with blood-plasma.

2. Sodium Hydroxide or Caustic Soda [NaOH] Methods of Preparation

(i) A 10% solution of Na_2CO_3 is treated with milk of lime (Causticizing process).

$$Na_2CO_3 + Ca(OH)_2 \longrightarrow CaCO_3 \downarrow + 2NaOH$$

(ii) Electrolytic process involves Nelson cell and Castner-Kellner cell.

A brine solution is electrolysed using a mercury cathode and a carbon anode. Sodium metal discharged at the cathode combines with Hg to form Na-amalgam. Chlorine gas is evolved at the anode.

The amalgam is treated with water to give sodium hydroxide and hydrogen gas.

$$2Na\text{-}Hg + 2H_2O \longrightarrow 2NaOH + 2Hg + H_2$$

Physical Properties

Sodium hydroxide is a white translucent solid. It is readily soluble in water. Crystals of NaOH are deliquescent.

Chemical Properties

1. It is a hygroscopic, deliquescent white solid, absorbs CO_2 and moisture from the atmosphere.

$$2NaOH + CO_2 \longrightarrow Na_2CO_3 + H_2O$$

2. **Reaction with salts**

Formation of insoluble hydroxides, e.g.

$$FeCl_3 + 3NaOH \longrightarrow Fe(OH)_3 \downarrow + 3NaCl$$

Formation of unstable hydroxides, e.g.

$$2AgNO_3 + 2NaOH \longrightarrow 2NaNO_3 + 2AgOH$$

$$2AgOH \longrightarrow \underset{\text{brown}}{Ag_2O\downarrow + H_2O}$$

3. **Reaction with metals**

Less electropositive metals like Zn, Al and Sn, etc give H_2 gas with NaOH.

$$Zn + 2NaOH \longrightarrow Na_2ZnO_2 + H_2 \uparrow$$

4. **Reaction with sand**

$$2NaOH + SiO_2 \longrightarrow \underset{\text{sodium silicate (glass)}}{Na_2SiO_3} + H_2O$$

5. A mixture of caustic soda (NaOH) and quicklime (CaO) is known as **sodalime**.

Uses of Sodium Hydroxide (NaOH)

(i) It is used as a reagent in laboratory.

(ii) It is used in manufacture of soap, paper, dyes, fat and oils etc.

(iii) It is also used to manufacture many chemical compounds like sodium hypochlorite, sodium chlorate etc.

(iv) It can be used in petrol-refining and for purification buxite-ore (leading of Al_2O_3).

3. Sodium Carbonate or Washing Soda ($Na_2CO_3 \cdot 10H_2O$)

Solvay process

CO_2 gas is passed through a brine solution saturated with NH_3.

$$2NH_3 + H_2O + CO_2 \longrightarrow (NH_4)_2CO_3$$

$$(NH_4)_2CO_3 + H_2O + CO_2 \longrightarrow 2NH_4(HCO_3)$$

$$NH_4(HCO_3) + NaCl \longrightarrow NaHCO_3 + NH_4Cl$$

Sodium bicarbonate is filtered and dried. It is ignited to give sodium carbonate.

$$2NaHCO_3 \xrightarrow{\Delta} Na_2CO_3 + CO_2 + H_2O$$

Properties

1. Sodium carbonate crystallises from water as decahydrate which effloresces on exposure to dry air forming monohydrate which on heating change to anhydrous salt (**soda-ash**).

$$Na_2CO_3 \cdot 10H_2O \xrightarrow[375\ K]{dry\ air} Na_2CO_3 \cdot H_2O + 9H_2O$$

$$Na_2CO_3 \cdot H_2O \xrightarrow{\Delta} \underset{soda\ ash}{Na_2CO_3 + H_2O}$$

2. On hydrolysis, it forms an alkaline solution.

$$Na_2CO_3 + 2H_2O \longrightarrow \underset{weak\ acid}{H_2CO_3} + \underset{strong\ base}{2NaOH}$$

or $\qquad CO_3^{2-} + 2H_2O \longrightarrow H_2CO_3 + 2OH^-$

3. Aqueous sodium carbonate solution react with CO_2 gas and forms sodium bicarbonate.

$$Na_2CO_3 + H_2O + CO_2 \longrightarrow 2NaHCO_3$$

Uses

1. It is used in water softening, laundering and cleaning.

2. It is used in paper, paints and textile industries.

4. Sodium Bicarbonate or Baking Soda (NaHCO$_3$)

Preparation

It is obtained as an intermediate product in Solvay process.

Properties

1. **Heating effect** : It gives CO_2 and Na_2CO_3 on heating.

$$2NaHCO_3 \xrightarrow{\Delta} Na_2CO_3 + CO_2\uparrow + H_2O$$

2. In aqueous medium, it is alkaline due to anionic hydrolysis.

$$NaHCO_3 + H_2O \longrightarrow NaOH + H_2CO_3$$

Uses

1. It is used as a constituent of baking powder which is a mixture of sodium bicarbonate, starch and potassium bitartrate or cream of tartar and in medicine to remove acidity of the stomach (as antacid).
2. $NaHCO_3$ is a mild antiseptic for skin infections.
3. It is used in fire extinguisher.

5. Microcosmic Salts ($Na(NH_4)HPO_4 \cdot 4H_2O$)

Preparation

It is prepared by dissolving Na_2HPO_4 and NH_4Cl in the molecular proportions in hot water followed by crystallisation.

$$Na_2HPO_4 + NH_4Cl \longrightarrow Na(NH_4)HPO_4 + NaCl$$
disodium hydrogen
phosphate

Properties

On heating, it forms a transparent glassy bead of metaphosphate, which gives coloured beads of orthophosphates when heated with coloured salts like that of transition metal ions($Cu^{2+}, Fe^{2+}, Mn^{2+}, Ni^{2+}, Co^{2+}$). This test is called **microcosmic bead test**.

$$Na(NH_4)HPO_4 \longrightarrow NH_3 + H_2O + NaPO_3$$
sodium metaphosphate

$$CuSO_4 \longrightarrow CuO + SO_3$$
$$CuO + NaPO_3 \longrightarrow CuNaPO_4$$
(blue bead)

It is especially used to detect silica which being insoluble in $NaPO_3$ and gives a cloudy bead.

Alkaline Earth Metals [Group-II]

Group-II elements are Be, Mg, Ca, Sr, Ba and Ra, which have two electrons in their valence shell. These are commonly called alkaline earth metals because their oxides are alkaline in nature and are found in earth's crust.

Mg is present in chlorophyll and Ca is present in bones as calcium phosphate.

General Characteristics of Alkaline Earth Metals

(i) **Electronic configuration** [noble gas] ns^2

Element	At. no.	Electronic configuration
Be	4	[He] $2s^2$
Mg	12	[Ne] $3s^2$
Ca	20	[Ar] $4s^2$
Sr	38	[Kr] $5s^2$
Ba	56	[Xe] $6s^2$
Ra	88	[Rn] $7s^2$ (Radioactive)

(ii) **Atomic radii and ionic radii** The atomic radii and ionic radii of these elements are quite large but smaller than those of the corresponding alkali metals, due to increased nuclear charge of these elements. The atomic as well as ionic radii goes on increasing down the group due to the gradual addition of extra energy levels.

(iii) **Density** These are much denser than alkali metals because of their smaller size and greater nuclear charge and mass. The density, however, first decreases from Be to Ca and then steadily increases from Ca to Ra due to difference in type of crystal structure.

(iv) **Melting and boiling points** These metals have higher melting and boiling points than those of alkali metals because of greater number of bonding electrons.

The melting and boiling points decrease on moving down the group with the exception of magnesium.

(v) **Metallic properties** These are silvery white metals, soft in nature but harder than alkali metals due to stronger metallic bonding.

(vi) **Ionization enthalpy** The first ionisation enthalpy of alkaline earth metals are higher than those of the corresponding alkali metals due to smaller size and ns^2 configuration.

The second ionisation enthalpy values are higher than their first ionisation enthalpy values but much lower than the second ionisation enthalpy values of alkali metals.

On moving down the group, due to increase in atomic size, the magnitude of ionisation enthalpy decreases.

(vii) **Electropositive character** These are strong electropositive elements due to their large size and comparatively low ionisation enthalpy.

On moving down the group, the electropositive character increases due to increase in atomic radii and decrease in ionisation enthalpy.

(viii) **Oxidation state** Alkaline earth metals uniformly show an oxidation state of +2.

In the solid state, the dipositive ions (M^{2+}) form strong lattices due to their small size and high charge (i.e. high lattice enthalpy).

⌐ In the aqueous solution, the M^{2+} cations are strongly hydrated due to their small size and high charge. The hydration energy released by the M^{2+} cation is very high. ⌐

(ix) **Flame colouration** Alkaline earth metal salts impart characteristic colours to the flame.

As we move down the group from Ca to Ba, the ionisation enthalpy decreases, hence the energy or the frequency of the emitted light increases. Thus,

Ca	Sr	Ba	Ra
brick red	crimson red	apple green	crimson

Be and Mg because of their high ionisation energies, do not impart any characteristic colour to the flame.

(x) **Crystal lattice** Be and Mg crystallises in hcp, Ca and Sr in ccp and Ba in bcc lattice.

Chemical Properties of Alkaline Earth Metals

Alkaline earth metals are quite reactive due to their low ionisation energies but less reactive than alkali metals. Reactivity of the group-2 elements increases on moving down the group because their ionisation enthalpy decreases.

(i) **Reaction with water** Group-2 elements are less reactive with water as compared to alkali metals.

$$M + 2H_2O \longrightarrow M(OH)_2 + H_2 \quad \text{(where, } M = \text{Mg, Ca, Sr or Ba)}$$

Be does not react even with boiling water and Ba react vigorously even with cold water. Thus, increasing order of reactivity with water is

$$\text{Mg} < \text{Ca} < \text{Sr} < \text{Ba}$$

A suspension of $Mg(OH)_2$ in water is called milk of magnesia.

⌐ $Ca(OH)_2$ solution (lime water) and $Ba(OH)_2$ solution (baryta) are used for the detection of CO_2. ⌐

(ii) **Reaction with oxygen** The affinity towards oxygen increases down the group. Thus, Be, Mg and Ca when heated with O_2 form monoxides while Sr, Ba and Ra form peroxides.

$$2M + O_2 \xrightarrow{\Delta} \underset{\text{metal oxide}}{2MO} \qquad (M = \text{Be, Mg, Ca})$$

$$M + O_2 \xrightarrow{\Delta} \underset{\text{metal peroxide}}{MO_2} \qquad (M = \text{Ba, Sr})$$

(iii) **Reaction with acids** Alkaline earth metals except Be, displace H_2 from acids.

$$M + H_2SO_4 \longrightarrow MSO_4 + H_2 \uparrow$$
$$(\text{where, } M = \text{Mg, Ca, Sr, Ba})$$

Reactivity increases on moving down the group from Mg to Ba. Only Mg displaces H_2 from a very dilute HNO_3.

(iv) **Reaction with hydrogen** Except Be, all other elements of group–2 combine with hydrogen on heating to form hydride (MH_2).

$$M + H_2 \longrightarrow MH_2$$

BeH_2 and MgH_2 are covalent and polymeric whereas the hydrides of Ca, Sr and Ba are ionic in nature.

(v) **Reaction with halogens** All the elements of group–2 combine with halogens at high temperature, forming their corresponding halides (MX_2).

$$M + X_2 \xrightarrow{\Delta} MX_2$$

Beryllium halides (BeF_2, $BeCl_2$, etc) are covalent, hygroscopic and fume in air due to hydrolysis, $BeCl_2$ exists as a dimer. The halides of other alkaline earth metals are fairly ionic and this character increases as the size of the metal increases.

The halides are soluble in water and their solubility decreases in the order

$$MgX_2 > CaX_2 > SrX_2 > BaX_2$$

(vi) **Reaction with nitrogen** These metals react with nitrogen to form nitrides of the types M_3N_2 which are hydrolysed with water to evolve NH_3.

$$3M + N_2 \longrightarrow M_3N_2$$
$$M_3N_2 + 6H_2O \longrightarrow 3M(OH)_2 + 2NH_3$$

(vii) **Reaction with carbon** These metals when heated with carbon, form their respective carbides of the general formula MC_2 (except Be).

$$M + 2C \xrightarrow{\Delta} MC_2$$

(where, M = Mg, Ca, Sr or Ba)

All these carbides are ionic in nature and react with H_2O to form acetylene (except Be_2C which gives methane).

$$CaC_2 + 2H_2O \longrightarrow Ca(OH)_2 + HC\equiv CH$$

(viii) **Reducing character** All the alkaline earth metals are strong reducing agents because of their lower electrode potentials but these are weaker than the corresponding alkali metals.

As we move down the group from Be to Ra, the reducing character increases due to decrease in ionisation enthalpy.

(ix) **Solubility in liquid ammonia** Like alkali metals, these metals also dissolve in liquid ammonia by giving coloured solutions.

$$M + (x + y)NH_3 \longrightarrow [M(NH_3)_x]^{2+} + 2[e(NH_3)_y]^-$$

The tendency to form ammoniates decreases with increase in size of the metal atom (i.e. on moving down the group).

(x) **Complex formation** It is favoured in case of alkaline earth metals because of their small sizes as compared to the alkali metals. Both Mg^{2+} and Ca^{2+} form six membered coordinate complexes with EDTA (ethylenediamminetetracetic acid) which are used to determine the hardness of water.

(xi) **Basic strength of oxides and hydroxides** BeO and $Be(OH)_2$ are amphoteric while the oxides and hydroxides of other alkaline earth metals are basic. The basic strength, however, increases from Be to Ba.

⌐ The basic character of hydroxides of group–2 elements is lesser than those of group-1 hydroxides because of the larger size of later than former group. ⌐

(xii) **Thermal stability and nature of bicarbonates and carbonates** Bicarbonates of these metals do not exist in solid state but are known in solution only. When these solutions are heated, these get decomposed to evolve CO_2.

$$M(HCO_3)_2 \xrightarrow{\Delta} MCO_3 + CO_2\uparrow + H_2O$$

The carbonates of alkaline earth metals can be regarded as salts of weak carbonic acid (H_2CO_3) and metal hydroxide, $M(OH)_2$. The carbonates decompose on heating forming metal oxide and CO_2.

$$MCO_3 \xrightarrow{\Delta} MO + CO_2 \uparrow$$

Anomalous Behaviour of Beryllium

Beryllium, differs from the rest of the members of its group due to the following reasons:

  (i) Beryllium has a small atomic and ionic size.
 (ii) It has no vacant d-orbitals.
(iii) It has a high charge density.

The points of difference are:

  (i) **Hardness** Beryllium is denser and harder than other members of the family.

 (ii) **Melting point** Beryllium has high melting point i.e. 1551 K while that of magnesium is 924 K.

(iii) **Ionisation potential** It has higher ionisation potential as compared to the rest of the members of this group.

(iv) **Reaction with acids** Due to lower oxidation potential of Be, it does not liberate hydrogen from acids readily.

 (v) **Reaction with water** Beryllium does not react with water even at higher temperature while other members of the family liberates hydrogen by reacting with water at room temperature.

(vi) **Amphoteric in character** Oxide (BeO) and hydroxide $[Be(OH)_2]$ of beryllium are amphoteric in character and dissolve in acids to form salt and beryllate in alkali.

(vii) **Formation of carbides** Beryllium when heated with carbon form Be_2C which on reaction with water gives methane. While other members of the group form ionic carbide MC_2 (acetylide) which on reaction with water evolve acetylene.

Diagonal Relationship Between Be and Al

The main identical physical and chemical properties of Be with aluminium are given below

	Group 1	Group 2	Group 13	Group 14
2nd period	Li	Be	B	C
3rd period	Na	Mg	Al	Si

(i) **Action of air** Both the metals are stable in air.

(ii) **Action with water** Be and Al do not decompose water even at 373 K. It is due to their less electropositive character.

(iii) **Electropositive character** Beryllium like aluminium is less electropositive due to their small ionic radii.

(iv) **Complex formation** Beryllium and aluminium form a number of complexes. Both form fluoro complex anions like BeF_4^{2-} and AlF_6^{3-} in solution.

(v) **Reaction with alkali** Beryllium and aluminium react with sodium hydroxide liberating hydrogen.

$$Be + 2NaOH \longrightarrow \underset{\text{sodium beryllate}}{Na_2BeO_2} + H_2 \uparrow$$

$$Al + 2NaOH + 2H_2O \longrightarrow \underset{\text{sodium metaaluminate}}{2NaAlO_2} + 3H_2 \uparrow$$

(vi) **Passive nature** Both these metals are rendered passive on reaction with concentrated nitric acid due to the formation of oxide layer on their surfaces.

(vii) **Amphoteric character of oxides** Oxides of both Be and Al are amphoteric in nature. So, they get dissolve in both, acids as well as in alkalies.

Uses of Alkaline Earth Metals and Their Compounds

1. Beryllium (Be) is used in corrosion resistant alloys.

2. Alloy of Mg with aluminium is used as structural material because of its high strength, low density and ease in machining.

3. Strontium carbonate is used for the manufacture of glass for colour TV picture tubes.

4. Hydrated calcium chloride, $CaCl_2 \cdot 6H_2O$ is widely used for melting ice on roads, particularly in very cold countries, because a 30% eutectic mixture of $CaCl_2/H_2O$ freezes at $-55°C$ as compared with $NaCl/H_2O$ at $-18°C$.

5. Barium sulphate being insoluble in water and opaque to X-rays, is used under the name barium meal to scan the X-ray of the human digestive system.

6. Magnesium is present in chlorophyll, a green pigment in plant, essential for photosynthesis.

7. Anhydrous $CaCl_2$ because of its hygroscopic nature is a good drying agent but it cannot be used to dry alcohols/ammonia/ amines.

8. Magnesium perchlorate $Mg(ClO_4)_2$ is used as a drying agent under the name anhydrone.

Note *Kidney stones generally consist of calcium oxalate, $CaC_2O_4 \cdot H_2O$ which dissolves in dilute strong acids but remains insoluble in bases.*

Compounds of Calcium

1. Calcium Oxide or Quick Lime or Lime [CaO]

Preparation

By the thermal decomposition of calcium carbonate.

$$CaCO_3 \xrightarrow{\text{1070-1270 K}} CaO + CO_2 \uparrow$$

Properties

1. It is a basic oxide.

2. Its aqueous suspension is known as **slaked lime**.

$$\underset{\text{burnt lime}}{CaO} + H_2 \xrightarrow{\text{hissing sound}} \underset{\text{slaked lime}}{Ca(OH)_2} + Heat$$

3. On heating with ammonium salts, it gives ammonia.

$$CaO + 2NH_4Cl \xrightarrow{\Delta} CaCl_2 + 2NH_3 + H_2O$$

4. It reacts with carbon to form calcium carbide.

$$CaO + 3C \longrightarrow \underset{\text{calcium carbide}}{CaC_2} + CO$$

5. It is used as basic flux, for removing hardness of water, for preparing mortar (CaO + sand + water).

2. Calcium Hydroxide or Slaked Lime or Lime Water [Ca(OH)$_2$]

Preparation

By dissolving quicklime in water.

$$CaO + H_2O \longrightarrow Ca(OH)_2; \qquad \Delta H = -63\,kJ$$

Properties

(i) Its suspension in water is known as milk of lime.

(ii) It gives $CaCO_3$ (milky) and then $Ca(HCO_3)_2$ with CO_2.

$$\underset{\text{lime water}}{Ca(OH)_2} + CO_2 \longrightarrow \underset{\text{milkiness}}{CaCO_3} + H_2O$$

$$CaCO_3 + H_2O + \underset{\text{excess}}{CO_2} \longrightarrow \underset{\text{soluble}}{Ca(HCO_3)_2}$$

(iii) It reacts with Cl_2 to give bleaching powder, $CaOCl_2$.

$$Ca(OH)_2 + Cl_2 \longrightarrow CaOCl_2 + H_2O$$

3. Calcium Carbonate or Limestone or Marble or Chalk [$CaCO_3$]

Preparation By passing CO_2 through lime water.

$$Ca(OH)_2 + CO_2 \longrightarrow CaCO_3{\downarrow} + H_2O$$

Properties It is insoluble in H_2O but dissolves in the presence of CO_2, due to the formation of calcium bicarbonate.

$$\underset{\text{insoluble}}{CaCO_3} + H_2O + CO_2 \longrightarrow \underset{\text{soluble}}{Ca(HCO_3)_2}$$

4. Gypsum, Calcium Sulphate Dihydrate ($CaSO_4 \cdot 2H_2O$)

It is also known as alabaster.

On heating at 390 K, it gives plaster of Paris.

It is added to cement to slow down its rate of setting.

5. Plaster of Paris or Calcium Sulphate Hemihydrate ($CaSO_4 \cdot \frac{1}{2}H_2O$)

When it is mixed with water, it forms first a plastic mass which sets into a solid mass with slight expansion due to dehydration and its reconversion into gypsum. It is obtained when gypsum is heated at 393 K.

$$CaSO_4 \cdot 2H_2O \longrightarrow CaSO_4 \cdot \frac{1}{2}H_2O + \frac{3}{2}H_2O$$

Above 393 K, no water of crystallization is left and anhydrous calcium sulphate is obtained. It is known as **dead burnt plaster**.

6. Bleaching Powder ($CaOCl_2$)

It is also called calcium chloro hypochlorite or chloride of lime.

Preparation

$$Ca(OH)_2 + Cl_2 \longrightarrow CaOCl_2 + H_2O$$

Properties

(i) Its aqueous solution gives Ca^{2+}, Cl^- and OCl^- ions.

(ii) With limited quantity of dil H_2SO_4, it gives nascent oxygen which is responsible for its oxidising and bleaching action.

$$2CaOCl_2 + H_2SO_4 \longrightarrow CaCl_2 + CaSO_4 + 2HClO$$
$$HClO \longrightarrow HCl + [O]$$

(iii) With excess of dil H_2SO_4 (or CO_2), it forms Cl_2, which is known as **available chlorine.**

$$CaOCl_2 + H_2SO_4 \longrightarrow CaSO_4 + H_2O + Cl_2\uparrow$$
$$CaOCl_2 + CO_2 \longrightarrow CaCO_3 + Cl_2$$

The average percentage of **available chlorine is 35-40%.** Theoretically it should be 49%, which diminishes on keeping the powder due to following change

$$6CaOCl_2 \longrightarrow 5CaCl_2 + Ca(ClO_3)_2$$

Uses It is used for bleaching, as disinfectant and germicide in sterlisation of water, for making wool unshrinkable and in the manufacture of chloroform.

7. Cement

Cement is an important building material. It is a product obtained by combining materials such as limestone (provides lime and clay provides alumina and silica, SiO_2 along with the oxides of iron and magnesium.) The average composition of portland cement is

CaO, 50-60%; SiO_2, 20-25%; Al_2O_3, 5-10%; MgO, 2-3%; Fe_2O_3, 1-2% and SO_3, 1-2%.

A mixture of lime (CaO) and sand in the ratio 1 : 3 with enough water to make a thick paste is called **mortar.**

By ash, a waste product of steel industry, has properties similar to cement and can be added to cement to reduce its cost without affecting its quality.

19

The *p*-Block Elements

In *p*-block elements, the last electron enters in the outermost *p*-orbital. There are six groups of *p*-block elements in the Periodic Table, numbering from 13 to 18. Their valence shell electronic configuration is ns^2np^{1-6} (except for He).

Group 13

It is also called boron family. It includes B, Al, Ga, In, Tl, Al is the most abundant metal and third most abundant element in the earth's crust.

General Physical Properties of Group 13 Elements

(i) **Electronic configuration** Their valence shell electronic configuration is ns^2np^1.

Element	Atomic number	Electronic configuration
Boron (B)	5	[He] $2s^2, 2p^1$
Aluminium (Al)	13	[Ne] $3s^2, 3p^1$
Gallium(Ga)	31	[Ar] $3d^{10}, 4s^2 4p^1$
Indium (In)	49	[Kr] $4d^{10}, 5s^2 5p^1$
Thallium (Tl)	81	[Xe] $4f^{14}, 5d^{10}, 6s^2 6p^1$

(ii) **Atomic radii and ionic radii** Group 13 elements have smaller size than those of alkaline earth metals due to greater effective nuclear charge, Z_{eff}.

Atomic radii increases on moving down the group with an anomaly at gallium (Ga). Unexpected decrease in the atomic size of Ga is due to the presence of electrons in *d*-orbitals which do not screen the attraction of nucleus effectively.

In general, the ionic radii regularly increases from B^{3+} to Tl^{3+}.

(iii) **Density** It increases regularly on moving down the group from B to Tl.

(iv) **Melting and boiling points** Melting point and boiling point of group 13 elements are much higher than those of group 2 elements. The melting point decreases from B to Ga and then increases, due to structural changes in the elements.

⌐ Boron has a very high melting point (2180°C) because of its three dimensional structure in which B atoms are held together by strong covalent bonds. ⌐

Low melting point (303 K) of Ga is due to the fact that it consists of Ga_2 molecules, and Ga remains liquid upto 2276 K. Hence, it is used in high temperature thermometer.

(v) **Ionisation enthalpy** (IE) The first ionisation enthalpy values of group 13 elements are lower than the corresponding alkaline earth metals, due to the fact that removal of electron is easy. [$ns^2 np^1$ configuration]. The ionisation energy increases as expected $IE_1 < IE_2 < IE_3$. The sum of Ist three ionisation energies for each of the element is very high.

On moving down the group, IE decreases from B to Al, but the next element Ga has slightly higher ionisation enthalpy than Al due to the poor shielding of intervening d-electrons. It again decreases in In and then increases in the last element Tl.

(vi) **Oxidation states** B and Al show an oxidation state of +3 only while Ga, In and Tl exhibit oxidation states of both +1 and +3. As we move down in the group 13, due to **inert pair effect**, the tendency to exhibit +3 oxidation state decreases and the tendency to attain +1 oxidation state increases.

Stability of +1 oxidation state follows the order (Al < Ga < In < Tl).

Inert pair effect is reluctance of the s-electrons of the valence shell to take part in bonding. It occurs due to poor shielding of the ns^2-electrons by the intervening d and f-electrons. It increases down the group and thus, the lower elements of the group exhibit lower oxidation states.

(vii) **Electropositive** (metallic) **character** These elements are less electropositive than the alkaline earth metals due to their smaller size and higher ionisation enthalpies.

On moving down the group, the electropositive character first increases from B to Al and then decreases from Ga to Tl, due to the presence of d and f-orbitals which causes poor shielding.

(viii) **Reducing character** It decreases down the group from Al to Tl because of the increase in electrode potential value for M^{3+}/M. Therefore, it follows the order

$$Al > Ga > In > Tl$$

(ix) **Complex formation** Due to their smaller size and greater charge, these elements have greater tendency to form complexes than the s-block elements.

(x) **Nature of compounds** The tendency of the formation of ionic compounds increases from B to Tl. Boron forms only covalent compounds whereas Al can form both covalent as well as ionic compounds. Gallium forms mainly ionic compounds, although anhydrous $GaCl_3$ is covalent.

Chemical Properties of 13 Group Elements

(i) **Action of air** Crystalline boron is unreactive whereas amorphous boron is reactive. It reacts with air at 700°C as follows

$$4B + 3O_2 \xrightarrow{\Delta} 2B_2O_3 \text{ (At high temperature)}$$

Al is stable in air due to the formation of protective oxide film.

$$4Al + 3O_2 \longrightarrow 2Al_2O_3$$

Thallium is more reactive than Ga and In due to the formation of unipositive ion, Tl^+.

$$4Tl + O_2 \longrightarrow 2Tl_2O$$

(ii) **Reaction with nitrogen**

$$2B + N_2 \xrightarrow{\Delta} \underset{\text{Boron nitride}}{2BN}$$

$$2Al + N_2 \xrightarrow{\Delta} \underset{\text{Aluminium nitride}}{2AlN}$$

(iii) **Action of water** Both B and Al do not react with water but amalgamated aluminium reacts with H_2O evolving H_2.

$$2Al(Hg) + 6H_2O \longrightarrow 2Al(OH)_3 + 3H_2 + 2Hg$$

Ga and In do not react with pure cold or hot water but Tl forms an oxide layer on the surface.

(iv) **Reaction with alkalies and acids** Boron dissolves in alkalies and gives sodium borates.

$$2B + 6NaOH \xrightarrow{\text{Fusion}} \underset{\text{Sodium borates}}{2Na_3BO_3 + 3H_2}$$

Aluminium also reacts with alkali and liberates hydrogen.

$$2Al(s) + 2NaOH(aq) + 6H_2O(l) \longrightarrow 2Na[Al(OH)_4](aq) + 3H_2(g)$$
[Sodiumtetrahydroxo
aluminate (III)]

Aluminium dissolves in dil. HCl and liberates dihydrogen

$$2Al(s) + 6HCl(aq) \longrightarrow 2Al^{3+}(aq) + 6Cl^-(aq) + 3H_2(g)$$

(v) **Reaction with carbon**

$$4B + C \xrightarrow{\Delta} \quad B_4C$$
Boron carbide

$$4Al + 3C \longrightarrow \quad Al_4C_3$$
Aluminium carbide

Aluminium carbide is ionic and forms methane with water.

(vi) **Hydrides** Elements of group 13 do not combine directly with H_2 to form hydrides, therefore their hydrides have been prepared by indirect methods, e.g.

$$4BF_3 + 3LiAlH_4 \xrightarrow{\text{Dry ether}} 2B_2H_6 + 3LiF + 3AlF_3$$
Diborane

Boron forms a number of hydrides, they are known as **boranes**. Boranes catch fire in the presence of oxygen.

$$B_2H_6 + 3O_2 \longrightarrow B_2O_3 + 3H_2O; \quad \Delta_c H° = -1976\,kJ\,mol^{-1}$$

Boranes are hydrolysed by water.

$$B_2H_6 + 6H_2O \longrightarrow 2H_3BO_3 + 6H_2 \uparrow$$

Boranes are stable but the stability of hydrides of Al, Ga, In, and Tl decreases on moving down the group because the strength of the *M*—H bond decreases.

Structure of diborane BH_3 does not exist as such, but exists as a dimer, i.e. B_2H_6 [diborane]. In the above structure, B atoms are in sp^3-hybrid state. There are six B—H bond, out of which four B—H bonds are normal bonds present in the same plane while rest two B—H bonds behave as bridge bonds, i.e. $3c - 2e$ (three centre-two electrons, also known as banana bond) and present above and below the plane of the molecules which do not have sufficient number of electrons to form covalent bonds.

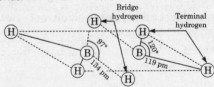

Aluminium (Al) forms a polymeric hydride of general formula $(AlH_3)_x$ which decomposes into its elements on heating.

(vii) **Oxides** Except, Tl all the elements of group 13 form oxides of general formula M_2O_3 on heating with oxygen.

$$4M + 3O_2 \xrightarrow{\Delta} 2M_2O_3$$

Tl forms thallium (I) oxide, Tl_2O which is more stable than thallium (III) oxide Tl_2O_3, due to inert pair effect.

(viii) **Nature of oxides and hydroxides** $B(OH)_3$ or H_3BO_3 is soluble in water, while other hydroxides are insoluble in water.

On moving down the group, there is a change from acidic to amphoteric and then to basic character of oxides and hydroxides of group 13 elements.

(ix) **Halides** All the elements of boron family (except Tl) form trihalides of type MX_3.

$$2B + 3X_2 \longrightarrow 2BX_3$$

$$B_2O_3 + 3C + 3Cl_2 \xrightarrow{\Delta} 2BCl_3 + 3CO$$

$$Al_2O_3 + 3C + 3Cl_2 \xrightarrow{\Delta} 2AlCl_3 + 3CO$$

All the boron trihalides $[BX_3]$ and aluminium trihalides AlX_3 (except AlF_3 which is ionic) are covalent compounds. AlX_3 exists as dimer while BX_3 is monomer because boron atom is too small to coordinate with four large halide ions. The energy released during the formation of the bridge structure is not sufficient for the cleavage of the typical $p\pi - p\pi$ bond in BF_3.

$[Al_2Cl_6]$

BF_3 is a colourless gas, BCl_3 and BBr_3 are colourless fuming liquids and BI_3 is a white solid at room temperature.

Trihalides of group 13 elements behave as Lewis acids because of their strong tendency to accept a pair of electrons. The relative strength of Lewis acids of boron trihalides is

$$BF_3 < BCl_3 < BBr_3 < BI_3$$

This is due to $p\pi\text{-}p\pi$ backbonding in BF_3 which makes it less electron deficient.

The halides of group 13 elements behave as Lewis acids and decreasing order of the acidic character is

$$BX_3 > AlX_3 > GaX_3 > InX_3 \quad \text{(where, } X = \text{Cl, Br or I)}$$

$TlCl_3$ decomposes to $TlCl$ and Cl_2 and hence, acts as an oxidising agent.

$$TlCl_3 \xrightarrow{\Delta} TlCl + Cl_2$$

Anomalous Behaviour of Boron

Boron shows anomalous behaviour with the other members of the group, due to the following reasons:

  (i) Smallest size in the group.

  (ii) High ionisation energy.

  (iii) Highest electronegativity in the group.

  (iv) Absence of vacant d-orbital.

A few points of difference are:

1. It is a non-metal while other members of the group are metallic.
2. It shows allotropy while other members do not.
3. It has the highest melting point and boiling point in group 13.
4. It forms only covalent compounds while other members form both ionic and covalent compounds.
5. The halides of boron exist as monomers while $AlCl_3$ exists as a dimer.
6. The oxides and hydroxides of boron are weakly acidic while those of aluminium are amphoteric and those of other elements are basic.
7. It can be oxidised by concentrated HNO_3 while aluminium becomes passive due to the formation of oxide layer on the surface.

$$2B + 6HNO_3 \longrightarrow \underset{\text{Boric acid}}{2H_3BO_3} + \underset{\text{Nitrogen dioxide}}{6NO_2}$$

Diagonal Relationship between Boron and Silicon

Boron exhibit resemblance with its diagonal element silicon of group 14.

1. Both B and Si are non-metals.
2. Both are semi-conductors.
3. Both B and Si form covalent hydrides, i.e. boranes and silanes respectively.
4. Both form covalent, and volatile halides which fume in moist air due to release of HCl gas.

$$BCl_3 + 3H_2O \longrightarrow H_3BO_3 + 3HCl\uparrow$$
$$SiCl_4 + 4H_2O \longrightarrow Si(OH)_4 + 4HCl\uparrow$$

5. Both form solid oxides which get dissolve in alkalies forming borates and silicates respectively.

6. Both react with electropositive metals and give binary compounds, which yield mixture of boranes and silanes on hydrolysis.

Boron and Its Compounds

Occurrence
It does not occur in free state. Its important minerals are
   (i) Borax (or Tincal), $Na_2B_4O_7 \cdot 10H_2O$
   (ii) Kernite, $Na_2B_4O_7 \cdot 4H_2O$
   (iii) Orthoboric acid, H_3BO_3

Isolation
Elemental boron is obtained by following methods:
   (i) By reduction of boric oxide with highly electropositive metals like K, Mg, Al, Na etc, in the absence of air.

$$B_2O_3 + 6K \xrightarrow{\Delta} 2B + 3K_2O$$

   (ii) By the reaction of boron halides with hydrogen,

$$2BCl_3 + 3H_2 \xrightarrow{1270K} 2B + 6HCl$$

Uses of Boron
   (i) As a semi-conductor.
   (ii) Boron steel rods are used to control the nuclear reactions.

$$_5B^{10} + _0n^1 \longrightarrow _5B^{11}$$

1. Borax or Sodium Tetraborate Decahydrate [$Na_2B_4O_7 \cdot 10H_2O$]

Preparation
It occurs naturally as tincal in dried up lakes. It is obtained by boiling of mineral colemanite with a solution of Na_2CO_3.

$$\underset{\text{Colemanite}}{Ca_2B_6O_{11}} + 2Na_2CO_3 \longrightarrow 2CaCO_3 \downarrow + 2NaBO_2 + \underset{\text{Borax}}{Na_2B_4O_7}$$

$NaBO_2$ can be removed by passing CO_2 through it.

$$4NaBO_2 + CO_2 \longrightarrow Na_2CO_3 + Na_2B_4O_7$$

Properties

1. Its aqueous solution is basic in nature.

$$Na_2B_4O_7 + 7H_2O \longrightarrow 2NaOH + 4H_3BO_3$$

2. On heating with ethyl alcohol and conc. H_2SO_4, it gives volatile vapours of triethylborate which burn with a green flame.

$$Na_2B_4O_7 + H_2SO_4 + 5H_2O \longrightarrow Na_2SO_4 + 4H_3BO_3$$

$$H_3BO_3 + 3C_2H_5OH \longrightarrow \underset{\text{Triethylborate}}{B(OC_2H_5)_3} + 3H_2O$$

3. **Action of heat**

$$Na_2B_4O_7 \cdot 10H_2O \xrightarrow[-10H_2O]{\text{Heat}}$$

$$Na_2B_4O_7 \xrightarrow{\Delta} \underset{\text{Sodium metaborate}}{2NaBO_2} + \underset{\text{Boric oxide}}{B_2O_3}$$

$$\underbrace{\qquad\qquad\qquad\qquad\qquad}_{\text{Glassy bead}}$$

Borax bead is used for the detection of coloured basic radicals under the name **borax bead test**, e.g.

$$\underset{\text{Cobalt sulphate}}{CoSO_4} \xrightarrow{\Delta} CoO + SO_3 ;$$

$$CoO + B_2O_3 \longrightarrow Co(BO_2)_2$$

$$\text{Cobalt metaborate (blue)}$$

Basic radical or salt	Fe	Cr	Ni
Colours of borax bead	Green	Green	Brown

2. Boric Acid or Orthoboric Acid [H_3BO_3 or $B(OH)_3$]

Preparation

By treating borax with dil. HCl or dil. H_2SO_4.

$$Na_2B_4O_7 + 2HCl + 5H_2O \longrightarrow 2NaCl + 4H_3BO_3$$

Properties

1. It is a weak monobasic acid (Lewis acid).

$$H_3BO_3 + 2H_2O \longrightarrow [B(OH)_4]^- + H_3O^+$$

2. With C_2H_5OH and conc H_2SO_4, it gives triethylborate.

$$H_3BO_3 + 3C_2H_5OH \xrightarrow{\text{Conc. } H_2SO_4} \underset{\text{Triethylborate}}{B(OC_2H_5)_3} + 3H_2O$$

3. **Heating effect**

$$H_3BO_3 \xrightarrow{273\text{ K}} HBO_2 \xrightarrow{473\text{ K}} H_2B_4O_7 \xrightarrow[\text{hot}]{\text{Red}} B_2O_3$$

| Orthoboric acid | Metaboric acid | Tetraboric acid | Boron trioxide (Boric anhydride) |

Uses

It is used as an antiseptic and eye lotion under the name 'boric lotion', and as a food preservative.

3. Borazine or Borazole, $[B_3N_3H_6]$

It is a colourless liquid having a six membered ring of alternating B and N atoms. It is also called 'inorganic benzene'. It is prepared by B_2H_6 as follows

$$\underset{1\quad:\quad 2}{3B_2H_6 + 6NH_3} \xrightarrow{\Delta} 2B_3N_3H_6 + 12H_2\uparrow$$

The π-electrons in borazine are only partially delocalised. It is more reactive than benzene.

Compounds of Aluminium

1. Anhydrous Aluminium Chloride $[AlCl_3 \text{ or } Al_2Cl_6]$
Preparation
It can not be prepared by heating $AlCl_3 \cdot 6H_2O$.

$$2AlCl_3 \cdot 6H_2O \xrightarrow{\Delta} 2Al(OH)_3 + 6HCl\uparrow$$

$$2Al(OH)_3 \xrightarrow{\text{Heat}} Al_2O_3 + 3H_2O$$

It can be prepared
(i) By passing dry chlorine or HCl gas over heated Al.

$$2Al + 3Cl_2 \xrightarrow{\text{Heat}} 2AlCl_3$$

$$2Al + 6HCl \xrightarrow{\text{Heat}} 2AlCl_3 + 3H_2$$

(ii) By heating a mixture of alumina and carbon in a current of dry chlorine.

$$Al_2O_3 + 3C + 3Cl_2 \xrightarrow{\Delta} 2AlCl_3 + 3CO$$

Properties

1. $AlCl_3$ fumes in moist air due to hydrolysis.

$$AlCl_3 + 3H_2O \longrightarrow Al(OH)_3 + 3HCl$$

2. It behaves as Lewis acid.

Uses

It is used as a catalyst in Friedel-Craft reaction and as a mordant dye.

2. Aluminium Oxide or Alumina [Al_2O_3]

It is the most stable compound of aluminium and occurs in nature as colourless corundum and several coloured oxides, (it is present in combination with different metal oxides) like ruby (red), topaz (yellow), sapphire (blue), and emerald (green), which are used as precious stones (gems).

Alum

The term alum is given to double sulphates of the type $X_2SO_4 \cdot Y_2(SO_4)_3 \cdot 24H_2O$ where, X represents a monovalent cation such as Na^+, K^+ and NH_4^+, while Y is a trivalent cation such a $Al^{3+}, Cr^{3+}, Fe^{3+}$ and Co^{3+} (Li^+ does not form alum).

Some important alums are:

  (i) Potash alum $K_2SO_4 \cdot Al_2(SO_4)_3 \cdot 24H_2O$

  (ii) Sodium alum $Na_2SO_4 \cdot Al_2(SO_4)_3 \cdot 24H_2O$

  (iii) Ammonium alum $(NH_4)_2SO_4 \cdot Al_2(SO_4)_3 \cdot 24H_2O$

  (iv) Ferric alum $(NH_4)_2SO_4 \cdot Fe_2(SO_4)_3 \cdot 24H_2O$

Potash alum is prepared in the laboratory by mixing hot equimolar quantities of K_2SO_4 and $Al_2(SO_4)_3$. The resulting solution on concentration and crystallisation gives potash alum.

Note 1. *A mixture of Al powder with NH_4NO_3 is called ammonol and is used in bombs.*

      2. *Al is the chief constituent of silvery paints.*

      3. *$Al_2(SO_4)_3$ is used for making fire proof clothes.*

Group 14

General Physical Properties of Group 14 Elements

(i) **Electronic configuration** Their valence shell electronic configuration is $ns^2\ np^2$

Element	Atomic number	Electronic configuration
Carbon (C)	6	[He] $2s^2\ 2p^2$
Silicon (Si)	14	[Ne] $3s^2\ 3p^2$
Germanium (Ge)	32	[Ar] $3d^{10}, 4s^2\ 4p^2$
Tin (Sn)	50	[Kr] $4d^{10}, 5s^2\ 5p^2$
Lead (Pb)	82	[Xe] $4f^{14}, 5d^{10}, 6s^2\ 6p^2$

(ii) **Metallic character** C and Si are non-metals, Ge is a metalloid and Sn and Pb are metals.

(iii) **Appearance** C is black, Si is light-brown, Ge is greyish, Sn and Pb are silvery white.

(iv) **Density** Density increases with increase in atomic number due to increase in mass per unit volume down the group.

(v) **Melting points and boiling points** The melting points and boiling points decrease from carbon to lead but carbon and silicon have very high melting and boiling points due to their giant structure.

(vi) **Oxidation state** They exhibit +2 and +4 oxidation state. The compounds of Pb in +4 oxidation state are powerful oxidising agents since, +2 oxidation state of Pb is more stable due to inert pair effect.

The compounds in +2 oxidation state are ionic in nature and in +4 oxidation state are covalent in nature (According to Fajan's rule).

(vii) **Ionisation enthalpy** It decreases from C to Sn. For Pb, it is slightly higher than Sn.

(viii) **Electronegativity values** The value decreases from C to Pb but not in a regular manner probably due to filling of d-orbitals in Ge and Sn and f-orbitals in Pb.

(ix) **Catenation** The greater the strength of element-element bond, the greater is the strength of catenation.

C $>>$ Si $>$ Ge $\approx$ Sn $>$ Pb (catenation).

(x) **Allotropy** All the elements of this group except Pb exhibit allotropy.

In cold countries, white tin changes to grey tin and results in decrease in density. This is called tin disease or tin plague.

(xi) **Valency** All elements exhibit tetravalency. In case of carbon, 406 kJ mol^{-1} of energy is required for promotion of $2s$-electron to $2p$. Formation of two extra bonds provide this energy.

(xii) **Atomic and ionic radii** Both increase from C to Pb.

(xiii) **Multiple bonding** Carbon forms $p\pi - p\pi$ bonds with itself and with S, N and O. Other elements show negligible tendency of this type due to their large size. Others form $d\pi - p\pi$ multiple bonds.

Chemical Properties of Group 14 Elements

(i) **Hydrides** All members of the group form covalent hydrides. Their number and ease of formation decreases down the group.

Hydrides of carbon are called hydrocarbons (alkanes, alkenes or alkynes).

Hydrides of Si and Ge are known as silanes and germanes.

The only hydrides of Sn and Pb are SnH_4 (stannane) and PbH_4 (plumbane).

Their thermal stability decrease down the group.

Their reducing character increases down the group.

(ii) **Halides** All the elements give tetrahedral and covalent halides of the type MX_4 except $PbBr_4$ and PbI_4.

Thermal stability

$$CX_4 > SiX_4 > GeX_4 > SnX_4 > PbX_4$$

Order of thermal stability with common metals

$$MF_4 > MCl_4 > MBr_4 > MI_4$$

Except CX_4 other tetrahalides can hydrolysed due to the presence of vacant d-orbitals.

$$SiX_4 + 2H_2O \longrightarrow SiO_2 + 4HX$$

Ease of hydrolysis: $SiX_4 > GeX_4 > SnX_4 > PbX_4$

Except C, other elements form dihalides of the type MX_2 which are more ionic and have higher melting points and boiling points, e.g. $SnCl_2$ is a solid whereas $SnCl_4$ is a liquid at room temperature.

$SnCl_2 \cdot 5H_2O$ is called **bitter of tin** and is used as a mordant in dyeing.

(iii) **Oxides** They form two types of oxides, mono-oxides of the type MO, e.g.

CO (neutral) and SiO, GeO, SnO, PbO(all basic) and dioxides of the type MO_2

$$\underbrace{CO_2, SiO_2}_{\text{Acidic}} \qquad \underbrace{GeO_2, SnO_2 \text{ and } PbO_2}_{\text{Amphoteric}}$$

CO_2 is linear gas at ordinary temperature. Solid CO_2 is known as **dryice** or **drikold**.

SiO_2 is a solid with three dimensional network in which Si is bonded to four oxygen atoms tetrahedrally and covalently. A mass of hydrated silica (SiO_2) formed from skeletons of minute plants, known as diatoms, is called Kieselguhr. It is a highly parous material and is used in the manufacture of dynamite.

Carbon

Free states (diamond, graphite, coal etc.) and combined states (oxides, carbonates, hydrocarbons etc.)

Allotropic Forms of Carbon

The crystalline forms include

(i) **Diamond** It is the hardest and has three dimensional polymeric structure in which hybridisation of C is sp^3. It is covalent solid, melting point 3650°C, density 3.51 g/cm^3 and bad conductor of heat and electricity.

(ii) **Graphite** It is dark grey, having hexagonal plates, hybridisation of each C is sp^2. It is good conductor of heat and electricity due to the presence of free electrons. It was also known as **black lead**. It is a very good lubricant. Graphite is thermodynamically most stable allotropes of carbon.

Aqua dag Suspensions of graphite in water.

Oil dag Suspension of graphite in oil lubricants.

(iii) **Fullerenes** Fullerenes are made by the heating of graphite in an electric arc in the presence of inert gases such as helium or argon. These are the only pure form of carbon because they have smooth structure without having dangling bonds. C_{60} molecule contains 12 five membered rings and 20 six membered rings. The five membered rings are connected to six membered rings while six membered rings are connected to both five and six membered rings. These are used in microscopic ball bearings, light weight batteries, in synthesis of new plastics and new drugs.

Amorphous forms of carbon are:

(i) **Coal** The different forms of coal are peat (60% C), lignite (70% C), Bituminous (78% C), Semibituminous (83% C) and anthracite (90% C). Bituminous is most common variety of coal.

(ii) **Coke** It is obtained by destructive distillation of coal.

$$\text{Coal} \xrightarrow{\text{DD}} \text{coke} (80° - 90\% \text{ C})$$

(iii) **Charcoal or wood charcoal** It is obtained by heating wood strongly in absence of air. When heated with steam, it becomes more activated. It is used to remove colouring matters and odoriferous gases.

(iv) **Bone black or animal charcoal** It is obtained by destructive distillation of bones in iron retort. By products are bone oil or pyridine. It is used as adsorbant. On burning, it gives bone ash which is calcium phosphate and used in the manufacture of phosphorous and phosphoric acid.

(v) **Lamp-black** It is obtained by burning vegetable oils in limited supply of air. It is used in the manufacture of printing ink, black paint, varnish and carbon paper.

(vi) **Carbon-black** It is obtained by burning natural gas in limited supply of air. It is added to rubber mixture for making automobile tyres.

Some Important Compounds of Carbon

Coal Gas

Preparation By destructive distillation of coal.

Composition

$$H_2 = 45 - 55\% \quad N_2 = 2 - 12\%$$
$$CH_4 = 25 - 35\% \quad CO_2 = 0 - 3\%$$
$$CO = 4 - 11\% \quad O_2 = 1 - 1.5\%$$

Ethylene, acetylene, benzene, etc = $3 - 5\%$

Uses It is used as illuminant, as fuel and to provide inert atmosphere in the metallurgical processes.

Natural Gas

It is found along with petroleum below the surface of earth.

Composition $CH_4 = 60 - 80\%$

Higher hydrocarbons = $2 - 12\%$

$C_2H_6 = 5 - 10\%, \quad C_3H_8 = 3 - 18\%$

Uses It is used as a fuel. Its partial combustion yields carbon black (reinforcing agent for rubber).

Oil Gas

Preparation

$$\text{Kerosene} \xrightarrow[\text{absence of air}]{\text{Heated in}} \text{Mixture of simple hydrocarbons}$$

Uses It is used as fuel in laboratories in Bunsen burners.

Wood Gas

Preparation Destructive distillation of wood gives wood gas (CH_4, C_2H_6, H_2)

Uses It is used as fuel.

Liquified Petroleum Gas (LPG)

It is used in cylinders for domestic purposes.

Composition *n*-butane + *Iso*-butane

Uses It is used as domestic fuel.

A strong foul smelling substance ethyl mercaptan or thioethanol (C_2H_5SH) is also added to LPG to detect its leakage because LPG is a colourless and odourless gas.

Carbon Monoxide (CO)

Preparation

(i) $2C(s) + O_2(g) \xrightarrow{\Delta} 2CO(g)$

(ii) $HCOOH \xrightarrow[\text{Conc. } H_2SO_4]{373\ K} H_2O + CO$

(iii) It is manufactured in the form of water gas and producer gas.

$$C(g) + H_2O(g) \xrightarrow{473\ K - 1273\ K} \underbrace{CO(g) + H_2(g)}_{\text{Water gas}}$$

$$2C(s) + O_2(g) + 4N_2(g) \xrightarrow{1273\ K} \underbrace{2CO(g) + 4N_2(g)}_{\text{Producer gas}}$$

Properties

It is colourless, odourless and almost water insoluble gas. It is a powerful reducing agent. CO is used in the extraction of many metals from their oxide ores. It is highly poisonous in nature because of its ability to form a complex with haemoglobin.

$$Fe_2O_3(s) + 3CO(g) \xrightarrow{\Delta} 2Fe(s) + 3CO_2(g)$$

$$ZnO(s) + CO(g) \xrightarrow{\Delta} Zn(s) + CO_2(g)$$

Carbon Dioxide (CO_2)

Preparation

$$C(s) + O_2(g) \xrightarrow{\Delta} CO_2(g)$$

$$CH_4(g) + 2O_2(g) \xrightarrow{\Delta} CO_2(g) + 2H_2O(g)$$

$$CaCO_3(s) + 2HCl(aq) \longrightarrow CaCl_2(aq) + CO_2(g) + H_2O(l)$$

Properties It is a colourless and odourless gas. With water, it forms carbonic acid. $H_2CO_3(aq) + H_2O(l) \rightleftharpoons HCO_3^-(aq) + H_3O^+(aq)$

Photosynthesis $6CO_2 + H_2O \xrightarrow[\text{Chlorophyll}]{h\nu} C_6H_{12}O_6 + 6O_2 + 6H_2O$

Compounds of Silicon

Silicates

Silicates are metal derivatives of silicic acid, H_2SiO_3 and can be obtained by fusing metal oxides or metal carbonates with sand. The basic structural unit of silicates is SiO_4^{4-}.

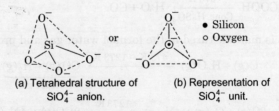

(a) Tetrahedral structure of SiO_4^{4-} anion.
(b) Representation of SiO_4^{4-} unit.
• Silicon
○ Oxygen

Types of silicates	No. of oxygen atom shared	Basic unit	Example
Orthosilicates	0	SiO_4^{4-}	Zircon ($ZrSiO_4$)
Pyrosilicates	1	$Si_2O_7^{6-}$	Thortveitite ($Sc_2Si_2O_7$)
Cyclic silicates	2	$Si_3O_9^{6-}$	Wallastonite ($Ca_3Si_3O_9$)
		$Si_6O_{18}^{12-}$	Beryl ($Be_3Al_2Si_6O_{18}$)
Chain silicates	2	$(SiO_3^{2-})_n$ and $(Si_4O_{11}^{6-})_n$	Pyroxenes, Kaolinite, talc ($3MgO \cdot 4SiO_2 \cdot H_2O$)
Sheet silicates	3	$(Si_2O_3^{2-})_n$, $(SiO_3)_n$	Zeolites, quartz
Three dimensional silicates	4		

Talc consists of planar sheets which can slip over one another due to weak forces of attraction, and is a constituent of talcum powder. That's why talcum powder has a slippery touch.

Mica (abrak) is naturally occurring aluminium silicate $[KH_2Al_3(SiO_4)_3]$ or $KAl_3Si_3O_{10}(OH)_2$.

Silicones

The linear, cyclic or cross linked polymeric compounds containing (R_2SiO) as a repeating units, are known as silicones. They are manufactured from alkyl substituted chlorosilanes.

$$2RCl + Si \xrightarrow[570\,K]{Cu\ powder} R_2SiCl_2 \xrightarrow[-2HCl]{+2H_2O} R_2Si(OH)_2$$

$$\text{Polymerisation} \downarrow -H_2O$$

$$-O-\left[\begin{array}{c} R \\ | \\ Si-O \\ | \\ R \end{array}\right]_n \begin{array}{c} R \\ | \\ Si- \\ | \\ R \end{array}$$

Silicones

Silicones are chemically inert, water repellent, heat resistant, good electrical insulators. These are used as lubricants (vaseline), insulators etc.

Silicon Dioxide (SiO_2)

Silicon dioxide is a covalent three dimensional network solid in which each silicon atom is covalently bonded in a tetrahedral manner to four oxygen atoms. Silica in its normal form is almost non-reactive because of high Si—O bond enthalpy. It is attacked by HF and NaOH.

$$SiO_2 + 2NaOH \longrightarrow Na_2SiO_3 + H_2O$$
$$SiO_2 + 4HF \longrightarrow SiF_4 + 2H_2O$$

Zeolites

If aluminium atoms replaces few silicon atoms in 3-dimensional network of silicon dioxide, overall structure known as alumino silicate, acquires a negative charge. Cations such Na^+, K^+ or Ca^{2+} balance the negative charge, e.g. feldspar and zeolites. ZSM-5 is used as a catalyst in petrochemical industry.

Carborundum

It is second hardest material known and has formula SiC (silicon carbide). It is used as high temperature semiconductor, in transistor diode rectifiers.

Glass

It is a transparent or translucent amorphous substance obtained by fusion of sodium carbonate (or sodium sulphate), calcium carbonate and sand (silica). It is not a true solid, so its melting point is not sharp.

General formula of glass is $Na_2O \cdot CaO \cdot 6SiO_2$.

Coloured glasses are obtained by adding certain substance to the molten mass.

Colour	Substance added
Blue	CoO
Green	Fe^{2+} and Cr
Yellow	Fe^{3+}, uranate of sodium
Purple	MnO_2
Lemon-yellow	CdS
Red	Cu_2O, selenium oxide
Amber	Organic matter and C
Ruby	$AuCl_3$

Different varities of glass

Glass type	Composition	Properties
Hard glass	$K_2O \cdot CaO \cdot 4SiO_2$	Resistant to acid and chemicals
Flint glass	$K_2O \cdot PbO \cdot 4SiO_2$	High refractive index so used in optical lenses and prisms
Pyrex glass	Mixture of borosilicate of Pb, Ca and Na	Low coefficient of thermal expansion so can with stand sudden changes in temperature
Crooke's glass	Contains CeO_2 along with general composition	Absorbs UV radiations so used in making goggles
Jena glass	Contains mixture of Zn and Ba borosilicates	Resistant to heat, shock, etc.
Quartz glass	Pure silica	Optical instruments (vetreosil)

Glass is attacked by HF. This property is used in the etching of glass.

$$Na_2SiO_3 + 8HF \longrightarrow 2NaF + H_2SiF_6 + 3H_2O$$
$$CaSiO_3 + 8HF \longrightarrow CaF_2 + H_2SiF_6 + 3H_2O$$
$$\text{Hydrofluoro}$$
$$\text{silicic acid}$$

Compounds of Lead

Chrome Yellow ($PbCrO_4$)

It is prepared by adding potassium chromate to lead chromate and is used as a yellow pigment under the name chrome yellow. On treating with alkali, it gives basic lead chromate or chrome red, $PbCrO_4 \cdot PbO$.

Basic lead carbonate, $Pb(OH)_2 \cdot 2PbCO_3$

It is also known as white lead and is prepared by adding sodium carbonate solution to any lead salt.

$$3Pb(NO_3)_2 + 3Na_2CO_3 + H_2O \longrightarrow Pb(OH)_2 \cdot 2PbCO_3$$
$$+ 6NaNO_3 + CO_2 \uparrow$$

It is used as white paint. The disadvantage of using white lead in paints is that, it turns black by the action of H_2S of the atmosphere.

> Lead poisoning is called plumbosolvency which increases in the excess of nitrates, organic acids and ammonium salts.

Group 15

The 15 group of the periodic table consists of nitrogen, phosphorus, arsenic, antimony and bismuth. These elements are known as **pnicogens** and their compounds as **pniconides**.

Occurrence

Molecular nitrogen comprises 78% by volume of the atmosphere. It occurs as sodium nitrate, $NaNO_3$ (called Chile saltpetre) and potassium nitrate (Indian saltpetre.) Phosphorus occurs in minerals of the apatite family, $Ca_9(PO_4)_6 \cdot CaX_2$ $(X = F, Cl, \text{ or } OH)$ (e.g. fluorapatite $Ca_9(PO_4)_6 \cdot CaF_2$) which are the main components of phosphate rocks.

Physical Properties of Group 15 Elements

(i) **Electronic configuration** Their valence shell electronic configuration is $ns^2 \ np^3$

Element	Atomic number	Electronic configuration
Nitrogen (N)	7	[He] $2s^2, 2p^3$
Phosphorus (P)	15	[Ne]$3s^2, 3p^3$
Arsenic (As)	33	[Ar] $3d^{10}, 4s^2, 4p^3$
Antimony (Sb)	51	[Kr] $4d^{10}, 5s^2, 5p^3$
Bismuth (Bi)	83	[Xe] $4f^{14}, 5d^{10}, 6s^2, 6p^3$

(ii) **Metallic character** N and P are non-metals, As and Sb are metalloids and Bi is metal.

(iii) **Physical state** Nitrogen is the first element after hydrogen which is diatomic gas in native form. All other elements in the group are solids.

(iv) **Atomicity** N_2 is diatomic while others are tetraatomic E_4.

(v) **Melting and boiling points** The melting point increases from nitrogen to arsenic. The boiling points increase regularly on moving down the group.

(vi) **Density** It increases down the group.

(vii) **Atomic radii** It increases with increase in atomic number as we go down the group.

(viii) **Allotropy** All the elements (except Bi) exhibit allotropy.

Nitrogen	— α-nitrogen, β-nitrogen
Phosphorus	— White, red, black
Arsenic	— Grey, yellow, black
Antimony	— Metallic yellow (explosive)

(ix) **Oxidation state**

N	P	As	Sb	Bi
−3 to +5	−3, +3, +4, +5	+3, +5	+3, +5	+3, +5

Nitrogen has a wide range of oxidation states.

The stability of +3 oxidation state increases and stability of +5 oxidation state decreases on moving down the group due to inert pair effect.

 (x) **Ionisation enthalpy** Ionisation energy of nitrogen is very high due to its small size and half-filled highly stable configuration. The ionisation energy decreases down the group.

(xi) **Electronegativity** It decreases from nitrogen to bismuth.

(xii) **Catenation** They exhibit the property of catenation but to lesser extent due to weak $E - E$ bond than 14 group elements.

(xiii) **Reactivity** Elemental nitrogen is highly unreactive because of its strong triple bond. (almost as inert as noble gases).

White phosphorus is extremely reactive and kept in water. It is inflammable and can be ignited at 45°C.

Chemical Properties of Group 15 Elements

 (i) **Hydrides** All the elements of this group form hydrides of type EH_3, which are covalent and pyramidal in shape. Thermal stability, basic strength, solubility in water, bond angle and strength of M—H bond of group 15 elements follows the order as mentioned

$$NH_3\,(107.4°) > PH_3\,(92°) > AsH_3\,(91°) > SbH_3\,(90°) > BiH_3$$

| Ammonia | Phosphine | Arsine | Stibine | Bismuthine |

Reducing character, covalent character, rate of combustion of group 15 elements follows the order

$$NH_3 < PH_3 < AsH_3 < SbH_3 < BiH_3$$

 (ii) **Halides** All the elements of this group form trihalides, MX_3 and except nitrogen all form pentahalides, MX_5, e.g. NCl_3, NI_3, $PCl_3, BiCl_3, AsCl_3, PCl_5$ etc. Trihalides (except of N) behave as Lewis acid and the order of their strength is $PCl_3 > AsCl_3 > SbCl_3$

Trihalides of N behave as Lewis base and has the following order of strength

$$NF_3 < NCl_3 < NBr_3 < NI_3$$

NCl_3 is an explosive compound.

(iii) **Oxides** All the elements of this group form oxides of the type M_2O_3 and M_2O_5.

Oxides of N : $\underbrace{N_2O_5,\ N_2O_4, N_2O_3}_{\text{Strongly acidic}}$ $\underbrace{NO\quad N_2O}_{\text{Neutral}}$

Oxides of P : $\underset{\text{Strongly acidic}}{P_4O_{10}\qquad P_2O_3}$

As_4O_6 is called white arsenic and is a poison.

The acidic strength of pentoxides and trioxides decrease on moving down the group, i.e.

$$N_2O_5 > P_2O_5 > As_2O_5 > Sb_2O_5$$

BiOCl is called pearl white.

Anomalous Behaviour of Nitrogen

Nitrogen differs from rest of the members of the group because of its small size, high electronegativity, high ionisation energy, absence of vacant d-orbitals and capacity to form $p\pi$-$p\pi$ multiple bonds.

Nitrogen is a diatomic gas (with triple bond) and chemically inert under ordinary conditions. It does not show pentavalency and distinctly non-metallic. It exhibits a large number of oxidation states and forms oxides such N_2O, NO, NO_2.

Nitrogen and Its Compounds

1. Dinitrogen (N_2)

Preparation

$$NH_4Cl(aq) + NaNO_2(aq) \longrightarrow N_2(g) + 2H_2O(l) + NaCl(aq)$$

$$(NH_4)_2Cr_2O_7 \xrightarrow{\text{Heat}} N_2 + 4H_2O + Cr_2O_3$$

$$Ba(N_3)_2 \longrightarrow Ba + 3N_2$$
$$\text{(Pure nitrogen)}$$

Properties

1. Nitrogen does not react with alkali metals except Li but reacts with alkaline earth metals to give metal nitride.

$$6Li + N_2 \xrightarrow{\text{Heat}} 2Li_3N$$

$$3Mg + N_2 \xrightarrow{\text{Heat}} Mg_3N_2$$

2. Reaction with oxygen

$$N_2(g) + O_2(g) \underset{}{\overset{2000\ K}{\rightleftharpoons}} 2NO(g)$$

3. Reaction with non-metals

$$2B + N_2 \xrightarrow{\text{Heat}} 2BN$$

4. Reaction with CaC_2

$$CaC_2 + N_2 \xrightarrow{\text{1273 K}} \underbrace{CaCN_2}_{\text{Nitrolim}} + C$$

Uses Liquid N_2 is used as refrigerant. N_2 is used in the manufacture of HNO_3, NH_3, $CaCN_2$ (calcium cyanamide) and other nitrogenous compounds. It is used for filling electric bulbs.

2. **Ammonia** (NH_3)

Preparation

(i) **Lab method**
$$2NH_4Cl + Ca(OH)_2 \longrightarrow CaCl_2 + 2NH_3 + 2H_2O$$

(ii) **Haber's process**

$$N_2 + 3H_2 \xrightarrow[\text{Low temperature, high pressure}]{\text{Fe/Mo}} 2NH_3;$$

$$\Delta_f H^\ominus = -46.1 \text{ kJ mol}^{-1}$$

(iii) $AlN + 3H_2O \longrightarrow Al(OH)_3 + NH_3$

(iv) $NH_2CONH_2 \xrightarrow{2H_2O} 2NH_3 + H_2O + CO_2$

Properties

1. It is a colourless gas with characteristic pungent odour. It is extremely soluble in water due to H-bonding.

2. It is a strong Lewis base and used in the metal ion detection as

$$Cu^{2+}(aq) + 4NH_3(aq) \longrightarrow [Cu(NH_3)_4]^{2+}$$
[Blue] [Deep blue]

$$Ag^+(aq) + Cl^-(aq) \longrightarrow AgCl(s)$$
(White ppt)

$$AgCl(s) + 2NH_3(aq) \longrightarrow [Ag(NH_3)_2]Cl(aq)$$
Soluble

3. Reaction with chlorine

When NH_3 is in excess, N_2 is the main product.

$$8NH_3 + 3Cl_2 \longrightarrow 6NH_4Cl + N_2 \uparrow$$

When Cl_2 is in excess, NCl_3 is the main product.

$$NH_3 + 3Cl_2 \longrightarrow NCl_3 + 3HCl$$

4. Reaction with Nesseler's reagent

$$NH_3 + \underbrace{2K_2HgI_4 + 3KOH}_{\text{Nessler's reagent}} \longrightarrow \underset{\substack{\text{Iodide of Millon's base} \\ \text{(brown ppt)}}}{H_2N-HgO-HgI} + 7KI + 2H_2O$$

Uses It is used as a refrigerant and to produce various nitrogenous fertilizers.

Oxides of Nitrogen

Compound	Common method of preparation	Physical appearance and chemical nature	Resonance structure
Dinitrogen oxide [N_2O] (laughing gas)	$NH_4NO_3 \xrightarrow{\Delta} N_2O$ $+ 2H_2O$	Colourless gas, neutral	$\ddot{N}{=}N{=}\ddot{O} \leftrightarrow {:}N{\equiv}N{-}\ddot{\ddot{O}}{:}$
Nitrogen monoxide [NO]	$2NaNO_2 + 2FeSO_4$ $+ 3H_2SO_4 \longrightarrow$ $Fe_2(SO_4)_3 +$ $2NaHSO_4 + 2H_2O$ $+ 2NO$	Colourless gas, neutral	${:}N{=}\ddot{O} \leftrightarrow {:}\dot{N}{=}\ddot{O}{:}$
Dinitrogen trioxide [N_2O_3]	$2NO + N_2O_4$ $\xrightarrow{250\,K} 2N_2O_3$	Blue solid, acidic	(resonance structure)
Nitrogen dioxide [NO_2]	$2Pb(NO_3)_2 \xrightarrow{673\,K}$ $4NO_2 + 2PbO + O_2$	Brown gas, acidic	(resonance structure)
Dinitrogen tetraoxide [N_2O_4]	$2NO_2 \xrightleftharpoons[\text{Heat}]{\text{Cool}} N_2O_4$	Colourless solid/liquid, acidic	(resonance structure)
Dinitrogen pentoxide [N_2O_5]	$4HNO_3 + P_4O_{10} \longrightarrow$ $4HPO_3 + 2N_2O_5$	Colourless solid, acidic	(resonance structure)

NO_2 contains odd number of valence electrons. On dimerisation, it is converted to stable N_2O_4 molecule with even number of electrons.

3. Nitric Acid (HNO_3)

It is a stronger acid than H_3PO_4.

Preparations

(i) Lab method

$$NaNO_3 + H_2SO_4 \,(conc.) \longrightarrow NaHSO_4 + HNO_3$$

(ii) Ostwald's process

$$4NH_3 + 5O_2 \xrightarrow[\text{500 K, 9 bar}]{\text{Pt/Rh gauge}} 4NO + 6H_2O$$

$$2NO + O_2 \rightleftharpoons 2NO_2$$

$$3NO_2(g) + H_2O(l) \longrightarrow 2HNO_3(aq) + NO(g)$$

Physical properties It is a syrupy, colourless, pungent liquid usually available as 68% and 15.7 M aqueous solution is often yellow due to small concentrations of NO_2.

Chemical Reactions

1. **Action of nitric acid on zinc under different conditions**

   Cold and dil HNO_3

   $$4Zn + 10HNO_3 \,(dilute) \longrightarrow 4Zn(NO_3)_2 + 5H_2O + N_2O\uparrow$$

   Cold and concentrated HNO_3

   $$Zn + 4HNO_3 \longrightarrow Zn(NO_3)_2 + 2H_2O + 2NO_2\uparrow$$

2. **Action of nitric acid on copper under different conditions**

   Cold and dil. HNO_3

   $$3Cu + 8HNO_3 \longrightarrow 3Cu(NO_3)_2 + 4H_2O + 2NO\uparrow$$

   Cold and concentrated HNO_3

   $$Cu + 4HNO_3 \longrightarrow Cu(NO_3)_2 + 2H_2O + 2NO_2$$

3. **Reaction with non-metals**

   $$I_2 + 10HNO_3 \longrightarrow 2HIO_3 + 10NO_2 + 4H_2O$$
   $$C + 4HNO_3 \longrightarrow CO_2 + 2H_2O + 4NO_2$$
   $$S_8 + 48HNO_3 \longrightarrow 8H_2SO_4 + 48NO_2 + 16H_2O$$
   $$P_4 + 20HNO_3 \longrightarrow 4H_3PO_4 + 20NO_2 + 4H_2O$$

4. Brown ring test of nitrate

$$NO_3^- + 3Fe^{2+} + 4H^+ \longrightarrow NO + 3Fe^{3+} + 2H_2O$$

$$[Fe(H_2O)_6]^{2+} + NO \longrightarrow [Fe(H_2O)_5NO]^{2+} + H_2O$$
$$\qquad\qquad\qquad\qquad\qquad\qquad [Brown]$$

5. Metals like Fe, Cr, Ni, Al or Co becomes inactive or passive due to stable oxide layers.

Structure of nitric acid

Uses It is used

1. in the manufacturing of fertilizers.
2. for purification of silver and gold.
3. in the manufacturing of explosives and as an oxidising agent.
4. as nitrating reagent.

Phosphorus and Its Compounds

Allotropic Forms of Phosphorus

Phosphorus exists in three main allotropic forms. These are as follows.

(i) White phosphorus (ii) Red phosphorus (iii) Black phosphorus

Black phosphorus is formed when red phosphorus is heated in a sealed tube at 803 K. It does not oxidise in air.

Some points of distinction between white and red phosphorus

S.No.	Property	White	Red
1.	Structure		
2.	Odour	Garlic smell	Odourless
3.	Conductivity	Bad conductor	Semi-conductor
4.	Physiological action	Poisonous translucent solid	Non-poisonous
5.	Hardness	Soft	Brittle
6.	Action of KOH	PH_3	No action
7.	Action of Cl_2	PCl_3 or PCl_5	On heating PCl_3 or PCl_5
8.	In dark	Shines	Does not shine

Match box side contains red P or P_2S_3 + glue and on tip of match stick, red P, $KClO_3$ chalk and glue is deposited.

Chemical Properties

1. With non-metals

$$P_4 + 5O_2 \longrightarrow P_4O_{10}$$
$$P_4 + 6Cl_2 \longrightarrow 4PCl_3$$
$$P_4 + 10Cl_2 \longrightarrow 4PCl_5$$

2. With compounds

$$P_4 + 3NaOH + 3H_2O \longrightarrow \underset{\substack{\text{Sodium} \\ \text{hypophosphite}}}{3NaH_2PO_2} + PH_3$$

$$P_4 + 20HNO_3 \longrightarrow \underset{\substack{\text{Orthophosphoric} \\ \text{acid}}}{4H_3PO_4} + 4H_2O + 20NO_2$$

Uses It is used in match boxes, explosives, as rat poison, in fertilizers and alloys.

Compounds of Phosphorus

1. Phosphine (PH_3)

Preparation It is prepared by following methods :

$$Ca_3P_2 + 6H_2O \longrightarrow 3Ca(OH)_2 + 2PH_3$$
$$Ca_3P_2 + 6HCl \longrightarrow 3CaCl_2 + 2PH_3$$
$$P_4 + 3NaOH + 3H_2O \longrightarrow PH_3 + \underset{\substack{\text{Sodium} \\ \text{hypophosphite}}}{3NaH_2PO_2}$$

$$PH_4I + KOH \longrightarrow KI + H_2O + PH_3$$

Properties

1. It is a colourless gas with rotten fish like smell and is highly poisonous. It explodes in contact with traces of oxidising agents like HNO_3, Cl_2 and Br_2 vapours.

$$3CuSO_4 + 2PH_3 \longrightarrow Cu_3P_2 + 3H_2SO_4$$
$$3HgCl_2 + 2PH_3 \longrightarrow Hg_3P_2 + 6HCl$$

2. Phosphine is weakly basic.

$$PH_3 + HBr \longrightarrow PH_4^+Br^-$$

Uses It is used to prepare smoke screens in warfare. A mixture of CaC_2 and Ca_3P_2 is used in Holme's signals.

2. Phosphorus Trichloride (PCl_3)

Preparation

$$P_4 + 6Cl_2 \longrightarrow 4PCl_3$$
$$P_4 + 8SOCl_2 \longrightarrow 4PCl_3 + 4SO_2 + 2S_2Cl_2$$

Properties It is a colourless oily liquid, having pyramidal shape [sp^3-hybridised]

$$PCl_3 + 3H_2O \longrightarrow H_3PO_3 + 3HCl$$
$$3CH_3COOH + PCl_3 \longrightarrow 3CH_3COCl + H_3PO_3$$
$$3C_2H_5OH + PCl_3 \longrightarrow 3C_2H_5Cl + H_3PO_3$$

Structure of PCl_3

3. Phosphorus Pentachloride (PCl_5)

Preparation

$$P_4 + 10Cl_2 \longrightarrow 4PCl_5$$
$$P_4 + 10SO_2Cl_2 \longrightarrow 4PCl_5 + 10SO_2$$

Structure PCl_5 in gaseous and liquid phases has sp^3d-hybridisation and its shape is trigonal bipyramidal. The three equatorial P—Cl bonds are equivalent while the two axial bonds are longer than equatorial bonds.

Properties In solid state, PCl_5 exists as an ionic solid, $[PCl_4]^+ [PCl_6]^-$ in which, the cation, $[PCl_4]^+$ is tetrahedral and the anion $[PCl_6]^-$ is octahedral.

$$PCl_5 + H_2O \longrightarrow POCl_3 + 2HCl$$
$$POCl_3 + 3H_2O \longrightarrow H_3PO_4 + 3HCl$$
$$C_2H_5OH + PCl_5 \longrightarrow C_2H_5Cl + POCl_3 + HCl$$
$$CH_3COOH + PCl_5 \longrightarrow CH_3COCl + POCl_3 + HCl$$
$$2Ag + PCl_5 \longrightarrow 2AgCl + PCl_3$$
$$Sn + 2PCl_5 \longrightarrow SnCl_4 + 2PCl_3$$

It is used in the synthesis of some organic compounds.
e.g. C_2H_5Cl, CH_3COCl.

Oxoacids of Phosphorus

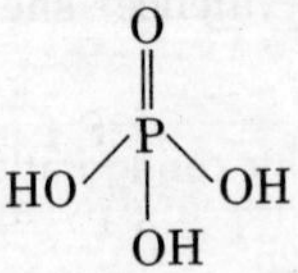

Orthophosphoric acid
(H_3PO_4)
(Oxidation state = + 5)

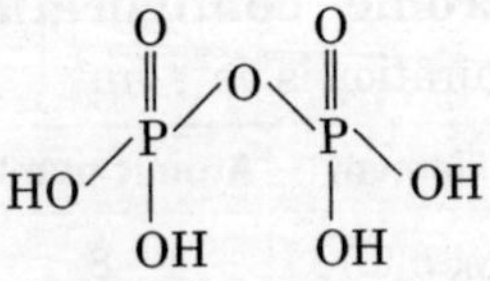

Pyrophosphoric acid
$(H_4P_2O_7)$
(Oxidation state = + 5)

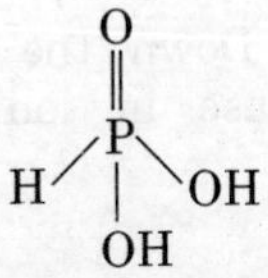

Orthophosphorous acid
(H_3PO_3)
(Oxidation state = +3)

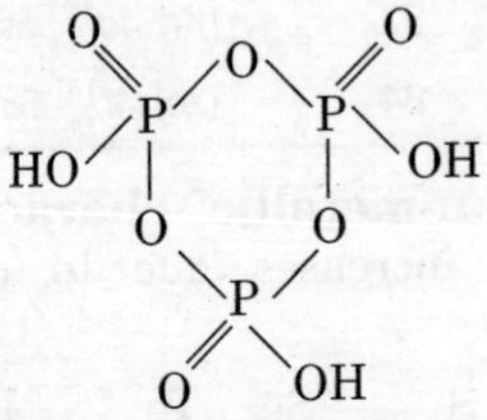

Cyclotrimetaphosphoric acid, $(HPO_3)_3$
(Oxidation state = + 5)

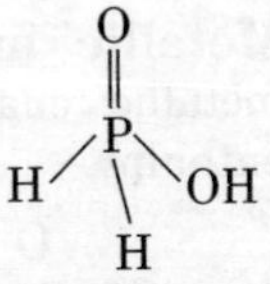

Hypophosphorous acid
(H_3PO_2)
(Oxidation state = + 1)

In toothpaste, $CaHPO_4 \cdot 2H_2O$ is added as mild abrasive and polishing agent.

These P—H bonds are not ionisable to give H^+ and do not play any role in basicity. Only those H-atoms which are attached with oxygen in P—OH form are ionisable and cause the basicity. Thus, H_3PO_3 and H_3PO_4 are dibasic and tribasic respectively as the structure of H_3PO_3 has two P—OH bonds and H_3PO_4 has three.

Group 16

The elements **oxygen** (O), **sulphur** (S), **selenium** (Se), **tellurium** (Te) and **polonium** (Po) belong to group 16 of the Periodic Table. These elements are known as **chalcogens**, i.e. ore forming elements.

The name sulphur has been derived from sanskrit word 'Sulveri' meaning 'killer of copper'.

Occurrence

Oxygen forms about 46.6% by mass of earth's crust. Combined sulphur exists primarily as sulphates such as gypsum $CaSO_4 \cdot 2H_2O$, epsom salt $MgSO_4 \cdot 7H_2O$; baryte, $BaSO_4$ and sulphide such as galena, PbS; (zinc) blende, ZnS; copper pyrites, $(CuFeS_2)$.

General Physical Properties of Group 16 Elements

(i) **Electronic configuration** Their valence shell electronic configuration is ns^2, np^4

Element	Atomic number	Electronic configuration
Oxygen (O)	8	[He] $2s^2\, 2p^4$
Sulphur (S)	16	[Ne] $3s^2\, 3p^4$
Selenium (Se)	34	[Ar] $3d^{10},\, 4s^2\, 4p^4$
Tellurium (Te)	52	[Kr] $4d^{10},\, 5s^2\, 5p^4$
Polonium (Po)	84	[Xe] $4f^{14},\, 5d^{10}, 6s^2\, 6p^4$

(ii) **Metallic and non-metallic character** Down the group metallic character increases due to decrease in ionisation enthalpy.

O　S　Se　Te　Po
Non-metals　Metalloids　Metal

(iii) **Abundance** O > S > Se > Te > Po

(iv) **Density** It increases down the group regularly.

(v) **Melting point and boiling point** Both show a regular increase down the group due to increase in molecular weight and van der Waals' forces of attraction.

(vi) **Oxidation state**

O	S	Se	Te	Po
–1, –2	–2 to +6	–2 to +6	–2 to +6	–2 to +6

In OF_2, the oxidation state of oxygen is +2.

(vii) **Ionisation energy** They possess a large amount of ionisation energy which decreases gradually from O to Po due to increase in size of atoms and increase in screening effect.

(viii) **Electron affinity** They have high electron affinity which decrease from O to Po. As the size of the atom increases, the extra added electron feels lesser attraction by nucleus and hence, electron affinity decreases.

(ix) **Electronegativity** It decreases down the group due to decrease in effective nuclear charge down the group.

(x) **Catenation** 16 group elements follow the order as shown below

S—S > Se—Se > O—O > Te—Te

(xi) **Atomicity** Oxygen is diatomic, sulphur and selenium are octa atomic with puckered ring structure.

(xii) **Allotropy**

Oxygen — Dioxygen (O_2) and ozone (O_3)

Sulphur — Rhombic (or α) sulphur, S_8

Monoclinic (or β) sulphur, S_8 (most stable), plastic sulphur

(xiii) **Atomic radii and ionic radii** They increase regularly from O to Po.

Chemical Properties of 16 Group Elements

(i) **Hydrides** All these elements form stable hydrides of the type H_2E. (Where, E = O, S, Se, Te and Po).

$$2H_2 + O_2 \rightleftharpoons 2H_2O$$

$$FeS + H_2SO_4 \longrightarrow H_2S + FeSO_4$$

H_2O is a liquid due to hydrogen bonding. While others are colourless gases with unpleasant smell.

⌐ Down the group acidic character increases from H_2O to H_2Se. All the hydrides except water possess reducing property and this character ┘ increases from H_2S to H_2Te.

(ii) **Halides** The stability of the halides decreases in the order

$$F^- > Cl^- > Br^- > I^-$$

Amongst hexahalides, hexafluorides are the only stable halides. All hexafluorides are gaseous in nature. SF_6 is exceptionally stable for steric reasons.

SF_4 is a gas, SeF_4 is a liquid and TeF_4 is a solid. These fluorides have sp^3d-hybridisation and see-saw geometry. They behave as Lewis acid as well as Lewis base e.g.

$$SF_4 + BF_3 \longrightarrow SF_4 \longrightarrow BF_3$$

$$SeF_4 + 2F^- \longrightarrow [SeF_6]^{2-}$$

The well known monohalides are dimeric in nature. Examples are $S_2F_2, S_2Cl_2, S_2Br_2, Se_2Cl_2$ and Se_2Br_2. These dimeric halides undergo disproportionation as given below

$$2Se_2Cl_2 \longrightarrow SeCl_4 + 3Se$$

(iii) **Oxides** They form AO_2 and AO_3 type oxides,

where $A = S, Se, Te$ or Po. Their acidic nature follow the order
$$SO_2 > SeO_2 > TeO_2 > PoO_2 \text{ and } SO_3 > SeO_3 > TeO_3$$
Ozone is considered as oxides of oxygen.

SO_2 is a gas having sp^2-hybridisation and V-shape.

SO_3 is a gas which is sp^2-hybridised and planar in nature.

SeO_2 is a volatile solid consists of non-planar infinite chains.

SeO_3 has tetrameric cyclic structure in solid state. SO_2 and SO_3 are the anhydrides of sulphurous (H_2SO_3) and sulphuric acid (H_2SO_4) respectively.

Note *In photocopying (xerox) machines Se acts as photoconductor.*

Anomalous Behaviour of Oxygen

Oxygen differs from rest of the members of the group because of its small size, high electronegativity and non-availability of d-orbitals for bonding.

Oxygen is a diatomic gas and is paramagnetic. It exhibit-2 oxidation state and forms $p\pi$-$p\pi$ bonds.

Oxygen and Its Compounds

1. Dioxygen

Priestley and **Scheele** prepared oxygen by heating suitable oxygen compounds.

Preparation By action of heat on oxygen rich compounds

(i) **From oxides** $2HgO \xrightarrow{\Delta} 2Hg + O_2 \uparrow$

$$2Ag_2O \longrightarrow 4Ag + O_2 \uparrow$$

$$2PbO_2 \longrightarrow 2PbO + O_2 \uparrow$$

(ii) **From peroxides and other oxides**

$$2H_2O_2 \xrightarrow{MnO_2} 2H_2O + O_2$$

(iii) **From certain compounds**

$$2KClO_3 \xrightarrow[MnO_2]{\Delta} 2KCl + 3O_2 \uparrow$$

$$2CaOCl_2 \longrightarrow 2CaCl_2 + O_2 \uparrow$$

Physical properties It is colourless, odourless, tasteless, slightly heavier than air and sparingly soluble in water.

Chemical properties On heating it combines directly with metals and non-metals, e.g.

$$C + O_2 \longrightarrow CO_2$$

$$P_4 + 5O_2 \longrightarrow P_4O_{10}$$

$$S + O_2 \longrightarrow SO_2$$

$$N_2 + O_2 \xrightarrow{3000^\circ C} 2NO$$

$$2Mg + O_2 \longrightarrow 2MgO$$

$$4Na + O_2 \longrightarrow 2Na_2O \longrightarrow Na_2O_2$$

Combination with O_2 is accelerated by using catalyst. Platinum is particularly an active catalyst.

$$2H_2 + O_2 \xrightarrow{Pt} 2H_2O$$

$$4NH_3 + 5O_2 \xrightarrow{Pt} 4NO + 6H_2O$$

Uses It is used in welding and cutting (oxy-hydrogen or oxy-acetylene) torch and in iron and steel industry to increase the content of blast in the Bessemer and open hearth process. It is also used for life support systems, e.g. in hospitals, for divers, miners and mountaineers.

Tests

1. With NO, it gives reddish brown fumes of NO_2.
2. It is absorbed by alkaline pyrogallol.

2. Ozone (O_3)

Preparation By passing silent electric discharge through cold, dry oxygen in ozoniser. (Lab method)

$$3O_2 \rightleftharpoons 2O_3; \Delta H^\ominus (298\,K) = +142\ kJ\ mol^{-1}$$

Physical properties It is pale blue gas with characteristic strong smell. It is slightly soluble in water.

Chemical Reactions

1. **Decomposition**

$$2O_3 \xrightarrow{573\,K} 3O_2; \Delta H = 284\ kJ/mol$$

2. **Oxidising action**

$$O_3 \longrightarrow O_2 + [O]$$

$$PbS + 4[O] \longrightarrow PbSO_4$$

$$H_2S + [O] \longrightarrow H_2O + S$$

$$2FeSO_4 + H_2SO_4 + [O] \longrightarrow Fe_2(SO_4)_3 + H_2O$$

3. It acts as a powerful oxidising agent. It liberates iodine from neutral KI solution and the liberated I_2 turns starch paper blue.

$$2KI + H_2O + O_3 \longrightarrow 2KOH + I_2 + O_2$$

$$I_2 + Starch \longrightarrow Blue\ colour$$

Uses It is used

1. as a germicide and disinfectant for sterlising water.
2. as a bleaching agent for oils, ivory wax and delicate fibres.
3. for detecting the position of double bond in unsaturated compounds.
4. in destroying odours coming from cold storage room, slaughter houses and kitchen of hotels.

Sulphur and its Allotropes

Sulphur forms numerous allotropes of which the yellow rhombic (α-sulphur) and monoclinic (β-sulphur) forms are the most important. The stable form at room temperature is rhombic sulphur which transforms to monoclinic sulphur when heated above 369 K.

Compounds of Sulphur

1. Sulphur Dioxide (SO_2)

Method of preparation

(i) By heating sulphur in air

$$S(s) + O_2(g) \xrightarrow{\Delta} SO_2(g)$$

(ii) Roasting iron pyrites in excess of air

$$4FeS_2(s) + 11O_2(g) \longrightarrow 2Fe_2O_3(s) + 8SO_2(g)$$

(iii) Lab method

$$SO_3^{2-}(aq) + 2H^+(aq) \longrightarrow H_2O(l) + SO_2(g)$$

Physical properties SO_2 is a colourless gas with pungent smell and is highly soluble in water.

$$SO_2(g) + H_2O(l) \rightleftharpoons H_2SO_3$$

Chemical reactions It turns lime water milky due to the formation of calcium bisulphite. However, in excess of SO_2 milkiness disappears due to the formation of calcium bisulphite.

$$Ca(OH)_2 + SO_2 \longrightarrow \underset{\text{Milkiness}}{CaSO_3} + H_2O$$

$$CaSO_3 + SO_2 + H_2O \longrightarrow \underset{\text{Soluble}}{Ca(HSO_3)_2} + H_2O$$

$$2NaOH + SO_2 \longrightarrow Na_2SO_3 + H_2O$$

$$Na_2SO_3 + H_2O + SO_2 \longrightarrow 2NaHSO_3$$

$$SO_2(g) + Cl_2(g) \longrightarrow SO_2Cl_2(l)$$

$$2SO_2(g) + O_2(g) \xrightarrow{V_2O_5} 2SO_3(g)$$

As a Reducing agent

$$2Fe^{3+} + SO_2 + 2H_2O \longrightarrow 2Fe^{2+} + SO_4^{2-} + 4H^+$$

$$5SO_2 + 2MnO_4^- + 2H_2O \longrightarrow 5SO_4^{2-} + 4H^+ + 2Mn^{2+}$$

when H_2S gas is passed through a saturated solution of SO_2 till its smell dissappears, it turns in a milky solution called the **Wacken roder's liquid**. When H_2S is passed through H_2SO_3, the reaction is called **Wacken roder's reaction.**

2. Oxoacids of Sulphur

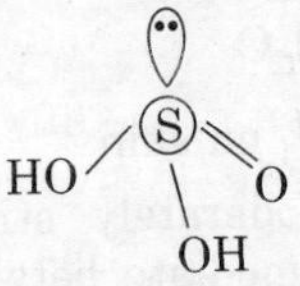

HO—S(=O)—OH with lone pair and =O
Sulphurous acid
(H_2SO_3)

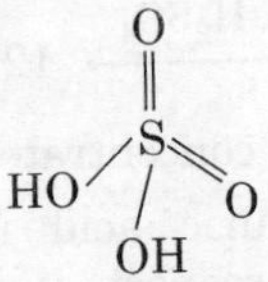

HO—S(=O)(=O)—OH
Sulphuric acid
(H_2SO_4)

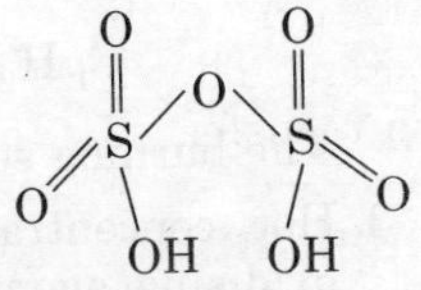

Oleum (pyrosulphuric acid)
($H_2S_2O_7$)

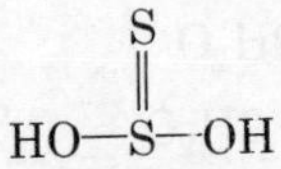

HO—S(=S)—OH
Thiosulphurous acid
($H_2S_2O_2$)

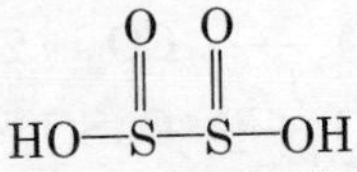

HO—S(=O)—S(=O)—OH
Dithionous acid
($H_2S_2O_4$)

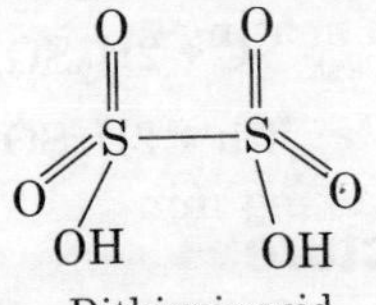

Dithionic acid
($H_2S_2O_6$)

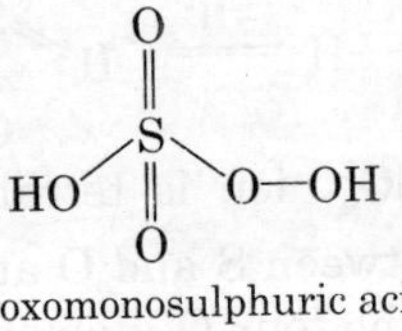

HO—S(=O)(=O)—O—OH
Peroxomonosulphuric acid
or Caro's acid
(H_2SO_5)

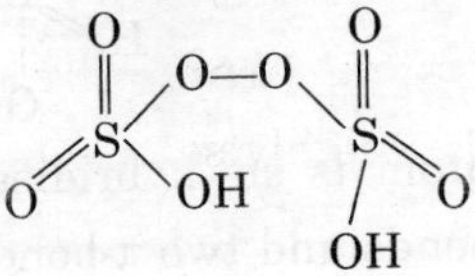

Peroxodisulphuric acid
($H_2S_2O_8$)

Uses

1. It is used in refining of petroleum and sugar.

2. It is used in bleaching wool and silk.

3. Sulphuric Acid (H_2SO_4)

Sulphuric acid is one of the most important industrial chemicals world wide. It is called the king of chemicals. It is manufactured by lead chamber process or **contact process.** Contact process involves three steps:

(i) Burning of sulphur or sulphur ores in air to generate SO_2.

(ii) Conversion of SO_2 to SO_3 by the reaction with oxygen in the presence of a catalyst (V_2O_5).

(iii) Absorption of SO_3 in H_2SO_4 to give oleum ($H_2S_2O_7$) which upon hydrolysis gives H_2SO_4.

Properties

1. Sulphuric acid is a colourless, dense, oily liquid.

$$MX + H_2SO_4 \longrightarrow 2HX + M_2SO_4$$

2. Concentrated sulphuric acid is a strong dehydrating agent.

$$C_{12}H_{22}O_{11} \xrightarrow{\text{conc. } H_2SO_4} 12C + 11H_2O$$

The burning sensation of concentrated H_2SO_4 on skin.

3. Hot concentrated sulphuric acid is a moderately strong oxidising agent. In this respect, it is intermediate between phosphoric acid and nitric acid.

$$3S + 2H_2SO_4 \text{ (conc.)} \longrightarrow 3SO_2(g) + 2H_2O$$

$$C + 2H_2SO_4 \text{(conc.)} \longrightarrow CO_2 + 2SO_2 + 2H_2O$$

$$Cu + 2H_2SO_4 \text{(conc.)} \longrightarrow CuSO_4 + SO_2 + 2H_2O$$

Structure

S-atom is sp^3-hybridised. SO_4^{2-} ion is tetrahedral. There are four σ-bonds and two π-bonds between S and O atoms (with two π-bonds delocalised over the S and the four O atoms).

Uses It is used in petroleum refining, in pigments paints and in detergents manufacturing.

3. Hypo

It is chemically sodium thiosulphate pentahydrate, $Na_2S_2O_3 \cdot 5H_2O$.

Preparation 1. It is prepared by boiling sodium sulphite solution with flowers of sulphur and stirring till the alkaline reaction has disappeared.

$$Na_2SO_3 + S \longrightarrow Na_2S_2O_3$$

2. It is also prepared by **spring's reaction.**

$$Na_2S + Na_2SO_3 + I_2 \longrightarrow Na_2S_2O_3 + 2NaI$$

Properties 1. It is a colourless, crystalline and efflorescent substance.

2. It gives white ppt with a dilute solution of $AgNO_3$ which quickly changes into black due to the formation of Ag_2S.

$$S_2O_3^{2-} + 2Ag^+ \longrightarrow \underset{\text{White ppt}}{Ag_2S_2O_3}$$

$$Ag_2S_2O_3 + H_2O \longrightarrow Ag_2S + H_2SO_4$$

Uses

1. Due to its property of dissolving silver halide, it is used in photography for fixing under the name hypo.

$$2Na_2S_2O_3 + AgBr \longrightarrow Na_3[Ag(S_2O_3)_2] + NaBr$$

ring bleaching, it is used as an antichlor.

$$Na_2S_2O_3 + Cl_2 + H_2O \longrightarrow Na_2SO_4 + S + 2HCl$$

3. It is used to remove iodine stain, for volumetric estimation of iodine and in medicines.

Group 17

The 17 group of Periodic Table contains five elements **fluorine** (F), **chlorine** (Cl), **bromine** (Br), **iodine** (I) and **astatine** (As) collectively known as halogens (salt forming elements). Astatine is artificially prepared radioactive element.

General Physical Properties of Group 17 Elements

(i) **Electronic configuration** Their valence shell electronic configuration is ns^2, np^5.

Element	Atomic number	Electronic configuration
Fluorine (F)	9	[He] $2s^2 2p^5$
Chlorine (Cl)	17	[Ne] $3s^2 3p^5$
Bromine (Br)	35	[Ar] $3d^{10}, 4s^2 4p^5$
Iodine (I)	53	[Kr] $4d^{10}, 5s^2 5p^5$
Astatine (At)	85	[Xe] $4f^{14}, 5d^{10}, 6s^2 6p^5$

(ii) **Physical state** Intermolecular forces in halogens are weak and increase down the group. Thus, F_2 and Cl_2 are gases, Br_2 is volatile liquid and I_2 is solid.

(iii) **Atomicity** All are diatomic in nature.

(iv) **Abundance** Being very reactive in nature, they are not found free in nature. Their presence in earth's crust follows the order

$$F_2 > Cl_2 > Br_2 > I_2$$

(v) **Colour** They absorb light in the visible range forming excited states and are thus, coloured in nature.

F_2	Cl_2	Br_2	I_2
Pale yellow	Yellowish green	Reddish brown	Deep violet

(vi) **Metallic character** All the elements are non-metals and metallic character increases down the group. Thus, I forms I^+.

(vii) **Oxidation state**

F	Cl	Br	I	At
-1	-1 to $+6$	-1 to $+6$	-1 to $+7$	$-1, +1, +5$

(viii) **Bond energy and bond length** The bond length increases from fluorine to iodine and in the same order bond dissociation energy decreases. However, the bond dissociation energy of F_2 is lesser due to its smaller size. The order of bond dissociation energy is $Cl_2 > Br_2 > F_2 > I_2$.

But the order of bond length is F—F < Cl—Cl < Br—Br < I—I

(ix) **Density** It increases down the group in a regular fashion and follows the order I > Br > Cl > F.

(x) **Ionisation enthalpy** The ionisation enthalpy of halogens is very high and decreases down the group. The iodine also forms I^+ and I^{3+} and forms compounds like ICl, ICN, IPO_4. In molten state, the compounds conduct electricity showing ionic character.

(xi) **Electron affinity** The halogens have the high values for electron affinity. The order of electron affinity is

$$Cl > F > Br > I$$

Due to small size of fluorine (hence, high electron density), the extra electron to be added feels more electron-electron repulsion. Therefore, fluorine has less value for electron affinity than chlorine.

(xii) **Reduction potentials and oxidising nature** $E°_{red}$ of halogens are positive and decrease from F to I. Therefore, halogens act as strong oxidising agents and their oxidising power decreases from fluorine to iodine. Fluorine is the strongest oxidising agent and is most reactive. That's why it is prepared by the electrolysis of a mixture of KHF_2 and anhydrous HF using Monel metal as a catalyst.

(xii) **Solubility**   Halogens are soluble in water which follows the order

$$F_2 > Cl_2 > Br_2 > I_2$$

The solubility of iodine in water is enhanced in the presence of KI.

$$KI + I_2 \rightleftharpoons KI_3 \rightleftharpoons K^+ + I_3^-$$

I_2 forms blue colour complex with starch.

Chemical Properties of Group 17 Elements

(i) **Hydrides**   HF is a low boiling liquid due to intermolecular hydrogen bonding, while HCl, HBr, HI are gases. The boiling point follows the trend

$$HF > HI > HBr > HCl$$

Some other properties show the following trend :

HI > HBr > HCl > HF	HI < HBr < HCl < HF
Acid strength, Reducing character, Bond length	Thermal stability, Dipole moment, Bond strength, Stability

(ii) **Oxides**   Fluorine forms two oxides, OF_2 and O_2F_2, but only OF_2 is thermally stable at 298 K. O_2F_2 oxidises plutonium to PuF_6 and the reaction is used for removing plutonium as PuF_6 from spent nuclear fuel.

Chlorine forms a number of oxides such as, Cl_2O, Cl_2O_3, Cl_2O_5, Cl_2O_7, ClO_2 and ClO_2 is used as a bleaching agent for paper pulp, textiles and in water treatment.

Br_2O, BrO_2, BrO_3 are the least stable bromine oxides and exist only at low temperatures. They are very powerful oxidising agents.

The iodine oxides, i.e. I_2O_4, I_2O_5, I_2O_7 are insoluble solids and decompose on heating. I_2O_5 is a very good oxidising agent and is used in the estimation of carbon monoxide.

(iii) **Reaction with alkali**

$$\underset{\text{(Cold dilute)}}{2F_2 + 2NaOH} \longrightarrow 2NaF + OF_2 + H_2O$$

$$\underset{\text{(Hot conc.)}}{2F_2 + 4NaOH} \longrightarrow 4NaF + O_2 + 2H_2O$$

Other halogens form hypohalite with dilute NaOH and halate with conc. NaOH,

$$X_2(g) + 2OH^- \xrightarrow{150°C} X^- + OX^- + H_2O$$

$$\text{(Cold, dilute)} \qquad\qquad \text{(Hypohalite ion)}$$

$$X_2(g) + 6OH^- \xrightarrow{70°C} 5X^- + XO_3^- + 3H_2O$$

$$\text{(Hot, conc.)} \qquad\qquad \text{(Halate ion)}$$

(iv) **Oxoacids of halogens** Higher oxoacids of fluorine such as HFO_2, HFO_3 do not exist because fluorine is most electronegative and has absence of d-orbitals. +3 oxidation state of bromine and iodine are unstable due to inert pair effect, therefore, $HBrO_2$ and HIO_2 do not exist. Acidic character of oxoacids decreases as the electronegativity of halogen atom decreases. Thus, the order of acidic strength.

HOF	>	HOCl	>	HOBr	>
(Hypofluorous acid)		(Hypochlorous acid)		(Hypobromous acid)	

$$\text{HOI}$$

$$\xrightarrow{\text{Acidic nature decreases}} \qquad \text{(Hypoiodous acid)}$$

For the oxoacids of same halogens, acidic strength and thermal stability increase as the number of O atoms increases.

Anomalour Behaviour of Fluorine

Fluorine (F) differs from other elements of the group because of its exceptionally small atomic and ionic size and low F—F bond dissociation energy. Fluorine is more reactive than other halogens. It always has oxidation state of −1, ionic and strongest oxidising agent. It also forms strong hydrogen bonds.

Interhalogen Compounds

Interhalogens are the compounds that are formed by two different halogens. Depending upon the ratio in which two halogens combine, they are known to be of four types viz. larger halogen always be the central atom.

Preparation

The type of interhalogen formed, however, depends upon the conditions. Some of the reactions are discussed below.

- $Cl_2(g) + F_2(g) \xrightarrow{437 \text{ K}} 2ClF(g)$
  Equal volume

- $Cl_2(g) + 3F_2(g) \xrightarrow{573 \text{ K}} 2ClF_3(g)$
  Excess

- $ClF(g) + F_2(g) \xrightarrow{475-575 \text{ K}} ClF_3(g)$

- $Br_2(l) + 3F_2(g) \longrightarrow 2BrF_3(l)$
  Diluted with water

- $Br_2(l) + 5F_2 \longrightarrow 2BrF_5$
  Excess

- $I_2 + Cl_2 \longrightarrow 2ICl$
  Equimolar

- $I_2 + 3Cl_2 \longrightarrow 2ICl_3$
  Excess

General and Physical Properties

(*i*) These are covalent compounds because of small electronegativity difference.

(*ii*) Interhalogen compounds can never have more than two different halogens in a molecule.

(*iii*) Interhalogen ions can be either cations or anions.

(*iv*) The interhalogen compounds are generally more reactive than the halogens (except F_2). This is because the $A—X$ bond in interhalogens is weaker than the $X—X$ bond in the halogens.

(*v*) Hydrolysis of interhalogens give halide and oxohalide.

(*vi*) Interhalogens compound fluorinate many metal oxides, metal halides and metals.

Chemical Properties

(*i*) **Reactivity** These compounds are generally more reactive than the halogens (except F_2). Their order is as follows

$$ClF_3 > BrF_3 > IF_7 > ClF > BrF_3 > IF_5 > BrF > IF_3 > IF$$

(*ii*) **Thermal stability**

Thermal stability	IF	BrF	ClF	ICl	IBr	BrCl
Electronegativity difference	1.5	1.2	1.0	0.5	0.3	0.2

(*iii*) **Hydrolysis** Interhalogen compounds when undergo hydrolysis gives halide ion derived from the *smaller halogen* along with a hypohalite (when XY) or halite (when XY_3) or halate (when XY_5) or perhalate (when XY_7) anion derived from the larger halogen.

Pseudohalogens and Pseudohalides

The substances behaving like halogens are known as pseudohalides. Some examples are

Pseudohalogen	Pseudohalide ion
$(CN)_2$ Cyanogen	$\overline{C}N$ Cyanide
$(OCN)_2$ Oxycyanogen	$\overline{O}CN$ Cyanate
	$\overline{S}CN$ Thiocyanate

Chlorine and Its Compounds

Occurrence

Common salt, NaCl is most important. Chlorine is also present in sea water and as rock salt.

Preparation of Chlorine

(i) **By oxidation of conc. HCl**

$$4NaCl + MnO_2 + 4H_2SO_4 \longrightarrow 4NaHSO_4 + MnCl_2 + 2H_2O + Cl_2$$

(ii) **Weldon's process**

$$MnO_2 + 4HCl \longrightarrow MnCl_2 + 2H_2O + Cl_2$$

(iii) **Deacon's process** In this process, HCl is oxidised by O_2 in the presence of $CuCl_2$ as catalyst at 400°C.

$$4HCl + O_2 \longrightarrow 2Cl_2 + 2H_2O$$

(iv) **Electrolytic process** By the electrolysis of brine solution in Nelson cell.

$$NaCl \rightleftharpoons Na^+ + Cl^-$$

$$2Na^+ + 2e^- \longrightarrow 2Na + H_2O \longrightarrow 2NaOH + H_2 \uparrow \text{ [at cathode]}$$

$$2Cl^- \longrightarrow 2Cl + 2e^- \longrightarrow Cl_2 \uparrow \qquad \text{[at anode]}$$

Properties

It is yellowish green gas, collected by upward displacement of air, poisonous in nature, soluble in water. It's aqueous solution is known as chlorine water.

Chemical Reactions

(i) **Action of water**

$$Cl_2 + H_2O \longrightarrow HOCl + HCl$$

$$HOCl \longrightarrow HCl + \underset{\text{Nascent oxygen}}{[O]}$$

Coloured matter + [O] $\longrightarrow$ colourless matter.

The bleaching action of chlorine is due to oxidation and is permanent.

(ii) **Action of hydrogen**

$$H_2 + Cl_2 \xrightarrow[\text{Charcoal catalyst}]{\text{UV light}} 2HCl$$

(iii) **Displacement reactions**

$$2KBr + Cl_2 \longrightarrow 2KCl + Br_2$$

$$2KI + Cl_2 \longrightarrow 2KCl + I_2$$

(iv) **Action of NaOH** (cold)

$$2NaOH + Cl_2 \longrightarrow NaCl + NaOCl + H_2O$$

Aqueous solution of NaOCl is called Javelle water.

(v) **Action of H$_2$S**

$$H_2S + Cl_2 \longrightarrow 2HCl + S$$

(vi) **Action of dry SO$_2$**

$$SO_2 + Cl_2 \longrightarrow SO_2Cl_2$$

(vii) **Action of CO**

$$CO + Cl_2 \longrightarrow \underset{\text{Phosgene}}{COCl_2}$$

(viii) **Oxidising properties**

$$SO_2 + Cl_2 + 2H_2O \longrightarrow H_2SO_4 + 2HCl$$

$$2FeSO_4 + Cl_2 + H_2SO_4 \longrightarrow Fe_2(SO_4)_3 + 2HCl$$

(ix) **Reaction with ammonia**

(a) When ammonia is in excess,

$$8NH_3 + 3Cl_2 \longrightarrow N_2 + 6NH_4Cl$$

(b) When chlorine is in excess,

$$NH_3 + 3Cl_2 \longrightarrow NCl_3 + 3HCl$$

(x) **Chromyl chloride test** When a mixture of chloride and solid K$_2$Cr$_2$O$_7$ is heated with concentrated H$_2$SO$_4$, in a dry test tube, deep red vapours of chromyl chloride are evolved.

$$Cl^- + K_2Cr_2O_7 + H_2SO_4 \longrightarrow \underset{\text{Red vapours}}{CrO_2Cl_2} + KHSO_4 + HSO_4^- + H_2O$$

When these vapours are passed through NaOH solution, the solution becomes yellow due to the formation of sodium chromate.

$$CrO_2Cl_2 + 4NaOH \longrightarrow \underset{\text{Yellow}}{Na_2CrO_4} + 2NaCl + 2H_2O$$

The yellow solution is neutralised with acetic acid and on addition of lead acetate, gives a yellow precipitate of lead chromate.

$$Na_2CrO_4 + Pb(CH_3COO)_2 \longrightarrow \underset{\text{Yellow ppt}}{PbCrO_4} + 2CH_3COONa$$

Uses

It is used as a bleaching agent, disinfectant and in the manufacture of CHCl$_3$, CCl$_4$, DDT, anti-knocking compounds and bleaching powder.

Hydrochloric Acid (HCl)

Preparation

$$NaCl + H_2SO_4 \xrightarrow{420\ K} NaHSO_4 + HCl$$

$$NaHSO_4 + NaCl \xrightarrow{823\ K} Na_2SO_4 + HCl$$

Properties

It is a colourless and pungent smelling gas. It is extremely soluble in water and ionises as below

$$HCl(g) + H_2O(l) \longrightarrow H_3O^+(aq) + Cl^-(aq)$$

Its other reaction are as

$$NH_3 + HCl \longrightarrow NH_4Cl$$
$$Na_2CO_3 + 2HCl \longrightarrow 2NaCl + H_2O + CO_2\uparrow$$
$$NaHCO_3 + HCl \longrightarrow NaCl + H_2O + CO_2\uparrow$$
$$Na_2SO_3 + 2HCl \longrightarrow 2NaCl + H_2O + SO_2\uparrow$$

Noble metals like gold, platinum can dissolve in aqua-regia [three part conc HCl and one part of conc HNO_3].

Uses

It is used in the manufacture of chlorides, cholrine, in textile and dyeing industries, in medicine and in extraction of glue from animal tissues and bones.

Iodine (I_2)

It's major source is deep sea weeds of laminaria variety. Their ashes which is called kelp contain 0.5% iodine as iodides.

Another source of I_2 is caliche or crude chile salt petre ($NaNO_3$) which contains 0.2%, $NaIO_3$.

Iodine is purified by sublimation.

It shows no reaction with water. Tincture of iodine is a mixture of I_2 and KI dissolved in rectified spirit.

Oxoacids of Halogens

Being highly electronegative and small size, fluorine forms only one oxoacid, HOF, as fluoric (I) acid or hypofluorus acid on reaction with water.

Other member of halogen form four series of oxoacids with formula HOX [halic (I) acid or hypohalous acid], HOXO [halic (III) acid or halous acid], HOXO$_2$ [halic (V) acid or halic acid] and HOXO$_3$ [halic (VII)] acid or perhalic acid].

Hypochelorous acid   Chlorous acid   Chloric acid   Perchloric acid

Structures of oxoacids of chlorine

18 Group

The 18 group of the Periodic Table consists of colourless, odourless gases at room temperature, isolated by William Ramsay in 1898 from air.

General/Physical Characteristics of Group 18 Elements

(i) **Electronic configuration** Their valence shell electronic configuration is ns^2np^6 except He.

Element	Atomic number	Electronic configuration
Helium (He)	2	$1s^2$
Neon (Ne)	10	$[He]\,2s^2 2p^6$
Argon (Ar)	18	$[Ne]\,3s^2 3p^6$
Krypton (Kr)	36	$[Ar]\,3d^{10},\,4s^2 4p^6$
Xenon (Xe)	54	$[Kr]\,4d^{10},\,5s^2 5p^6$
Radon (Rn)	86	$[Xe]\,4f^{14},\,5d^{10},\,6s^2 6p^6$

(ii) **Physical state** They are all gases under ordinary conditions of temperature and pressure.

(iii) **Abundance** In 1.0% air, the abundance follows the order

$$Ar > Ne > He > Kr > Xe$$

(iv) **Atomicity** The $C_p / C_V = 1.67$ shows their monoatomic nature. However under high energy conditions, several molecular ions such as He_2^+, HeH^+, HeH^{2+} and Ar_2^+ are formed in discharge tubes. They only survive momentarily and are detected spectroscopically.

(v) **Melting and boiling points** Due to the increase in magnitude of van der Waals' forces, the melting point and boiling point increases from He to Rn.

(vi) **Atomic radii** The atomic radii increases from He to Rn. It corresponds to the van der Waals' radii. So it has greatest atomic size in respective period.

(vii) **Density** The density of noble gases increases down the group (except density of Ne < He) .

(viii) **Heat of vaporisation** They have very low values of heat of vaporisation due to weak van der Waals' forces of attraction. The value increases down the group.

(ix) **Solubility in water** They are slightly soluble in water and solubility increases from He to Rn.

(x) **Liquefication** It is extremely difficult to liquify inert gases due to weak van der Waals' forces of attraction among their molecules. Hence, they posses low value of critical temperature also.

(xi) **Ionisation energy** All noble gases possess very stable outer electronic configuration (ns^2 and $ns^2 np^6$). Therefore, ionisation energy of noble gases is very high and decreases down the group.

(xii) **Electron affinity** Due to the presence of stable electronic configuration, they have no tendency to accept additional electron. Therefore, electron affinity of the elements of this group is almost zero.

Chemical Properties of Group 18 Elements

The noble gases are inert in nature because of their completely filled subshells. In 1962, the first compound of noble gases was prepared. It is hexafluoroplatinate (prepared by Bartlett).

$$Xe + PtF_6 \longrightarrow Xe[PtF_6]$$

Now, many compounds of Xe and Kr are known with fluorine and oxygen.

Preparation of Compounds of Xenon

(i) $\underset{\text{(Xe in excess)}}{Xe(g)} + F_2(g) \xrightarrow{\text{673 K, 1 bar}} XeF_2(s)$

(ii) $\underbrace{Xe(g) + 2F_2(g)}_{\text{(1 : 5 ratio)}} \xrightarrow{\text{873 K, 7 bar}} XeF_4(s)$

(iii) $\underbrace{Xe(g) + 3F_2(g)}_{\text{(1 : 20 ratio)}} \xrightarrow{\text{573 K, 60-70 bar}} XeF_6(s)$

(iv) $XeF_4 + O_2F_2 \longrightarrow XeF_6 + O_2$

Chemical Reactions of Xenon Compounds

$$XeF_2 + PF_5 \longrightarrow [XeF]^+ [PF_6]^-$$

$$XeF_4 + SbF_5 \longrightarrow [XeF_3]^+ [SbF_6]^-$$

$$XeF_6 + H_2O \longrightarrow XeOF_4 + 2HF$$

$$XeF_6 + 2H_2O \longrightarrow XeO_2F_2 + 4HF$$

$$2XeF_4 + 3H_2O \longrightarrow Xe + XeO_3 + 4HF + F_2$$

$$XeF_6 + 3H_2O \longrightarrow XeO_3 + 6HF$$

Partial hydrolysis of XeF_6 gives oxyfluorides, $XeOF_4$ and XeO_2F_2.

XeF_2, XeF_4 and XeF_6 are colourless, crystalline solids and sublime readily at 298 K. They are powerful fluorinating agents.

XeF_6 cannot be stored in glass vessels because it reacts with silica of glass and finally give explosise XeO_3.

$$2XeF_6 + SiO_2 \longrightarrow 2XeOF_4 + SiF_4$$
$$2XeOF_4 + SiO_2 \longrightarrow 2XeO_2F_2 + SiF_4$$
$$2XeO_2F_4 + SiO_2 \longrightarrow 2XeO_3 + SiF_4$$

XeO_4^{2-} is called xenontetronide ion and XeO_6^{4-} is called perxenate ion. They form clathrates with many inorganic and organic molecules.

Structure of Xenon Compounds

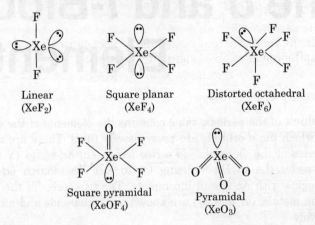

Linear (XeF₂) Square planar (XeF₄) Distorted octahedral (XeF₆)

Square pyramidal (XeOF₄) Pyramidal (XeO₃)

Uses of Noble Gas

1. A mixture of $He + O_2$ is used for respiration by deep sea divers. He is also used to fill balloons and air ships because of its non-inflammable nature.

2. Ne is used in discharge lamps and signs, in botanical gardens and the greenhouses as it stimulates growth of plants and accelerate chlorophyll formation.

3. Ar is used for filling incandescent metal filament electric bulbs and to provide an inert atmosphere in high temperature metallurgical processes.

4. Rn is used in the treatment of cancer.

20

The *d* and *f*-Block Elements

The **d-block** of the periodic table contains the elements of the groups 3-12 in which the *d*-orbitals are progressively filled. There are mainly three series of the elements, *3d*-series (Sc to Zn) *4d*-series (Y to Cd) and *5d*-series (La to Hg omitting Ce to Lu). The fourth *6d*-series which begins with Ac is still incomplete. The two series of the inner-transition metals, (4*f* and 5*f*) are known as lanthanoids and actinoids respectively.

Transition Elements

Elements having partially filled *d*-orbitals in ground state or in excited state, are known as transition elements. They have been placed in the centre of the Periodic Table between *s*-block and *p*-block elements.

Iron is the most abundant and widely used transition metal.

General Electronic Configuration of Transition Elements

Transition elements have the electronic configuration $(n-1)d^{1-10}\ ns^{0-2}$. Zn, Cd, Hg, the end members of first three series have general electronic configuration $(n-1)d^{10}ns^2$. These elements do not show properties of transition elements to any extent and are called **non-typical transition elements**.

Electronic configuration of transition elements

3d-Series			4d-Series			5d-Series		
At. no.	Element	Electronic configuration	At. no.	Element	Electronic configuration	At. no.	Element	Electronic configuration
21	Sc	[Ar]$3d^1 4s^2$	39	Y	[Kr]$4d^1 5s^2$	57	La	[Xe]$5d^1 6s^2$
22	Ti	[Ar]$3d^2 4s^2$	40	Zr	[Kr]$4d^2 5s^2$	72	Hf	[Xe]$4f^{14} 5d^2 6s^2$
23	V	[Ar]$3d^3 4s^2$	41	Nb	[Kr]$4d^4 5s^1$	73	Ta	[Xe]$4f^{14} 5d^3 6s^2$
24	Cr	[Ar]$3d^5 4s^1$	42	Mo	[Kr]$4d^5 5s^1$	74	W	[Xe]$4f^{14} 5d^4 6s^2$
25	Mn	[Ar]$3d^5 4s^2$	43	Tc	[Kr]$4d^5 5s^2$	75	Re	[Xe]$4f^{14} 5d^5 6s^2$
26	Fe	[Ar]$3d^6 4s^2$	44	Ru	[Kr]$4d^7 5s^1$	76	Os	[Xe]$4f^{14} 5d^6 5s^2$
27	Co	[Ar]$3d^7 4s^2$	45	Rh	[Kr]$4d^8 5s^1$	77	Ir	[Xe]$4f^{14} 5d^7 6s^2$
28	Ni	[Ar]$3d^8 4s^2$	46	Pd	[Kr]$4d^{10} 5s^0$	78	Pt	[Xe]$4f^{14} 5d^9 6s^1$
29	Cu	[Ar]$3d^{10} 4s^1$	47	Ag	[Kr]$4d^{10} 5s^1$	79	Au	[Xe]$4f^{14} 5d^{10} 6s^1$
30	Zn	[Ar]$3d^{10} 4s^2$	48	Cd	[Kr]$4d^{10} 5s^2$	80	Hg	[Xe]$4f^{14} 5d^{10} 6s^2$

General Physical Properties of Transition Elements

(i) **Atomic and ionic size** Ions of the same charge in a given series exhibit regular decrease in radius with increasing atomic number, because the new electron enters in a *d*-orbital and nuclear charge increases by unity.

In last of the series, a small increase in size is observed due to electron-electron repulsion.

Atomic and ionic radii increase from 3d-series to 4d-series but the radii of the third (5d) series elements are virtually the same as those of the corresponding member of the second series. It can be explained on the basis of lanthanoid contraction [poor shielding of 4f].

(ii) **Ionisation enthalpies** In a series as we move from left to right, ionization enthalpy increases due to increase in nuclear charge but not in regular trend.

The irregular trend in the first ionisation enthalpy of the 3d metals, though of little chemical significance, can be accounted by considering that the removal of one electron alters the relative energies of 4s and 3d-orbitals.

(iii) **Oxidation states** Transition metals show variable oxidation state due to two incomplete outermost shells. Only stable oxidation states of the first row transition metals are

Sc(+3), Ti(+4), V(+5), Cr(+3, +6), Mn(+2, +7),

Fe(+2, +3), Co(+2, +3), Ni(+2), Cu(+2), Zn(+2).

The transition elements in their lower oxidation states (+2 and +3) usually form ionic compounds. In higher oxidation state, compounds are normally covalent.

Only Os and Ru show +8 oxidation states in fluorides and oxides.

Ni and Fe in $Ni(CO)_4$ and $Fe(CO)_5$ show zero oxidation state.

(iv) **Enthalpy of atomisation** Transition elements exhibit higher enthalpies of atomisation. Because of the presence of a large number of unpaired electrons in their atoms, they have stronger interatomic interactions and hence, stronger bonds.

(v) **Trends in the M^{2+}/M standard electrode potentials** $E^\circ_{M^{2+}/M}$ is governed by three factors. Enthalpy of sublimation, enthalpy of ionisation and enthalpy of hydration.

The irregular trend of M^{2+}/M electrods potentials in 3d-series is due to irregular variation in ionisation enthalpy and heat of sublimation.

Except copper, 3d series elements are good reducing agents.

If sum of the first and second ionisation enthalpies is greater than hydration enthalpy, standard potential $(E^\circ_{M^{2+}/M})$ will be positive and reactivity will be lower and *vice-versa*.

Trends in the M^{3+}/M^{2+} Standard Electrode Potentials

An examination of the $E^\ominus (M^{3+}/M^{2+})$ values shows the varying trends. The low value for Sc^{3+}/Sc^{2+} reflects the stability of Sc^{3+} which has a noble gas configuration. The highest value for Zn^{3+}/Zn^{2+} is due to the removal of an electron from the stable d^{10} configuration of Zn^{2+}.

(vi) **Melting and boiling point** Due to strong metallic bond, they have high mp and bp. The mp of these elements become maximum in the middle and then decreases with the increase in atomic number. Manganese and technetium show abnormal values in the trend. Tungsten has the highest m.p. (3410°C).

Mercury is liquid at room temperature (mp – 38.9°C) due to absence of unpaired electrons, and weak metallic bonding.

(vii) **Density** d-block elements have high density because of their small atomic size and strong metallic bonding.

Densities of 3d series elements

Density	Sc	Ti	V	Cr	Mn	Fe	Co	Ni	Cu	Zn
g/cm³	3.0	4.54	6.12	7.19	7.40	7.87	8.74	8.90	8.92	7.13

Osmium has slightly lower density (22.52 g cm^{-3}) as compared to iridium (22.61 g cm^{-2}). Thus, iridium has the highest density among transition metals.

(viii) **Atomic volume**   Atomic volume decreases along the period due to decrease in atomic size.

(ix) **Chemical reactivity** d-block elements are less reactive due to high ionisation energies. Some are almost inert and known as noble metals, e.g. Au, Pt, Os, Ir, etc.

(x) **Complex formation**   They are well known to form a large number of complex compounds mainly due to

   (a) small atomic size and high nuclear charge

   (b) presence of partially filled or vacant d-orbitals, e.g. $K_4[Fe(CN)_6]$

(xi) **Magnetic properties**

   (a) **Paramagnetic** nature is due to the presence of unpaired electrons in d-orbitals. Paramagnetic character increases with increase in the number of unpaired electrons (n) and highest for Mn(II) [among $3d$-series].

   (b) Diamagnetic substances are repelled by applied magnetic field and have no unpaired electron.

   (c) In ferromagnetism, permanent magnetic character is acquired by substance, e.g. Fe.

   Magnetic moment (μ) is given by

   $$\mu = \sqrt{n\,(n+2)} \text{ BM,} \qquad \text{(Bohr magneton)}$$

(xii) **Coloured ions**   Colour exhibited by transition metal ions is due to the presence of unpaired electrons in d-orbitals and is due to the d-d transitions of electrons. When visible light is incident on the ion, an electron from a lower energy d-orbital is excited to a higher energy d-orbital.

Colour of a complex depends on the metal, its oxidation state and its ligands, e.g. $[Cu(H_2O)_4]^{2+}$ is pale blue while $[Cu(NH_3)_4]^{2+}$ is dark blue. $CuSO_4 \cdot 5H_2O$ is blue in colour and anhydrous $CuSO_4$ is colourless.

Charge transfer also gives intense colour e.g. MnO_4^- ion does not contain any unpaired d-electron. Its purple colour is due to charge transfer from O to Mn, thus O^{2-} changes to O^- and Mn(VII) to Mn(VI). Charge transfer is possible only when the energy levels on the two different atoms involved are fairly close.

(xiii) **Catalytic properties** The transition metals and their compounds behave like catalyst due to

(a) the presence of partially filled d-orbitals resulting in variable oxidation states.

(b) formation of intermediate complex with reactants by lowering the energy of activation.

(c) their rough surface area, e.g. provides active sites for adsorption of reactant molecules.

Iron, in the preparation of NH_3 (Haber's process), finely divided nickel for hydrogenation, Pt in the preparation of nitric acid (Ostwald's process) etc.

Some important catalysts having transition metals are

1. Zeigler Natta catalyst : $TiCl_4 + (C_2H_5)_3 Al$
2. Lindlar's catalyst : $Pd/BaSO_4$
3. Wilkinson's catalyst : $[Ph_3P]_3 RhCl$
4. Adam's catalyst : Pt/PtO
5. Brown's catalyst or P-2 catalyst : Nickel boride

(xiv) **Formation of alloys** d-block elements have a strong tendency to form alloys, because their atomic sizes are very similar and in the crystal lattice, one metal can be readily replaced by another. Alloys so formed have high m.p. The metals Mo, W, Cr, Ni, and V are used for the production of stainless steel.

Amalgam is an alloy formed by mercury with other metals. Iron and platinum do not form any alloy with mercury.

List of Alloys

Alloy	Composition (%)	Uses
Stainless steel	Fe = 73, Cr = 18, Ni = 8, C (traces)	Cutlery, machine parts
Coinage alloy or Coinage silver	Ag = 92.5, Cu = 7.5	Coins, Jewellery
Dental alloy	Ag = 33, Hg = 52, Sn = 12.5, Cu = 2, Zn = 0.5	For filling teeth
Brass	Cu = 80, Zn = 20	Utensils, condenser tubes
Bronze	Cu = 80, Sn = 20	Utensils, statues, coins
Gun metal	Cu = 87, Sn = 10, Zn = 3	Gun, gears
Bell metal	Cu = 80, Sn = 20	Bells, Gongs
German silver	Cu = 60, Zn = 20, Ni = 20	Cutlery, resistant wires
Duralumin	Al = 95, Cu = 4, Mg and Mn = 1	Air ships
Misch metal	Ce(25%) + lanthanide metals + 5% Fe + traces of S, C, Si, Ca, Al	Lighter flints

(xv) **Interstitial compounds** The vacant space present in a crystal lattice is known as interstitial site or void. The non-metal atoms (e.g. H, N, C, etc.) due to their small size when occupy such place, the resulting compound is known as interstitial compound. Such compounds are hard and rigid, e.g. cast iron and steel.

(xvi) **Non-stoichiometric compounds** The compounds not having the elements in the exact ratio as in the ideal crystal are known as non-stoichiometric compounds, e.g. in $Fe_{0.94}O_1$, the Fe : O is approx 0.94 : 1 and not exactly 1 : 1. It is due to the variability of oxidation state in the transition metal.

(xvii) **Spinel** These are the mixed oxides in which oxygen atoms constitute a fcc lattice, e.g. $ZnFe_2O_4$. It is a normal spinel in which the trivalent ions occupy the octahedral holes and divalent ions occupy the tetrahedral holes.

In inverse spinel, the trivalent ion occupy the tetrahedral holes and divalent ion occupy the octahedral holes. e.g. $FeFe_2O_4$ or Fe_3O_4.

Some important reagents having transition metals

1. **Baeyer's reagent** Dilute alkaline $KMnO_4$, used to test the presence of unsaturation.

2. **Tollen's reagent** Ammoniacal solution of $AgNO_3$, i.e. $[Ag(NH_3)_2]OH$, used to test the aldehyde group.

3. **Nessler's reagent** Alkaline solution of K_2HgI_4 is used to test $NH_3(g)$ and NH_4^+.

4. **Benedict's solution** $CuSO_4$ solution + sodium citrate + Na_2CO_3, used to test the aldehyde group.

5. **Lucas reagent** HCl (conc.) + anhydrous $ZnCl_2$, used to distinguish between 1°, 2° and 3° alcohols.

Applications of Transition Elements

1. A mixture of TiO_2 and $BaSO_4$ is called titanox and a mixture of $ZnS + BaSO_4$ is called lithopone.

2. $TiCl_2$ and TiO_2 are used in smoke screens. TiO_2 is also used as white pigment of paints.

3. Tentalum is used in surgical venals and analytical weights.

4. Chromium is used in stainless steel and chrome plating.

5. Mo is used in X-rays tubes. Pt is used in resistance thermometers.

6. Cd is used for making joints in jewellery.

7. Ce is used as a scavenger of oxygen and sulphur in many metals.

Compounds of *d*-block Elements

1. Potassium Dichromate ($K_2Cr_2O_7$)

Ore Ferrochrome or chromite ($FeO \cdot Cr_2O_3$) or ($FeCr_2O_4$)

Preparation

$$4FeO \cdot Cr_2O_3 + 8Na_2CO_3 + 7O_2 \longrightarrow \underset{\text{Yellow}}{8Na_2CrO_4} + 2Fe_2O_3 + 8CO_2\uparrow$$

$$2Na_2CrO_4 + 2H^+ \longrightarrow \underset{\text{Orange}}{Na_2Cr_2O_7} + 2Na^+ + H_2O$$

$$Na_2Cr_2O_7 + 2KCl \longrightarrow K_2Cr_2O_7 + 2NaCl$$

Sodium dichromate is more soluble than potassium dichromate.

Chromates and dichromates are interconvertible in aqueous solution depending upon pH of the solutions.

Chromate ion   Dichromate ion

Properties Sodium and potassium dichromates are strong oxidising agents, thus, acidified $K_2Cr_2O_7$ will oxidise iodides to iodine, sulphides to sulphur, tin (II) to tin (IV) and iron (II) salts to iron (III).

$$Cr_2O_7^{2-} + 14H^+ + 6I^- \longrightarrow 2Cr^{3+} + 7H_2O + 3I_2$$

$$Cr_2O_7^{2-} + 3H_2S + 8H^+ \longrightarrow 2Cr^{3+} + 3S + 7H_2O$$

$$Cr_2O_7^{2-} + 14H^+ + 3Sn^{2+} \longrightarrow 3Sn^{4+} + 2Cr^{3+} + 7H_2O$$

Uses

1. $K_2Cr_2O_7$ is used as an oxidising agent in volumetric analysis.
2. It is used in mordant dyes, leather industry, photography (for hardening of film).
3. It is used in chromyl chloride test.
4. It is used in cleaning glassware.

2. Potassium Permanganate ($KMnO_4$)

Ore Pyrolusite (MnO_2)

Preparation

$$2MnO_2 + 4KOH + O_2 \longrightarrow \underset{\text{Green}}{2K_2MnO_4} + 2H_2O$$

$$3MnO_4^{2-} + 4H^+ \longrightarrow 2MnO_4^- + MnO_2 + 2H_2O$$

Commercial preparation

$$MnO_2 \xrightarrow[\text{with air or KNO}_3]{\text{Fused with KOH, oxidised}} \underset{\text{Manganate ion}}{MnO_4^{2-}}$$

$$MnO_4^{2-} \xrightarrow[\text{(alkaline medium)}]{\text{Electrolytic oxidation}} \underset{\substack{\text{Permanganate ion} \\ \text{(purple)}}}{MnO_4^-}$$

Properties $KMnO_4$ acts as strong oxidising agent.

1. In the presence of dilute H_2SO_4, $KMnO_4$ is reduced to manganous salt.

$$MnO_4^- + 8H^+ + 5e^- \longrightarrow Mn^{2+} + 4H_2O$$

Acidic $KMnO_4$ solution oxidises oxalates to CO_2, iron(II) to iron (III), nitrites to nitrates and iodides to iodine. The half-reactions of reductants are

$$5C_2O_4^{2-} \longrightarrow 10CO_2 + 10e^-$$
$$5Fe^{2+} \longrightarrow 5Fe^{3+} + 5e^-$$
$$5NO_2^- + 5H_2O \longrightarrow 5NO_3^- + 10H^+ + 10e^-$$
$$10I^- \longrightarrow 5I_2 + 10e^-$$

To acidify $KMnO_4$, only H_2SO_4 is used and not HCl or HNO_3 because HCl reacts with $KMnO_4$ and produce Cl_2 while HNO_3, itself acts as oxidising agent.

2. In alkaline medium, $KMnO_4$ is reduced to insoluble MnO_2.

$$MnO_4^- + 3e^- + 2H_2O \longrightarrow MnO_2 + 4OH^-$$

Alkaline or neutral $KMnO_4$ solution oxidises I^- to IO_3^-, $S_2O_3^{2-}$ to SO_4^{2-}, Mn^{2+} to MnO_2, etc.

Aqueous $KMnO_4$ reacts with NH_3 to liberate N_2 gas.

$$2KMnO_4 + 2NH_3 \longrightarrow 2KOH + 2MnO_2 + N_2 + 2H_2O$$

Uses $KMnO_4$ is used

(i) in laboratory preparation of Cl_2.

(ii) as an oxidising agent and disinfectant.

(iii) in making Baeyer's reagent.

(iv) for the bleaching of wool, cotton, silk and other textile fibres and for the decolourisation of oils are also dependent on its strong oxidising power.

Structures

Permanganate ion   Manganate ion

3. Copper Sulphate ($CuSO_4 \cdot 5H_2O$)

It is also known as blue vitriol.

Method of preparation   It is obtained by the action of dil H_2SO_4 on copper scrap in the presence of air.

$$2Cu + 2H_2SO_4 + \underset{(Air)}{O_2} \longrightarrow CuSO_4 + 2H_2O$$

Properties

1. On heating it turns white due to loss of water of crystallisation. At 1000 K, $CuSO_4$ decomposes into CuO and SO_3.

$$CuSO_4 \xrightarrow{1000 \text{ K}} CuO + SO_3$$

2. It gives blue solution with NH_4OH and white ppt of Cu_2I_2 with KI.

Uses   It is used in electroplating, as mordant in dyeing, in making bordeaux mixture [($Ca(OH)_2 + CuSO_4$)], etc.

4. Silver Nitrate ($AgNO_3$)

It is also called Lunar caustic.

Method of preparation   It is prepared by heating silver with dilute nitric acid.

$$3Ag(s) + \underset{\text{Dilute}}{4HNO_3(aq)} \xrightarrow{\Delta} 3AgNO_3(aq) + NO(g) + 2H_2O(l)$$

Properties

1. It is colourless, crystalline compound which blackens when comes in contact of organic substances (skin, cloth, etc.)
2. With potassium dichromate, it gives red ppt of Ag_2CrO_4.
3. On strong heating, it decomposes to metallic silver.

$$2AgNO_3(s) \xrightarrow{\Delta} 2Ag(s) + 2NO_2(g) + O_2(g)$$

4. Ammoniacal solution of silver nitrate is known as Tollen's reagent.

Uses   It is used as laboratory reagent, in silvering of mirror, in the preparation of inks and hair dyes, etc.

Inner-Transition (*f*-block) Elements

The elements in which the filling of atomic orbitals by electrons in valence shell take place in *f*-subshells, two levels inside the outer subshell, are known as inner-transition elements. They are also known as *f*-block elements.

Classification of *f*-Block Elements

They have been classified into two series.

(a) **4*f*-series** (first inner-transition series) The last electron enters in 4*f*-orbital. The elements belonging to this series are also known as **lanthanoids**.

(b) **5*f*-series** (second inner-transition series) The last electron enters in 5*f*-orbital. The elements belonging to this series are also known as **actinoids**.

Lanthanides

The fifteen elements from lanthanum (at. no. 57) to lutetium (at. no. 71) are known as **lanthanoids** or **rare earths**. Their properties are as follows :

Electronic Configuration

The general electronic configuration of these elements is $[Xe]4f^{0-14}5d^{0-1}6s^2$. The lanthanum, electronic configuration $[Xe]4f^05d^16s^2$ and lutetium, electronic configuration $[Xe]4f^{14}5d^16s^2$, have no partially filled 4*f*-orbital in their ground state, are considered as lanthanoids due to their properties close to these elements.

Oxidation State

The most common and most stable oxidation state of lanthanides is +3 but some elements also exhibit +2 and +4 oxidation states in which they leave behind stable ions, e.g.

$$Eu^{2+} = [Xe]4f^7, \quad Yb^{2+} = [Xe]4f^{14}$$
$$Ce^{4+} = [Xe]4f^0, \quad Tb^{4+} = [Xe]4f^7$$

An aqueous solution of Ce^{4+} is a good oxidising agent. The Eu^{2+} and Yb^{2+} can exist in aqueous solution and are good reducing agents. But there are exceptions also, e.g.

$$Sm^{2+} = [Xe]4f^6; \quad Tm^{2+} = [Xe]4f^{13}; \quad Pr^{4+} = [Xe]4f^1$$

Magnetic Properties

Magnetic properties have spin and orbit contributions. Hence, magnetic moments are given by the formula,

$$\mu = \sqrt{4S(S+1) + L(L+1)}$$

Where, L = orbital quantum number, S = spin quantum number

All lanthanoid ions with the exception of La^{3+}, Lu^{3+} and Ce^{4+}, are paramagnetic in nature. For the first row transition elements, the orbital contribution is usually quenched out by interaction with the electric fields of the ligands in its environment. Thus, as a first approximation the magnetic moment can be calculated using the simple spin only formula.

$$\mu_s = \sqrt{n(n+2)}$$

Lanthanoid Contraction

Steady decrease in the atomic and ionic (Ln^{3+}) radii as the atomic number of the lanthanoid elements increases is called lanthanoid contraction. This is because the additional electron goes to $4f$-subshell. These $4f$-orbitals being large and diffuse, have poor shielding effect. The effective nuclear charge increases which causes the contraction in the size of electron charge cloud. This contraction in size is quite regular and is known as lanthanoid contraction.

The f-f transitions are possible due to absorption of light from the visible region.

Consequences of Lanthanoid Contraction

 (i) Covalent character of cations increases.

 (ii) The electronegativity of trivalent ions increases slightly.

 (iii) There is decrease in basic strength of oxides and hydroxides from La to Lu.

 (iv) There is small increase in standard electrode potential values.

 (v) Sizes of Zr and Hf; Nb and Ta are similar, so they are called **chemical twins.**

Colour

The species containing unpaired electrons are coloured and so on in the case of lanthanoid ions.

Melting and Boiling Points

Lanthanoids have high melting and boiling points but there is no regular trend.

Density

Lanthanoids have densities varying from 6.67 to 9.7 g cm^{-3}, but there is no regular trend for these values.

Electronegativity

For lanthanoids, the electronegativity values are almost same as that of s-block elements. Lanthanoids form ionic compounds.

Ionisation Energies

The ionisation energy values of lanthanoids are not very high due to their large size and comparable with those of alkaline earth metals.

Complex Compound

Due to their large ionic size, they have little tendency to form complexes.

Chemical Reactivity

Due to their low values of ionisation energies, the lanthanoids are very reactive.

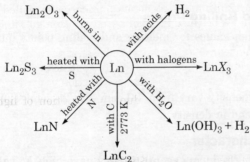

Chemical reactions of lanthanoids

Alloys

They form alloy especially with iron *e.g.* misch metal which consists of a lanthanoids metal 94 ~ 95%, iron ~ 5% and S, C, Ca and Al in traces. Mg mixed with 3% misch metal is used for making jet engine parts.

Actinoids

The fourteen elements from actinium (at. no. 89) on wards to lawrencium (at. no. 103) are known as actinoids and constitute the 5f-series. From neptunium to onwards, the elements are man-made (artificially prepared) and also known as **transuranic elements**.

Electronic Configuration

The last electron in such elements enters in the 5f atomic orbital. Their general electronic configuration is

$$[Rn]5f^{0-14}6d^{0-1}7s^2$$

There is not much difference between the energies of 5f and 6d, so it is difficult to predict whether the electron has entered in 5f or 6d.

Oxidation State

The common oxidation state is +3 but other oxidation states are also exhibited by actinoids upto the maximum being +7.

Magnetic Properties

The magnetic moments of actinoid ions are smaller than theoretical values. It is hard to interpret due to large spin orbit coupling.

Actinoid Contraction

It is similar to lanthanide contraction due to poor shielding of $5f$-electrons. It is greater than lanthanoid contraction.

Melting and Boiling Points

They have high values for melting and boiling points but there is no regular trend.

Density

The value of density vary from 7.0 gcm^{-3} to 20 gcm^{-3}. Again there is no regular trend in density.

Reducing character

They are strong reducing agents as they have high $E°$ values approximately 2.0 V.

Reactivity

Actinoids are very reactive in nature and combine with oxygen and halogens like lanthanoids.

Coloured Ions

Actinoid ions are coloured due to the presence of unpaired electrons and f-f transitions.

Complex Formation

They have higher tendency to form complex compounds.

21

Coordination Compounds

Coordination compounds are those molecular compounds which retain their identity in solid state as well as in dissolved state. In these compounds, the central metal atom or ion is linked by ions or molecules with **coordinate bonds.** e.g. potassium ferrocyanide, $K_4[Fe(CN)_6]$.

$$K_4[Fe(CN)_6] \overset{aq}{\rightleftharpoons} 4K^+ + [Fe(CN)_6]^{4-}$$

Central metal atom
↓ ↙ Ligands
$K_4[Fe(CN)_6]$ ← Coordination sphere (entity)
↑ ↑
Counter ion   Coordination number

Double Salts

These are the addition molecular compounds which are stable in solid state but dissociate into constituent ions in the solution. e.g. Mohr's salt, $[FeSO_4 \cdot (NH_4)_2SO_4 \cdot 6H_2O]$ get dissociated into Fe^{2+}, NH_4^+ and SO_4^{2-} ions.

Terms Related to Coordination Compounds

1. Complex Ion or Coordination Entity

It is an electrically charged species in which central metal atom or ion is surrounded by number of ions or neutral molecules.

(i) **Cationic complex entity** It is the complex ion which carries positive charge, e.g. $[Pt(NH_3)_4]^{2+}$.

(ii) **Anionic complex entity** It is the complex ion which carries negative charge, e.g. $[Fe(CN)_6]^{4-}$.

2. Central Atom or Ion

The atom or ion to which a fixed number of ions or groups are bound, is called central atom or ion. It is also referred as Lewis acid. e.g. in $[NiCl_2(H_2O)_4]$, Ni is central metal atom. It is generally transition element or inner-transition element. These central atoms/ions are also referred to as Lewis acids.

3. Ligands

Ligand is electron donating species (ions or molecules) bound to the central atom in the coordination entity.

These may be charged or neutral. Ligands are of the following types:

(i) **Unidentate** It is a ligand, which has one donor site, i.e. the ligand bound to a metal ion through a single donor site, e.g. H_2O, NH_3, etc.

(ii) **Didentate** It is the ligand, which has two donor sites.

e.g.
$$\begin{array}{ll} \underset{|}{COO^-} & \underset{|}{CH_2-NH_2} \\ COO^- & CH_2-NH_2 \\ \text{(Oxalate ion)} & \text{(Ethylene diamine)} \\ \text{(ox)} & \text{(en)} \end{array}$$

(iii) **Polydentate** It is the ligand, which has several donor sites.

e.g. $[EDTA]^{4-}$ is hexadentate ligand.

$$\begin{array}{c} H_2C-N \diagup \overset{CH_2COO^-}{\underset{CH_2COO^-}{\diagdown}} \\ | \\ H_2C-N \diagup \overset{CH_2COO^-}{\underset{CH_2COO^-}{\diagdown}} \end{array}$$

[Ethylenediamminetetraacetate ion]

(iv) **Ambidentate ligands** These are the monodentate ligands which can ligate through two different sites, e.g. NO_2^-, SCN^-, etc.

(v) **Chelating ligands** Di or polydentate ligands cause cyclisation around the metal atom which are known as chelates. Such ligands uses two or more donor atoms to bind a single metal ion and are known as chelating ligands.

More the number of chelate rings, more is the stability of complex.

The stabilisation of coordination compounds due to chelation is known as **chelate effect**.

⌐ π-acid ligands are those ligands which can form σ-bond and π-bond
by accepting an appreciable amount of π electron density from metal
atom pulling facts to empty π or $\overset{*}{\pi}$ -orbitals. ⌐

4. Coordination Number

It is defined as the number of coordinate bonds formed by central metal atom, with the ligands.

e.g. in $[PtCl_6]^{2-}$, Pt has coordination number 6.

In case of monodentate ligands,

Coordination number = number of ligands

In polydentate ligands,

Coordination number = number of ligands × denticity

5. Coordination Sphere

The central metal/ion and the ligands attached to it, are enclosed in square bracket which is known as coordination sphere. The ionisable group written outside the bracket is known as **counter ions**.

6. Coordination Polyhedron

The spatial arrangement of the ligands which are directly attached to the central atom or ion, is called coordination polyhedron around the central atom or ion. e.g. $[Co(NH_3)_6]^{3+}$ is octahedral, $[Ni(CO)_4]$ is tetrahedral and $[PtCl_4]^{2-}$ is square planar.

7. Oxidation Number of Central Atom

The charge of the complex if all the ligands are removed along with the electron pairs that are shared with the central atom, is called oxidation number of central atom.

e.g. $[Cu(CN)_4]^{3-}$, oxidation number of copper is +1, and represented as Cu(I).

Types of Complexes

Homoleptic Complexes

Complexes in which the metal atom or ion is linked to only one kind of donor atoms, are called homoleptic complexes. e.g. $[Co(NH_3)_6]^{3+}$.

Heteroleptic Complexes

Complexes in which the metal atom or ion is linked to more than one kind of donor atoms are called heteroleptic complexes. e.g. $[Co(NH_3)_4Cl_2]^+$.

Labile and Inert Complexes

Complexes in which the ligand substitution is fast are known as **labile complexes** and in which ligand substitution is slow, are known as **inert complexes**.

Effective Atomic Number (EAN)

This concept was proposed by Sidgwick. In a complex, the EAN of metal atom is equal to the total number of electrons present in it.

$$EAN = Z - ON \text{ of metal} + 2 \times CN$$

(where, Z = atomic number of metal atom

ON = oxidation number of metal

and CN = coordination number of complex)

An ion with central metal atom having EAN equal to next inert gas will be more stable.

IUPAC Naming of Complex Compounds

Naming is based on set of rules given by IUPAC.

1. Name of the compound is written in two parts (i) name of cation, and (ii) name of anion.

2. The cation is named first in both positively and negatively charged coordination complexes.

3. The dissimilar ligands are named in an alphabetical order before the name of central metal atom or ion.

4. For more then one similar ligands, the prefixes di, tri, tetra, etc are added before its name. If the di, tri, etc already appear in the complex then bis, tris, tetrakis are used.

5. If the complex part is anion, the name of the central metal ends with suffix 'ate'.

6. Names of the anionic ligands end in 'O', names of positive ligands end with 'ium' and names of neutral ligands remains as such. But exception are there as we use aqua for H_2O, ammine for NH_3, carbonyl for CO and nitrosyl for NO.

7. Oxidation state for the metal in cation, anion or neutral coordination compounds is indicated by Roman numeral in parentheses.

8. The name of the complex part is written as one word.

9. If the complex ion is a cation, the metal is named same as the element.

10. The neutral complex molecule is named similar to that of the complex cation.

Some examples are

(i) $[Cr(NH_3)_3(H_2O)_3]Cl_3$

triamminetriaquachromium (III) chloride

(ii) $[Co(H_2NCH_2CH_2NH_2)_3]_2(SO_4)_3$

tris (ethane-1,2-diammine) cobalt (III) sulphate

(iii) $[Ag(NH_3)_2][Ag(CN)_2]$

diamminesilver (I) dicyanoargentate(I)

(iv) $K_4[Fe(CN)_6]$

potassiumhexacyanoferrate (II)

Isomerism in Coordination Compounds

Coordination compounds exhibit the following types of isomerism:

1. Structural Isomerism

In this isomerism, isomers have different bonding pattern. Different types of structural isomers are

(i) **Linkage isomerism** This type of isomerism is shown by the coordination compounds having ambidentate ligands.
e.g.$[Co(NH_3)_5(NO_2)]Cl$ and $[Co(NH_3)_5(ONO)]Cl$ or pentammine nitrito-N-cobalt (III) chloride and pentamminenitrito-O-cobalt (III) chloride.

(ii) **Coordination isomerism** This type of isomerism arises from the interchange of ligands between cationic and anionic complexes of different metal ions present in a complex, e.g.
$[Cr(NH_3)_6][Co(CN)_6]$ and $[Co(NH_3)_6][Cr(CN)_6]$

(iii) **Ionisation isomerism** This isomerism arises due to exchange of ionisable anion with anionic ligand, e.g.
$$[Co(NH_3)_5SO_4]Br \quad \text{and} \quad [Co(NH_3)_5Br]SO_4$$
$$\text{(Red)} \qquad\qquad\qquad \text{(Violet)}$$

(iv) **Solvate isomerism** This is also known as hydrate isomerism. In this isomerism, water is taken as solvent. It has different number of water molecules in the coordination sphere and outside it, e.g.
$[Co(H_2O)_6]Cl_3$, $[Co(H_2O)_4Cl_2]Cl \cdot 2H_2O$, $[Co(H_2O)_3Cl_3]\cdot 3H_2O$

2. Stereoisomerism

Stereoisomers have the same chemical formula and chemical bonds but they have different spatial arrangement. These are of two types :

(i) **Geometrical isomerism** Geometrical isomers are further of two types i.e. *cis* and *trans* isomers. This isomerism is common in complexes with coordination number 4 and 6.

Geometrical isomerism in complexes with coordination number 4

(i) Tetrahedral complexes do not show geometrical isomerism.

(ii) Square planar complexes of formula $[MX_2L_2]$ (X and L are unidentate) show geometrical isomerism. The two X ligands may be arranged adjacent to each other in a *cis* isomer, or opposite to each other in a *trans*-isomer, e.g.

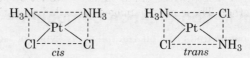

(iii) Square planar complex of the type $[MABXL]$ (where A, B, X, L, are unidentate ligands) shows three isomers, two *cis* and one *trans*.

The structures of these isomers can be written by fixing the position of one ligand and placing other ligands *trans* to it.

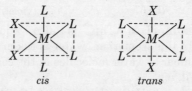

e.g. $[Pt(NH_3)(Br)(Cl)(Py)]$.

Geometrical isomerism in complexes with coordination number 6

Octahedral complexes of formula $[MX_2L_4]$, in which the two X ligands may be oriented *cis* or *trans* to each other, e.g. $[Co(NH_3)_4Cl_2]^+$.

Octahedral complexes of formula $[MX_2A_2]$, where X are unidentate ligands and A are didentate ligand, form *cis* and *trans* isomers, e.g. $[CoCl_2(en)_2]$.

In octahedral complexes of formula $[MA_3X_3]$, if three donor atoms of the same ligands occupy adjacent positions at the corners of an octahedral face, it is known as **facial (*fac*) isomer,** when the positions are around the meridian of the octahedron, it is known as **meridional** (*mer*) **isomer**. e.g. $[Co(NH_3)_3(NO_2)_3]$

$$\begin{array}{cc}
\text{fac} & \text{mer}
\end{array}$$

(ii) **Optical isomerism** These are the complexes which have chiral structures. It arises when mirror images cannot be superimposed on one another. These mirror images are called **enantiomers**. The two forms are called *dextro* (*d*) and *laevo* (*l*) forms.

Tetrahedral complexes with formula $[M(AB)_2]$ show optical isomers and octahedral complexes (*cis* form) exhibit optical isomerism.

Bonding in Coordination Compounds

Werner's Theory

Metals exhibit two types of valencies in the formation of complexes. These are primary valencies and secondary valencies.

1. Primary valencies correspond to oxidation number (ON) of the metal and are satisfied by anions. These are ionisable and non-directional.

2. Secondary valencies correspond to coordination number (CN) of the metal atom and are satisfied by ligands. These are non-ionisable and directional. Hence, geometry is decided by these valencies.

3. Metal ion should satisfy both primary and secondary valancies.

Limitations

Werner theory was unable to account for the following.

(*i*) Definite geometry of coordination compounds.

(*ii*) Presence of magnetic and optical properties of coordination compounds.

To overcome the limitations of Werner's theory, various theories were put forward such as valence bond theory, cyrstal field theory.

Valence Bond Theory (VBT)

This theory was proposed by L. Pauling in 1930 s. According to this theory, when a complex is formed, the metal ion/atom provides empty orbitals to the surrounding ligands. Coordination number shows the number of such empty orbitals, i.e. number of empty orbitals is equal to the coordination number. These empty orbitals hybridised before participation in bonding and the nature of hybridisation depends on the nature of metal and on the nature of approaching ligand.

Inner orbital Complexes or Outer Orbital Complexes

When outer d-orbital nd shells are used in bonding, the complexes are called **outer orbital complexes.** They are formed due to weak field ligands or high spin ligands and hybridisation is sp^3d^2. They have octahedral geometry.

When d-orbitals of $(n-1)$ shell are used, these are known as **inner orbital complex.**

They are formed due to strong field ligands or low spin ligands and hybridisation is d^2sp^3. They have also octahedral geometry.

1. **6-ligands** (unidentate), **octahedral entity**

   (i) **Inner orbital complex** $[Co(NH_3)_6]^{3+}$

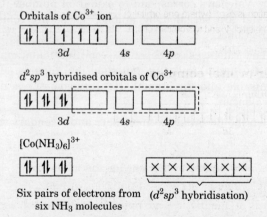

Orbitals of Co^{3+} ion

d^2sp^3 hybridised orbitals of Co^{3+}

$[Co(NH_3)_6]^{3+}$

Six pairs of electrons from six NH_3 molecules

$(d^2sp^3$ hybridisation)

All electrons are paired, therefore complex will be diamagnetic in nature.

(ii) **Outer orbital complex, $[CoF_6]^{3-}$**

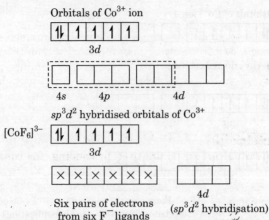

Orbitals of Co^{3+} ion

sp^3d^2 hybridised orbitals of Co^{3+}

Complex has unpaired electrons, therefore, it will be paramagnetic in nature.

2. 4-ligands (unidentate) tetrahedral entity

S.No.	Inner orbital complexes	Outer orbital complexes
(a)	Strong field or low spin ligands	Weak field or high spin ligands
(b)	Hybridisation is dsp^2 (where one orbital of 3d, one orbital of 4s and two orbitals of 4p)	Hybridisation is sp^3 (where one orbital of 4s and three orbitals of 4p)
(c)	Square planar shape	Tetrahedral shape

(i) Inner orbital complex, $[Ni(CN)_4]^{2-}$

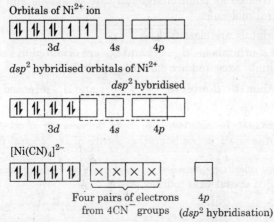

Orbitals of Ni^{2+} ion

dsp^2 hybridised orbitals of Ni^{2+}

All electrons are paired so complex will be diamagnetic in nature.

(ii) **Outer orbital complex, $[CoCl_4]^-$**

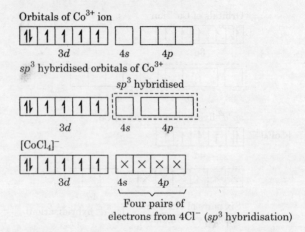

Orbitals of Co^{3+} ion

sp^3 hybridised orbitals of Co^{3+}

sp^3 hybridised

$[CoCl_4]^-$

Four pairs of
electrons from $4Cl^-$ (sp^3 hybridisation)

Since, complex has unpaired electrons, so it will be paramagnetic in nature.

Limitations of VBT

This theory could not explain the quantization of the magnetic data, existence of inner orbital and outer orbital complex, change of magnetic moment with temperature and colour of complexes.

Crystal Field Theory (CFT)

This theory was proposed by H. **Bethe** in 1929 and **van Vleck. Orgel,** in 1935, applied this theory to coordination compounds. In this theory, ligands are treated as point charges in case of anions and dipoles in case of neutral molecules.

The five d-orbitals are classified as

(i) Three d-orbitals i.e. d_{xy}, d_{yz} and d_{zx} are oriented in between the coordinate axes and are called t_{2g}-orbitals.

(ii) The other two d-orbitals, i.e. $d_{x^2-y^2}$ and d_{z^2} oriented along the axes are called e_g-orbitals.

Due to approach of ligands, the five degenerate d-orbitals split. Splitting of d-orbitals depends on the nature of the crystal field.

The energy difference between t_{2g} and e_g level is designated by Δ and is called **crystal field splitting energy**.

By using spectroscopic data for a number of coordination compounds, having the same metal ions but different ligand, the crystal field splitting for each ligand has been calculated. A series in which ligand are arranged in order of increasing magnitude of crystal field splitting, is called **spectrochemical series**.

Spectrochemical series

$$I^- < Br^- < SCN^- < Cl^- < S^{2-} < F^- < OH^-$$

$$< C_2O_4^{2-} < H_2O < NCS^- < EDTA^{4-} < NH_3 < en < CN^- < CO.$$

Crystal Field Splitting in Octahedral Complexes

In case of octahedral complexes, energy separation is denoted by Δ_o (where subscript o is for octahedral).

In octahedral complexes, the six-ligands approach the central metal ion along the axis of $d_{x^2-y^2}$ and d_{z^2} orbitals. These are e_g orbitals. Energy of e_g set of orbitals > energy of t_{2g} set of orbitals.

The energy of e_g orbitals will increase by $(3/5)$ Δ_o and t_{2g} will decrease by $(2/5)$ Δ_o.

If $\Delta_o < P$, the fourth electron enters one of the e_g orbitals giving the configuration $t_{2g}^3 e_g^1$. Ligands for which $\Delta_o < P$ are known as weak field ligands and form high spin complexes.

If $\Delta_o > P$, it becomes more energetically favourable for the fourth electron to occupy a t_{2g} orbital with configuration $t_{2g}^4 e_g^o$. (where, P = energy required for e^- pairing in an orbital). Ligands which produce this effect are known as strong field ligands and form low spin complexes.

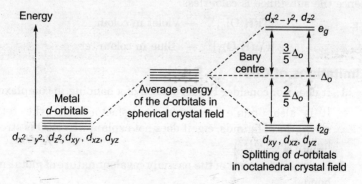

Splitting of d-orbitals
in octahedral crystal field

Crystal Field Splitting in Tetrahedral Complexes

In tetrahedral complexes, four ligands may be imagined to occupy the alternate corners of the cube and the metal ion at the center of the cube.

In such complexes d-orbital splitting is inverted and is smaller as compared to the octahedral field splitting.

Energy of t_2 set of orbitals > Energy of e set of orbitals.

Orbital splitting energies are so low that pairing of electrons are not possible so these form high spin complexes.

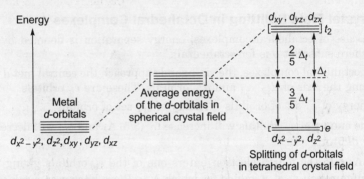

Splitting of d-orbitals in tetrahedral crystal field

Colour in Coordination Compounds

The crystal field theory attributes the colour of the coordination compounds due to d-d transition of the electron, i.e. electron jump from t_{2g} level to higher e_g level.

In the absence of ligands, crystal field splitting does not occur and hence the substance is colourless.

e.g. $[Ti(H_2O)_6]^{3+}$ — Violet in colour

                $[Cu(H_2O)_4]^{2+}$ — Blue in colour, etc.

Limitations of CFT

1. It does not consider the formation of π bonding in complexes.

2. It is also unable to account satisfactorily for the relative strengths of ligands, e.g. it does not explain why H_2O is stronger ligand than OH^-.

3. It gives no account of the partialy covalent nature of metal-metal bonds.

Ligand Field or Molecular Orbital Theory

This theory was put forward by Hund and Mulliken. According to this theory, all the atomic orbitals of the atom participating in molecule formation get mixed to give rise an equivalent number of new orbitals, called the molecular orbitals. The electrons are now under the influence of all the nuclei.

Stability of Coordination Compounds

The stability of complex in solution refers to the degree of association between the two species involved in the state of equilibrium. It is expressed as stability constant (K).

e.g. $$M^+ + nL^{x-} \rightleftharpoons [ML_n]^{y-}; \qquad K = \frac{[(ML_n)^{y-}]}{[M^+][L^{x-}]^n}$$

The factors on which stability of the complex depends :

(i) **Charge on the central metal atom** As the magnitude of charge on metal atom increases, stability of the complex increases.

(ii) **Nature of metal ion** The stability order is $3d < 4d < 5d$ series.

(iii) **Basic nature of ligands** Strong field ligands form stable complex.

The instability constant or the **dissociation constant** of compounds is defined as the reciprocal of the formation or stability constant.

Importance and Applications of Coordination Compounds

1. They are used in many qualitative and quantitative analysis.
2. Hardness of water is estimated by simple titration with Na_2 EDTA.
3. Purification of metals can be achieved through formation and subsequent decomposition of their coordination compounds.
4. They have great importance in biological systems.
5. They are used as catalyst for many industrial processes.
6. In medicinal chemistry, there is a growing interest of chelating therapy.

Organometallic Compounds

They contain one or more metal-carbon bond in their molecules. They are of the following types:

1. Sigma (σ) Bonded Compounds

Metal-carbon bond is sigma bond, e.g. $(C_2H_5)_4Pb$, $Zn(C_2H_5)_2$, R—Mg—X, etc.

2. Pi(π) Bonded Compounds

In which molecules/ions containing π bonds act as a ligand, e.g. ferrocene, dibenzene chromium and Zeise's salt.

> Zeise's salts is $K[PtCl_3(\eta^2 - C_2H_4)]$ in which ethylene acts as a ligand which do not have a lone pair of electron.
> In ferrocene, $Fe(\eta^5 - C_5H_5)_2$, η represents the number of carbon atoms with which metal ion is directly attached.

3. σ and π Bonded Compounds

Metal carbonyls are their examples. Metal-carbon bond of metal carbonyls have both σ and π-bond character. They have CO molecule as ligand, e.g.

$[Ni(CO)_4]$ $Fe(CO)_5$

> Wilkinson's catalyst $(Rh(PPh_3)_3Cl)$ is used as homogeneous catalyst in the hydrogenation of alkenes. *Ziegler-Natta* catalyst $[TiCl_4 + (C_2H_5)_3Al]$ acts as heterogeneous catalyst in the polymerisation of ethylene.

22
Environmental Chemistry

Environmental chemistry is the branch of chemistry which is concerned with the chemical phenomenon occurring in the environment.

Classification of Environment

1. Atmosphere

Atmosphere is a gaseous mixture of air that surrounds the earth. Its different layers are as follows :

(i) **Troposphere** It is the lowest region of the atmosphere extending from earth's surface to the lower boundary of the stratosphere. It contains water vapours and is greatly affected by air pollution. It extends upto the height of ~ 10 km from sea level.

(ii) **Stratosphere** The layer of the earth's atmosphere above the troposphere and below the mesosphere, is called stratosphere. Ozone layer is present in this region.

(iii) **Mesosphere** It is the region of the earth's atmosphere above the stratosphere and below the thermosphere. It is the coldest region (temperature -2 to $-92°C$) of atmosphere.

(iv) **Thermosphere** The upper region of the atmosphere above the mesosphere is called thermosphere It is the hottest region (temperature up to $1200°C$).

(v) **Exosphere** It is the uppermost region of atmosphere. It contains atomic and ionic O_2, H_2 and He.

2. Hydrosphere

It is the aqueous envelop of the earth, e.g. oceans, lakes etc.

3. Lithosphere

The solid rocky portion of the earth constitute the lithosphere.

4. Biosphere

The biological envelop which supports the life is called biosphere. e.g. animals, human beings.

Environmental Pollution

It may be described as contamination of environment with harmful wastes mainly arising from certain human activities. These activities release materials which pollute atmosphere, water and soil.

Types of Pollutions

(i) **Natural pollution** This type of pollution is caused by the natural sources, e.g. volcanic eruptions, release of methane by paddy fields and cattles, forest fires etc.

(ii) **Man-made pollution** This type of pollution is resulting from human activities like burning of the fuels, deforestation, industrial effluents, pesticides etc.

Pollutants

Any substance produced either by a natural source or by human activity which causes adverse effect on the environment is called pollutant.

Pollutants can be of the following types depending upon the following factors :

Classification on the Basis of Their Degradation

(i) **Biodegradable pollutants** Pollutants capable of being degraded by biological or microbial actions are called biodegradable pollutants, e.g. domestic sewage.

(ii) **Non-biodegradable pollutants** The substances which are normally not acted upon by microbes are called non-biodegradable pollutants. These undergo biological magnification.

They can further be of two types :

(i) Wastes, e.g. glass, plastic, phenols.

(ii) Poisons, e.g. radioactive substances, Hg salts, pesticides, heavy metals.

Classification on the Basis of Their Occurrence in Nature

(i) **Primary pollutants** These are present in same form in which these are added by man, e.g. DDT, pesticides, fertilizers etc.

(ii) **Secondary pollutants** These occur in different forms and are formed by the reaction between the primary pollutants in the presence of sunlight, e.g. HNO_3, H_2SO_4, PAN, ozone etc.

Classification on the Basis of Their Existence in Nature

(i) **Quantitative pollutants** These are naturally present in nature and also added by man. These become pollutants when their concentration reaches beyond a threshold value in the environment, e.g. CO_2, nitrogen oxide etc.

(ii) **Qualitative pollutants** These are not present in the nature but are added by nature only due to human activities, e.g. pesticides, fungicides, herbicides etc.

Tropospheric Pollution

It is caused by gaseous pollutants and particulate matter.

Gaseous air pollutants Oxides of sulphur (SO_x), oxides of nitrogen (NO_x), oxides of carbon (CO, CO_2), hydrogen sulphide (H_2S), hydrocarbons. Ozone and other oxidants etc.

Particulate pollutants Dust, fumes, mist, smoke, smog etc.

Air Pollution

Air pollution occurs when the concentration of a normal component of the air or a new chemical substance added or formed in air, build up to undesirable proportions causing harm to humans, animals, vegetation and materials.

Air Pollutants

The chemical substances and particles causing pollution are called air pollutants. The major air pollutants are :

(i) **Oxides of sulphur** The most common species is sulphur dioxide (SO_2) It is produced by petrol combustion, coal combustion, petrol refining and smelting operation.

It obstruct the movement of air in and out of lungs. It is particularly poisonous to trees causing chlorosis and dwarfing. In the presence of air, it is oxidised to SO_3 which is also an irritant.

$$2SO_2 + O_2 \text{ (air)} \longrightarrow 2SO_3$$

Taj Mahal is reported to be affected by SO_2 and other pollutants released by oil refinery of Mathura. The SO_3 reacts with water in the air (or in the lungs) to form H_2SO_4.

(ii) **Oxides of nitrogen** NO_2 and NO are obtained by combustion of coal, gasoline, natural gas, petroleum refining, chemical industries and tobacco smoke. In upper atmosphere, these are emitted by high flying jets and rockets.

Breathing NO_2 causes chlorosis to plants and chronic lung conditions leading to death in human beings. These oxides destroy ozone (O_3) layer.

$$2NO(g) + O_2(g) \longrightarrow 2NO_2(g)$$
$$NO(g) + O_3(g) \longrightarrow NO_2(g) + O_2(g)$$

(iii) **Smoke and dust** These are obtained in cement works, iron and steel works, gas works, power generating stations. Coal miners suffer from black lung disease and textile workers suffer from white lung disease.

(iv) **Ammonia** It is produced by fertilizer works.

(v) **Mercaptans** These are obtained from oil refineries, coke ovens etc.

(vi) **Zn and Cd** These are obtained from zinc and cadmium industries.

(vii) **Freon** (or CFC's) Their source is refrigerator.

(viii) **Hydrocarbons** These are formed by incomplete combustion of fuel used in automobiles. These are carcinogenic. They harm plants and also break down of tissues.

(ix) **Oxides of Carbon**

(a) **Carbon monoxide** (CO) It is produced by incomplete combustion of gasoline in motor vehicles, wood, coal, inceneration and forest fires. It induces headache, visual difficulty, coma or death. It blocks the normal transport of oxygen from the lungs to other parts of the body, by combining with haemoglobin of the blood. (Its affinity towards haemoglobin is about 300 times more than the oxygen.)

(b) **Carbon dioxide** (CO_2) causes mild narcotic effects, stimulation of the respiratory centre and leads to asphyniation. The increasing concentration of CO_2 also changes the climatic conditions, especially by raising the global temperature. This phenomenon is known as the **green house effects**.

Green House Effect and Global Warming

The phenomenon in which atmosphere of earth traps the heat coming from the sun and prevents it from escaping into the outer space is called green house effect. Certain gases, called green house gases [carbon dioxide, methane, ozone, chlorofluoro carbon compounds (CFCs) and water vapour] in the atmosphere absorb the heat given by earth and radiate back it to the surface of the earth. Thus, warming of the earth led to the warming of air due to green house gases, which is called global warming.

Consequences of Green House Effect
(or Global Warming)

1. The green house gases are useful in keeping the earth warm with an average temperature of about 15° to 20°C.

2. There may be less rainfall in this temperature zone and more rainfall in the dried areas of the world.

3. Increase in the concentration of CO_2 in the atmosphere leads to increase in the temperature of the earth's surface. As a result, evaporation of surface water will increase which further help in the rise of temperature and results in the melting of glaciers and polar ice caps and hence, level of sea water may rise.

Acid Rain

The pH of normal rain water is 5.6 due to the formation of H^+ ions by dissolution of CO_2 from atmosphere.

$$H_2O(l) + CO_2(g) \rightleftharpoons H_2CO_3(aq)$$
$$\text{Carbonic acid}$$

$$H_2CO_3(aq) \rightleftharpoons H^+(aq) + HCO_3^-(aq)$$

when the pH of rain water drops below 5.6 it is called acid rain (by Robert Augus.) Oxides of N and S are responsible for making rain water acidic. Much of the NO_x and SO_x entering in the atmosphere are converted into HNO_3 and H_2SO_4 respectively. The detailed photochemical reactions occurring in the atmosphere are given as

$$NO + O_3 \longrightarrow NO_2 + O_2$$
$$2NO_2 + O_2 \longrightarrow 2NO_3$$
$$NO_2 + NO_3 \longrightarrow N_2O_5$$
$$N_2O_5 + H_2O \longrightarrow 2HNO_3$$

HNO_3 is removed as a precipitate or as particulate nitrates after reaction with bases (like NH_3, particulate lime etc).

$$SO_2(g) + \frac{1}{2} O_2(g) + H_2O(l) \xrightarrow[\text{Soot particles}]{\text{(Hydrocarbon, NO}_x)} H_2SO_4(aq)$$

The presence of hydrocarbons and NO_x step up the oxidation rate of the reaction. Soot particles are also known to be strongly involved in catalysing the oxidation of SO_2. Acid rain causes extensive damage to buildings and sculptural materials of marble, limestone, slate, mortar etc.

$$CaCO_3 + H_2SO_4 \longrightarrow CaSO_4 + CO_2 + H_2O$$

Particulate Pollutants

These are the minute solid particles or liquid droplets in air. Particulates in the atmosphere may be viable or non-viable.

1. Viable particulates : bacteria, fungi, algae etc.

2. Non-viable particulates : smoke, dust, mists, fumes.

Smog

It is a mixture of smoke (composed of tiny particles of carbon, ash and oil etc from coal combustion) and fog in suspended droplet form. It is of two types:

(i) London Smog or Classical Smog

It is mixture of coal, smoke plus fog. The fog part is mainly SO_2 and SO_3. Chemically, it is a reducing mixture and so, it is called reducing smog. It causes bronchial irritation and acid rain. It occurs in cool humid climate.

(ii) Photochemical Smog or Los Angeles Smog

The oxidised hydrocarbons and ozone in a warm, dry and sunny climate cause photochemical smog. Its brown colour is due to the presence of NO_2. It occurs in very large populations and in high vehicular density cities.

The nitrogen dioxide by absorbing sunlight in blue and UV region decomposes into nitric oxide and atomic oxygen followed by a series of the other reactions producing O_3, formaldehyde, acrolein and peroxyacetylnitrates.

$$NO_2(g) + h\nu \longrightarrow NO(g) + O(g), \quad O(g) + O_2(g) \longrightarrow O_3(g)$$

$$RH + O \longrightarrow R\overset{\bullet}{O}, \quad R\overset{\bullet}{O} + O_2 \longrightarrow R\overset{\bullet}{O}_3$$

$$R\overset{\bullet}{O}_3 + NO \longrightarrow R\overset{\bullet}{O}_2 + NO_2$$

$$R\overset{\bullet}{O}_2 + NO_2 \longrightarrow \text{Peroxyacetylnitrate}$$

Hydrocarbons $+ O_2, NO_2, NO, O, O_3 \longrightarrow$ Peroxides, formaldehyde, peroxyacetylnitrate (PAN), acrolein etc.

It is oxidising in nature and causes irritation to eyes, lungs, nose, asthamatic attack and damage to plants.

Stratospheric Pollution (Depletion of Ozone Layer)

Ozone is a light bluish gas and absorbs UV radiations of the sun which are harmful to living beings, but now a days ozone layer is being depleted by CFCs (chlorofluorocarbons).

UV radiations cause the chlorofluorocarbons to dissociate to form highly reactive chlorine free radical which reacts with ozone to form chlorine monoxide.

$$CF_2Cl_2(g) + h\nu \longrightarrow \underset{\text{(Free radical)}}{Cl^\bullet(g)} + ClF_2(g)$$

$$^\bullet Cl(g) + O_3(g) \longrightarrow ClO^\bullet(g) + O_2(g)$$

$$ClO^\bullet(g) + O(g) \longrightarrow Cl^\bullet(g) + O_2(g)$$

$Cl^\bullet$ (free radical) can react with more O_3. Many O_3 molecules can thus be destroyed for each chlorine atom produced. It has been shown that over one thousand ozone molecules can be destroyed by one Cl free radical.

The Ozone Hole

Ozone hole is formed over Antarctica, and some parts of non-polar regions also. In other parts of stratosphere NO_2, CH_4 react with $ClO^\bullet$ and $Cl^\bullet$ respectively and act as natural sink for $ClO^\bullet$ and $Cl^\bullet$

$$ClO^\bullet(g) + NO_2(g) \longrightarrow ClONO_2(g)$$

$$Cl^\bullet(g) + CH_4(g) \longrightarrow {}^\bullet CH_3(g) + HCl(g)$$

These reactions consume $Cl^\bullet$ and $ClO^\bullet$ hindrance to ozone depletion.

In Antarctica, during winters, special types of clouds, called polar stratospheric clouds (PSCs) are formed. These clouds are of two types

Type I Clouds They contain some solidified nitric acid trihydrate ($HNO_3 \cdot 3H_2O$) formed at about $-77°C$.

Type II Clouds They contain some ice formed at about $-85°C$. These clouds play important role in ozone depletion by hydrolysing chlorine nitrate.

$$ClONO_2(g) + H_2O(g) \longrightarrow HOCl(g) + HNO_3(g)$$

$$ClONO_2(g) + HCl(g) \longrightarrow Cl_2(g) + HNO_3(g)$$

Hypochlorous acid and Cl_2 are formed which are reconverted into reactive chlorine atoms with the help of sunlight which causes ozone depletion.

Polar vortex During winters, when polar stratospheric clouds are formed over Antarctica, stable wind patterns in the stratosphere encircle the continent which is called **polar vortex**. It is tight whirlpool of winds which is so rigid that air within it is isolated from the sun and forms the warmer air of temperate region to fill up ozone hole. After the spring, the intensity of sunlight increases and the vortex breaks down and ozone rich air from the temperate region rushes in and replenishes the ozone hole.

Consequences of Depletion of Ozone Layer

(a) **Loss of sight** The UV radiation damage the cornea and lens of the eyes.

(b) **Effect on immune system** The UV radiations are also likely to suppress immune system.

(c) **Skin cancer** The UV radiation is known to be cancer causing agent.

Water Pollution

The contamination of water by foreign substances which would constitute a health hazard and make it unfit for all purposes (domestic, industrial or agriculture etc) is known as water pollution. The polluted water may have foul odour, bad taste, unpleasant colour etc.

Maximum prescribed concentration of some metals in drinking water is as follows

Metal	Maximum concentration in ppm
Fe	0.2
Al	0.2
Cu	3.0
Zn	5.0
Mn	0.05
Cd	0.005

Sources of Water Pollution

(i) **Domestic sewage** Discharge from kitchens, baths, etc.

(ii) **Industrial water** Wastes from manufacturing processes which includes acids, alkalies, pesticides, insecticides, metals, fungicides etc.

(iii) **Oil** From oil spills or washings of automobiles.

(iv) **Atomic explosion** Processing of radioactive materials.

(v) **Suspended particles (organic or inorganic)** Viruses, bacteria, algae, protozoa etc.

(vi) **Wastes from fertilizer** Industries such as phosphates, nitrates, ammonia etc.

(vii) **Clay** Ores, minerals, fine particles of soil.

Effects of Impurities in Water

(a) **Fluorides** Mottling of teeth enamel, above 1 mg/L fluoride causes fluorosis.

(b) **Sulphates** Sulphates of Na, K, Mg causes diarrhoea.

(c) **Lead** It damages kidney, liver, brain and central nervous system.

(d) **Cadmium and mercury** They causes kidney damage.

(e) **Zn** It causes dizziness and diarrhoea.

(f) **Arsenic** It can cause cramps and paralysis.

(g) **Phosphates from fertilizers** They promote algae growth and reduce dissolved oxygen concentration of water. This process is known as **eutrophication.**

Aerobic and Anaerobic Oxidation

The oxidation of organic compounds present in sewage in the presence of good amount of dissolved or free oxygen (approx. 8.5 mg/L) by aerobic bacteria is called **aerobic oxidation**. When dissolved or free oxygen is below a certain value, the sewage is called **stale.**

Anaerobic bacteria bring out putrification by producing $H_2S, NH_3, CH_4, (NH_4)_2S$ etc. This type of oxidation is called **anaerobic oxidation**.

The optimum value of dissolved oxygen for good quality of water is 4-6 ppm (4-6 mg/L). The lower the concentration of dissolved oxygen, the more polluted is the water.

Biological oxygen demand (BOD) It is defined as the amount of free oxygen required for biological oxidation of the organic matter under aerobic conditions at 20°C for a period of five days. Its unit is mg/L or ppm. Clean water would have BOD value of less than 5 ppm whereas highly polluted water could have a BOD value of 17 ppm or more.

An average sewage has BOD of 100 to 150 mg/L.

Chemical oxygen demand (COD) It is the measure of all types of oxidisable impurities (biologically oxidisable and biologically inert organic matter such as cellulose) present in the sewage. COD values are higher than BOD values.

Control of Water Pollution

(i) Recycling of waste water

(ii) Use of chemicals : Lead poisoning can be cured by giving the patient an aqueous solution of calcium complex of EDTA. Lead ions displace calcium in the EDTA complex to form chelated lead and Ca^{2+}. The soluble lead chelate is excreted with the urine.

$$Ca—EDTA + Pb^{2+} \longrightarrow Pb – EDTA + Ca^{2+}$$

(iii) Special techniques such as adsorption, ion exchangers, reverse osmosis, electrodialysis etc.

(iv) Waste water reclamation

Sewage Treatment

It involves the following steps:

(i) **Preliminary process** Passing sewage through screens to remove large suspended matter and then through mesh screens to remove solids, gravels, silt etc.

(ii) **Settling process** (sedimentation) The residual water when allowed to stand in tanks, the oils and grease, float on the surface and skimmed off and solids settle down. The colloidal material is removed by adding alum, ferrous sulphate etc. Primary sludge can be separated.

(iii) **Secondary treatment or biological treatment** It is aerobic chemical oxidation or aeration which converts carbon of the organic matter to CO_2, nitrogen into NH_3 and finally into nitrite and nitrates, dissolved bases form salts such as NH_4NO_2, NH_4NO_3 and $Ca(NO_3)_2$ etc., and secondary sludge is obtained.

(iv) **Tertiary treatment** It is treatment of waste water with lime for removal of phosphate which is then coagulated by adding alum and ferric chloride and removed by filtration.

Water is disinfected by adding chlorine.

Secondary sludge forms a good fertilizer for soil as it contains nitrogen and phosphorus compounds.

Soil or Land Pollution

The addition of substances in an indefinite proportion changes the productivity of the soil. This is known as soil or land pollution.

Sources of Soil Pollution

(i) Agricultural pollutants e.g. chemicals like pesticides, fertilizers, bacteriocides, fumigants, insecticides, herbicides, fungicides.

(ii) Domestic refuge and industrial wastes.

(iii) Radioactive wastes from research centres and hospitals.

(iv) Soil conditioners containing toxic metals like Hg, Pb, As, Cd etc.

(v) Farm wastes from poultries, dairies and piggery farms.

Control of Soil Pollution

(i) **Use of manures** Manures prepared from animal dung is much better than the commonly used fertilizers.

(ii) **Use of bio-fertilizers** These are the organisms which are inoculated in order to bring about nutrient enrichment of the soil. *e.g.,* nitrogen fixing bacteria and blue-green algae.

(iii) **Proper sewage system** A proper sewage system must be employed and sewage recycling plants must be installed.

(iv) **Salvage and recycling** Rag pickers remove a large number of waste articles such as paper, polythene, card board, rags, empty bottles and metallic articles. These are subjected to recycling and this helps in checking soil pollution.

Radioactive Pollution

Cosmic rays that reach the earth from outer space and terrestrial radiation from radioactive elements are natural radiations. This natural or background radiation is not a health hazard due to its low concentration.

Man made sources of radiations include mining and refining of plutonium and thorium, atomic reactors and nuclear fuel. These are produced during preparation of radio-isotopes. These are of two types : electromagnetic (radio waves UV, IR, α-rays) and particulate.

Other Sources of Radioactive Pollution

(i) **Atomic explosions** Atomic explosions produce radioactive particles which are thrown high up into the air as huge clouds. The process releases large amount of energy as heat. Due to atomic explosion nuclear fall out. These radioactive elements may reach the human beings through food chain.

(ii) **Radioactive wastes** Wastes from atomic power plants come in the form of spent fuels of uranium and plutonium. People working in such power plants, nuclear reactors, fuel processors etc., are vulnerable to their exposure.

(iii) **Radio isotopes** Many radioactive isotopes like C^{14}, I^{125}, P^{32} and their compounds are used in scientific researches. The waste water of these research centres contains the radioactive elements which may reach the human beings through water and food chains.

Effects of Radiations

1. Strontium-90 accumulates in the bones to cause bone cancer and tissue degeneration in number of organs.

2. I-131 damages WBCs, bone marrow, lymph nodes and causes skin cancer, sterility and defective eye sight.

3. These may cause ionisation of various body fluids, chromosomal aberrations and gene mutations.

4. Radioactive iodine may also cause cancer of thyroid glands.

5. Cesium-137 brings about nervous, muscular and genetic change.

6. Uranium causes skin cancers and tumours in the miners.

7. Radon-222 causes leukemia, brain tumours and kidney cancers.

Bhopal Gas Tragedy

In Dec. 2, 1984 a dense cloud of methyl isocyanate gas (MIC) leaked from a storage tank of the Union Carbide Ltd plant in Bhopal. It caused a great loss of life to people and animals. Methyl isocyanate was prepared by the reaction of methyl amine with phosgene and stored in abundance.

$$CH_3NH_2 + COCl_2 \longrightarrow CH_3—N{=}C{=}O + 2HCl$$

Methyl amine Phosgene   MIC

Green Chemistry–An Alternative Tool for Reducing Pollution

Green chemistry may be called chemistry involved in the design, development, and implementation of chemical products and processes to reduce or eliminate the use and generation of substances hazardous to human health and the environment.

Thus, the goal of green chemistry is to promote the development of products and processes that reduce or eliminate the use or generation of toxic substances associated with the design, manufacture, and use of hazardous chemicals. Some important principles and method of green chemistry are :

1. It is better to prevent waste than to treat or clean up waste after it is formed.

2. Synthetic methods should be designed to maximize the incorporation of all materials used in the process into the final product.

3. Whenever possible, synthetic methodologies should be designed to use and generate substances that possess little or no toxicity to human health and the environment.

4. Chemical products should be designed to preserve efficiency of function while reducing toxicity.

5. The use of auxiliary substance (e.g. solvents, separation agents etc.) should be avoided as far as possible.

6. Energy requirements should be recognised for their environmental and economic impacts and should be minimized.

7. Synthetic methods should be conducted at ambient temperature and pressure.

Green Chemistry in Day-to-Day life

(i) **Dry cleaning of clothes** Tetra chloroethene ($Cl_2C = CCl_2$) was earlier used as solvent for dry cleaning. Now-a-days hydrogen peroxide (H_2O_2) is used for the purpose of bleaching clothes in the process of laundary.

(ii) Bleaching of paper

(ii) Synthesis of chemicals

$$CH_2 = CH_2 + O_2 \xrightarrow[\substack{Pt\ (II)/Cu\ (II) \\ (in\ water)}]{Catalyst} CH_3CHO\,(90\%)$$

23

Purification and Characterisation of Organic Compounds

Purification of Organic Compounds

Organic compounds extracted from a natural source or synthesized in the laboratory requires purification. Various methods are used for the purification and are based on the nature of the compound and the impurity present in it. The purity of a compound is ascertained by determining its melting point or boiling point or by chromatographic and spectroscopic techniques.

Methods of Purification of Solids

(i) **Cystallisation** In this process, a saturated solution of impure substance is prepared in hot solvent and heated with animal charcoal which adsorbs the impurities. The solution is filtered and filtrate on cooling deposits crystals of pure compound. Success of the process depends upon the selection of the solvent. The impurities must be least soluble.

> A process in which crystal formation is initiated by adding crystals of pure substance, is known as **seeding**.

(ii) **Fractional crystallisation** It is based on the different solubilities of different compounds in a solvent. The compound having less solubility crystallises out first on cooling leaving behind others in solution. Sometimes mixture of two solvents, e.g. alcohol and water, chloroform and petroleum ether, give better results.

(iii) **Sublimation** Some solids directly convert into vapours when heated without converting into liquid. These are known as sublimate and this process is called sublimation. The substances which sublime can be purified by this method provided the impurities present does not sublime. Camphor, naphthalene and anthracene are purified by sublimation.

Methods of Purification of Liquids

(i) **Simple distillation** The vaporisation of a liquid by heating and subsequent condensation of vapours by cooling is known as distillation. The liquids boiling under ordinary conditions of temperature and pressure without decomposition and containing non-volatile impurities are purified by simple distillation.

(ii) **Fractional distillation** It is employed for separating mixture of two or more volatile liquids having boiling points close to each other, e.g. acetone (boiling point 60°C) and methanol (boiling point 65°C). Components of petroleum are separated by this method. The vapours of the liquids are passed through the fractionating column which provides greater space for their cooling. The vapours of high boiling substance condense and fall back into distillation flask.

(iii) **Distillation under reduced pressure or vacuum distillation** Some liquids decompose when heated to their boiling points, e.g. glycerol. Such liquids can be purified by distillation under reduced pressure much below than their boiling points.

(iv) **Steam distillation** The liquids insoluble in water, steam volatile in nature, having high molecular weight and high vapour pressure are purified by steam distillation provided the impurities present are not steam volatile. The liquid boils when the sum of vapour pressures due to the organic liquid (p_1) and that due to water (p_2) becomes equal to the atmospheric pressure (p). i.e. $p = p_1 + p_2$. Since, p_1 is lower than, p the organic liquid vaporises at lower temperature than its boiling point. e.g. o-hydroxy acetophenone and p-hydroxy acetophenone are separated by this method.

(v) **By separating funnel** In this method, a mixture of two immiscible liquids can be separated and the process is also called differential extraction.

Chromatographic Method

It was discovered by **Tswett** (1906).

It is based upon the principle of selective adsorption of various components of a mixture between the two phases : stationary or fixed phase and mobile phase.

The various chromatographic techniques are:

1. Adsorption Chromatography

Stationary phase – solid or ion exchange resin. Mobile phase –liquid or gas.

It includes liquid-solid chromatography, gas-solid chromatography or ion exchange chromatography.

Two types of chromatographic techniques based on the principle of differential adsorption are as follows.

(a) Column Chromatography

It is an example of adsorption chromatography. Adsorbents used are alumina, silica gel, cellulose powder, animal charcoal, keiselguhr etc.

Liquid solvents used are benzene, petroleum ether, alcohol etc.

When the solvent is poured over the mixture present at the top of a column packed with adsorbent, the components are separated into number of layers called **zones, bands** or **chromatograms** due to preferential adsorption.

(b) Thin Layer Chromatography

It involves separation of substances of a mixture over a thin layer of an adsorbent coated on glass plate. The thin layer (about 0.2 mm thick) of an adsorbent (silica gel or alumina) is spread over a glass plate of suitable size. The plate is known as thin layer chromatography plate or chromoplate.

The solution of the mixture to be separated is applied as small spot about 2 cm above one end of TLC plate. The glass plate is then placed in a closed jar containing the eluant. As the solvent rises up the plates, the component of mixture moves up along with the eluant to different distance depending on their degree of adsorption and separation takes place.

Retardation Factor i.e. R_f Value

$$R_f = \frac{\text{distance moved by the substance from base line } (x)}{\text{distance moved by the solvent from base line } (y)}$$

2. **Partition Chromatography**

Fixed phase-liquid supported on inert solid. Mobile phase –liquid or gas.

This process is known as liquid-liquid partition chromatography or liquid-gas partition chromatography on the basis of its different phases.

3. **Paper Chromatography**

The principle of paper chromatography is based on the fact that solutes have the capacity to migrate through filter paper at different rates as a solution is drawn into strip of paper by capillary action.

In paper chromatography, the dissolved substance is applied as a small spot about 2-3 cm from the edge of a strip or square of filter paper and is allowed to dry. This strip is then suspended in a large close container where atmosphere is saturated with the solvent system. The end containing the sample is dipped into the mobile phase which has already been saturated with the stationary phase. When the solvent front has reached at the other end of the paper, the strip is removed and the zones are located by analytical methods.

> The ratio of the distance travelled by a component to the distance travelled by the solvent front is characteristic of each component and is known as the R_f value.
>
> $$R_f = \frac{\text{distance in cm from starting line to the centre of zone}}{\text{distance in cm from starting line to the solvent front}}$$

Elution The continuous pouring of solvent from the top of the column is known as elution or running of column. Solvent is known as **eluant**.

The most weakly adsorbed component is eluted first by least polar solvent while more strongly adsorbed component is eluted later by highly polar solvents.

Chemical Methods of Purification

The substance to be purified is treated with a suitable chemical reagent to form a stable derivative. It is then separated by suitable method and decomposed to get the pure compounds.

Examples

   (i) Mixture of amines (1°, 2° and 3°) is separated by **Hinsberg's method**.

   (ii) Acetic acid from pyroligneous acid is separated by forming calcium salt.

(iii) Acids are separated by forming sodium derivatives with $NaHCO_3$.

(iv) Absolute alcohol is obtained from rectified spirit by quick lime process and azeotropic distillation.

Azeotropic Distillation

Azeotropes are constant boiling mixtures which distil off without any change in composition at a fixed temperature. Therefore, **components of an azeotropic mixture cannot be separated by fractional distillation.** A very common example of azeotropic mixture is rectified spirit which contains 95.87% ethyl alcohol and 4.23% water by weight which boils at 351.1 K.

Such mixtures are separated by adding another component which generate a new lower boiling azeotrope that is heterogeneous (i.e. producing two immiscible liquid phases). e.g. C_6H_6 is added to H_2O and ethyl alcohol azeotrope to separate them.

Qualitative Analysis of Organic Compounds

1. Detection of Carbon and Hydrogen

This is done by heating the given organic compound with dry cupric oxide in a hard glass test tube when carbon present is oxidised to carbon dioxide and hydrogen is oxidised to water.

$$C + 2CuO \xrightarrow{\Delta} CO_2 + 2Cu$$

$$2H + CuO \xrightarrow{\Delta} H_2O + Cu$$

Carbon dioxide turns lime water milky.

$$\underset{\text{From C}}{Ca(OH)_2 + CO_2} \longrightarrow \underset{\text{Milky}}{CaCO_3\downarrow + H_2O}$$

Water condenses on the cooler parts of the test tube and turns anhydrous copper sulphate blue.

$$\underset{\text{White}}{CuSO_4 + 5H_2O} \longrightarrow \underset{\text{Blue}}{CuSO_4 \cdot 5H_2O}$$

Lassaigne's Test

The organic compound is fused with a small piece of Na metal. When element (N, S, X) of the organic compound combine to give $NaCN, Na_2S$ or NaX, the red hot tube is plunged in distilled water, boiled and filtered. The filtrate is called **Lassaigne's extract** or **sodium extract**. The Lassaigne's extract is usually alkaline. If not, it is made alkaline by adding a few drops of a dilute solution of sodium hydroxide. The purpose of fusing the organic compounds with sodium metal is to convert halogens, N, S, P etc., present in the organic compound to their corresponding soluble sodium salts (ionic compounds).

$$Na + C + N \xrightarrow{\Delta} NaCN$$

$$2Na + S \xrightarrow{\Delta} Na_2S$$

$$Na + X \xrightarrow{\Delta} NaX \qquad \text{(where, } X = Cl, Br, I)$$

1. Detection of Nitrogen

To a part of this Lassaigne's extract a few drops of a freshly prepared solution of ferrous sulphate is added, because a dilute solution of $FeSO_4$ after a long time oxidise to basic ferric sulphate which is useless for analysis. The contents are warmed a little, cooled and then acidified with dil. H_2SO_4. Appearance of a green or Prussian blue colouration indicates the presence of nitrogen.

$$6CN^- + Fe^{2+} \longrightarrow [Fe(CN)_6]^{4-}$$

$$3[Fe(CN)_6]^{4-} + 4Fe^{3+} \xrightarrow{xH_2O} \underset{\text{Prussian blue}}{Fe_4[Fe(CN)_6]_3 \cdot xH_2O}$$

If S is also present alongwith N, a red colour in place of Prussian blue in the test of nitrogen appears, due to the formation of $Fe(SCN)^{2+}$.

Hydrazine does not give Lassaigne's test for nitrogen since it does not contain carbon. In order to test the presence of N in such compounds, during fusion with Na, some charcoal or preferably starch (which contains C but not N, S, halogens etc.) is added. Under these conditions, C of starch or charcoal combines with N of the compound to form NaCN which will now give a positive test for nitrogen.

⌐ Lassaigne's test is not shown by diazonium salts because diazonium salts usually lose N_2 on heating much before they have a chance to ⌐ react with fused sodium metal.

2. Detection of Sulphur

(i) Sodium fusion extract is acidified with acetic acid and lead acetate is added to it. A black precipitate of PbS indicates the presence of sulphur.

$$S^{2-} + Pb^{2+}$$
$$\downarrow$$
$$PbS$$
$$\text{Black}$$

(ii) On treating sodium fusion extract with sodium nitroprusside, apperance of a violet colour further indicates the presence of sulphur.

$$S^{2-} + [Fe(CN)_5NO]^{2-} \longrightarrow \underset{\text{Violet}}{[Fe(CN)_5NOS]^{4-}}$$

3. Detection of Halogens

The sodium fusion extract is acidified with nitric acid and then treated with silver nitrate.

$$X^- + Ag^+ \longrightarrow AgX$$

X represents a halogen —Cl, Br, or I.

AgCl-white ppt, AgBr-dull yellow ppt, AgI-bright yellow ppt.

Note *Beilstein test is also a test for halogen but it is not a confirmatory test.*

4. Detection of Phosphorus

The compound is heated with an oxidising agent (sodium peroxide). By this the phosphorus present in the compound is oxidised to phosphate. The solution is boiled with nitric acid and then treated with ammonium molybdate. A yellow colouration or precipitate indicates the presence of phosphorus.

$$Na_3PO_4 + 3HNO_3 \longrightarrow H_3PO_4 + 3NaNO_3$$

$$H_3PO_4 + 12(NH_4)_2MoO_4 + 21HNO_3 \longrightarrow \underset{\substack{\text{Ammonium} \\ \text{phosphomolybdate} \\ \text{(yellow ppt)}}}{(NH_4)_3PO_4 \cdot 12MoO_3}$$
$$+ 21NH_4NO_3 + 12H_2O$$

Quantitative Estimation of Elements

1. Estimation of Carbon and Hydrogen (Liebig's Method)

When a known mass of organic compound is strongly heated with dry CuO, C and H present are quantitatively oxidised to CO_2 and H_2O respectively.

$$C_xH_y + \left(x + \frac{y}{4}\right)O_2 \longrightarrow xCO_2 + \frac{y}{2}H_2O$$

By knowing the amount of CO_2 and H_2O from known weight of organic compound, the percentage of carbon and hydrogen can be computed.

The water is absorbed in anhydrous $CaCl_2$.

The carbon dioxide is absorbed in concentrated solution of KOH.

$$\text{Percentage of carbon} = \frac{12}{44} \times \frac{\text{mass of } CO_2 \times 100}{\text{mass of organic substance}}$$

$$\text{Percentage of hydrogen} = \frac{2}{18} \times \frac{\text{mass of } H_2O \times 100}{\text{mass of organic substance}}$$

On heating with CuO, elements other than C and H are also modified as follows :

When organic compound contains nitrogen, the oxides of nitrogen (NO, N_2O etc.) are absorbed by caustic potash. These are removed by the use of bright copper gauge.

$$4Cu + 2NO_2 \longrightarrow 4CuO + N_2$$
$$Cu + N_2O \longrightarrow CuO + N_2$$

Nitrogen is not absorbed by KOH solution.

> When organic compound contains halogens, they are removed by using silver gauge by forming non-volatile silver halide.
> When sulphur is present, it is removed by forming lead sulphate by using fused lead chromate and halogens form lead halides.

Estimation of Nitrogen

(i) **Duma's method** This method is used for nitrogenous compounds. Though tedious but it is better than Kjeldahl's method.

In this method, the nitrogenous compound is heated strongly with CuO in the atmosphere of CO_2 and the mixture obtained is passed over a roll of heated bright Cu gauze. The oxides of nitrogen again reduce to N_2. The resultant mixture is passed in KOH. All gases except N_2 are fairly absorbed. Nitrogen is collected over KOH and its volume at NTP is measured.

$$C_xH_yN_z + (2x + y/2)\,CuO \longrightarrow xCO_2 + y/2\,H_2O + z/2\,N_2 + (2x + y/2)\,Cu$$

$$\text{Percentage of nitrogen} = \frac{28 \times \text{volume of } \dot{N}_2 \text{ at NTP} \times 100}{22400 \times \text{wt. of organic compound}}$$

$$= \frac{\text{mass of nitrogen} \times 100}{\text{mass of organic substance}}$$

(ii) Kjeldahl's method

In this method, nitrogen containing compound is heated with conc. H_2SO_4. The acid mixture obtained is then heated with excess of NaOH. The liberated ammonia gas is absorbed in an excess of standard solution of H_2SO_4. The amount of NH_3 produced is determined by estimating the amount of H_2SO_4 consumed in reaction.

Organic compound + conc. H_2SO_4 + (small amount of K_2SO_4 and

$$CuSO_4 \rightarrow (NH_4)_2SO_4 \xrightarrow{2NaOH} Na_2SO_4 + 2NH_3 + 2H_2O$$

$$2NH_3 + H_2SO_4 \longrightarrow (NH_4)_2SO_4$$

Ammonia is passed through H_2SO_4 or HCl of known volume and normality. The volume of acid neutralised by NH_3 is calculated by neutralising the acid left by NaOH solution.

$$\text{Percentage of nitrogen} = \frac{1.4 \times N \times V}{\text{mass of organic compound}}$$

N = normality of acid

V = volume of acid in mL neutralised by ammonia.

(In practice, K_2SO_4 is added to raise the boiling point of H_2SO_4 and $CuSO_4$ is added to catalyse the reaction).

Kjeldahl's method is not reliable as results obtained are generally low. It cannot be applied to compounds containing nitrogen directly linked to oxygen or nitrogen such as nitro, nitroso, azo and nitrogen present in ring as in pyridine.

Estimation of Halogen (Carius Method)

In this method, halogen containing compound is heated with fuming HNO_3 in presence of $AgNO_3$ contained in carius tube. On heating, C and H are oxidised to CO_2 and H_2O and halogen present forms AgX.

Organic compound + Fuming HNO_3 + $AgNO_3 \rightarrow AgX$

It is estimated gravimetrically.

Percentage of halogen

$$= \frac{\text{Atomic mass of halogen atom} \times \text{mass of } AgX \times 100}{\text{mol. mass of } AgX \times \text{mass of organic compound}}$$

Estimation of Sulphur

In this method, sulphur containing compound is heated in carius tube with Na_2O_2 or fuming HNO_3. On heating S is oxidised to H_2SO_4. It is precipitated as $BaSO_4$ by adding excess of $BaCl_2$ solution in water.

Organic compound + Oxidising agent (Na_2O_2 or fuming HNO_3) $\rightarrow$

$H_2SO_4 \xrightarrow{BaCl_2} BaSO_4$.

It is estimated gravimetrically,

$$\text{Percentage of sulphur} = \frac{32 \times \text{mass of } BaSO_4 \times 100}{233 \times \text{mass of organic compound}}$$

Estimation of Phosphorus

In this method, organic compound is heated with fuming HNO_3 that converts 'P' present in compound to phosphoric acid. It is precipitated as $(NH_4)_3PO_4 \cdot 12MoO_3$ by adding NH_3 and ammonium molybdate. Alternatively, phosphoric acid may be precipitated as $MgNH_4PO_4$ by adding magnesia mixture which on ignition yields $Mg_2P_2O_7$.

Organic compound + Fuming nitric acid $\rightarrow H_3PO_4$

$$\xrightarrow[\substack{\text{mixture} \\ (MgSO_4 + NH_4OH + NH_4Cl)}]{\text{Magnesia}} MgNH_4PO_4 \xrightarrow[\substack{\text{(magnesium} \\ \text{pyrophosphate)}}]{\text{Ignition}} Mg_2P_2O_7$$

$$\text{Percentage of phosphorus} = \frac{62 \times \text{mass of } Mg_2P_2O_7 \times 100}{222 \times \text{mass of organic compound}}$$

Now a days CHN elemental analyser is used to estimate the C, H and N in the organic compound.

Estimation of Oxygen

The mixture of gaseous product containing oxygen is converted to carbon monoxide. This mixture is passed through warm iodine pentoxide (I_2O_5) when carbon monoxide is oxidised to carbon dioxide producing iodine.

$$\text{Compound} \xrightarrow{\text{Heat}} O_2 + \text{Other gaseous products}$$

$$2C + O_2 \xrightarrow{1373 \text{ K}} 2CO \times 5$$

$$I_2O_5 + 5CO \longrightarrow I_2 + 5CO_2 \times 2$$

$$\therefore \text{Percentage of oxygen} = \frac{32 \times m_1 \times 100}{88 \times m} \%$$

m = mass of organic compound taken.

m_1 = mass of carbon dioxide produced.

24

General Organic Chemistry

Organic Chemistry

The hydrides of carbon (hydrocarbons) and their derivatives are called **organic compounds.** The branch of chemistry which deals with these compounds is called **organic chemistry.**

Berzelius (1808) defined organic chemistry as 'the chemistry of substances found in living matter and gave the vital force theory. Synthesis of urea, the first organic compound synthesised in laboratory, by Wohler, gave death blow to the vital force theory.

$$(NH_4)_2SO_4 + 2KCNO \xrightarrow[-K_2SO_4]{} 2NH_4CNO \xrightarrow{\Delta} \underset{\text{urea}}{NH_2CONH_2}$$

Acetic acid is the first organic compound synthesised from its elements.

Reasons for Large Number of Organic Compounds

(a) **Catenation** It is the tendency of self combination and is maximum in carbon. A carbon atom can combine with other carbon atoms by single, double or triple bonds. Thus, it forms more compounds than the others.

(b) **Tetravalency and small size** Carbon being tetravalent, is capable of bonding with four other C-atoms or some other monovalent atoms. Carbon can form compound with oxygen, hydrogen, chlorine, sulphur, nitrogen and phosphorus. These compounds have specific properties depending upon the nature of the element or group attached with the carbon.

Furthermore, these compounds are exceptionally stable because of the small size of carbon.

General Characteristics of Organic Compounds

1. These are the compounds of carbon with H, O, N, S, P, F, Cl, Br and I.

2. These are generally found in living organisms.
   e.g. carbohydrates, proteins etc.
3. These may be gases, liquids or solids.
4. Being covalent in nature, these have low boiling point and melting point and soluble in organic solvents.
5. These are generally volatile and inflammable.
6. They do not conduct electricity because of the absence of free ions.
7. They posses distinct colour and odour.

Representation of Different Formula

An organic compounds can be represented by the following ways :

1. Complete formula

In it, all the bonds present between any two atoms are shown clearly.

e.g.

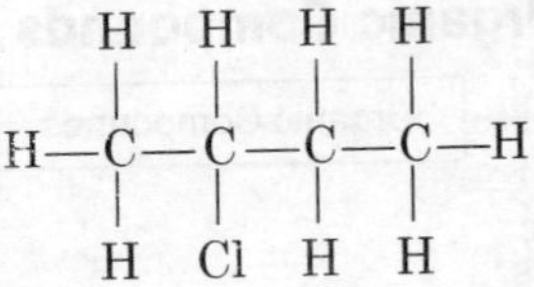

$$H-\underset{\underset{H}{|}}{\overset{\overset{H}{|}}{C}}-\underset{\underset{Cl}{|}}{\overset{\overset{H}{|}}{C}}-\underset{\underset{H}{|}}{\overset{\overset{H}{|}}{C}}-\underset{\underset{H}{|}}{\overset{\overset{H}{|}}{C}}-H$$

2. Condensed Formula

In it, all the bonds are not shown clearly.

e.g. $CH_3\underset{\underset{Cl}{|}}{CH}CH_2CH_3$ or $CH_3CH(Cl)CH_2CH_3$

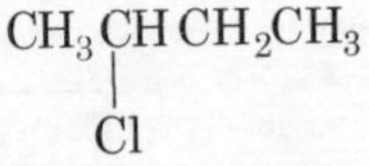

3. Bond Line Formula

In it, every fold and free terminal represents a carbon and lines represent the bonds. e.g.

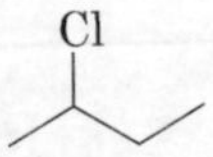

In such formulae, it is assumed that required number of H-atoms are present, **wherever**, they are necessary (to satisfy tetravalency of carbon), e.g.

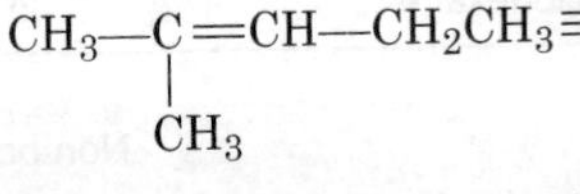

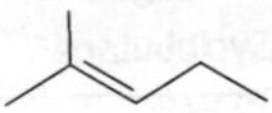

$$CH_3-\underset{\underset{CH_3}{|}}{C}=CH-CH_2CH_3 \equiv$$

$$CH_2=CH-C\equiv C-OH \equiv$$

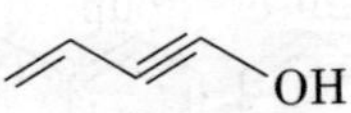

$$CH_3-CH_2-COOH \equiv$$

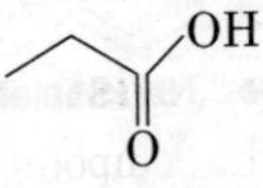

Three-dimensional Representation of Organic Molecule

The three-dimensional (3-D) structure of organic molecule can be represented on paper by using certain convention, e.g. by using solid (◄—) and dashed (⅏⅏⅏) wedge formula, the 3-D image of a molecule from a two-dimensional picture can be perceived. 3-D representation of methane molecule on paper has been shown below :

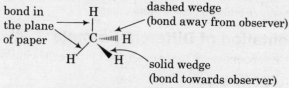

wedge-and-dash representation of CH_4.

Classification of Organic Compounds

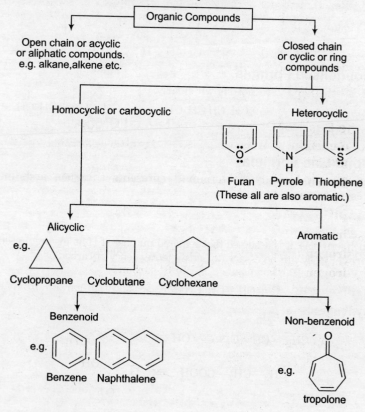

Classification of Carbon Atoms

1. On the Basis of Number of C Attached

(i) **Primary carbon atom**   When carbon atom is attached with one other carbon atom only, it is called primary or $1°$ carbon atom.

(ii) **Secondary carbon atom**   When carbon atom is attached with two other carbon atoms, it is called secondary or $2°$ carbon atom.

(iii) **Tertiary carbon atom**   When carbon atom is attached with three other carbon atoms, it is called tertiary or $3°$ carbon atom.

(iv) **Quaternary carbon atom**   When carbon atom is attached with four other carbon atoms, it is called quaternary or $4°$ carbon atom.

Reactivity order of carbon atoms is as follows $3° > 2° > 1°$.

e.g.

$$\underset{1°}{CH_3}-\underset{2°}{CH_2}-\underset{4°}{C}-\underset{3°}{CH}-\underset{1°}{CH_3}$$

with $\underset{1°}{CH_3}$ above the C and $\underset{1°}{CH_3}$ $\underset{1°}{CH_3}$ below.

On the Basis of Position of Functional Group

(i) **α-carbon**   Carbon which is directly attached to the functional group.

(ii) **β-carbon**   Carbon which is directly attached to the α-carbon.

Classification of Hydrogen Atoms

$1°$-hydrogen (primary)   attached to $1°$-carbon.

$2°$-hydrogen (secondary)   attached to $2°$-carbon.

$3°$-hydrogen (tertiary)   attached to $3°$-carbon.

α-hydrogen(s)   Hydrogens which are attached to α-carbon atom.

β-hydrogen(s)   Hydrogens which are attached to β-carbon atom.

e.g.

$$\underset{\beta}{CH_3}-\underset{\alpha}{CH_2}-Cl,$$

$$\underset{\beta}{CH_3}-\underset{\alpha}{CH_2}-COOH$$

$$\underset{\beta}{CH_3}-\underset{\alpha}{CH_2}-CHO$$

Functional Group

The atom, e.g. —Cl, —Br etc., or group of atoms e.g. —COOH, —CHO, which is responsible for the chemical properties of the molecule, is called functional group.

Double and triple bonds are also functional groups.

$$R-OH$$

R is called alkyl group, it contains only single bond; alkenyl group contains double bond and alkynyl group contains triple bond.

Homologous Series

The series in which the molecular formula of adjacent members differ by a —CH_2 unit, is called **homologous series** and the individual members are called **homologues**. e.g. The homologous series of alkene group is

$$\left.\begin{array}{l} C_2H_4 \\ C_3H_6 \\ C_4H_8 \\ C_5H_{10} \end{array}\right\} \text{ difference of —}CH_2 \text{ unit or 14 unit mass}$$

The general characteristics of this series are :

1. All the homologues contain same functional group. That's why their chemical properties are almost similar.

2. All the members of a series have same general formula, e.g.

Series	General formula
Alkanes	C_nH_{2n+2}
Alkenes	C_nH_{2n}
Alkynes	C_nH_{2n-2}
Alcohol and ether	$C_nH_{2n+2}O$
Aldehyde and ketone	$C_nH_{2n}O$
Acid and ester	$C_nH_{2n}O_2$

3. All the members can be prepared by almost similar methods.

4. With increase in the molecular weight of a series, the physical properties varies gradually.

Nomenclature of Organic Compounds

Trivial System

It is the oldest system in which names are derived from source or some property. These are mainly derived from Latin or Greek names. e.g. acetic acid (acetum = vinegar), oxalic acid (oxalus), malic acid (pyrus malus), citric acid (citrum), formic acid (obtained from red ant (formicus)].

IUPAC System

The IUPAC (International Union of Pure and Applied Chemistry) system, given in 1957, is superior and widely used. IUPAC amends these rules from time to time. Here, we are following the 1993 recommendations of IUPAC nomenclature. Following rules are used to write the IUPAC name of an organic compound.

Rule I

Longest chain rule The chain containing the principal functional group, secondary functional group and multiple bonds as many as possible is the longest possible chain. In the absence of functional group, secondary group and multiple bonds, the chain containing the maximum number of C-atoms will be the longest possible chain. e.g.

Choose the word root from the table given below for the longest possible chain.

Word Root for Carbon Chain

Chain length	Word root	Chain length	Word root
C_1	Meth-	C_7	Hept
C_2	Eth-	C_8	Oct
C_3	Prop-	C_9	Non
C_4	But-	C_{10}	Dec
C_5	Pent	C_{11}	Undec
C_6	Hex-	C_{12}	Dodec

Rule 2

Lowest number rule Numbering is done in such a way so that
  1. branching if present gets the lowest number.
  2. the sum of numbers of side chain is lowest.
  3. principal functional group gets the lowest number.

Select the principal functional group from the preference series :

$$—COOH > —SO_3H > —COOR > —COX > —CONH_2 > CN > —NC$$

$$> —CHO > \!\!\! > \!\!\! C=O > —OH > —SH$$

$$> —NH_2 > —OR > —\underset{\underset{O}{\diagdown\diagup}}{C}—C— \; > = > \equiv > NO_2 > X > R$$

Functional group other than the principal functional group are called substituents.

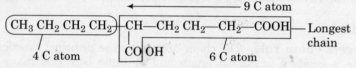

Rule 3.

Naming the prefixes and suffixes Prefix represents the substituent and suffix is used for principal functional group.

Primary prefixes are cyclo, bicyclo, di, tri, tetra, tries, tetrakis etc.

Primary suffix are ene, ane, or yne used for double, single and triple bonds respectively.

Substituent	Prefix	Substituent	Prefix
—F	Fluoro	—N=N—	diazo
—Cl	Chloro	—N=O	nitroso
—Br	Bromo	—NO_2	nitro

Secondary suffixes are tabulated below :

S. No.	Class	Formula	Prefix	Suffix
1.	Acid halides	$\overset{O}{\overset{\|}{—C—X}}$	halocarbonyl	—oyl halide —carbonyl halide
2.	Alcohols	—OH	hydroxy	—ol
3.	Aldehydes	—CHO	formyl	—al —carbaldehyde
4.	Ketones	$>\!\!C=O$	oxo	—one

S. No.	Class	Formula	Prefix	Suffix
5.	Amides	$-CONH_2$	carbamoyl	—amide
6.	Amine	$-NH_2$	amino	—amine
7.	Carboxylic acid	$-COOH$	carboxy	—carboxylic acid
8.	Ester	$-COOR$	oxy carbonyl	—alkyl alkanoate
9.	Nitriles	$-CN$	cyano	—nitrile
10.	Sulphonic acid	$-SO_2-OH$	sulpho	—sulphonic acid

Hence, according to the rules, given above, the IUPAC name of a compound can be written as

Prefixes + root word + suffixes primary prefix + secondary prefix
+ root word + primary suffix + secondary suffix

e.g.

$$\overset{4}{C}H_3\ \overset{3}{C}H-\overset{2}{C}H_2\ \boxed{\overset{1}{C}HO}$$ —— principal functional group (–al)

$\boxed{OH}$— substituent (hydroxy)

4–hydroxybutanal

↑ prefix ↑ root word ↑ suffix

If more than two similar functional groups are present, all the groups are considered as substituent, e.g.

$$\overset{3}{C}H_2-\overset{2}{C}H-\overset{1}{C}H_2$$
$$|\qquad\quad|\qquad\quad|$$
$$CN\quad\ \ CN\quad CN$$

propane-1, 2, 3-cyanide

Naming Alicyclic Compounds

For alicyclic compounds, prefix cyclo is used e.g.

$$CH_3-\overset{1}{C}H-\overset{2}{C}H_3$$
$$|$$
$$1$$

cyclohexane   1-(1-methylethyl) cyclohexane

If the alkyl chain contains a greater number of C-atoms than the ring, the ring is designated as substituent, e.g.

$$\triangleright-\overset{1}{C}H_2\ \overset{2}{C}H_2\ \overset{3}{C}H_2\ \overset{4}{C}H_3$$

cyclopropylbutane

If side chain contains a multiple bond or a functional group, the ring is treated as a substituent e.g.

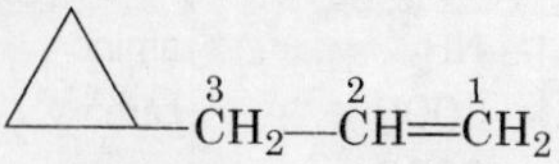

3-cyclo propylprop-1-ene

Other examples are :

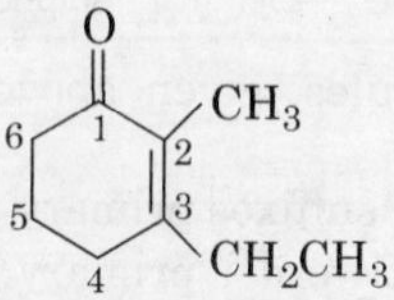

3-ethyl-2-methylcyclohex-2-en-1-one

Naming Spiro Compounds

Prefix 'spiro' is used for the compounds in which one carbon is common between two rings :

Here, smaller ring is numbered first, e.g.

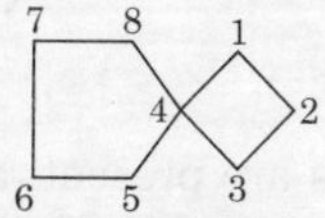

spiro [3.4] octane
↑
number of atoms in ring
in ascending order

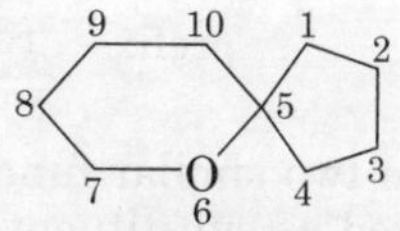

6-oxaspiro [4.5] decane

Naming Bicyclo Compounds

Prefix 'bicyclo' is used for such compounds, e.g.

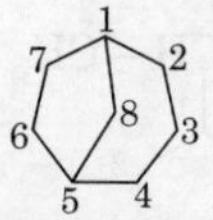

bicyclo [3.2.1] octane
↑
number of atoms in each ring
in descending order

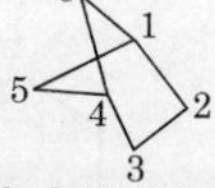

bicyclo [2.1.1] hexane

In bicyclo compounds, numbering is done first in larger ring, then in smaller ring.

Naming Aromatic Compounds

IUPAC accepted their common trivial names, e.g.

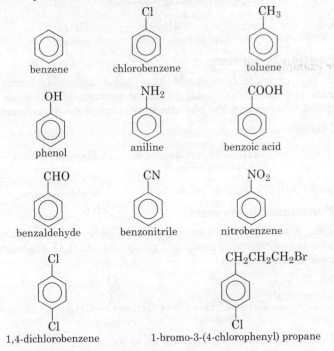

benzene	chlorobenzene	toluene
phenol	aniline	benzoic acid
benzaldehyde	benzonitrile	nitrobenzene
1,4-dichlorobenzene		1-bromo-3-(4-chlorophenyl) propane

Isomerism

The compound having same molecular formula but differ in properties are known as isomers and the phenomenon is known as isomerism.

There are two main types of isomerism i.e.

1. Structural Isomerism

In this type of isomerism, compounds have same molecular formula but different structures.

It can further be of following types :

(i) Chain Isomerism

It arises when two or more compounds have similar molecular formula but different carbon skeletons, e.g. for C_5H_{12}. we have

$$CH_3—CH_2—CH_2—CH_2—CH_3$$
$$n-\text{pentane}$$

$$CH_3—CH_2—CH—CH_3 \;;\; H_3C—\underset{\underset{CH_3}{|}}{\overset{\overset{CH_3}{|}}{C}}—CH_3$$

$$\underset{CH_3}{|}$$

iso– pentane   *neo*– pentane

(ii) Position Isomerism

When two or more compounds have same molecular formula but different position of functional groups or substituents, they are called positional isomers and the phenomenon is called position isomerism.

e.g. C_3H_7Cl

$$CH_3—CH_2—CH_2—Cl,$$
1–chloropropane

$$CH_3—\underset{\underset{Cl}{|}}{CH}—CH_3$$
2–chloropropane

(iii) Functional Isomerism

It arises when two or more compounds have the same molecular formula but different functional group. e.g. C_3H_6O represents an aldehyde and a ketone as

$$CH_3—CH_2—CHO, \quad CH_3—\overset{\overset{O}{\|}}{C}—CH_3$$
Propanal   Propanone

• C_2H_6O represents an alcohol and an ether.

$$CH_3—CH_2—\overset{\bullet\bullet}{\underset{\bullet\bullet}{O}}H, \; CH_3—\overset{\bullet\bullet}{\underset{\bullet\bullet}{O}}—CH_3 \text{ etc.}$$
ethanol   dimethyl ether

(iv) Metamerism

It arises due to different alkyl groups on either side of the same functional group in a molecule, *e.g.,*

$$CH_3—\overset{\bullet\bullet}{\underset{\bullet\bullet}{O}}—C_3H_7, \; C_2H_5—\overset{\bullet\bullet}{\underset{\bullet\bullet}{O}}—C_2H_5$$
1-methoxypropane   diethyl ether

(v) Tautomerism

It is a special type of functional isomerism which arises in carbonyl compounds containing α-H atom. e.g.

$$CH_3—\overset{\overset{O}{\|}}{C}—H \;\rightleftharpoons\; CH_2{=}\overset{\overset{OH}{|}}{C}—H$$
keto form   enol form
(acetaldehyde)

α-hydrogen

cyclohexanone   enol form
(keto form)

2. Stereoisomerism

The compounds having same molecular formula but different spatial arrangement of atoms or groups are called **stereoisomers** and the phenomenon is called **stereoisomerism**.

Stereoisomerism is of two types : optical isomerism and geometrical isomerism.

(i) Optical Isomerism

Compounds having similar physical and chemical properties but differ only in behaviour towards plane polarised light are called enantiomers or optical isomers and the phenomenon is known as optical isomerism. e.g.

2-butanol

mirror

The isomer which rotate the plane of polarised light towards right (clockwise) is known as **dextrorotatory** or **d-form** while that which rotates towards left (anticlockwise) is known as **laevorotatory** or **l-form**.

Generally asymmetric or chiral compounds show optical isomerism. Chiral compounds are those which contain chiral centre i.e. chiral carbon, the carbon all the four valencies of which are satisfied by four different groups. Allenes, spiranes and biphenyl compounds, although have absence of chiral centre, but are asymmetric. That's why they are also optically active.

Number of optical active isomers = 2^n (where, n = chiral carbon). If two end are similar number of optical active isomers = 2^{n-1} (if n = even) and *meso* form = $2^{\frac{n-1}{2}}$. If n = odd, number of optical active isomers = $2^{n-1} - 2^{(n-1)/2}$.

Terms Related to Optical Isomerism

(a) **Enantiomers** The non-superimposable mirror images are called **enantiomers.** e.g.

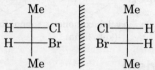

(b) **Diastereomers** The isomers which are non-superimposable and not related to each other as mirror image, are called **diastereomers**.

```
        Me                    Me
        |                     |
  H ———|— Cl            H ———|— Cl
  H ———|— Br            Br ———|— H
        |                     |
        Me                    Me
```
diastereomers

They have different physical and chemical properties.

(c) *Meso* **form** The compound in which half part of a molecule is the mirror image of other half, is called *meso* form. Generally, a *meso* compound have two or more chiral centres and a plane of symmetry.

It is optically inactive due to internal compensation, thus, it is not possible to convert it into *d* and *l*-form e.g.

```
             COOH
              |
       H ——— *C — OH
      --------|-------------- plane of symmetry
       H ——— C — OH
              |*
             COOH
```
meso compound

(d) **Racemic mixture** It is a mixture of enantiomers in 1 : 1. It is optically inactive due to external compensation.

> Separation of a racemic mixture into *d* and *l* form is called **resolution**. It can be done by mechanical method, biochemical method and chemical method.

(e) **Atropisomers** These are the isomers that can be interconvertable by rotation about single bond but for which the rotation barrier is large enough that they can be separated and do not convert readily at room temperature.

(f) **Specific rotation** It is given by the expression

$$[\alpha] = \frac{\alpha}{l \times d} = \frac{\text{observed rotation (degree)}}{\text{length} \times \text{density}}$$

Nomenclature of Enantiomers

(i) *D-L* **configuration** The optical isomer in which H is present towards left hand side and the other group towards right hand side, is *D*-form while in which, H is present towards right and the other group occupy the left position, is *L*-form. This system is applicable mainly for compounds containing one chiral atom.

(ii) **Threo-erythro system** When the same groups are present at the same side of the carbon chain, the form is called erythro form. When the same groups are present on the opposite side of the carbon chain, the form is called threo form. e.g.

erythro form   threo form

(iii) *R-S* **system** This system was proposed by Cahn, Ingold and Prelog. In this system, configuration *R* is given to the isomer in which sequence of groups is clockwise and *S* is given to the isomer in which sequence of groups is anticlockwise.

Priority sequence is decided by following rules :

1. Priority is given to the atom having high atomic number, e.g. in Cl, Br and F, the priority order is Br > Cl > F.

2. In case of group of atoms, priority is decided by the atomic number of first atom. e.g. in —COOH, —OH and —NH$_2$ priority order is

$$\text{—OH} > \text{—NH}_2 > \text{—COOH}$$

3. If the first atom of the group of atoms is same, the priority is decided by second atom of the group, e.g. among —COOH, —CH$_2$OH and—CHO, priority order is

$$\text{—COOH} > \text{—CHO} > \text{—CH}_2\text{OH}$$

4. When a multiple bond is present in a group, the atom at the end of the multiple bond is like as if it is equal to equivalent number of single bond, e.g.

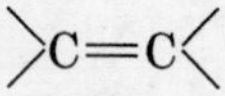

$$>C=C< \quad \text{is equivalent to}$$

$$\begin{array}{cc} -\overset{|}{C}-\overset{|}{C}- \\ -\overset{|}{C} \quad \overset{|}{C}- \\ \underset{|}{N} \quad \underset{|}{C} \end{array}$$

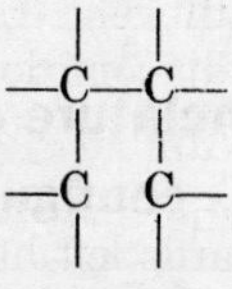

Similarly, $-C\equiv N$ is equivalent to

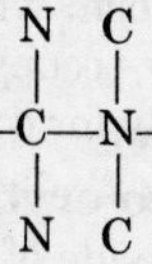

$$\begin{array}{cc} N \quad C \\ -\overset{|}{C}-\overset{|}{N}- \\ \underset{|}{N} \quad \underset{|}{C} \end{array}$$

e.g.

④ H—C—CH₃ ③ with OH ① on top, NH₂ ② on bottom

$$(4) H-\overset{\overset{\displaystyle OH ①}{|}}{\underset{\underset{\displaystyle NH_2 ②}{|}}{C}}-CH_3 ③ \equiv$$

Interconversion →

Clockwise;
R configuration

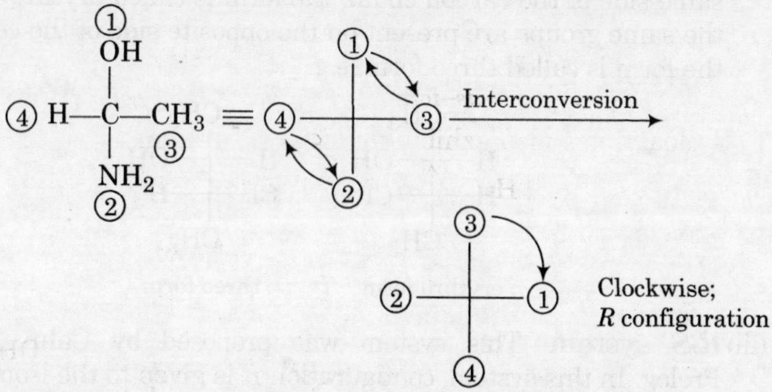

Priority order OH > NH₂ > CH₃ > H

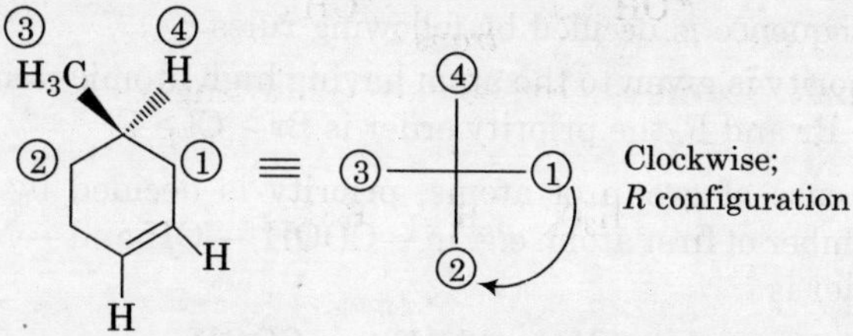

Clockwise;
R configuration

(ii) Geometrical Isomerism

The isomers having same molecular formula but different spatial arrangement of atoms about the double bond are known as geometrical isomers and this phenomenon is called geometrical isomerism, e.g.

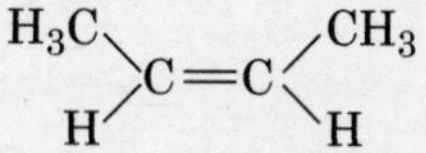

$$\underset{H}{\overset{H_3C}{>}}C=C\underset{H}{\overset{CH_3}{<}} \qquad \underset{H}{\overset{H_3C}{>}}C=C\underset{CH_3}{\overset{H}{<}}$$

cis-2-butene 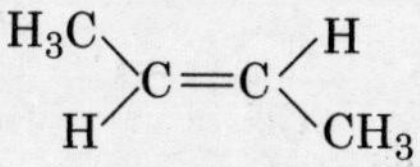   *trans*-2-butene

For exhibiting geometrical isomerism, the essential conditions are :
1. The compound must contain at least one double bond.
2. The groups present at the double bonded carbon atoms, must be different. However, one similar group should be present at the adjacent double bonded carbon atoms.

Number of geometrical isomers (if two ends are not similar = 2^n where, n = number of double bonds).

Types of Geometrical Isomers

(a) ***Cis-trans* isomers** In *cis*-isomer, similar groups are present on the same side of the double bond and in *trans*-isomer, similar groups are present on the opposite side of the double bond. e.g.

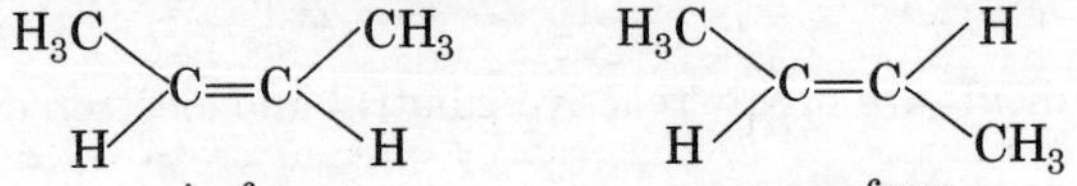

cis–form   *trans*–form

Cycloalkanes also exhibit *cis-trans* isomerism.

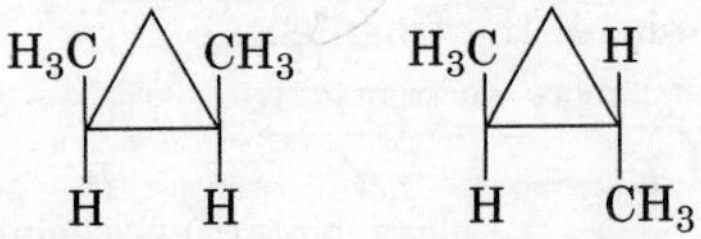

cis-form   *trans*-form

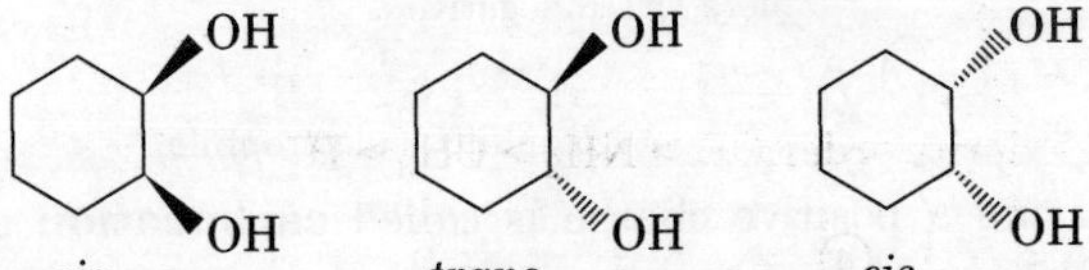

cis   *trans*   *cis*

(b) ***Syn-anti* isomers** compounds containing C=N bond (as in aldoxime), N=N bond (as in H_2N_2O) exhibit this type of isomerism. e.g.

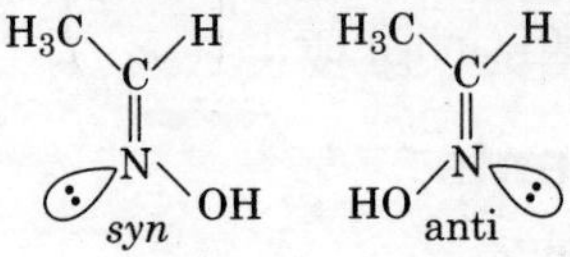

syn   *anti*

(c) ***E-Z* isomers** In *E*-isomer, bulkier (heavier) groups are present on the opposite side of the double bond and in *Z*-isomer, heavier groups are present on the same side of the double bond. *E* is *entgegen* means opposite and *Z* is *Zusammen* means together, e.g.

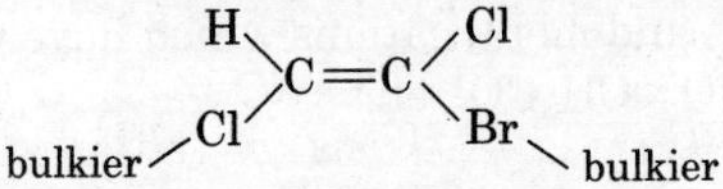

bulkier   bulkier
Z isomer    *Z*-3-hexene

Fission of a Covalent Bond

1. Homolytic Fission

In this, one of the electrons of the shared pair in a covalent bond goes with each of the bonded atoms. The neutral chemical species thus formed, is called free radical. Generally, homolytic fission takes place in non-polar, covalent molecules in the presence of sunlight or high temperature.

$$A \overset{\curvearrowleft \curvearrowright}{\text{---}} B \xrightarrow{\text{Sunlight}} \underbrace{A^\bullet + B^\bullet}_{\text{free radicals}}$$

e.g. $$Cl_2 \xrightarrow{\text{Sunlight}} 2Cl^\bullet$$

Free radicals are highly reactive, neutral and electron deficient species.

2. Heterolytic Fission

In this, the bond breaks in such a fashion that the shared pair of electrons goes with one of the fragments.

$$A \overset{\curvearrowright}{\underset{}{\text{---}}} B \xrightarrow{\text{more electronegative}} \underset{\text{electrophile}}{A^+} + \underset{\text{nucleophile}}{B^-}$$

or $$A \overset{\curvearrowleft}{\underset{}{\text{---}}} B \xrightarrow{\text{less electronegative}} \underset{\text{nucleophile}}{A^-} + \underset{\text{electrophile}}{B^+}$$

Carbon bearing a positive charge is called **carbocation** and carbon bearing negative charge is called **carbanion**.

> Heterolytic fission generally takes place in polar covalent molecules but in non-polar molecules, it takes place in the presence of catalyst like $AlCl_3$ (anhy.), $FeCl_3$(anhy.) etc.

Attacking Reagents

These are of two types :

1. Electrophiles or Electrophilic Reagents

These are electron deficient species i.e. behave as Lewis acids. The following species behave as electrophiles :

(i) All non-metal cations and metal cations which have vacant d-orbitals. e.g. Cl^+, NO_2^+, CH_3CO^+ etc.

(ii) Lewis acids (incomplete octet), e.g. BF_3, $ZnCl_2$ (anhydrous), $FeCl_3$ (anhydrous), $AlCl_3$ (anhydrous), $\ddot{C}H_2$ etc.

(iii) Non-metal (acidic) oxides e.g. CO_2, SO_2 etc.

2. Nucleophiles or Nucleophilic Reagents

These are electron rich species i.e. behave as Lewis bases.

These attack at electron deficient area.

The following species behave as nucleophiles :

(i) All anions e.g. Cl^-, NH_2^-, OH^- etc.

(ii) Lewis bases e.g. $\ddot{:}NH_3$, H_2O, $R—\overset{\cdot\cdot}{\underset{\cdot\cdot}{O}}—R$, $R—\overset{\cdot\cdot}{\underset{\cdot\cdot}{O}}H$ etc.

(iii) Benzene, alkenes etc.

Nucleophilicity order is

$$H^- > CH_3^- > NH_2^- > RO^- > OH^-$$

In case of same nucleophilic site, nucleophilicity parallels basicity i.e. as the basicity increases, nucleophilicity also increases.

⌐ If nucleophilic sites (or attacking atoms) are different nucleophilicity varies inversely with electronegativity. ⌐

3. Ambiphiles

These species behave like both electrophiles as well as nucleophiles.

Organic compounds containing a multiple bond between carbon and a more electronegative atom can act as ambiphiles. e.g.

$$\overset{H}{\underset{H}{>}}\overset{\delta+}{C}=\overset{\delta-}{\ddot{O}\ddot{:}} \quad ; \quad CH_3—\overset{\delta+}{C}\equiv\overset{\delta-}{N}\ddot{:}$$

electrophile nucleophile   electrophile nucleophile

Reaction Intermediates

These are formed as a intermediate during the course of a reaction. These are short lived and highly reactive.

Free radicals, carbocations, carbanions, carbenes and nitrenes are important reactions intermediates.

1. **Free Radicals**

These are the product of homolysis and contain an odd electron. These are highly reactive planar species with sp^2-hybridisation.

Their order of stability is

$$(C_6H_5)_3\overset{\bullet}{C} > (C_6H_5)_2\overset{\bullet}{C}H > C_6H_5\overset{\bullet}{C}H_2$$

$$> CH_2=CH-\overset{\bullet}{C}H_2 > 3° > 2° > 1° > CH_2=\overset{\bullet}{C}H$$

2. **Carbocations**

These are the product of heterolysis and contain a carbon bearing positive charge. These are electron deficient species. Carbocations contain six electrons in the valence shell.

These are also planar chemical species, i.e. sp^2-hybridised with an empty p-orbital.

The stability order of carbocations is :

$$(C_6H_5)_3C^+ > (C_6H_5)_2\overset{+}{C}H > (CH_3)_3\overset{+}{C} > C_6H_5\overset{+}{C}H_2 > 2°$$

$$> CH_2=CH-\overset{+}{C}H_2 > 1° > \overset{+}{C}_6H_5 > CH_2=\overset{+}{C}H$$

3. **Carbanions**

These are also the product of heterolysis and contain a carbon bearing negative charge and 8 electrons in its valence shell.

These have pyramidal shape with sp^3-hybridised carbon (having one lone pair)

The order of stability of carbanions is

$$(C_6H_5)_3C^- > (C_6H_5)_2\overset{-}{C}H > C_6H_5\overset{-}{C}H_2 > CH_2=CH-\overset{-}{C}H_2$$

$$> \overset{-}{C}H_3 > 1° > 2° > 3° \text{ carbanions}$$

4. **Carbenes**

These are divalent carbon species having two non-bonding electrons along with two bond pairs.

These are obtained by photolysis or pyrolysis, e.g.

$$\underset{\text{ketene}}{CH_2=C=O} \xrightarrow[\text{or } \Delta]{h\nu} :CH_2 + :C=O$$

These being electron deficient behave as Lewis acids. These are of two types :

(i) **Singlet carbene** In it, the C-atom is sp^2-hybridised. The unhybridised orbitals contain no electrons and a hybridised orbital contains two electrons :

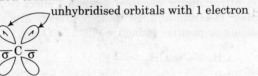

Singlet carbene has bent structure and is less stable than triplet carbene.

The order of stability of singlet carbenes is

$$\overset{..}{C}H_2 > \overset{..}{C}F_2 > \overset{..}{C}Cl_2 > \overset{..}{C}Br_2$$

(ii) **Triplet carbene** In it, the central C-atom is sp-hybridised. The unhybridised orbitals contain 1 electron each.

unhybridised orbitals with 1 electron

$$\overline{\sigma}\,C\,\overline{\sigma}$$

Triplet carbene has linear geometry.

5. Nitrene

These are neutral monovalent nitrogen species in which N atom has two unshared pair of electrons with a mono valent atom or group attached.

These are obtained by thermolysis of azides and as reactive as carbenes.

These are of two types : singlet nitrene and triplet nitrene

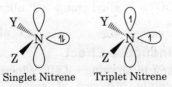

Singlet Nitrene   Triplet Nitrene

6. Arynes

It contains a formal carbon-carbon triple bond in aromatic molecule.

The additional bond is formed between two neighbouring C-atoms by sideways overlapping of two sp^2-orbitals. The new bond lies along with side of the ring and has little interaction with the π electron cloud lying above and below the ring. The sideways overlapping is weak and thus, makes the benzene more reactive.

Inductive Effect

It is just like shifting of shared pair of electrons in polar covalent molecules. If shared pair is more shifted towards the more electronegative atom, the less electronegative atom acquires slight positive charge and more electronegative atom acquires partial negative charge, e.g.

$$\overset{+\delta}{CH_3} \longrightarrow \overset{-\delta}{Cl}$$

It is a permanent effect and propagates through carbon chain. Atoms or groups having greater electron affinity than hydrogen, are said to have electron attracting or negative inductive effect ($-I$) while that having, smaller electron affinity than hydrogen are said to have electron releasing or positive inductive effect ($+I$). e.g.

$$\overset{+\delta\delta}{CH_3} \longrightarrow \overset{+\delta}{CH_2} \longrightarrow \overset{-\delta}{Cl}$$

$$\overset{+\delta\delta\delta}{CH_3} \longrightarrow \overset{+\delta\delta}{CH_2} \longrightarrow \overset{+\delta}{CH_2} \longrightarrow \overset{-\delta}{Cl}$$
$$\text{1°alkyl halide}$$

Here, Cl has $-I$ effect and alkyl group has $+I$ effect.

Order of groups producing $-I$ effect is

$$\overset{+}{R_3}N > NO_2 > CN > SO_3H > CHO > CO > COOH > F >$$
$$Cl > Br > I > OH > OR > NH_2 > C_6H_5 > H$$

Order of groups producing $+I$ effect is

$$O^- > \text{—}COO^- > 3° \text{ alkyl group} > 2° \text{ alkyl group}$$
$$> 1° \text{ alkyl group} > CH_3 > H$$

Applications of Inductive Effect

1. Presence of groups showing $+I$ effect increases the stability of carbocation while presence of groups showing $-I$ effect decreases their stability.

2. Strength of acid increases with the attachment of group showing $-I$ effect and decreases with the attachment of group showing $+I$ effect.

3. Presence of $+I$ effect showing groups increases the basic strength of amines.

4. Reactivity of carbonyl compound is increased by $-I$ effect showing groups.

5. Reactivity of alkyl halides towards S_N1 is increased by $+I$ showing groups.

Electromeric Effect

It is defined as the polarity produced in a multiple bonded compound as a reagent approaches it. In the presence of attacking reagent, the two π electrons are completely transferred to any of the one atom. This effect is temporary.

This may be of $+E$ type (when displacement of electron pair is away from the atom or group) or of $-E$ type (when the displacement is towards the atom or group). e.g.

Hyperconjugation

It involves delocalisation of σ electron of a C—H bond of an alkyl group attached directly to an atom of unsaturated system or to an atom with an unshared p-orbital.

This effect is also called **no bond resonance or Baker Nathan effect**.

Applications of Hyperconjugation

(i) **Stability of alkenes** More the number of α-hydrogen atoms, more stable is the alkene.

$$\overset{\alpha}{H_3C}-C\overset{\overset{\alpha}{\overset{\displaystyle CH_3}{\big|}}}{=}C\overset{\overset{\displaystyle \alpha}{\displaystyle CH_3}}{\underset{\underset{\displaystyle \alpha}{\displaystyle CH_3}}{<}} > \overset{\alpha}{CH_3}CH=C\overset{\overset{\displaystyle \alpha}{\displaystyle CH_3}}{\underset{\underset{\displaystyle \alpha}{\displaystyle CH_3}}{<}} > \overset{\alpha}{CH_3}-CH=CH-\overset{\alpha}{CH_3}$$

(ii) **Stability of carbocation** Greater the number of alkyl groups attached to a positively charged carbon atom, the greater is the stability.

$$(CH_3)_3 C^+ > (CH_3)_2 \overset{+}{CH} > CH_3 -\overset{+}{CH_2} > \overset{+}{CH_3}$$

Resonance Effect

When all the properties of a molecule cannot be shown by a single structure and two or more structures are required to show all the properties of that molecule, then the structures are called **resonating structures** or **canonical forms** and the molecule is referred as resonance hybrid. This phenomenon is called resonance.

In resonance,

1. The arrangement of atoms must be identical in all the formulae.

2. The energy content of all the canonical forms must be nearly same.

3. Each canonical form must have the same number of unpaired electrons.

It involves delocalisation of π electrons. This effect may be of $+R$ type or $-R$ type.

Positive Resonance Effect $(+R)$

Electron donating groups with respect to conjugate system show $+R$ effect. Central atom of functional groups should be more electronegative than the surrounding atoms or groups to show $+R$ effect. e.g. halogens, —OH, —OR, —OCOR, —NH$_2$,—NHCOR etc.

Electron donating groups producing, $+R$ effect are *ortho* and *para* directing. They activate the benzene ring towards the electrophilic substitution reactions except halogens. Halogens slightly deactivate the benzene ring towards the electrophilic substitution reaction. More the E.D.G, more is the basic nature.

Negative Resonance Effect (−R)

Electron withdrawing groups with respect to conjugate system show − R effect. Central atom of functional groups should be less electronegative than surrounding atoms or groups to show −R effect. e.g. halogens, — COOH, — COOR, — CHO,— CN,—NO$_2$ etc.

Electron withdrawing group (E.W.G.) producing − R effect are *meta* directing. They deactivate the benzene ring towards the electrophilic substitution reaction. More the E.W.G, more is the acidic nature.

Stability of Canonical Forms

It can be judged by the following rules :

1. Non-polar structure is more stable than the polar structure.

2. Among polar structures, structure with maximum number of covalent bonds is most stable.

3. The structure with maximum charge separation is more stable.

4. Structure with positive charge on more electropositive element and negative charge on more electronegative element is more stable.

Resonance Energy

Number of π bonds ∝ contributing structures ∝ resonance energy ∝ stability.

In benzene, resonance energy is 36 kcal/mol.

Relation Between Resonance and Bond order

$$\text{Bond order} = \frac{\text{Total number of bonds betwen two atoms}}{\text{Total number of resonating structures}}$$

e.g. $BO = \dfrac{2+1}{2} = 1.5$

Types of Organic Reactions

Reactions are of following types :

1. Addition Reactions

These reactions are given by unsaturated compounds or compounds containing multiple bonds.

In these reactions, the reagent adds to the substrate molecule.

These are of two types (depending upon the nature of attacking species) :

(i) **Electrophilic addition reactions** In these reactions, H^+ (or electrophile) is added to the substrate in the rate determining step.

These reactions are given by alkenes and alkynes. e.g.

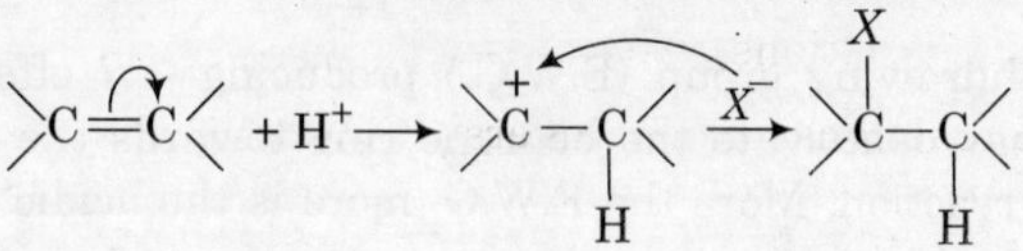

(ii) **Nucleophilic addition reactions** In these reactions, nucleophile is added to the substrate in the rate determining step.

These reactions are given by carbonyl compounds. e.g.

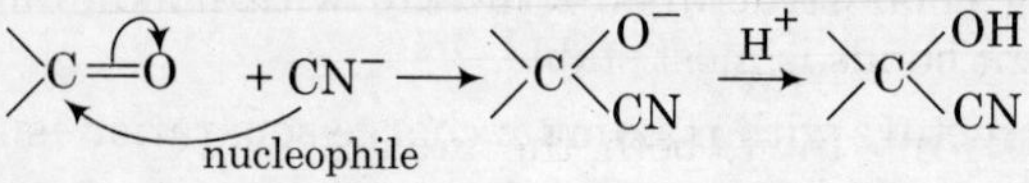

2. Substitution Reactions

In these reactions, one atom or group of atoms, called the leaving group, is substituted by a nucleophile or an electrophile. On this basis these reactions are of two types :

(i) **Electrophilic substitution reactions** When leaving group is replaced by an electrophile, the reaction is called electrophilic substitution reaction.

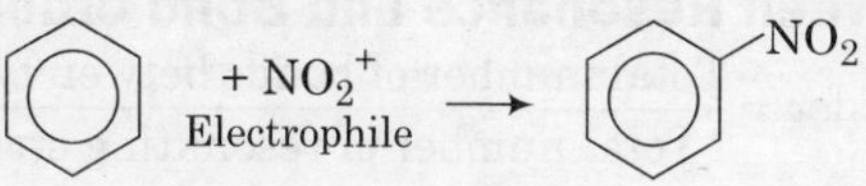

(ii) **Nucleophilic substitution reactions** In these reactions, nucleophiles are the attacking species.

These are of two types :

(a) S_N1 **(Nucleophilic substitution unimolecular)** reaction is a two step process, e.g.

$$R—X \longrightarrow R^+ + X^-$$

$$\underset{\text{nucleophile}}{R^+ + \quad OH^-} \longrightarrow ROH$$

For such reaction, rate = $k\,[R - X]$
The reactivity of alkyl halides towards S_N1 reaction is $3° > 2° > 1°$ alkyl halide.

(b) S_N2 **(Nucleophilic substitution bimolecular)** reaction is a single step process e.g.

$$\underset{\text{nucleophile}}{OH^-} + R—X \longrightarrow H\overset{\delta-}{O}...R...\overset{\delta-}{X} \longrightarrow R—OH + X^-$$

For such reactions, rate = $k\,[RX]\,[OH^-]$

These reactions involve inversion of configuration.

For such reactions the order of reactivity of alkyl halide is
$$1° > 2° > 3°$$

3. Elimination Reactions

In these reactions, two groups from the same or adjacent atoms are lost and electron deficient or unsaturated compound is formed.

These can be of two types :

(i) α-**elimination** In it, both the groups are eliminated from the same carbon atom. Such reactions are rare. e.g.

$$CHCl_3 \longrightarrow :\overset{-}{C}Cl_3 \longrightarrow \underset{\text{carbene}}{:CCl_2}$$

(ii) β-**elimination** Here, the groups are eliminated from the adjacent carbon atoms. These can further be E_1 or E_2 reactions .e.g.

4. Rearrangement Reactions

Reactions involving the migration of an atom or a group from one atom to another within the same molecule are called rearrangement reactions.

e.g. Hofmann bromamide reaction involving the conversion of 1° amides to 1° amines on treatment with Br_2 in the presence of KOH.

This reaction involves the migration of alkyl group, R from C to N to form alkyl isocyanate.

25
Hydrocarbons

Hydrocarbons are the organic compounds containing carbon and hydrogen only, e.g. alkane, alkene and alkynes.

Classification of Hydrocarbons

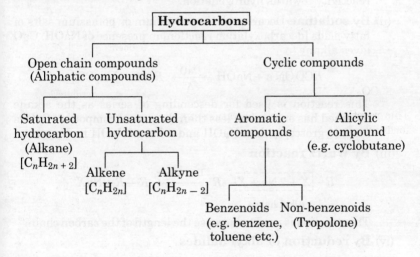

Alkanes

Alkanes are saturated, open chain hydrocarbons containing carbon-carbon single bonds, e.g. methane (CH_4), ethane (C_2H_6), propane (C_3H_8), etc.

These hydrocarbons are inert under normal conditions [i.e. do not react with acids, bases and other reagents]. Hence, they were earlier known as **paraffins** (Latin : *parum*-little; *affins*-affinity)

Alkanes exhibit **chain isomerism** and **position isomerism**.

Structure

Alkanes possess only sigma bonds. In these molecules, carbon atom lies at centre and hydrogen atoms lie at the corners of regular tetrahedron. All H—C—H bond angles are 109.5°.

Methods of Preparation of Alkanes

(i) **From hydrogenation of alkenes and alkynes**

$$CH_2 {=\!=} CH_2 + H_2 \xrightarrow{\ Pt/Pd/Ni\ } CH_3 {-\!-} CH_3$$
Ethene   Ethane

$$CH_3 {-\!-} C {\equiv} C {-\!-} H + 2H \xrightarrow{\ Pt/Pd/Ni\ } CH_3 {-\!-} CH_2 {-\!-} CH_3$$
Propane

Ease of hydrogenation depends on the steric crowding across the multiple bond. More is the steric crowding, the less is the reactivity towards hydrogenation.

(ii) **By sodalime** Decarboxylation of sodium or potassium salts of fatty acids [decarboxylation reaction] in presence of NaOH, CaO gives alkane.

$$R\overset{\ominus}{COO}\overset{\oplus}{N}a + NaOH \xrightarrow[\Delta]{\ CaO\ } R{-\!-}H + Na_2CO_3$$

This reaction is used for descending of series as the alkane obtained has one carbon less than the parent compound. CaO is more hygroscopic than NaOH and it keeps NaOH in dry state.

(iii) **By Wurtz reaction**

$$R{-\!\!}\overline{\underline{X + 2\,Na + X}}{\!-\!}R \xrightarrow{\ Dry\ ether\ } R{-\!-}R + NaX$$
Alkyl halide

This reaction is used to increase the length of the carbon chain.

(iv) **By reduction of alkyl halides**

$$R{-\!-}X + 2[H] \xrightarrow{\ Zn{-\!-}Cu/Alcohol\ } R{-\!-}H + HX$$

Reducing agents like Zn/HCl, HI/Red P, H_2/Pd can also be used.

(v) **By Kolbe's electrolysis**

$$2CH_3\overset{-}{CO}\overset{\oplus}{O}Na + 2H_2O \xrightarrow{\ Electrolysis\ }$$

$$CH_3{-\!-}CH_3 + 2NaOH + 2CO_2 + H_2$$

Only alkanes with even number of carbon atoms can be formed. Alkane and CO_2 are liberated at anode while H_2 is liberated at cathode.

(vi) **Clemmensen's reduction**

$$\underset{\substack{H_3C \\ H}}{\Large{>}}\!\!\!\underset{ethanal}{C\!=\!O} + 4[H] \xrightarrow{\text{Zn—Hg/HCl}} \underset{ethane}{H_3C\text{—}CH_3} + H_2O$$

(vii) **From compounds containing oxygen** Alcohols, aldehydes, ketones, carboxylic acids and their derivatives give alkane when treated with hot conc. HI and red P in a sealed tube.

$$R\text{OH} + 2HI \xrightarrow[150°C]{\text{Red P}} R\text{—H} + H_2O + I_2 \uparrow$$

$$\underset{H}{R\text{—}C\!=\!O} + 4HI \xrightarrow[150°C]{\text{Red P}} \underset{H}{R\text{—}CH_2} + H_2O + I_2 \uparrow$$

$$R\text{COOH} + 6HI \xrightarrow[150°C]{\text{Red P}} R\text{—}CH_3 + 2H_2O + 3I_2 \uparrow$$

(viii) **Wolff-Kishner's reduction**

$$\underset{H_3C}{\overset{H_3C}{>}}\!\!C\!=\!O + H_2\,N\text{—}NH_2 \xrightarrow{-H_2O}$$

$$\underset{H_3C}{\overset{H_3C}{>}}\!\!C\!=\!N\text{—}NH_2 \xrightarrow[435\text{–}473\,K,\,-N_2]{\text{KOH/Glycol}} \underset{Propane}{H_3C\text{—}CH_2\text{—}CH_3}$$

(ix) **From carbides**

$$\underset{\substack{\text{Aluminium} \\ \text{carbide}}}{Al_4C_3} + \underset{\text{Steam}}{12H_2O} \longrightarrow 4Al(OH)_3 + \underset{\text{Methane}}{3CH_4}$$

and, $$\underset{\text{Beryllium carbide}}{Be_2C} + 4H_2O \longrightarrow 2Be(OH)_2 + \underset{\text{Methane}}{CH_4}$$

(x) **Corey-House synthesis** This method can be used to prepare alkanes having odd number of carbon atoms.

$$RX + 2Li \xrightarrow{\text{Ether}} R\text{—Li} + LiX$$

$$2R\text{—Li} + CuI \longrightarrow LiR_2Cu$$

$$LiR_2Cu + R'X \longrightarrow \underset{\text{Alkane}}{R\text{—}R'} + R\text{—Cu} + LiX$$

Physical Properties of Alkanes

(i) The first four members are colourless gas, next thirteen members are colourless liquids and next higher members are colourless solids.

(It can be explained on the basis of magnitude of attraction forces.)

(ii) Boiling point of alkanes decreases on branching.

$$BP \propto VAF \text{ (van der Waals' forces)}$$

$$VAF \propto \text{molecular mass} \quad \text{or} \quad VAF \propto SA \text{ (Surface area)}$$

So, boiling point order can be given as

n-octane > iso-octane > 2, 2, 3, 3-tetramethyl butane

(iii) Alkanes with even number of carbon atoms have higher melting points as compared to next higher or lower alkanes with odd number of carbon atoms.

(iv) Alkanes being non-polar in nature, soluble in non-polar solvents but insoluble in polar solvent such as water.

Chemical Properties of Alkanes

(i) **Halogenation of alkanes**

(a) Chlorination

$$CH_4 + Cl_2 \xrightarrow[-HCl]{h\nu} CH_3Cl \xrightarrow[\substack{Cl_2 \\ -HCl}]{h\nu} CH_2Cl_2 \xrightarrow[-HCl]{Cl_2/h\nu} CHCl_3$$

$$\xrightarrow[-HCl]{Cl_2/h\nu} CCl_4$$

(b) Bromination of alkanes proceeds in the same way but not so easily.

(c) Iodination

$$CH_4 + I_2 \rightleftharpoons CH_3I + HI$$

Order of reactivity of halogens is

$$F_2 > Cl_2 > Br_2 > I_2$$

Order of reactivity of hydrogen of alkane is

$$3° > 2° > 1°$$

Mechanism of halogenation of alkanes proceed *via* free radical formation, i.e. the attacking reagent is a halogen free radical ($X^\bullet$). It is a chain reaction.

(ii) Combustion

$$C_nH_{2n+2} + \frac{(3n+1)}{2}O_2 \longrightarrow nCO_2 + (n+1)H_2O$$

Due to the evolution of a large amount of heat during combustion, alkanes are used as fuels.

(iii) Controlled oxidation

(i) $2CH_4 + O_2 \xrightarrow{\text{Cu / 523 K / 100 atm}} 2\,CH_3OH$
   $9:1$ methanol

(ii) $CH_4 + O_2 \xrightarrow[\Delta]{\text{Mo}_2\text{O}_3} HCHO + H_2O$

(iii) $2CH_3{-}CH_3 + 3O_2 \xrightarrow[\Delta]{(CH_3COO)_2Mn} 2CH_3COOH + 2H_2O$

(iv) $CH_4 + \underset{\text{limited}}{O_2} \xrightarrow{\text{Burn}} \underset{\substack{\text{carbon} \\ \text{black}}}{C} + 2H_2O$

(iv) Isomerisation

$$CH_3(CH_2)_4CH_3 \xrightarrow[\text{HCl}]{\text{Anhy. AlCl}_3} CH_3{-}\underset{\underset{CH_3}{|}}{CH}{-}(CH_2)_2CH_3$$
2-methylpentane

$$+ CH_3{-}CH_2\underset{\underset{CH_3}{|}}{CH}{-}CH_2CH_3$$
3-methylpentane

(v) Aromatisation

(vi) Reaction with steam

$$CH_4 + H_2O \xrightarrow[\Delta]{Ni} CO + 3H_2$$

(vii) **Pyrolysis**

$$C_{12}H_{26} \xrightarrow{\text{Pt or Pd or Ni}} C_7H_{16} + C_5H_{10} + \text{Other products}$$

(viii) **Nitration**

$$C_6H_{13}-H + HO-NO_2 \xrightarrow{\Delta} \underset{\text{Nitrohexane}}{C_6H_{13}NO_2} + H_2O$$

(ix) **Sulphonation**

$$C_6H_{13}-H + HOSO_3H \text{ (conc.)} \xrightarrow{400°C} \underset{\text{Hexane sulphonic acid}}{C_6H_{13}-SO_3H} + H_2O$$

Reactions for Methane (CH_4)

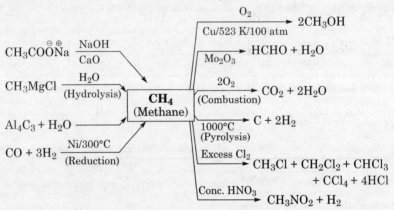

(Methane cannot be prepared by Wurtz reaction, Kolbe's electrolytic process and by reduction of alkenes or alkynes).

Reactions for Ethane (C_2H_6)

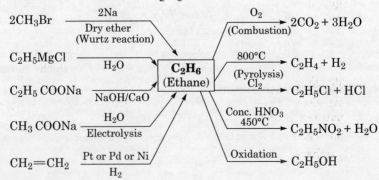

Conformations of Alkanes

Alkanes have C—C sigma (σ) bonds and rotation about C—C single bond is allowed. This rotation results in different spatial arrangements of atoms in space which can change into one another, such spatial arrangements are called conformations or conformers or rotamers.

Conformations of ethane

(i) **Sawhorse projections**

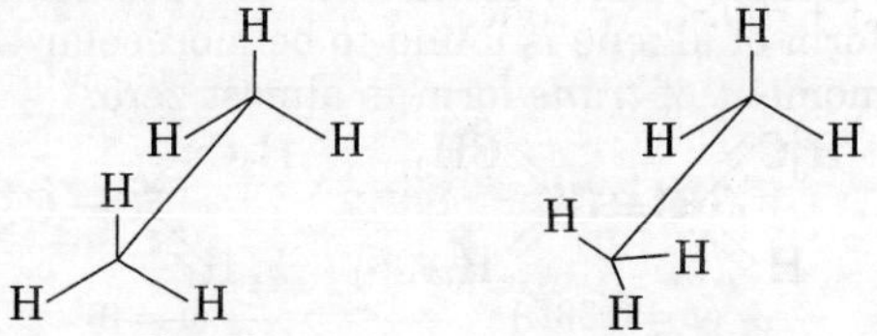

eclipsed   staggered

(ii) **Newman projections**

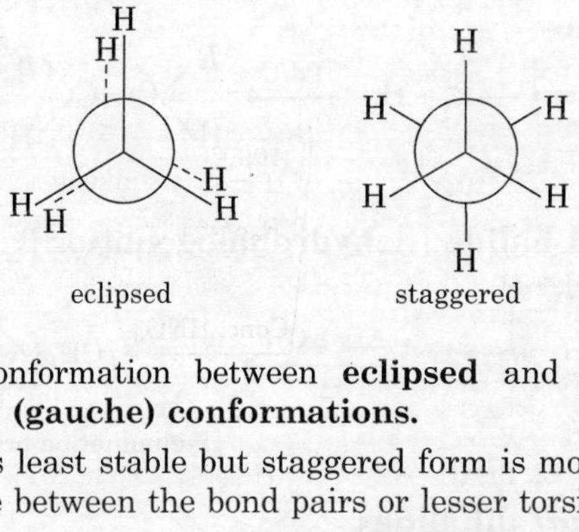

eclipsed   staggered

Intermediate conformation between **eclipsed** and **staggered** are known as **skew (gauche) conformations**.

Eclipsed form is least stable but staggered form is most stable due to greater distance between the bond pairs or lesser torsional strain.

The energy difference between the two extreme forms is of the order of 12.5 kJ mol^{-1}.

Alkenes

These are unsaturated non-cyclic hydrocarbons which have sp^2-hybridisation with 120° bond angle.

Alkenes are also called **olefins** [oil forming] which indicates their high reactive nature.

Alkenes have general formula C_nH_{2n}, where $n = 2, 3, 4 \ldots$

e.g., C_2H_4 (ethene), C_3H_6 (propene), etc.

Structure

Alkenes possess atleast one π bond and have triangular planar shape with a bond angle of 120° between C—H bonds.

Isomerism in Alkenes

Alkene show both structural isomerism and geometrical isomerism.

Structural isomerism exhibited by alkenes are chain isomerism and position isomerism.

Alkenes also exhibit stereoisomerism as geometrical (*cis-trans*) isomerism. *cis*-form of alkene is found to be morepolar than *trans*-form because dipolemoment of *trans*-form is almost zero.

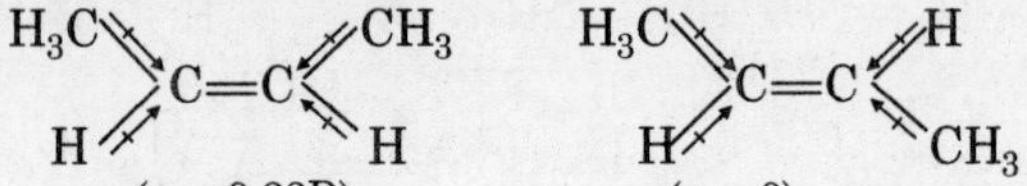

(μ = 0.33D)
[*cis*-but-2-ene]

(μ = 0)
[*trans*-but-2-ene]

Methods of Preparation of Alkenes

(i) **From alkynes**

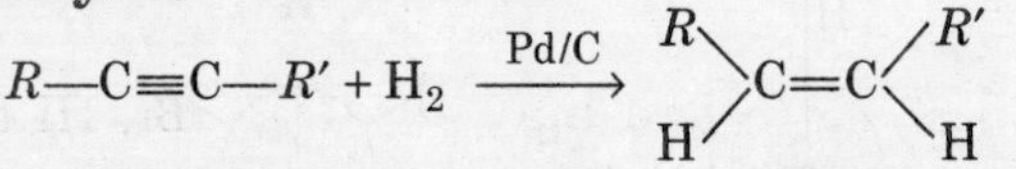

$$R—C{\equiv}C—R' + H_2 \xrightarrow{Pd/C} \underset{\text{cis-alkene}}{\begin{array}{c} R \\ H \end{array} C{=}C \begin{array}{c} R' \\ H \end{array}}$$

(ii) **From alkyl halide [dehydrohalogenation]**

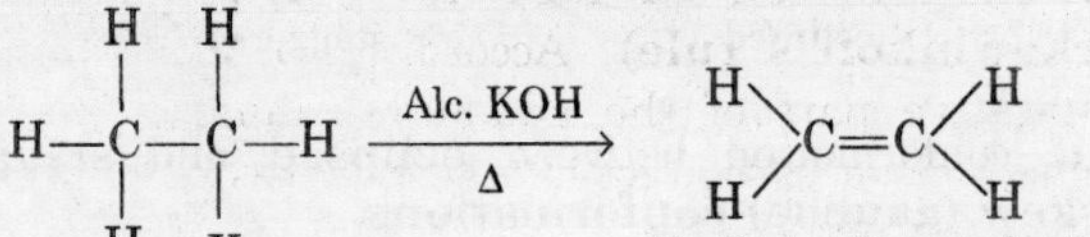

[X = Cl, Br, I]

[β-elimination product]

(iii) **From *vicinal* dihalides**

$$CH_2Br—CH_2Br + Zn \longrightarrow CH_2{=}CH_2 + ZnBr_2$$

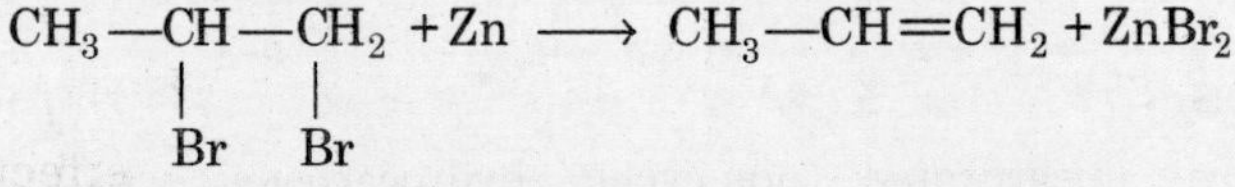

$$\underset{\underset{Br \quad Br}{\mid \quad \mid}}{CH_3—CH—CH_2} + Zn \longrightarrow CH_3—CH{=}CH_2 + ZnBr_2$$

(iv) **From alcohols by acidic dehydrogenation**

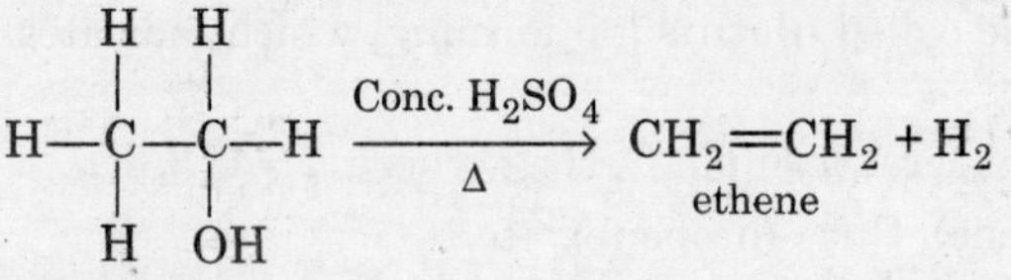

ethanol

$$\xrightarrow[\Delta]{\text{Conc. } H_2SO_4} \underset{\text{ethene}}{CH_2{=}CH_2} + H_2$$

Physical Properties of Alkenes

Alkene as a class resemble alkanes in physical properties, except in types of isomerism and difference in polar nature.

C_1 to C_3 are gases, the next fourteen are liquids and the higher members are solids.

Alkenes show a regular increase in boiling point with increase in size.

Chemical Properties of Alkenes

(i) Addition of halogens

$$CH_2{=}CH_2 + Br{-}Br \xrightarrow{CCl_4} \underset{\underset{Br \quad\; Br}{|\qquad\;|}}{CH_2{-}CH_2}$$

$$\underset{ethene}{}$$

1,2-dibromoethane

$$\underset{propene}{CH_3{-}CH{=}CH_2} + Cl{-}Cl \longrightarrow \underset{\underset{Cl \quad\;\; Cl}{|\qquad\;\;\;|}}{CH_3{-}CH{-}CH_2}$$

1,2-dichloropropane

(ii) Addition of hydrogen halides

HCl, HBr, HI add up to alkenes to form alkyl halides as per their reactivity order

$$HI > HBr > HCl$$

Addition reaction of HBr to unsymmetrical alkenes (Markownikoff's rule) According to Markownikoff's rule, the negative part of the addendum (adding molecule) gets attached to that carbon atom which possesses lesser number of hydrogen atom.

$$\underset{\underset{prop\text{-}1\text{-}ene}{\underset{H \;\; H \;\; H}{|\quad\;|\quad\;|}}}{H{-}C{-}C{=}C{-}H} + HBr \longrightarrow \underset{\underset{2\text{-}bromopropane}{\underset{H}{|}}}{H_3C{-}C{-}CH_3}$$

Anti-Markownikoff addition or peroxide effect or Kharash effect In the presence of organic peroxide, addition of only HBr molecule on unsymmetrical alkene takes place contrary to the Markownikoff's rule.

$$\underset{prop\text{-}1ene}{CH_3{-}CH{=}CH_2} + HBr \xrightarrow[(C_6H_5CO)_2O_2]{} \underset{1\text{-}bromopropane}{CH_3CH_2CH_2Br}$$

(iii) **Addition of sulphuric acid**

$$CH_3—CH=CH_2 + HOSO_2OH \underset{\text{[cold and conc.]}}{\longrightarrow} CH_3CH(OSO_3H)CH_3$$
propyl hydrogen sulphate

(iv) **Addition of water**

$$CH_3—\underset{\underset{CH_3}{|}}{C}=CH_2 + H_2O \xrightarrow{H^+} \underset{H_3C}{\overset{H_3C}{>}}\underset{\underset{OH}{|}}{C}—CH_3$$

2-methylpropene   2-methylpropan-2-ol

(v) **Oxymercuration-demercuration** This reaction is an example of hydration of alkene according to Markownikoff's rule.

$$\underset{\text{3,3-dimethylbut-1-ene}}{(CH_3)_3—CH=CH_2} \xrightarrow[\text{THF, H}_2\text{O}]{(CH_3COO)_2Hg}$$

$$(CH_3)_3C—\underset{\underset{OOCCH_3}{|}}{CH}—CH_2Hg\,OOCCH_3 \xrightarrow[\text{NaOH}]{\text{NaBH}_4} (CH_3)_3C—\underset{\underset{OH}{|}}{CH}—CH_3$$

3,3-dimethylbutan 2-ol

It is an *anti*-addition reaction.

It is better than catalytic hydration by dil. H_2SO_4, as it avoids rearrangement.

(vi) **Hydroboration oxidation**

$$6(R—CH=CH_2) + B_2H_6 \longrightarrow \underset{\text{trialkyl borane}}{2(R—CH_2CH_2)_3B} \xrightarrow[+6H_2O_2]{OH^-}$$

$$\underset{\text{primary alcohol}}{6RCH_2CH_2OH + 2H_3BO_3}$$

This reaction involved *syn*-addition of reagent.

(vii) **Oxidation** Alkenes decolourise cold dilute aqueous solution of potassium permanganate (Baeyer's reagent). It is used as a test for unsaturation.

$$CH_2=CH_2 + H_2O + [O] \xrightarrow[273\ K]{\text{Dil. KMnO}_4} \underset{\underset{OH\quad OH}{|\qquad|}}{CH_2—CH_2}$$

ethane–1,2–diol
or glycol

Acidic $KMnO_4$ or acidic $K_2Cr_2O_7$ oxidise alkenes to ketones and/or acids depending upon the nature of alkene and the experimental conditions.

$$(CH_3)_2C\!\!=\!\!CH_2 \xrightarrow{\ KMnO_4/H^+\ } (CH_3)_2CO + CO_2 + H_2O$$
$$\underset{\text{2-methyl propene}}{} \qquad \underset{\text{propan-2-one}}{}$$

$$CH_3\!\!-\!\!CH\!\!=\!\!CH\!\!-\!\!CH_3 \xrightarrow{\ KMnO_4/H^+\ } 2CH_3COOH$$
$$\underset{\text{but-2-ene}}{} \qquad\quad \underset{\text{ethanoic acid}}{}$$

(viii) **Ozonolysis**

$$\underset{H_3C}{\overset{H_3C}{>}}C\!\!=\!\!CH_2 + O_3 \xrightarrow{\ Zn/H_2O\ } \underset{H_3C}{\overset{H_3C}{>}}C\!\!=\!\!O + HCHO + H_2O_2$$

$$Zn + H_2O_2 \longrightarrow ZnO + H_2O$$

(ix) **Polymerisation**

$$n(CH_2\!\!=\!\!CH_2) \xrightarrow[\text{catalyst}]{\text{High temperature/pressure}} \underset{\text{polythene}}{-[CH_2\!\!-\!\!CH_2\!\!-\!\!]_n}$$

$$n(CH_3\!\!-\!\!CH\!\!=\!\!CH_2) \xrightarrow[\text{catalyst}]{\text{High temperature/pressure}} \begin{bmatrix} -CH\!-\!CH_2- \\ | \\ CH_3 \end{bmatrix}_n$$

(x) **Reaction with sulphur monochloride**

$$2\underset{CH_2}{\overset{CH_2}{\|}} + S_2Cl_2 \longrightarrow S\!\!\underset{CH_2CH_2Cl}{\overset{CH_2CH_2Cl}{<}} + S$$
$$\underset{\substack{\text{mustard gas}\\ \text{(war gas)}}}{}$$

(xii) **Diels-Alder reaction** (*via* conjugated dienes)

conjugated   dienophile   cyclohexene
diene

Dienes having alternate single (–) and double bonds (=) are called conjugated alkenes. These give Diels (-) Alder reaction.

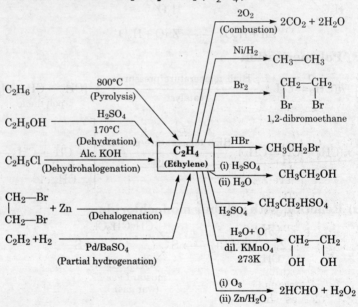

(xiii) **Substitution reactions** These occur at very high temperature at allylic position.

$$CH_3CH{=}CH_2 + Cl_2 \xrightarrow[\Delta]{500°C} ClCH_2{-}CH{=}CH_2 + HCl$$

propene   allyl choride
(3-chloroprop-1-ene)

Reactions for Ethene [Ethylene] (C_2H_4)

$C_2H_6 \xrightarrow{\text{800°C (Pyrolysis)}}$

$C_2H_5OH \xrightarrow{\text{H}_2\text{SO}_4 \text{ 170°C (Dehydration)}}$

$C_2H_5Cl \xrightarrow{\text{Alc. KOH (Dehydrohalogenation)}}$

$\begin{matrix} CH_2{-}Br \\ | \\ CH_2{-}Br \end{matrix} + Zn \xrightarrow{\text{(Dehalogenation)}}$

$C_2H_2 + H_2 \xrightarrow{\text{Pd/BaSO}_4 \text{ (Partial hydrogenation)}}$

C_2H_4 (Ethylene)

$\xrightarrow[\text{(Combustion)}]{2O_2} 2CO_2 + 2H_2O$

$\xrightarrow{Ni/H_2} CH_3{-}CH_3$

$\xrightarrow{Br_2} \begin{matrix} CH_2{-}CH_2 \\ | \quad\quad | \\ Br \quad\ Br \end{matrix}$ 1,2-dibromoethane

$\xrightarrow{HBr} CH_3CH_2Br$

$\xrightarrow[\text{(ii) H}_2\text{O}]{\text{(i) H}_2\text{SO}_4} CH_3CH_2OH$

$\xrightarrow{H_2SO_4} CH_3CH_2HSO_4$

$\xrightarrow[\substack{\text{dil. KMnO}_4 \\ \text{273K}}]{H_2O+O} \begin{matrix} CH_2{-}CH_2 \\ | \quad\quad | \\ OH \quad OH \end{matrix}$

$\xrightarrow[\text{(ii) Zn/H}_2\text{O}]{\text{(i) O}_3} 2HCHO + H_2O_2$

Alkynes

These are unsaturated hydrocarbons with general formula C_nH_{2n-2} e.g. C_2H_2 (ethyne), C_3H_4 (propyne).

Structure

$H{-}C{\equiv}C{-}H$ contains 3σ and 2π-bonds and bond length is 120 pm. In acetylene, $H{-}C{-}C$ bond angle is 180°. In alkynes, position of triple bond is determined by ozone (O_3). In alkynes show position chain functional and ring **chain isomerism.**

Methods of Preparation of Alkynes

(i) From calcium carbide

$$CaCO_3 \xrightarrow{\Delta} CaO + CO_2$$

$$CaO + C \longrightarrow CaC_2 + CO$$

$$CaC_2 + 2H_2O \longrightarrow Ca(OH)_2 + C_2H_2$$

(ii) From *vicinal* dihalides

$$H_2C-CH_2 \quad \xrightarrow[\substack{Alcohol \\ -KBr \\ -H_2O}]{KOH} \quad \overset{H}{\underset{H}{>}}C=C\overset{H}{\underset{Br}{<}}$$
$$\underset{Br \quad Br}{}$$

$$\xrightarrow[NaNH_2]{} \bigg| -NaBr, -NH_3$$

$$HC\equiv CH$$

(iii) From tetrahalides

$$Br_2CH-CHBr_2 + 2Zn \xrightarrow[\Delta]{CH_3OH} H-C\equiv C-H + 2ZnBr_2$$

Physical Properties of Alkynes

(i) The first two members are gases, next eight members (C_5-C_{12}) are liquids and higher members are solids.

(ii) They are all colourless and odourless with the exception of acetylene which has slightly garlic odour due to the presence of PH_3 and H_2S as impurities.

(iii) Alkynes are insoluble in water but soluble in organic solvents like ethers, carbon tetrachloride and benzene.

(iv) Melting point, boiling point and density increase with increase in molar mass.

Chemical Properties of Alkynes

Alkynes also exhibit electrophilic addition reaction but less reactive than alkenes because the dissociation of π-electron cloud requires more energy. Alkynes show electrophilic as well as nucleophilic addition reactions.

(i) Acidic character of alkyne

$$HC\equiv CH + Na \longrightarrow \underset{\substack{Monosodium \\ acetylide}}{HC\equiv C^-Na^+} + \frac{1}{2}H_2$$

$$H-C\equiv \bar{C}Na^+ + Na \longrightarrow \underset{Disodium\ acetylide}{Na^+-C\equiv \bar{C}Na^+} + \frac{1}{2}H_2$$

$$CH_3-C\equiv C-H + NaNH_2 \longrightarrow \underset{Sodium\ propynide}{CH_3-C\equiv \bar{C}Na^+} + NH_3$$

These reactions are not shown by alkenes, alkanes and non-terminal alkynes, hence used for distinction between alkane, alkene and alkyne. Acetylenic hydrogens are acidic in nature due to 50% s-character in *sp*-hybridised orbitals.

Acidity of alkynes is lesser than water.

Acidic behaviour order

(a) $\underset{sp}{HC \equiv CH} > \underset{sp^2}{CH_2 = CH_2} > \underset{sp^3}{CH_3 - CH_3}$

(b) $HC \equiv CH > CH_3 - C \equiv CH >> CH_3 - C \equiv C - CH_3$

(ii) **Electrophilic addition reactions**

$$-C \equiv C- + HZ \xrightarrow{H^+} \underset{\text{vinyl cation}}{-\overset{\overset{\displaystyle H}{|}}{C} = \overset{\oplus}{C}-} + :Z^- \longrightarrow -\overset{\overset{\displaystyle H}{|}}{C} = \overset{\overset{\displaystyle Z}{|}}{C}-$$

The addition product formed depends upon the stability of vinylic cation. Addition on unsymmetrical alkynes takes place according to Markownikoff's rule.

Few addition reactions are as follows :

(a) Addition of dihydrogen

$$\underset{\text{propyne}}{H_3CC \equiv C-H} + H_2 \xrightarrow{Pt/Pd/Ni} \underset{\text{propene}}{[CH_3 - CH = CH_2]}$$

$$\xrightarrow{H_2} \underset{\text{propane}}{CH_3CH_2CH_3}$$

(b) Addition of halogens

$$HC \equiv CH + Cl-Cl \longrightarrow \underset{\text{1,2-dichloropropene}}{[ClHC = CHCl]}$$

$$\downarrow Cl_2$$

$$\underset{\substack{\text{1,1,2,2-tetrachloroethane} \\ \text{or westron}}}{\overset{\overset{\displaystyle Cl \quad\;\; Cl}{|\qquad |}}{HC - CH}}$$
$$\underset{}{\underset{|\qquad |}{Cl \quad\;\; Cl}}$$

$$\downarrow -HCl$$

$$\underset{\substack{\\ \text{westrosol(1, 1, 2–trichloroethene)}}}{\overset{\overset{\displaystyle CH = CCl_2}{|}}{Cl}}$$

(c) Addition of hydrogen halides

$$CH_3 - C \equiv CH \xrightarrow{HBr} CH_3 - \underset{\underset{Br}{|}}{C} = CH_2 \xrightarrow{HBr} CH_3 - \underset{\underset{Br}{|}}{\overset{\overset{Br}{|}}{C}} - CH_3$$

$$\qquad\qquad\qquad\qquad\quad \text{2-bromopropene} \qquad\qquad \text{2,2-dibromopropane}$$

(d) Addition of water

$$\underset{\text{propyne}}{CH_3 - C \equiv CH} + HOH \xrightarrow[\text{333 K}]{Hg^{2+}/H^+} CH_3 - \underset{\underset{O-H}{|}}{C} = CH_2$$

$$\downarrow \text{isomerisation}$$

$$CH_3 - \underset{\underset{O}{\parallel}}{C} - CH_3$$

$$\text{propanone}$$

(iii) Cyclic polymerisation

$$\xrightarrow[\substack{\text{tube} \\ \text{873 K}}]{\text{Red hot iron}}$$

(iv) Reaction with AsCl₃ (arsenic trichloride)

$$\underset{CH}{\overset{CH}{\underset{\parallel}{}}} + \underset{AsCl_2}{\overset{Cl}{\underset{|}{}}} \xrightarrow{\text{Anhy. AlCl}_3} \underset{CHAsCl_2}{\overset{CHCl}{\underset{\parallel}{}}}$$

$$\qquad\qquad\qquad\qquad \underset{\text{(poisonous gas)}}{\text{Lewisite}}$$

(v) Oxidation

$$\underset{CH}{\overset{CH}{\underset{\parallel}{}}} + 4\,[O] \xrightarrow{\text{Alk. KMnO}_4} \underset{COOH}{\overset{COOH}{\underset{|}{}}}$$

$$\qquad\qquad\qquad\qquad\quad \text{Oxalic acid}$$

$$\underset{CH}{\overset{CH}{\underset{\parallel}{}}} + 3[O] + H_2O \xrightarrow{\text{Acidic}}_{\text{KMnO}_4} \underset{\text{Formic acid}}{2HCOOH}$$

$$\underset{CH}{\overset{CH}{\underset{\parallel}{}}} + H_2O + [O] \xrightarrow{K_2Cr_2O_7} \underset{\text{Acetic acid}}{CH_3COOH}$$

(vi) Ozonolysis

$$CH \equiv CH + O_3 \xrightarrow[\text{Zn/H}_2\text{O}]{\text{CCl}_4} \underset{\text{glyoxal}}{CHO-CHO} \longrightarrow \underset{\text{formic acid}}{2HCOOH}$$

Higher alkynes give diketones which are further oxidised to carboxylic acid.

(vii) Linear polymerisation

$$2HC \equiv CH \xrightarrow[\text{NH}_4\text{Cl}]{\text{Cu}_2\text{Cl}_2} CH_2 = CH - C \equiv CH$$

$$\xrightarrow{HC \equiv CH} \underset{\text{divinyl acetylene}}{CH_2 = CH - C \equiv C - CH = CH_2}$$

Reactions for Acetylene (C_2H_2)

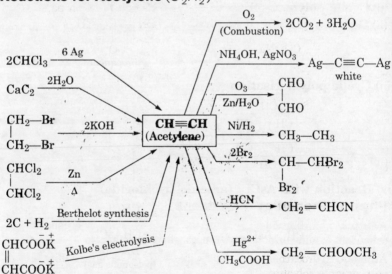

Benzene

The parent member of the family of aromatic hydrocarbons is benzene (molecular formula. C_6H_6). It has hexagonal ring of six carbon atoms with three double bonds at alternate positions. It is resonance stabilised and the structure may be represented as given ahead.

Structure of Benzene

On the basis of Kekule, structure of benzene has cyclic arrangement of six carbon atoms with alternate single and double bonds and one hydrogen atom attached to each carbon atom.

Aromaticity

Aromatic compound should possess the following characteristics :

(i) Planarity.

(ii) Complete delocalisation of the π electrons in the ring.

(iii) Presence of $(4n + 2)\pi$ electrons in the ring where n is an integer $(n = 0, 1, 2, \dots)$. This is often referred to as Huckel rule.

Methods of Preparation

(i) **Cyclic polymerisation of ethyne** Refer to text on page 371.

(ii) **Decarboxylation of aromatic acids**

(iii)

Physical Properties of Benzene

Aromatic hydrocarbons are non-polar molecules and are usually colourless liquids or solids with a characteristic aroma.

Aromatic hydrocarbons are immiscible with water but readily miscible with organic solvents.

Aromatic compounds burn with sooty flame.

Chemical Reactions of Benzene

Benzene gives electrophilic substitution reactions.

According to experimental evidences, electrophilic substitution reaction involve following three steps :

(a) Generation of electrophile

(b) Formation of carbocation intermediate

(c) Removal of proton from the carbocation intermediate.

Common electrophilic substitution reactions are as follows :

(i) Nitration

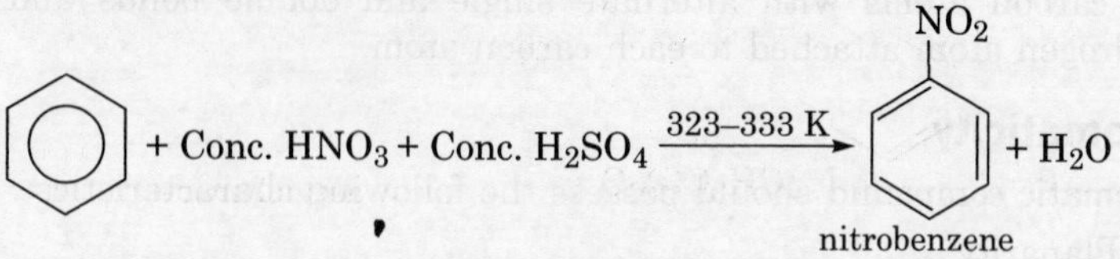

+ Conc. HNO$_3$ + Conc. H$_2$SO$_4$ $\xrightarrow{\text{323–333 K}}$ nitrobenzene + H$_2$O

(ii) Halogenation

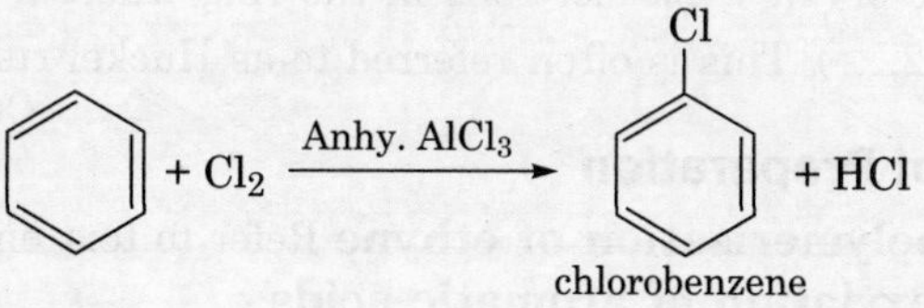

+ Cl$_2$ $\xrightarrow{\text{Anhy. AlCl}_3}$ chlorobenzene + HCl

(iii) Sulphonation

+ H$_2$SO$_4$ (fuming sulphuric acid) $\xrightarrow{\Delta}$ benzene sulphonic acid + H$_2$O

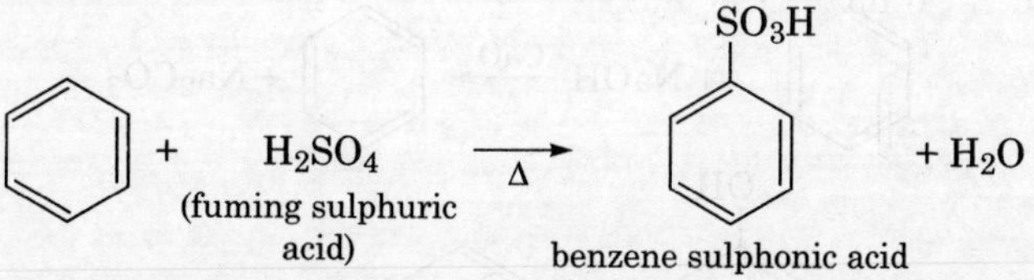

(iv) Friedel-Crafts alkylation reaction

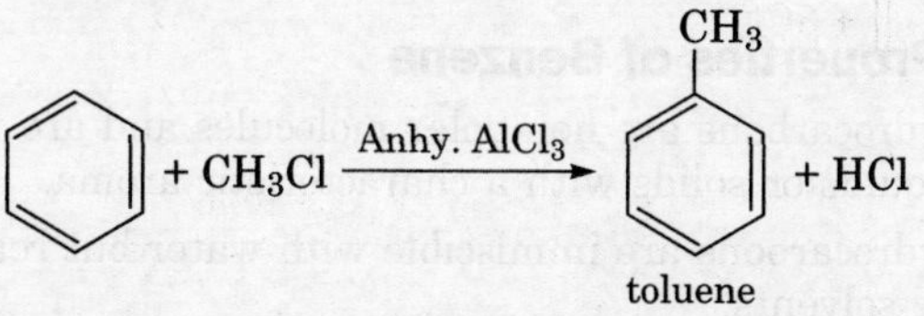

+ CH$_3$Cl $\xrightarrow{\text{Anhy. AlCl}_3}$ toluene + HCl

When Friedel-Craft alkylation is carried out with CH$_3$Cl the product obtained is C$_6$H$_5$CH$_3$. In case the alkylation is carried out with higher alkyl halide, e.g. n-propyl chloride, then the electrophile n-propyl carbocation (CH$_3$—CH$_2$—$\overset{+}{\text{C}}$H$_2$) which is a primary carbocation rearranges to form more stable secondary carbocation (*iso*-propyl carbocation) and the main product formed will be *iso*-propyl benzene.

(v) **Friedel-Crafts acylation reaction**

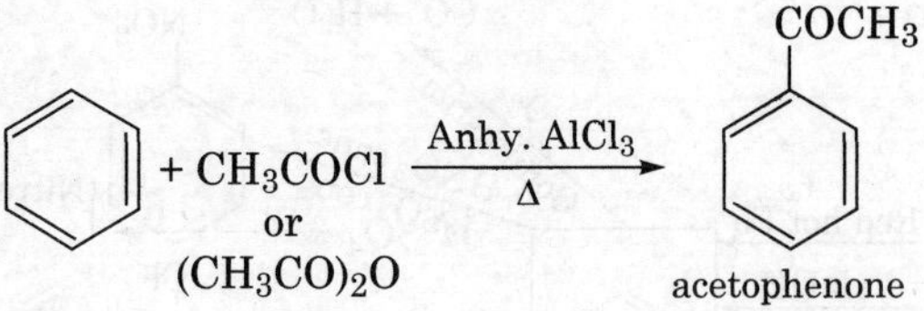

acetophenone

(vi) **With Cl_2** In excess of chlorine, benzene yields hexachlorobenzene $[C_6Cl_6]$.

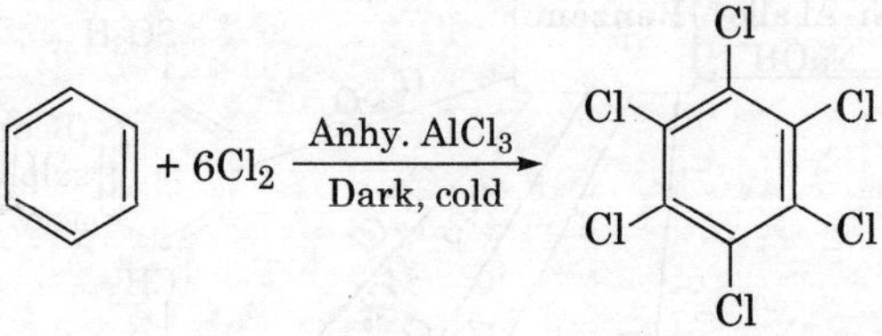

hexachlorobenzene

Benzene also undergoes addition reactions *e.g.*,

(i)

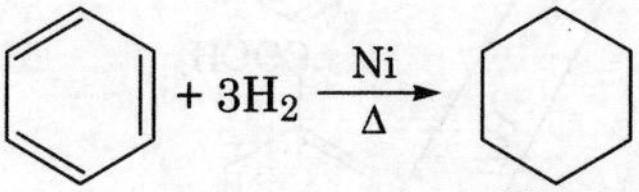

cyclohexane

(ii)

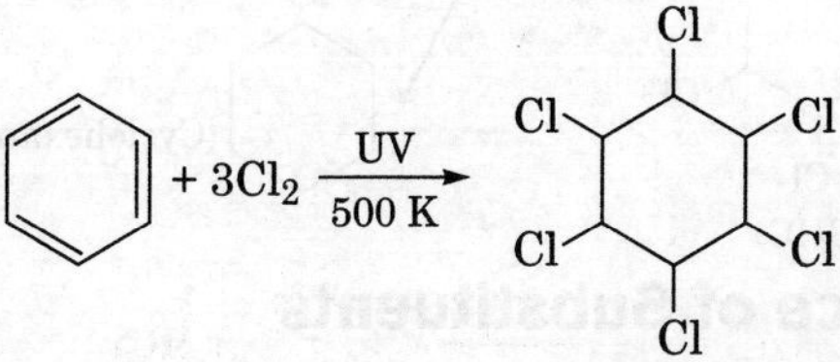

benzene hexachloride
(BHC or Gammexane or lindane)

Combustion $2C_6H_6 + 15O_2 \longrightarrow 12CO_2 + 6H_2O$

Reactions for Benzene

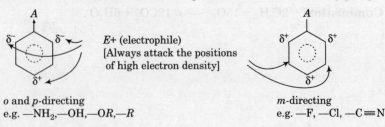

$3CH\equiv CH \xrightarrow{\text{Red hot Fe}}$

$C_6H_5CO\overset{-}{O}\overset{+}{Na} \xrightarrow[\text{CaO}]{\text{NaOH}}$

$C_6H_5OH \xrightarrow{Zn,\Delta}$

$C_6H_5N_2{}^+Cl^- \xrightarrow{H_3PO_2}$

$C_6H_5Cl \xrightarrow[\text{NaOH}]{\text{Ni–Al alloy}}$

Benzene

$\xrightarrow[\text{Combustion}]{O_2} CO_2 + H_2O$

$\xrightarrow[\text{H}_2\text{SO}_4 \text{ conc.}]{\text{HNO}_3 \text{ conc.}}$ NO$_2$ (Nitrobenzene)

$\xrightarrow[\text{Anhy. AlCl}_3]{Cl_2}$ Cl (Chlorobenzene)

$\xrightarrow{H_2SO_4}$ SO$_3$H (Benzene sulphonic acid)

$\xrightarrow[\text{Anhy. AlCl}_3]{CH_3Cl}$ CH$_3$ (Toluene)

$\xrightarrow[\text{Anhy. AlCl}_3]{CH_3COCl}$ COCH$_3$ (Acetophenone)

$\xrightarrow{H_2}$ (Cyclohexane)

$\xrightarrow[\text{500K}]{\text{UV, Cl}_2}$

Cl, Cl, Cl, Cl, Cl, Cl
(BHC)

Directive Influence of Substituents on Benzene Ring

The first substituent on benzene ring directs the next incoming group.

A

δ^- δ^-
δ^+

$E+$ (electrophile)
[Always attack the positions of high electron density]

o and p-directing
e.g. —NH$_2$, —OH, —OR, —R

A

δ^+ δ^+
δ^+

m-directing
e.g. —F, —Cl, —C≡N

Carcinogenicity and Toxicity

Benzene and polynuclear hydrocarbons containing more than two benzene rings fused together are toxic and said to possess cancer producing (carcinogenic) property. e.g.

1-2-benzanthracene   3-methylcholanthrene

Petroleum

It is a dark coloured oily liquid with offensive odour, found at various depths in many region below the earth's surface. It is also called **rock oil, mineral oil** or **crude oil.** It is covered by an atmosphere of a gaseous mixture known as **natural gas.**

It contains mainly alkanes, cycloalkanes, aromatic hydrocarbons, sulphur, nitrogen and oxygen compounds.

When subjected to fractional distillation, it gives different fractions at different temperatures.

S.No.	Fraction	Boiling range	Composition	Uses
1.	Uncondensed gases	Room temperature	$C_1 - C_4$	Fuel gases, refrigerants, production of carbon black, hydrogen.
2.	Crude naphtha (Its refractionation gives	30–150°	$C_5 - C_{10}$	
	(i) Petroleum ether	30 – 70°	$C_5 - C_6$	Solvent
	(ii) Gasoline	70 – 120°	$C_6 - C_8$	Fuel, petrol gas
	(iii) Benzene derivative	120 – 150°	$C_8 - C_{10}$	Solvent, drycleaning
3.	Kerosene	150–250°	$C_{11} - C_{16}$	Fuel, illuminants, oil gas

S.No.	Fraction	Boiling range	Composition	Uses
4.	Heavy oil (Its refractionation gives (i) Gas oil (ii) Fuel oil (iii) Diesel oil	250–400°	$C_{15} - C_{18}$	Fuel for diesel engines
5.	Residual oil (Its vacuum distillation gives (i) Lubricating oil (ii) Paraffin wax (iii) Vaseline (iv) Pitch	Above 400°C	$C_{17} - C_{40}$ $C_{17} - C_{20}$ $C_{20} - C_{30}$ $C_{20} - C_{30}$ $C_{30} - C_{40}$	Lubrication Candles, boot polish Toilets, lubrication Paints, road surfacing
6.	Petroleum coke			As fuel

LPG (Liquified Petroleum gas)

It is a mixture of butane and *iso*-butane with a small amount of propane. A strong foul smelling substance, called ethyl mercaptan (C_2H_5SH) is added to LPG cylinders, to help in the detection of gas leakage.

CNG (Compressed Natural Gas)

It consists mainly of methane (95%), which is a relatively unreactive hydrocarbon and makes its nearly complete combustion possible.

Artificial Methods for Manufacturing Petrol

From higher alkanes, petrol or gasoline is obtained by cracking or pyrolysis.

From coal, petrol can be synthesised by following two processes :

(i) **Bergius process**

$$\text{Coal} + H_2 \xrightarrow[\substack{450\text{-}500°C \\ 250 \text{ atm}}]{FeO_3} \text{Mixture of hydrocarbons or crude oil.}$$

The yield of gasoline by this method may be as high as 60%.

(ii) **Fischer- Tropsch process**

$$C + H_2O \underset{\text{steam}}{\xrightarrow{1200°C}} \underbrace{CO + H_2}_{\text{water gas}} \xrightarrow[\substack{200°C \\ 5\text{-}10 \text{ atm}}]{Co/Ni} \text{mixture of hydrocarbons.}$$

The best catalyst for this process is a mixture of Co, thoria, magnesia and kieselguhr.

The overall yield in this process is slightly higher than Bergius process.

Octane Number

The quality of petrol is expressed in terms of octane number which is defined as the percentage of *iso*-octane by volume in a mixture of *iso*-octane and *n*-heptane which has the same antiknock properties as the fuel under test.

The octane number is 100 for *iso*-octane (2,2,4-trimethylpentane)

Natural gas has octane number 130.

TEL (tetraethyl lead) is used as antiknocking compound.

Octane number is increased by isomerisation, alkylation or aromatisation.

Cetane Number

Quality of diesel oils is measured in terms of cetane number which is defined as the percentage of cetane (hexadecane) by volume in a mixture of cetane and α-methyl naphthalene which has the same ignition property as fuel oil under similar experimental conditions.

It is 100 for cetane and 0 for α-methyl naphthalene.

26

Haloalkanes and Haloarenes

The replacement of hydrogen atom(s) in hydrocarbon, aliphatic or aromatic, by halogen atom(s) results in the formation of alkyl halide (haloalkane) and aryl halide (haloarene), respectively.

Classification of Halogen Derivatives

On the basis of number of halogen atoms present, halogen derivatives are classified as mono, di, tri, tetra, etc., halogen derivatives, e.g.

$$C_2H_5X$$
monohaloalkane

monohaloarene

$$\begin{array}{c} CH_2{-}X \\ | \\ CH_2{-}X \end{array}$$
dihaloalkane

$$\begin{array}{c} CH_2{-}X \\ | \\ CH{-}X \\ | \\ CH_2{-}X \end{array}$$
trihaloalkane

On the basis of the nature of the carbon to which halogen atom is attached, halogen derivatives are classified as 1°, 2°, 3°, allylic, benzylic, vinylic and aryl derivatives, e.g.

$$\begin{array}{c} H \\ | \\ R'{-}C{-}X \\ | \\ H \end{array}$$
primary (1°)

$$\begin{array}{c} R' \\ | \\ R''{-}C{-}X \\ | \\ H \end{array}$$
secondary (2°)

$$\begin{array}{c} R' \\ | \\ R''{-}C{-}X \\ | \\ R''' \end{array}$$
tertiary (3°)

On the basis of hybridisation of carbon atom of C—X bond

On the basis of hybridisation of carbon atom of C—X bond showing allylic (sp^3 CH$_2X$ and sp^2/sp^3), benzylic (sp^3 CH$_2X$), vinylic (sp^2), and aryl (sp^2) halides.

Nature of C—*X* Bond

Due to high electronegativity of halogen (X) atom, the C—X bond is polar. This bond of haloarene is less polar than that of haloalkanes.

General Methods of Preparation of Haloalkanes

From Alcohols

$$R\text{—OH} \quad \text{Alcohol}$$

- $\xrightarrow[\text{(Lucas reagent)}]{\text{HCl + Anhy. ZnCl}_2} R\text{—Cl} + H_2O$ (Groove's process)
- $\xrightarrow[\text{Reflux}]{\text{NaBr + H}_2\text{SO}_4} R\text{—Br} + H_2O$
- $\xrightarrow{\text{PX}_3} 3R\text{—}X + H_3PO_3$ (X = Cl, Br)
- $\xrightarrow{\text{PCl}_5} R\text{—Cl} + POCl_3 + HCl$
- $\xrightarrow[\text{SOCl}_2]{\text{Pyridine}} R\text{—Cl} + SO_2\uparrow + HCl\uparrow$ (Darzen procedure)

In Groove's method, $ZnCl_2$ is used to weaken the C—OH bond. In case of 3° alcohols, $ZnCl_2$ is not required.

The reactivity order of halogen acids is HI > HBr > HCl.

⌐ Darzen procedure is the best method for preparing alkyl halides from alcohols since both the byproducts (SO_2 and HCl) are gaseous and escape easily. ⌐

Free Radical Halogenation of Alkanes

$$CH_3CH_2CH_2CH_3 \xrightarrow[\text{UV light or heat}]{\text{Cl}_2} \underset{\text{Chlorobutane}}{CH_3CH_2CH_2CH_2Cl}$$

$$+ \underset{\underset{\underset{\text{2-chlorobutane}}{Cl}}{|}}{CH_3CH_2CH\,CH_3}$$

Addition of Hydrogen Halides on Alkenes

$$H-\underset{\underset{H}{|}}{\overset{\overset{H}{|}}{C}}-C=\underset{\underset{H}{|}}{\overset{\overset{H}{|}}{C}}-H + HBr \longrightarrow H-\underset{\underset{H}{|}}{\overset{\overset{H}{|}}{C}}-\underset{\underset{Br}{|}}{\overset{\overset{H}{|}}{C}}-\underset{\underset{H}{|}}{\overset{\overset{H}{|}}{C}}-H$$

2- bromopropane (major)

$$H-\underset{\underset{H}{|}}{\overset{\overset{H}{|}}{C}}-C=\underset{\underset{H}{|}}{\overset{}{C}}- + HBr \xrightarrow{\text{Organic peroxide}} H-\underset{\underset{H}{|}}{\overset{\overset{H}{|}}{C}}-\underset{\underset{H}{|}}{\overset{\overset{H}{|}}{C}}-\underset{\underset{H}{|}}{\overset{\overset{H}{|}}{C}}-Br$$

1- bromopropane (major)

And from Alkynes

Finkelstein Reaction

$$R-X + NaI \xrightarrow{\text{Acetone}} R-I + NaX$$
$$(X = Cl, Br)$$

Swarts Reaction

$$H_3C-Br + AgF \longrightarrow H_3C-F + AgBr$$

Hg_2F_2, CoF_2 and SbF_3 can also be used as a reagent for Swarts reaction.

Hunsdiecker Reaction

$$CH_3CO\overset{-}{O}\overset{+}{Ag} + Br_2 \xrightarrow{CCl_4} CH_3Br + AgBr + CO_2\uparrow$$

Physical Properties of Haloalkanes

1. Boiling point orders

   (i) $R-I > R-Br > R-Cl > R-F$

   (ii) $CH_3-(CH_2)_2-CH_2Br > (CH_3)_2 CHCH_2Br > (CH_3)_3 CBr$

   (iii) $CH_3CH_2CH_2X > CH_3CH_2X > CH_3X$

2. Bond strength of haloalkanes decreases as the size of the halogen atom increases.

   Thus, the order of bond strength is

   $$CH_3F > CH_3Cl > CH_3Br > CH_3I$$

3. Dipole moment decreases as the electronegativity of the halogen decreases.

4. Haloalkanes though polar but are insoluble in water as they do not form hydrogen bonding with water.

5. Density order is

$$RI > RBr > RCl > RF \qquad \text{(for the same alkyl group)}$$
$$CH_3I > C_2H_5I > C_3H_7I$$

Chemical Reactions of Haloalkanes

Nucleophilic Substitution Reactions (S_N reactions)

General reaction : $\overset{-}{Nu} + \underset{|}{\overset{|}{-C}} \overset{\delta+}{-} \overset{\delta-}{X} \longrightarrow \underset{|}{\overset{|}{-C}}-Nu + X^-$

C_2H_5—Br

KOH (aq) → C_2H_5OH + KBr
(ethyl alcohol)

NH_3 → $C_2H_5NH_2$, $(C_2H_5)_2NH$, $(C_2H_5)_3N$
$(C_2H_5)_4N^+Br^-$ (Hofmann ammonolysis)

KCN → C_2H_5CN + KBr
(ethyl cyanide)

AgCN → C_2H_5NC + AgBr
(ethyl isocyanide)

KNO_2 → C_2H_5—ONO + KBr
ethyl nitrite

$AgNO_2$ → $C_2H_5NO_2$ + AgBr
nitroethane
(Williamson's synthesis)

$R'ONa$, Δ → C_2H_5—O—R' + NaBr

Na—C≡C—H, Δ → C_2H_5—C≡CH + NaBr
but-1-yne

$R'COOAg$, Δ → C_2H_5—O—$\overset{\overset{O}{\|}}{C}$—$R'$ + AgBr

KCN is predominantly ionic and provides cyanide ions in solution, which is ambident nucleophile and bind with carbon side to form cyanide as the major product, while AgCN is covalent and form isocyanide as the major product.

Like KCN, KNO_2 form R—ONO as K—O bond is ionic while $AgNO_2$ produces R—NO_2 as product because Ag—O bond is covalent in nature. Vinyl chloride is less reactive towards nucleophilic substitution reactions due to resonance.

Nucleophilic substitution reactions are of two types :

(a) S_N1 **type** (Unimolecular nucleophilic substitution)

These reactions proceed in two steps:

$$CH_3-\underset{\underset{CH_3}{|}}{\overset{\overset{CH_3}{|}}{C}}-X \xrightarrow[-X^- \text{ (Slow)}]{\text{Step 1}} CH_3-\overset{+}{C}\underset{CH_3}{\overset{CH_3}{<}} \xrightarrow[+ Nu^- \text{ (Fast)}]{\text{Step 2}}$$

alkyl halide   planar carbocation

$$CH_3-\underset{\underset{CH_3}{|}}{\overset{\overset{CH_3}{|}}{C}}-Nu$$

substitution product

Rate, $r = k\,[RX]$. It is a first order reaction.

Rate of S_N1 reaction depends upon the stability of carbocation formed.

Reactivity order of alkyl halide towards S_N1 mechanism

$$3° > 2° > 1°$$

Polar solvents, low concentration of nucleophiles and weak nucleophiles favours S_N1 mechanism.

In S_N1 reactions, partial racemisation occurs due to the possibility of frontal as well as backside attack on planar carbocation.

Nu⁻ backside attack   planar carbocation   Nu⁻ frontal attack → retention product + inversion product (enantiomeric forms) racemisation

(b) S_N2 **type** (Bimolecular nucleophilic substitution) These reactions proceed in one step and is a second order reaction with $r = k[RX]\,[Nu]$.

During S_N2 reaction, inversion of configuration occurs **(Walden inversion)** i.e. starting with *dextro*rotatory halide a *laevo* product is obtained and *vice-versa, e.g.*,

Reactivity of alkyl halides toward S_N2 mechanism is $1° > 2° > 3°$

Rate of reaction in S_N2 mechanism depends on the strength of the attacking nucleophile. Strength of some common nucleophiles is

$$:CN^- > :I^- > :OR^- > :OH^- > CH_3COO:^- > H_2O > F^-$$

Non-polar solvents, strong nucleophiles and high concentration of nucleophiles favour S_N2 mechanism.

Relative rates of some alkyl halides in S_N1 and S_N2 reactions are in the order

$$S_N1 : (CH_3)_3CX > C_6H_5{-}CH_2{-}X > CH_2{=}CH{-}CH_2X$$
$$> (CH_3)_2CHX > CH_3CH_2X > CH_3X$$

$$S_N2 : \underbrace{C_6H_5CH_2X > CH_2{=}CH{-}CH_2X}_{\text{resonance stabilised}} > CH_3X$$

$$> CH_3CH_2X > (CH_3)_2CHX > (CH_3)_3CX$$

Resonating structures of benzyl carbocations and allylic carbocation are

$$H_2C{=}C{-}\overset{\oplus}{C}H_2 \longleftrightarrow H_2\overset{\oplus}{C}{-}C{=}CH_2$$
$$\quad\quad\; | \quad\quad\quad\quad\quad\quad\quad |$$
$$\quad\quad\; H \quad\quad\quad\quad\quad\quad\quad H$$

Relative reactivity of alkyl halides having same alkyl group is

$$RI > RBr > RCl > RF$$

Elimination Reactions

Dehydrohalogenation is a β-elimination reaction in which halogen is lost from α-carbon atom and the hydrogen from the β-carbon according to Saytzeff rule, e.g.

$$CH_3 \overset{\overset{\displaystyle Br}{|}}{\underset{\text{2-bromobutane}}{-CH_2-CH-CH_3}} \xrightarrow[\text{– KBr, – H}_2\text{O}]{\text{Alc. KOH}} \underset{\substack{\text{but-2-ene} \\ \text{(major)}}}{CH_3-CH=CH-CH_3}$$

$$+ \underset{\text{but-1-ene (minor)}}{CH_3CH_2CH=CH_2}$$

Ease of dehydrohalogenation among alkyl halides

$$3° > 2° > 1°$$

i.e.

$$(CH_3)_3 CCl > (CH_3)_2 CHCl > CH_3CH_2Cl$$

Reduction

$$C_2H_5 - Br + H_2 \xrightarrow{\text{Ni, 575 K}} C_2H_6 + HBr$$

$$C_2H_5I + HI \xrightarrow{\text{Red P, 420 K}} C_2H_6 + I_2$$

Reaction with Metals

(i) **Wurtz reaction**

$$RX + 2Na + XR \xrightarrow{\text{Dry ether}} R—R \text{ (alkane)} + 2NaX$$

(ii) **Reaction with Mg**

$$C_2H_5Br + Mg \xrightarrow{\text{Dry ether}} \underset{\text{(Grignard's reagent)}}{C_2H_5—Mg—Br}$$

Grignard reagent is never isolated in the solid state as it explodes in dry state. So it is used in ethereal solution.

Isomerisation

$$\underset{\text{1-chloropropane}}{CH_3CH_2CH_2—Cl} \xrightarrow[\text{or anhy. AlCl}_3]{573 \text{ K}} \underset{\text{2-chloropropane}}{CH_3 \overset{\overset{\displaystyle Cl}{|}}{-CH-CH_3}}$$

General Methods of Preparation of Aryl Halides (Haloarenes)

By Halogenation of Aromatic Hydrocarbons

$$\text{C}_6\text{H}_6 + \text{Cl}_2 \xrightarrow[\text{310–320 K}]{\text{FeCl}_3, \text{ dark}} \text{C}_6\text{H}_5\text{Cl} + \text{HCl}$$

It is an electrophilic substitution reaction.

By Side Chain Halogenation

$$\text{CH}_3 \text{ (toluene)} + \text{Cl}_2 \xrightarrow[\text{Sunlight, } -\text{HCl}]{\text{383 K}} \text{CH}_2\text{Cl} \xrightarrow[\text{Sunlight, } -\text{HCl}]{\text{Cl}_2} \text{CHCl}_2 \xrightarrow[\text{Sunlight, } -\text{HCl}]{\text{Cl}_2} \text{CCl}_3$$

Benzotrichloride

(It involves free radical mechanism.)

From Benzene Diazonium Salt

$$\text{C}_6\text{H}_5\text{N}_2^+\text{Cl}^-$$

$$\xrightarrow{\text{CuCl/HCl}} \text{C}_6\text{H}_5\text{Cl} + \text{N}_2$$
$$\xrightarrow{\text{CuBr/HBr}} \text{C}_6\text{H}_5\text{Br} + \text{N}_2 \quad \Big] \text{ Sandmeyer reaction}$$

$$\xrightarrow{\text{Cu/HCl}} \text{C}_6\text{H}_5\text{Cl} + \text{N}_2$$
$$\xrightarrow{\text{Cu/HBr}} \text{C}_6\text{H}_5\text{Br} + \text{N}_2 \quad \Big] \text{ Gattermann reaction}$$

$$\xrightarrow[\text{273 K}]{\text{HBF}_4} \text{C}_6\text{H}_5\text{N}_2^+\text{BF}_4^- \xrightarrow[-\text{N}_2, -\text{BF}_3]{\Delta} \text{C}_6\text{H}_5\text{F}$$
(Balz Schiemann reaction)

$$\xrightarrow{\text{KI}, \Delta} \text{C}_6\text{H}_5\text{I} + \text{N}_2 + \text{KCl}$$

From Phenol

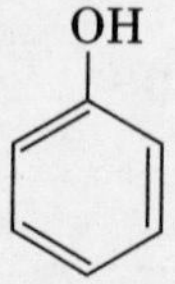

OH
+ PCl$_5$ $\longrightarrow$ C$_6$H$_5$Cl + HCl + POCl$_3$

Physical Properties of Aryl Halides

1. Aryl halides are colourless liquids or colourless solids with characteristic odour.

2. Boiling point generally increases with increase in the size of aryl group or halogen atom. Boiling point order

   Ar—I > Ar—Br > Ar—Cl > Ar—F

3. The melting point of *p*-isomer is more than *o*- and *m*-isomer. This is because of more symmetrical nature of *p*-isomer.

4. Due to resonance in chlorobenzene, C—Cl bond is shorter and hence, its dipole moment is less than that of cyclohexylchloride.

Chemical Properties of Aryl Halides

1. Nucleophilic Substitution Reactions

Aryl halides are less reactive towards nucleophilic substitution reaction. Their low reactivity is attributed due to the following reasons:

(i) Due to resonance, C—X bond has partial double bond character.

(ii) Stabilisation of the molecule by delocalisation of electrons.

(iii) Instability of phenyl carbocation.

However, aryl halides having electron withdrawing groups (like —NO$_2$, —SO$_3$H, etc.) at *ortho* and *para* positions undergo nucleophilic substitution reaction easily.

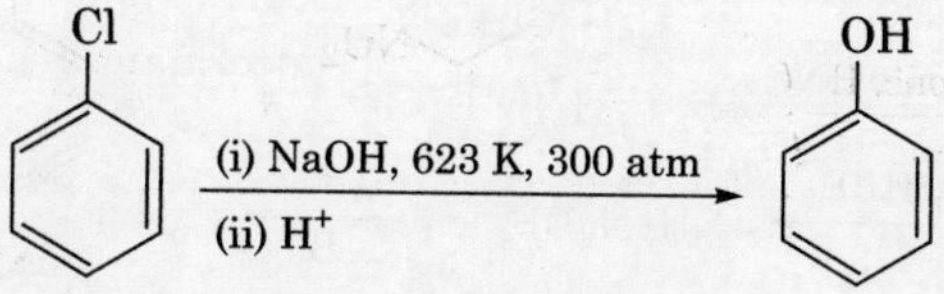

Cl
$\xrightarrow[\text{(ii) H}^+]{\text{(i) NaOH, 623 K, 300 atm}}$
OH

Presence of electron withdrawing group (—NO$_2$) increases the reactivity.

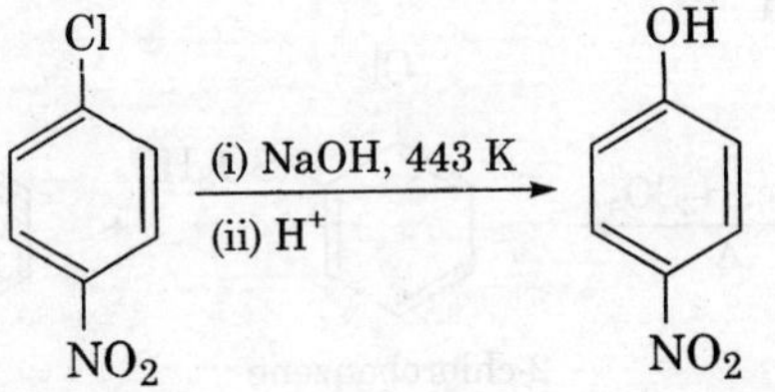

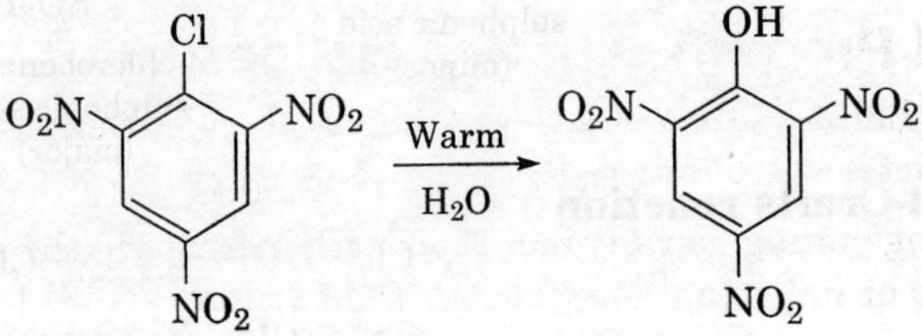

2. **Electrophilic Substitution Reactions**

Halogens are deactivating but *o, p*-directing. Thus, chlorination, nitration, sulphonation and Friedel Craft's reaction give a mixture of *o*- and *p*- chloro substituted derivatives.

(i) **Halogenation**

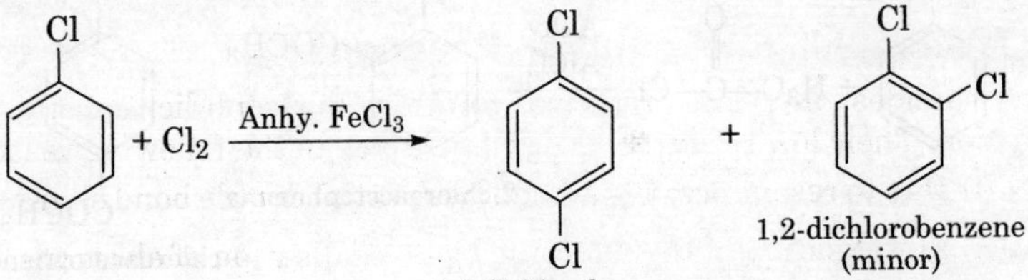

1,4-dichlorobenzene
(major)

1,2-dichlorobenzene
(minor)

(ii) **Nitration**

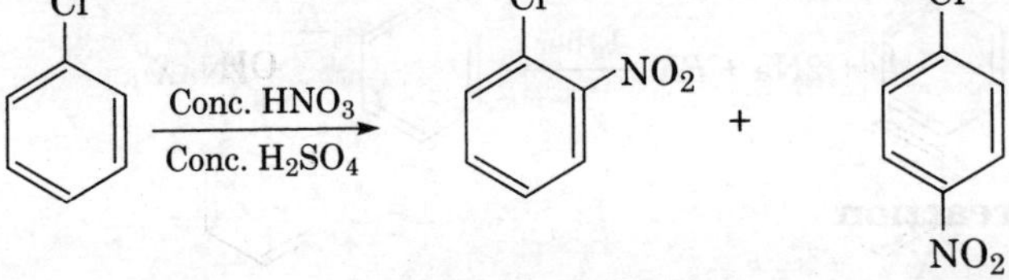

1-chloro-2-nitrobenzene
(minor)

1-chloro-4-nitrobenzene
(major)

(iii) **Sulphonation**

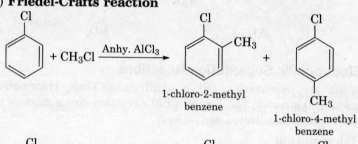

2-chlorobenzene
sulphonic acid
(minor)

+

4-chlorobenzene
sulphonic acid
(major)

(iv) **Friedel-Crafts reaction**

Cl
+ CH₃Cl →(Anhy. AlCl₃)→

1-chloro-2-methyl
benzene

+

1-chloro-4-methyl
benzene

Cl
+ H₃C—C—Cl →(Anhy. AlCl₃)→
      ‖
      O

2-chloroacetophenone

+

4-chloroacetophenone

3. Reaction with Metals

(i) **Wurtz Fittig reaction**

X
⟨benzene⟩ + 2Na + RX →(Ether)→ ⟨benzene⟩—R + 2NaX

(ii) **Fittig reaction**

X
2 ⟨benzene⟩ + 2Na →(Ether)→ ⟨biphenyl⟩ + 2NaX

Diphenyl

(iii) **Ullmann reaction**

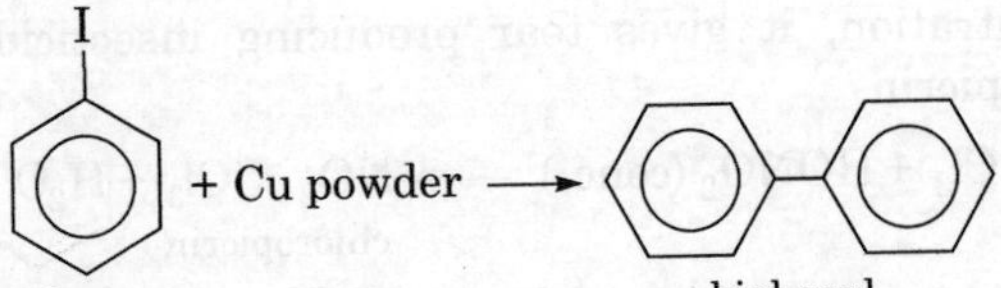

iodobenzene + Cu powder → biphenyl

Dihalogen Derivatives

$$CH_3-CH_2-\underset{\underset{Cl}{|}}{CH}-\underset{\underset{Cl}{|}}{CH_2}$$
(*Vic* or *vicinal*-dihalide)

$$CH_3CH_2CH\underset{Cl}{\overset{Cl}{<}}$$
(*Gem* or *geminal*-dihalide)

$$ClCH_2-CH_2-CH_2-CH_2-Cl$$
(Isolated dihalides)

Dichloromethane (CH_2Cl_2) is widely used as a solvent, as a propellant in aerosols. Direct contact of dichloromethane in humans causes intense burning and mild redness of the skin.

Trihalogen Derivatives

1. **Chloroform** [Trichloromethane, $CHCl_3$]

Methods of preparation

(i) $CH_4 + 3Cl_2 \xrightarrow[\text{Controlled chlorination}]{\text{Sunlight}} CHCl_3 + 3HCl$

(ii) Haloform reaction

$$C_2H_5OH + Cl_2 \longrightarrow CH_3CHO + 2HCl \text{ [Oxidation]}$$
$$CH_3CHO + 3Cl_2 \longrightarrow CCl_3 \cdot CHO + 3HCl \text{ [Chlorination]}$$
$$2CCl_3 \cdot CHO + Ca(OH)_2 \longrightarrow 2CHCl_3 + (HCOO)_2Ca$$
[Hydrolysis]

Properties

(i) Oxidation of $CHCl_3$ gives poisonous gas phosgene (carbonyl chloride).

$$2CHCl_3 + O_2 \xrightarrow{\text{Light}} \underset{\text{phosgene}}{2COCl_2} + 2HCl$$

To avoid this oxidation, $CHCl_3$ is stored in dark brown bottles and filled to the brim. 1% ethanol is added to chloroform which converts harmful phosgene gas into diethyl carbonate.

(ii) $CHCl_3$ is widely used in the production of freon refrigerant R—22.

(iii) On nitration, it gives tear producing insecticide substance chloropicrin.

$$CHCl_3 + HONO_2 \text{ (conc.)} \longrightarrow \underset{\text{chloropicrin}}{NO_2 \cdot CCl_3} + H_2O$$

(iv) On dehalogenation, it gives C_2H_2 (acetylene).

$$CHCl_3 + 6Ag + CHCl_3 \underset{\Delta}{\longrightarrow} CH \equiv CH + 6AgCl$$

(v) When subjected to hydrolysis, it gives formate.

$$CHCl_3 + 3NaOH \longrightarrow HC {\overset{OH}{\underset{OH}{\underset{-2H_2O}{\longrightarrow}}}} HCOO^- \overset{+}{N} a$$

2. Iodoform (tri-iodomethane, CHI_3)

Iodoform is prepared by iodoform reaction.

$$CH_3COCH_3 + 3I_2 + 4NaOH \longrightarrow$$
$$CHI_3 \downarrow + 3NaI + CH_3COONa + 3H_2O$$

Compounds containing either CH_3CO— or $CH_3CH(OH)$ group form yellow coloured iodoform with I_2 and NaOH.

Iodoform when comes in contact with organic matter, decomposes easily to free iodine, an antiseptic. Due to its objectionable smell, it has been replaced by other formulations containing iodine.

Polyhalogen Derivatives

1. Tetrachloromethane (Carbon Tetrachloride, CCl_4)

Preparation

(i) $CH_4 + 4Cl_2 \xrightarrow{\text{Sunlight}} CCl_4 + 4HCl$

(ii) $CHCl_3 + Cl_2 \xrightarrow{h\nu} CCl_4 + 2HCl$

CCl_4 is a colourless, non-inflammable, poisonous liquid, soluble in alcohol and ether.

Uses

Carbon tetrachloride is used

(i) as a solvent for oils, fats, resins

(ii) in dry cleaning

(iii) as fire extinguisher under the name '**pyrene**'.

2. **Freons**

The chlorofluorocarbon compounds of methane and ethane are collectively known as freons. These are usually produced for aerosol propellants, refrigeration and air conditioning purposes. Carbon tetra chloride when reacts with antimony trifluoride in the presence of $SbCl_5$ as catalyst, dichlorofluromethane (freon) is obtained.

3. **DDT** (*p, p'*-Dichlorodiphenyltrichloroethane)

2,2- bis (4-chlorophenyl) -1,1,1- trichloroethane

DDT is the first chlorinated organic insecticide. Its stability and fat solubility is a great problem.

It is prepared from chloral and chlorobenzene in the presence of conc. H_2SO_4.

4. **Perchloroethane** (C_2Cl_6)

It is used as moth repellant and is also known as artificial camphor.

27

Alcohols, Phenols and Ethers

Alcohols and Phenols

Alcohols and phenols are formed when a hydrogen atom in hydrocarbon, aliphatic and aromatic respectively, is replaced by hydroxyl group (—OH group).

Classification of Alcohols and Phenols

In alcohols, —OH group is attached to sp^3-hybridised carbon. These alcohols are usually classified as **primary, secondary** and **tertiary** alcohols.

$$R-\overset{\overset{H}{|}}{\underset{\underset{H}{|}}{C}}-OH \qquad R-\overset{\overset{R}{|}}{\underset{\underset{H}{|}}{C}}-OH \qquad R-\overset{\overset{R}{|}}{\underset{\underset{R}{|}}{C}}-OH$$

primary (1°)   secondary (2°)   tertiary (3°)

Alcohols may be

(i) monohydric-containing one —OH group,

(ii) dihydric-containing two —OH groups and

(iii) polyhydric-containing three or more —OH groups.

In allylic alcohols, —OH group is attached to sp^3-hybridised carbon but next to C=C bond. e.g. CH_2=CH—CH_2OH, in benzylic alcohol the — OH group is attached to sp^3 hybridised carbon atom next to an aromatic ring e.g. ($C_6H_5CH_2OH$).

In phenols, — OH group is attached to sp^2-hybridised carbon. These may also be monohyric, dihydric, etc. The dihydric phenol further may be *ortho*, *meta*, or *para* derivative.

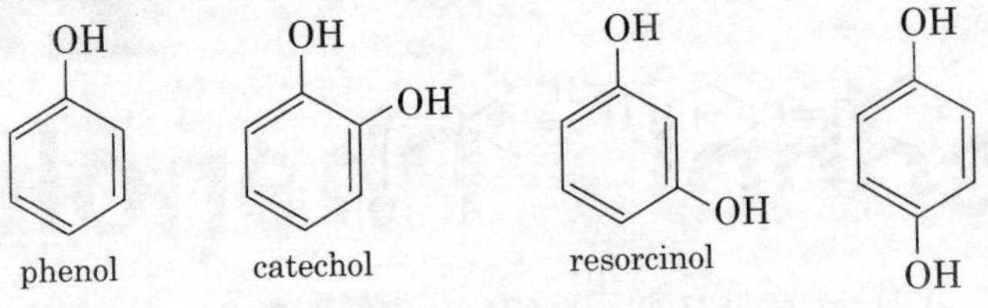

phenol   catechol   resorcinol   quinol or hydroquinone

Structure of Alcohols and Phenols

The oxygen atom of alcohols is sp^3-hybridised and they have tetrahedral position of hybrid atomic orbitals.

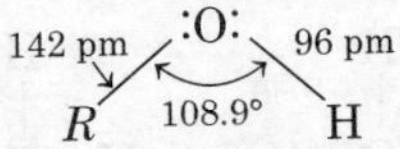

The value of $\angle ROH$ bond angle depends upon the R group. For methyl alcohol, it is ($\angle C - \overset{..}{\underset{..}{O}} - H$) 108.9° due to repulsion of lone pairs.

In phenols, the —OH group is attached to sp^2-hybridised carbon and thus, the C—O bond acquires a partial double bond character due to resonance.

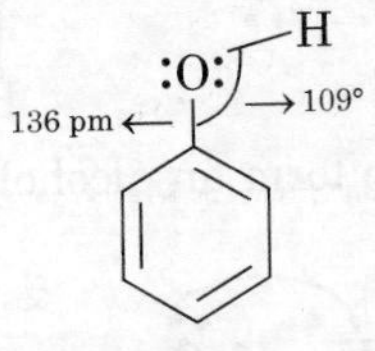

Nomenclature of Alcohol and Phenols

In IUPAC system, alcohol or alkanols are named by replacing the last word '*e*' of the corresponding alkane by 'ol'. e.g.

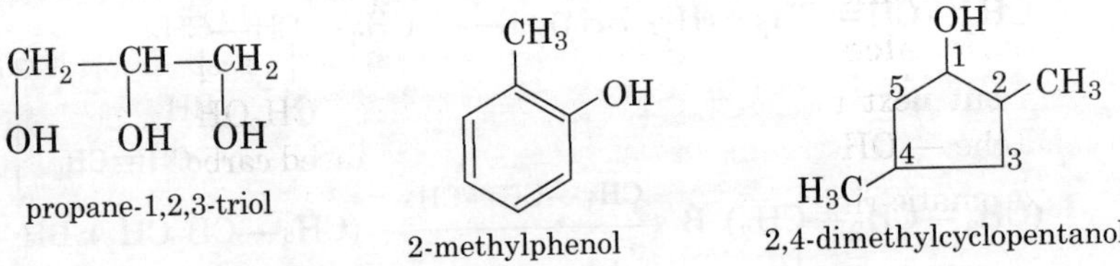

propane-1,2,3-triol

2-methylphenol

2,4-dimethylcyclopentanol

Preparation of Alcohols

(i) From alkenes

(a) By acid catalysed hydration in accordance with Markownikoff's rule.

$$>C=C< + H_2O \underset{}{\overset{H^+}{\rightleftharpoons}} >\underset{H}{C}-\underset{OH}{C}<$$

$$CH_3-CH=CH_2 + H_2O \underset{}{\overset{H^+}{\rightleftharpoons}} CH_3-\underset{OH}{CH}-CH_3$$

Mechanism

Step I Protonation of alkene by attack of H_3O^+

$$H_2O + H^+ \longrightarrow H_3O^+$$

$$>C=C< + H-\underset{+}{\overset{H}{O}}-H \rightleftharpoons H-\underset{H}{\overset{H}{C}}-\underset{H}{\overset{H}{C}}{}^+ + H_2\ddot{\underset{\bullet\bullet}{O}}$$

Step II Nucleophilic attack

$$H-\underset{H}{\overset{H}{C}}-\underset{H}{\overset{H}{C}}{}^+ + H_2\ddot{\underset{\bullet\bullet}{O}} \rightleftharpoons H-\underset{H}{\overset{H}{C}}-\underset{H}{\overset{H}{C}}-\underset{\oplus}{\overset{H}{O}}-H$$

Step III Deprotonation to form an alcohol

$$H-\underset{H}{\overset{H}{C}}-\underset{H}{\overset{H}{C}}-\overset{H}{\underset{\oplus}{O}}-H + H_2\ddot{\underset{\bullet\bullet}{O}} \longrightarrow H-\underset{H}{\overset{H}{C}}-\underset{H}{\overset{OH}{C}}-H + H_3\overset{+}{O}$$

(b) By hydroboration-oxidation

$$CH_3-CH=CH_2 + (H-BH_2)_2 \longrightarrow CH_3-\underset{H}{\overset{}{CH}}-\underset{BH_2}{\overset{}{CH_2}}$$

$$\downarrow CH_3-CH=CH_2$$

$$(CH_3-CH_2-CH_2)_3 B \xleftarrow{\cdot CH_3-CH=CH_2} (CH_3-CH_2CH_2)_2BH$$

$$3H_2O_2,\bar{O}H \downarrow H_2O$$

$$3CH_3CH_2CH_2OH + B(OH)_3$$

(ii) From carbonyl compounds

(a) By reduction of aldehydes and ketones

$$R\text{—CHO} + H_2 \xrightarrow{Pd} RCH_2\text{—OH}$$

$$RCOR' \xrightarrow{NaBH_4} R\text{—}\underset{\underset{\displaystyle OH}{|}}{CH}\text{—}R'$$

Aldehydes yield primary alcohols whereas ketones give secondary alcohols, when subjected to reduction.

(b) By reduction of carboxylic acids and ester

$$RCOOH \xrightarrow[\text{(ii) } H_2O]{\text{(i) LiAlH}_4} RCH_2OH$$

$$RCOOR' \xrightarrow[\text{Catalyst}]{H_2} RCH_2OH + R'OH$$

Reduction of aldehyde, ketones and esters with Na/alcohol is called Bouvaoult-blanc reduction.

(iii) From Grignard's reagents

The reaction produces a primary alcohol with methanal, a secondary alcohol with aldehydes (except methanal) and tertiary alcohol with ketones.

$$HCHO + RMgX \longrightarrow RCH_2\overset{-}{O}\overset{+}{M}gX \xrightarrow{H_2O} RCH_2OH + Mg\diagdown\begin{smallmatrix}X\\OH\end{smallmatrix}$$

$$RCHO + R'MgX \xrightarrow{H_2O} R\text{—}\underset{\underset{\displaystyle OMgX}{|}}{\overset{\overset{\displaystyle R'}{|}}{CH}}\xrightarrow[-Mg(OH)X]{H_2O} R\text{—}\underset{\underset{\displaystyle OH}{}}{\overset{\overset{\displaystyle R'}{|}}{CH}}\text{—OH}$$

$$RCOR + R'MgX \longrightarrow R\text{—}\underset{\underset{\displaystyle R}{|}}{\overset{\overset{\displaystyle R'}{|}}{C}}\text{—}\overset{-}{O}\overset{+}{M}gX \xrightarrow[-Mg(OH)X]{H_2O} R\text{—}\underset{\underset{\displaystyle R}{|}}{\overset{\overset{\displaystyle R'}{|}}{C}}\text{—OH}$$

(iv) Hydrolysis of alkyl halides

$$R-X + KOH(aq) \longrightarrow ROH + KX$$

To avoid dehydrohalogenation of RX, mild alkalies like moist silver oxide is used.

Ease of hydrolysis of alkyl halides $RI > RBr > RCl >$ and $t(3°) > s(2°) > p(1°)$ alkyl halides.

(v) Hydrolysis of ethers

$$R-\overset{\cdot\cdot}{O}-R + H_2O \xrightarrow{H_2SO_4} 2ROH$$

(vi) From primary amines By treatment with nitrous acid.

$$RNH_2 + HONO \xrightarrow{(NaNO_2 + HCl)} ROH + N_2\uparrow + H_2O$$

Methylamine does not give methyl alcohol when treated with HNO_2. It gives CH_3OCH_3 and CH_3ONO.

(vii) By alcoholic fermentation

$$\underset{\text{sucrose}}{C_{12}H_{22}O_{11}} + H_2O \xrightarrow{\text{Invertase}} \underset{\text{glucose}}{C_6H_{12}O_6} + \underset{\text{fructose}}{C_6H_{12}O_6}$$

$$\underset{\text{glucose and fructose}}{C_6H_{12}O_6} \xrightarrow{\text{Zymase}} \underset{\text{ethyl alcohol}}{2C_2H_5OH} + 2CO_2(g)$$

Preparation of Phenols

(i) From haloarenes

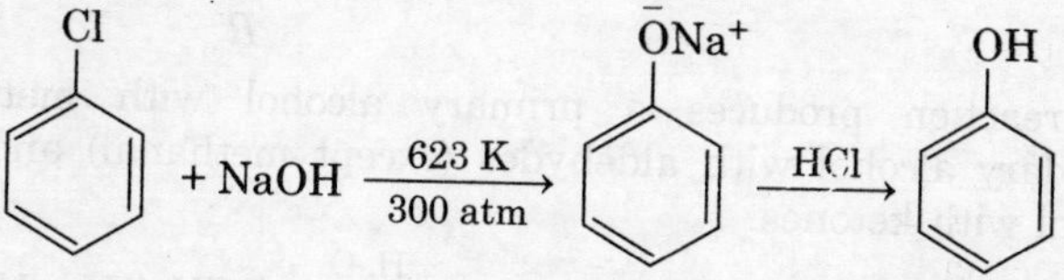

(ii) From benzene sulphonic acid

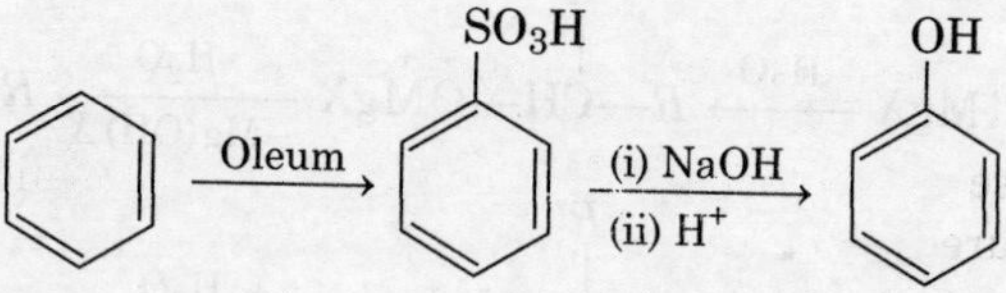

Benzene sulphonic acid

(iii) **From diazonium salts**

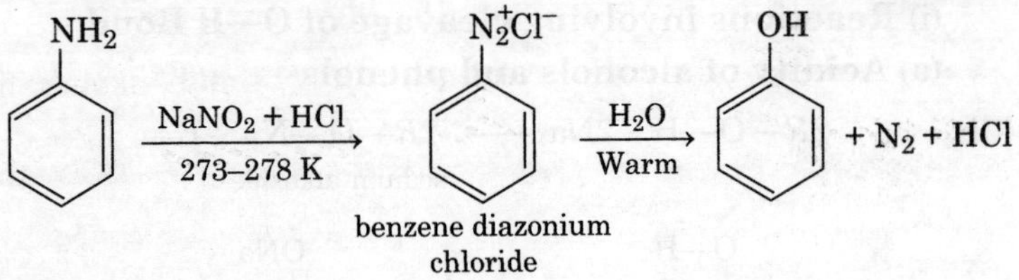

benzene diazonium
chloride

(iv) **From cumene**

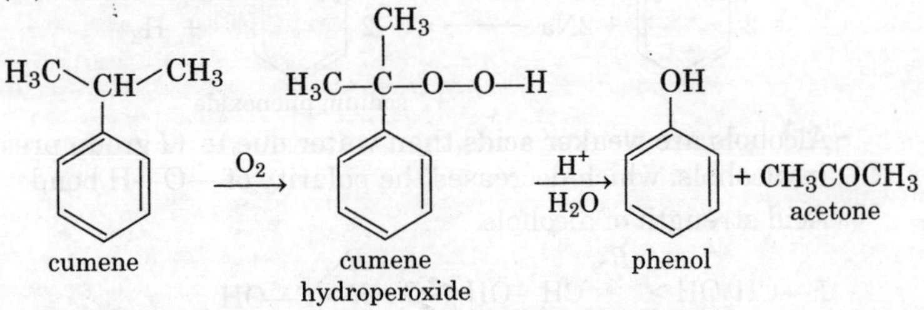

| cumene | cumene hydroperoxide | phenol |

Physical Properties of Alcohols

1. Lower alcohols are colourless liquids, members from C_5-C_{11} are oily liquids and higher members are waxy solids.

2. The hydroxyl groups in alcohols can form H-bonds with water, so alcohols are miscible with water. The solubility decreases with increase in molecular mass.

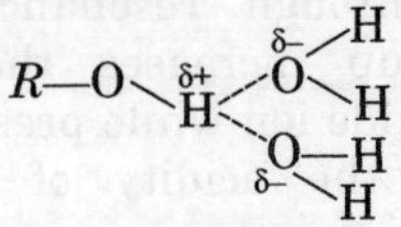

3. Boiling points of alkanols are higher than expected because of the presence of intermolecular hydrogen bonding in the polar molecules.

The boiling point decreases in the order 1° > 2° > 3° as the van der Waals' forces of attraction decreases.

Physical Properties of Phenols

1. These are colourless liquids or crystalline solids but become coloured due to slow oxidation with air.

2. Phenol is also called carbolic acid.

3. Because of the presence of polar —OH bond, phenols form intermolecular H-bonding with other phenol molecules and with water.

Chemical Reactions Common to Alcohols and Phenols

(i) **Reactions involving cleavage of O—H Bond**

(a) **Acidity of alcohols and phenols**

$$2R—O—H + 2Na \longrightarrow 2R—\overset{-}{O}—\overset{+}{Na} + H_2$$
$$\text{sodium alkoxide}$$

Alcohols are weaker acids than water due to $+I$ group present in alcohols, which decreases the polarity of —O—H bond.

Acid strength of alcohols

$$R\rightarrow CH_2OH > \overset{R}{\underset{R}{\diagdown}}CH—OH \gg \overset{R}{\underset{R}{\diagdown}}R\rightarrow C—OH$$

primary   secondary   tertiary

Electron releasing group increases electron density on oxygen and decreases the polarity of —OH bond.

Order of acidity is

$$RCOOH > H_2CO_3 > C_6H_5OH > H_2O > R—OH.$$

Phenol is more acidic than alcohols due to stabilisation of phenoxide ion through resonance. Presence of electron withdrawing group increases the acidity of phenol by stabilising phenoxide ion while presence of electron releasing group decreases the acidity of phenol by destabilising phenoxide ion.

Thus, increasing acidic strength is

o-cresol < p-cresol < m-cresol < phenol < o-nitrophenol < 2, 4, 6-trinitrophenol (picric acid)

Higher K_a and lower pK_a value corresponds to the stronger acid.

(b) **Esterification**

$$Ar/R—O—H + R'COOH \overset{H^+}{\rightleftharpoons} Ar/R — OCOR' + H_2O$$

$$Ar/R—OH + (R'CO)_2O \overset{H^+}{\rightleftharpoons} Ar/R — OCOR' + R'COOH$$

$$R/Ar — OH + R'COCl \xrightarrow[\text{Pyridine}]{} R/Ar — OCOR' + HCl$$

The reaction with $R'COOH$ and $(R'CO)_2O$ is reversible, so conc. H_2SO_4 is used to remove water.

The reaction with $R'COCl$ is carried out in the presence of pyridine so as to neutralise HCl which is formed during the reaction.

The introduction of acetyl (CH_3CO—) group in phenols is known as **acetylation.**

Acetylation of salicylic acid produces aspirin.

acetic anhydride

salicylic acid

acetyl salicylic acid (aspirin)

(ii) **Reaction involving cleavage of C—O bond in alcohols** In these reactions, the reactivity order of different alcohols is :

methyl alcohol   primary alcohol   secondary alcohol   tertiary alcohol

Alkyl group (due to +I effect) increases the electron density on the carbon and oxygen atom of C—OH bond. As a result, the bond cleavage becomes easy. Greater the number of alkyl groups present, more will be the reactivity of alcohol. Thus, the relative order of reactivity of the alcohols is justified.

(a) **Reaction with halogen acids** Alcohols can be converted into haloalkanes by the action of halogen acids.

$$R—OH + HX\ (HCl, HBr, HI) \longrightarrow R—X + H_2O$$

For a given alcohol order of reactivity of HX is

$$H—I > H—Br > H—Cl$$

For a given halogen acid order of reactivity of alcohols

Tertiary > Secondary > Primary

Mixture of anhyd. $ZnCl_2$ and conc. HCl (Lucas reagent) is used to distinguish 1°, 2° and 3° alcohols (discussed later).

(b) **Reaction with phosphorus halides**

$$ROH + PCl_5 \longrightarrow RCl + POCl_3 + HCl$$
$$3ROH + PBr_3 \longrightarrow 3RBr + H_3PO_3$$
$$3ROH + PI_3 \longrightarrow 3RI + H_3PO_3$$

(c) **Reaction with thionyl chloride**

$$ROH + SOCl_2 \longrightarrow RCl + SO_2\uparrow + HCl\uparrow$$

(d) **Dehydration of alcohols** It requires acid as catalyst and the reaction proceeds *via* intermediate carbonium ion. Acidic catalyst converts hydroxyl group into a good leaving group.

Since, the rate determining step is the formation of carbocation, the ease of dehydration is

$$3° > 2° > 1°$$

$$C_2H_5OH \xrightarrow[443\ K]{H_2SO_4} CH_2{=}CH_2 + H_2O$$

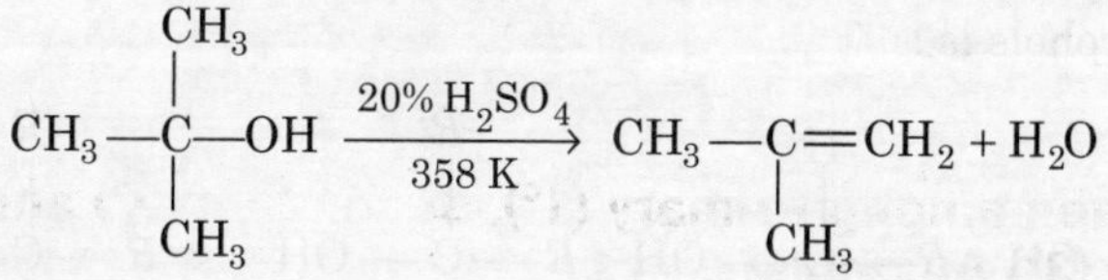

$$CH_3-\underset{\underset{CH_3}{|}}{\overset{\overset{CH_3}{|}}{C}}-OH \xrightarrow[358\ K]{20\%\ H_2SO_4} CH_3-\underset{\underset{CH_3}{|}}{C}{=}CH_2 + H_2O$$

Mechanism

Step I Formation of protonated alcohol

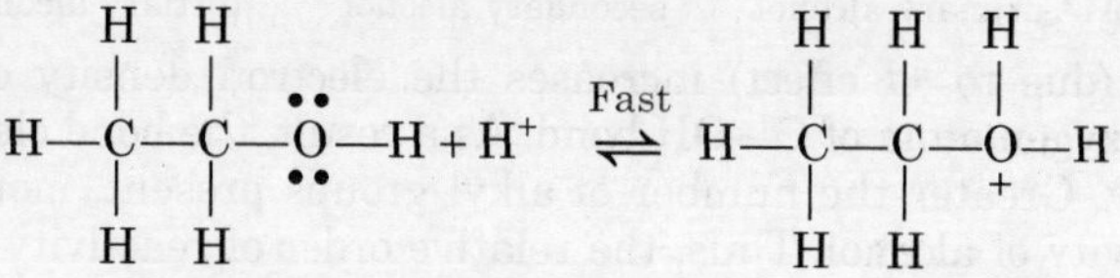

Step II Formation of carbocation

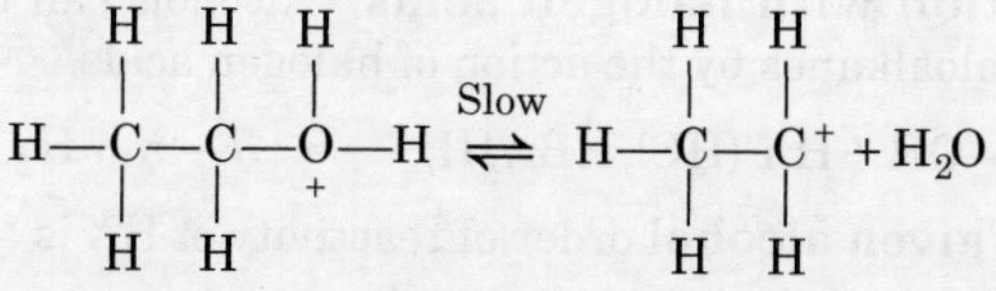

Step III Formation of ethene by elimination of a proton

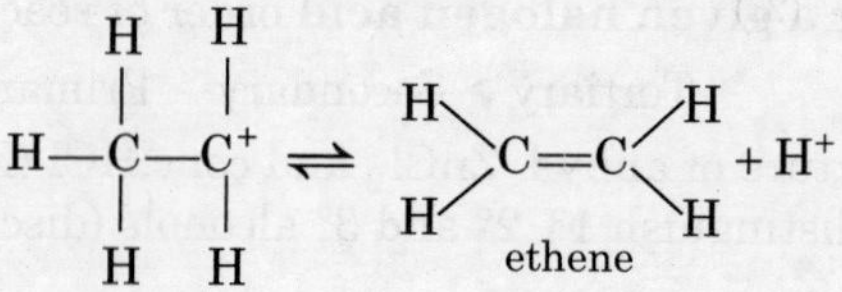

ethene

In dehydration reaction, highly substituted alkene is the major product and if the major product is capable of showing *cis-trans* isomerism, *trans*-product is the major product. **(Saytzeff's rule)**.

A common reagent that selectively oxidises a primary alcohol to an aldehyde (and no further) is pyridinium chlorochromate (PCC).

$$CH_3CH\!=\!CH\!-\!CH_2OH \xrightarrow{PCC} CH_3CH\!=\!CH\!-\!CHO$$

(e) **Oxidation reaction** This reaction is used to distinguish between 1°, 2° and 3° alcohols. Generally , alk. $KMnO_4$ and acid. $K_2Cr_2O_7$ is used as reagent (discussed later in this chapter)

(f) **Dehydrogenation**

$$\underset{\text{1° alcohol}}{RCH_2OH} \xrightarrow{Cu/300°C} \underset{\text{aldehyde}}{RCHO + H_2 \uparrow}$$

$$\underset{\text{2° alcohol}}{RCHOH\!-\!R} \xrightarrow{Cu/300°C} \underset{\text{ketone}}{R\cdot CO\cdot R + H_2 \uparrow}$$

$$\underset{\text{3° alcohol}}{(CH_3)_3COH} \xrightarrow{Cu/300°C} \quad \underset{\text{alkene (\textit{iso}-butylene)}}{\begin{array}{c} H_3C \\ H_3C \end{array}\!\!\!\diagdown\!\!\!C\!=\!CH_2 \ + H_2O}$$

Distinction among Primary (1°), Secondary (2°) and Tertiary (3°) Alcohols

1°, 2° and 3° alcohols are distinguished by Lucas test, oxidation and reduced copper.

Victor Meyer's test is also used to distinguish them.

In this test, primary (1°) alcohols give red colour, secondary (2°) alcohols give blue colour and tertiary (3°) alcohols give no colouration.

$$\underset{(1°)}{RCH_2OH} \xrightarrow{P/I_2} RCH_2I \xrightarrow{AgNO_2} RCH_2NO_2$$

$$\xrightarrow{HNO_2} \underset{\text{nitrolic acid}}{R\!-\!\underset{\underset{NOH}{\|}}{C}\!-\!NO_2} \xrightarrow{Alkali} \text{Blood red colour}$$

$$\underset{(2°)}{R_2CHOH} \xrightarrow{P/I_2} R_2CHI \xrightarrow{AgNO_2} R_2CHNO_2$$

$$\xrightarrow{HNO_2} \underset{\text{pseudonitrol}}{R_2\!-\!\underset{\underset{N=O}{|}}{C}\!-\!NO_2} \xrightarrow{Alkali} \text{Blue colour}$$

$$R_3C\!-\!OH \xrightarrow{\text{P/I}_2} R_2CI \xrightarrow{\text{AgNO}_2} R_3CNO_2 \xrightarrow{\text{HNO}_2} \text{No reaction}$$
$$\underset{(3°)}{}$$

Lucas reagent (mixture of anhyd. $ZnCl_2$ and conc. HCl) is used to distinguish 1°, 2° and 3° alcohols.

Lucas test

Primary alcohols	Secondary alcohols	Tertiary alcohols
$RCH_2OH \xrightarrow[\text{Anhy.ZnCl}_2]{\text{Conc HCl}} (X)$	$R_2CH\!-\!OH \xrightarrow[\text{Anhy.ZnCl}_2]{\text{Conc HCl}}$	$R_3C\!-\!OH \xrightarrow[\text{Anhy.ZnCl}_2]{\text{Conc HCl}}$
No reaction and hence, no white cloudiness or turbidity at room temperature.	R_2CHCl White cloudiness or turbidity appears with in about 5 minutes.	R_3CCl White cloudiness or turbidity appears immediately.

Oxidation reactions Oxidising reagents used for the oxidation of alcohols are neutral, acidic or alkaline $KMnO_4$ and acidified $K_2Cr_2O_7$.

Primary alcohols	Secondary alcohols	Tertiary alcohols
CH_3CH_2OH	$CH_3CH(OH)\!-\!CH_3$	$(CH_3)_3C\!-\!OH$
$\downarrow[O]$	$\downarrow[O]$	$\downarrow[O]$
CH_3CHO	CH_3COCH_3	$CH_3COCH_3 + CO_2 + H_2O$
$\downarrow[O]$	$\downarrow[O]$	$\downarrow[O]$
CH_3COOH	$CH_3COOH + CO_2 + H_2O$	$CH_3COOH + CO_2 + H_2O$

Chemical Reactions only for Phenols

(i) **Electrophilic substitution reactions** The —OH group attached to the benzene ring activates it towards electrophilic substitution at *ortho* and *para* positions.

(a) **Halogenation**

2,4,6-tribromophenol

With calculated amount of Br_2 in CS_2 or $CHCl_3$, it gives *ortho* and *para* product.

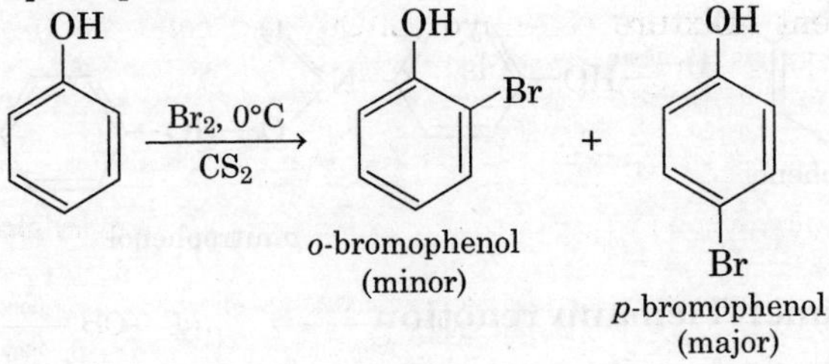

o-bromophenol
(minor)

p-bromophenol
(major)

(b) Sulphonation

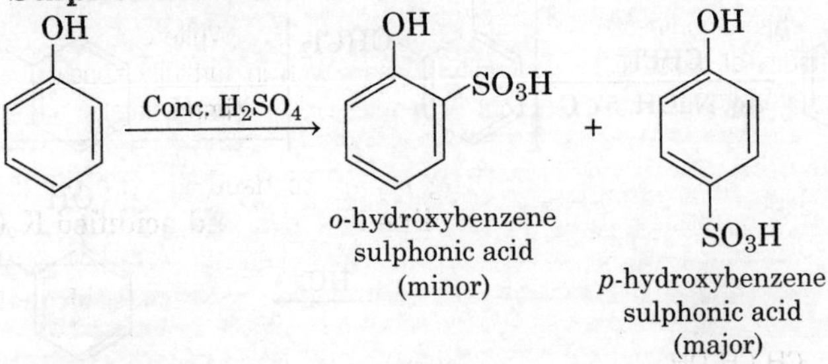

o-hydroxybenzene
sulphonic acid
(minor)

p-hydroxybenzene
sulphonic acid
(major)

(c) Nitration

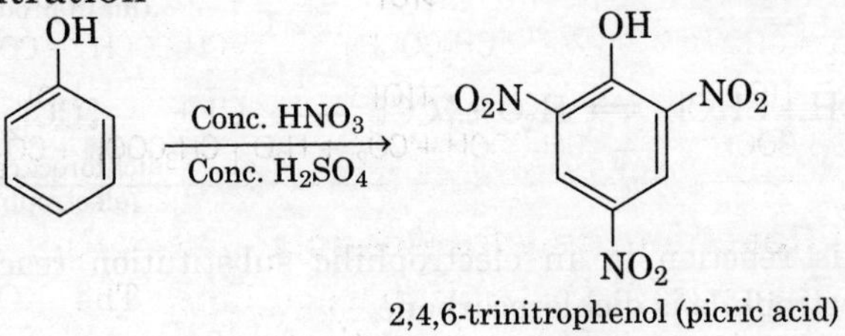

2,4,6-trinitrophenol (picric acid)

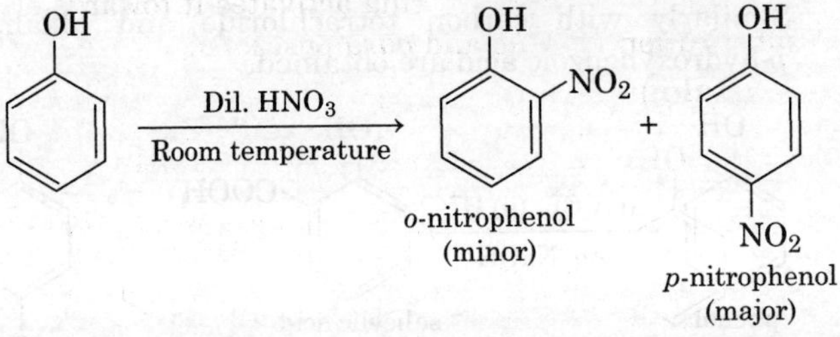

o-nitrophenol
(minor)

p-nitrophenol
(major)

The *ortho* and *para* isomers can be separated by steam distillation. This is because o-nitrophenol is steam volatile due to intramolecular hydrogen bonding while p-nitrophenol is less volatile due to intermolecular hydrogen bonding which causes the association of molecules.

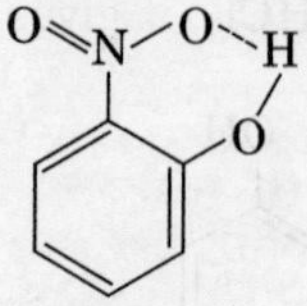

o-nitrophenol

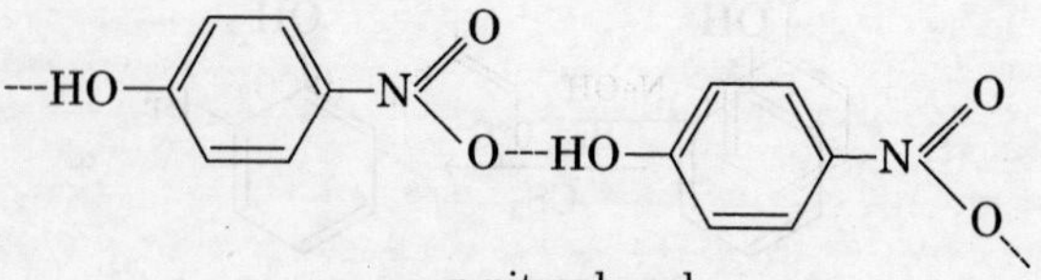

p-nitrophenol

(d) Reimer-Tiemann reaction

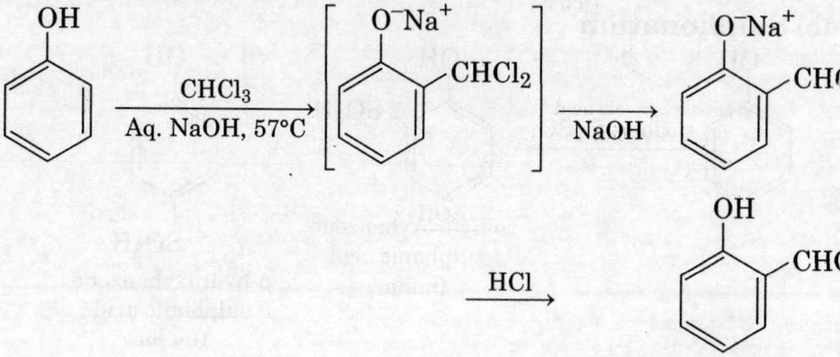

salicylaldehyde
(main product)

$$OH^- + CHCl_3 \rightleftharpoons H_2O + :\bar{C}Cl_3 \longrightarrow \bar{C}l + \underset{\substack{\text{dichlorocarbene} \\ \text{(electrophile)}}}{:CCl_2}$$

This reaction is an electrophilic substitution reaction and electrophile is dichlorocarbene.

Similarly with carbon tetrachloride and alkali, *o*- and *p*-hydroxybenzoic acid are obtained.

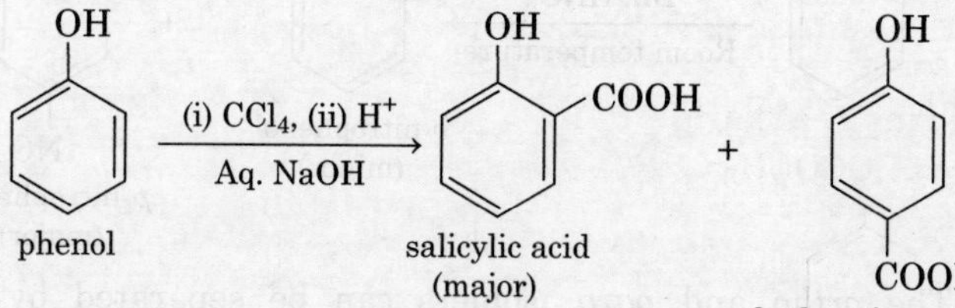

phenol

salicylic acid
(major)

p-hydroxybenzoic acid
(minor)

(ii) Kolbe's reaction

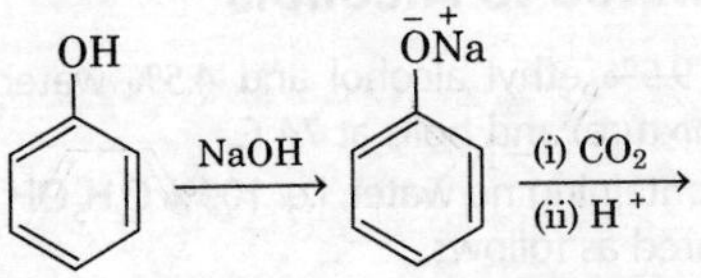
OH
NaOH
$\overset{-}{O}\overset{+}{Na}$
(i) CO_2
(ii) H^+

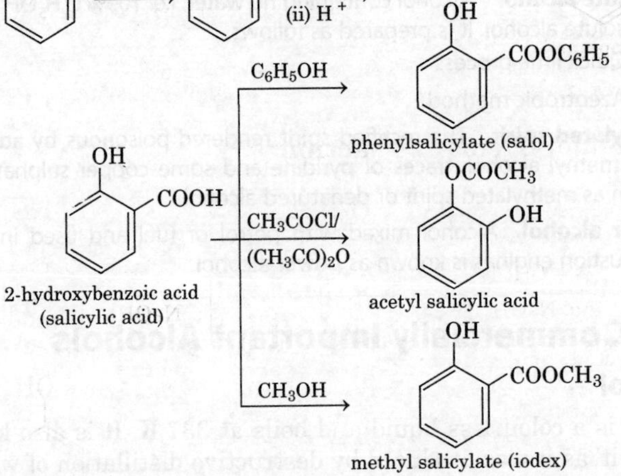
OH
COOH
2-hydroxybenzoic acid
(salicylic acid)
C_6H_5OH
OH
$COOC_6H_5$
phenylsalicylate (salol)
$CH_3COCl/$
$(CH_3CO)_2O$
$OCOCH_3$
OH
acetyl salicylic acid
CH_3OH
OH
$COOCH_3$
methyl salicylate (iodex)

(iii) Reaction with zinc dust

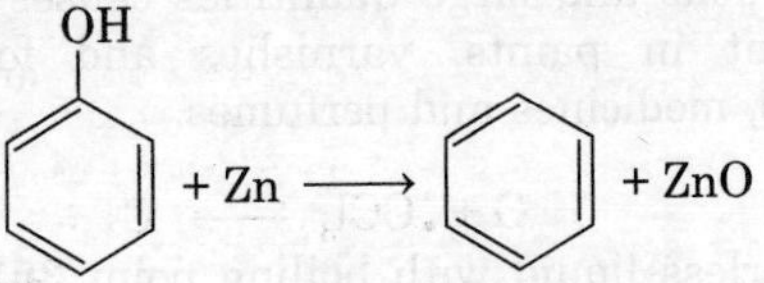
OH
+ Zn
+ ZnO

(iv) Oxidation

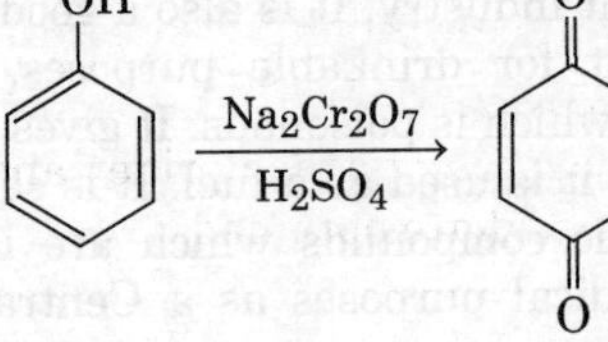
OH
$Na_2Cr_2O_7$
H_2SO_4
O
O

benzoquinone

(v) Fries rearrangement

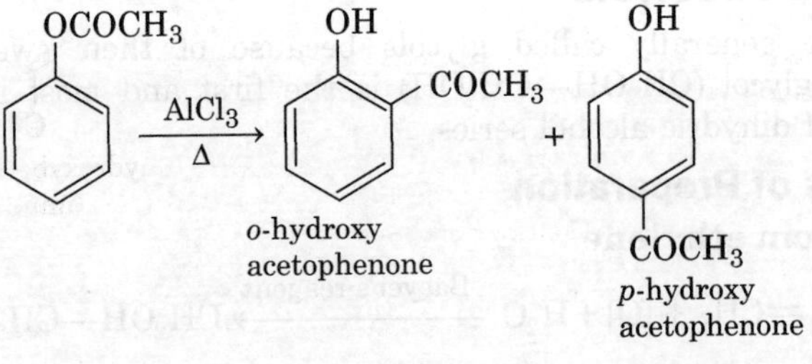
$OCOCH_3$
$AlCl_3$
Δ
OH
$COCH_3$
+
OH
o-hydroxy
acetophenone
$COCH_3$
p-hydroxy
acetophenone

Terms Related to Alcohols

(a) **Rectified spirit** It contains 9.5% ethyl alcohol and 4.5% water. It is an azeotrope (constant boiling mixture) and boils at 74°C.

(b) **Absolute alcohol** Alcohol containing no water, i.e. 100% C_2H_5OH is known as absolute alcohol. It is prepared as follows.

   (i) Quick lime process

   (ii) Azeotropic method

(c) **Methylated spirit** The rectified spirit rendered poisonous by addition of 4-5% methyl alcohol, traces of pyridine and some copper sulphate and is known as methylated spirit or denatured alcohol.

(d) **Power alcohol** Alcohol mixed with petrol or fuel and used in internal combustion engines is known as power alcohol.

Some Commercially Important Alcohols

Methanol

Methanol is a colourless liquid and boils at 337 K. It is also known as 'wood spirit' as it was produced by destructive distillation of wood. It is highly poisonous in nature. Ingestion of even small quantities of methanol is hazardous and large quantities causes even death. It is used as a solvent in paints, varnishes and for manufacturing formaldehyde dyes, medicines and perfumes.

Ethanol

Ethanol is a colourless liquid with boiling point 351 K. It is used in alcoholic beverages, produced by fermentation of sugars by yeast. It is used as a solvent in paint industry. It is also a good industrial solvent, hence, it is made unfit for drinkable purposes, by addition of a denaturant like CH_3OH which is poisonous. It gives carbon dioxide and water on burning. Thus, it is used as a fuel. It is safe and can be used to dissolve many organic compounds which are insoluble in water. Ethanol is used for medical purposes as a Central Nervous System (CNS) depressant.

Dihydric Alcohols

These are generally called glycols because of their sweet taste. Ethylene glycol (CH_2OH—CH_2OH) is the first and most important member of dihydric alcohol series.

Methods of Preparation

   (i) **From ethylene**

$$CH_2{=}CH_2 + [O] + H_2O \xrightarrow{\text{Baeyer's reagent}} CH_2OH{-}CH_2OH$$

(1% alkaline $KMnO_4$ is called Baeyer's reagent)

$$CH_2 = CH_2 \xrightarrow[Na_2SO_3/H_2O]{OsO_4/pyridine} CH_2OH-CH_2OH$$

(ii) **By reduction of glyoxal**

$$\begin{array}{c} CHO \\ | \\ CHO \\ \text{glyoxal} \end{array} + [H] \xrightarrow{LiAlH_4} \begin{array}{c} CH_2OH \\ | \\ CH_2OH \\ \text{ethylene glycol} \end{array}$$

Physical Properties

1. It is a colourless, syrupy liquid with sweet taste.

2. Because of its tendency of formation of H-bonds, it is miscible with H_2O and ethanol but not with ether.

Chemical Properties

It gives all the general reactions of —OH group.

$$\begin{array}{c} CH_2OH \\ | \\ CH_2OH \\ \text{(Glycol)} \end{array}$$

$\xrightarrow{Na/50^\circ C}$ $\begin{array}{c} CH_2O\overset{\ominus}{N}\overset{\oplus}{a} \\ | \\ CH_2OH \end{array}$ $\xrightarrow{Na}_{160^\circ C}$ $\begin{array}{c} CH_2O\overset{\ominus}{N}\overset{\oplus}{a} \\ | \\ CH_2O\overset{\ominus}{N}\overset{\oplus}{a} \end{array}$

$\xrightarrow{PCl_5}$ $\begin{array}{c} CH_2Cl \\ | \\ CH_2OH \end{array}$ $\xrightarrow{PCl_5}$ $\begin{array}{c} CH_2Cl \\ | \\ CH_2Cl \end{array}$

$\xrightarrow{2PI_3}$ $\begin{array}{c} CH_2I \\ | \\ CH_2I \\ \text{(unstable)} \end{array}$ $\xrightarrow{-I_2}$ $\begin{array}{c} CH_2 \\ \| \\ CH_2 \end{array}$

$\xrightarrow[{[O]}]{Dil\ HNO_3}$ $\begin{array}{c} COOH \\ | \\ COOH \\ \text{oxalic acid} \end{array}$

$\xrightarrow[K_2Cr_2O_7/H^+]{KMnO_4/H^+ or}$ $\begin{array}{c} 2HCOOH \\ \text{formic acid} \end{array}$

$\xrightarrow[(CH_3COO)_4Pb]{HIO_4\ or}$ $\begin{array}{c} 2HCHO \\ \text{formaldehyde} \end{array}$

$\xrightarrow[\Delta]{Conc\ H_2SO_4}$ $O\begin{array}{c} \diagup CH_2-CH_2 \diagdown \\ \diagdown CH_2-CH_2 \diagup \end{array}O$
1,4-dioxane

$\xrightarrow[-H_2O,\Delta]{H_3PO_4}$ $O\begin{array}{c} \diagup CH_2\ CH_2OH \\ \diagdown CH_2\ CH_2OH \end{array}$
diethylene glycol

The per-iodic acid cleavage of 1,2-glycols is sometimes called Malaprade reaction.

Trihydric Alcohols

Glycerol or glycerine, CH_2OH—$CH(OH)$—CH_2OH is the first member of this group. Its IUPAC name is propane-1,2,3-triol.

Method of Preparation

It is obtained as a by product in saponification reaction.

$$
\begin{array}{l}
CH_2OOCR \\
| \\
CHOOCR \\
| \\
CH_2OOCR \\
\text{fat or oil}
\end{array}
+ 3NaOH \xrightarrow{\text{Hydrolysis}}
\begin{array}{l}
CH_2OH \\
| \\
CHOH \\
| \\
CH_2OH \\
\text{glycerol}
\end{array}
+ 3R\overset{-}{C}O\overset{+}{O}Na \atop \text{soap}
$$

(where, $R = C_{17}H_{35}$ or $C_{15}H_{31}$ or $C_{17}H_{33}$)

Physical Properties

1. It is a colourless, odourless, viscous and hygroscopic liquid.
2. It is sweet in taste and steam volatile.
3. It is soluble in water but insoluble in ether.
4. Due to excessive H-bonding, it is highly viscous and has high boiling point.

Chemical Properties

It gives all the general reactions given by —OH group but 2° OH is less reactive as compared to 1°.

Some of its specific reactions are :

(i) **Reaction with HI**

$$
\begin{array}{l}
CH_2OH \\
| \\
CHOH \\
| \\
CH_2OH \\
\text{glycerol}
\end{array}
\xrightarrow[\text{warm}]{3HI}
\begin{array}{l}
CH_2I \\
| \\
CHI \\
| \\
CH_2I \\
\text{(unstable due to} \\
\text{large size of I)}
\end{array}
\xrightarrow{-I_2}
\begin{array}{l}
CH_2 \\
\| \\
CH \\
| \\
CH_2I \\
\text{allyl iodide}
\end{array}
$$

(ii) **Reaction with HNO_3**

$$
\begin{array}{l}
CH_2OH \\
| \\
CHOH \\
| \\
CH_2OH \\
\text{glycerol}
\end{array}
+ 3HNO_3 \atop \text{(conc.)}
\xrightarrow[-3H_2O]{H_2SO_4 \text{ (conc.)}}
\begin{array}{l}
CH_2ONO_2 \\
| \\
CHONO_2 \\
| \\
CH_2ONO_2 \\
\text{glyceryl trinitrate (TNG)}
\end{array}
$$

Glyceryl trinitrate or trinitroglycerine, when adsorbed on Keiselghur is known as **dynamite**. Mixture of TNG and cellulose trinitrate is called **blasting gelatin**.

(iii) **Reaction with oxalic acid**

(a) **At 110°C**

$$
\begin{array}{c}
\text{CH}_2\text{OH} \\
| \\
\text{CHOH} \\
| \\
\text{CH}_2\text{OH}
\end{array}
+
\underset{\text{oxalic acid}}{\begin{array}{c}
\text{HOOC} \\
| \\
\text{COOH}
\end{array}}
\xrightarrow[-\text{H}_2\text{O}]{110°\text{C}}
\underset{\text{glycerol mono oxalate}}{\begin{array}{c}
\text{CH}_2\text{OOC}\cdot\text{COOH} \\
| \\
\text{CHOH} \\
| \\
\text{CH}_2\text{OH}
\end{array}}
$$

$$
\xrightarrow[-\text{CO}_2]{110°\text{C}}
\underset{\substack{\text{glycerol} \\ \text{monoformate}}}{\begin{array}{c}
\quad\quad\overset{\text{O}}{\overset{\|}{}} \\
\text{CH}_2\!-\!\text{O}\!-\!\text{C}\!-\!\text{H} \\
| \\
\text{CHOH} \\
| \\
\text{CH}_2\text{OH}
\end{array}}
\xrightarrow[\text{(hydrolysis)}]{\text{H}_2\text{O}}
\underset{\substack{\text{formic acid}}}{\text{HCOOH}}
+
\underset{\text{glycerol}}{\begin{array}{c}
\text{CH}_2\text{OH} \\
| \\
\text{CHOH} \\
| \\
\text{CH}_2\text{OH}
\end{array}}
$$

(b) **At 260°C**

$$
\begin{array}{c}
\text{CH}_2\text{OH} \\
| \\
\text{CHOH} \\
| \\
\text{CH}_2\text{OH}
\end{array}
+
\begin{array}{c}
\text{HOOC} \\
| \\
\text{HOOC}
\end{array}
\xrightarrow{260°\text{C}}
\underset{\text{glycerol dioxalate}}{\begin{array}{c}
\text{CH}_2\!-\!\text{O}\!-\!\text{CO} \\
\quad\quad\quad\;| \\
\text{CH}\!-\!\text{O}\!-\!\text{CO} \\
| \\
\text{CH}_2\text{OH}
\end{array}}
\xrightarrow[\Delta]{-\,2\text{CO}_2}
\underset{\text{allyl alcohol}}{\begin{array}{c}
\text{CH}_2 \\
\| \\
\text{CH} \\
| \\
\text{CH}_2\text{OH}
\end{array}}
$$

(iv) **Dehydration**

$$
\begin{array}{c}
\text{CH}_2\text{OH} \\
| \\
\text{CHOH} \\
| \\
\text{CH}_2\text{OH}
\end{array}
\xrightarrow[-2\text{H}_2\text{O}]{\text{KHSO}_4 \text{ or } \text{P}_2\text{O}_5,\,\Delta}
\begin{array}{c}
\text{CH}_2 \\
\| \\
\text{CH} \\
| \\
\text{CHO}
\end{array}
$$

acraldehyde
or acrolein (bad smelling compound)

(v) **Oxidation** Different products are obtained by different oxidising agents.

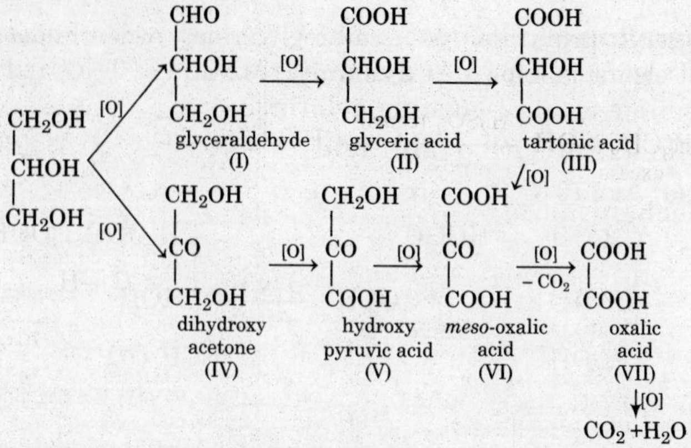

$$
\begin{array}{ccc}
\underset{\substack{\text{glyceraldehyde}\\(I)}}{\begin{array}{l}CHO\\|\\CHOH\\|\\CH_2OH\end{array}}\xrightarrow{[O]}&\underset{\substack{\text{glyceric acid}\\(II)}}{\begin{array}{l}COOH\\|\\CHOH\\|\\CH_2OH\end{array}}\xrightarrow{[O]}&\underset{\substack{\text{tartonic acid}\\(III)}}{\begin{array}{l}COOH\\|\\CHOH\\|\\COOH\end{array}}
\end{array}
$$

CH_2OH
|
$CHOH$ $\xrightarrow{[O]}$
|
CH_2OH $\xrightarrow{[O]}$

$$
\begin{array}{cccc}
\underset{\substack{\text{dihydroxy}\\\text{acetone}\\(IV)}}{\begin{array}{l}CH_2OH\\|\\CO\\|\\CH_2OH\end{array}}\xrightarrow{[O]}&\underset{\substack{\text{hydroxy}\\\text{pyruvic acid}\\(V)}}{\begin{array}{l}CH_2OH\\|\\CO\\|\\COOH\end{array}}\xrightarrow{[O]}&\underset{\substack{\text{meso-oxalic}\\\text{acid}\\(VI)}}{\begin{array}{l}COOH\\|\\CO\\|\\COOH\end{array}}\xrightarrow[-CO_2]{[O]}&\underset{\substack{\text{oxalic}\\\text{acid}\\(VII)}}{\begin{array}{l}COOH\\|\\COOH\end{array}}
\end{array}
$$

$\downarrow[O]$

$CO_2 + H_2O$

In the above reaction conc. HNO_3 gives II; dil HNO_3 gives II and III; $Bi(NO_3)_3$ or $NaNO_3$ gives VI; Fenton's reagent or NaOBr or Br_2 water in Na_2CO_3 gives a mixture of I and IV. Solid $KMnO_4$ oxidises glycerol to VII and CO_2 and H_2O. With HIO_4 (periodic acid), glycerol gives HCOOH and HCHO.

Ethers

Ethers are the organic compounds in which two alkyl or aryl groups are attached to a divalent oxygen, known as **ethereal oxygen**. These are represented by the general formula $R—O—R'$ where R may be alkyl or aryl groups. e.g.

Simple ethers $CH_3—O—CH_3$, $C_2H_5—O—C_2H_5$
                 dimethyl ether   diethyl ether
Mixed ethers $CH_3—O—C_2H_5$, $CH_3—O—C_3H_7$
                 ethyl methyl ether   methyl n-propyl ether

These are the functional isomers of alcohols. These also exhibit chain isomerism and metamerism.

Structure of Ether

The hybridisation of O atom in ethers is sp^3 (tetrahedral) and its shape is V-shape.

For dimetnyl ether

$$H_3C \overset{\displaystyle \ddot{O}}{\underset{117.7°}{\diagup \diagdown}} CH_3$$

Nomenclature of Ethers

In the IUPAC system, ethers are regarded as 'alkoxyalkanes' in which the ethereal oxygen is taken along with smaller alkyl group while the bigger alkyl group is regarded as a part of the alkane.

Preparation of Ethers

(i) **By dehydration of alcohols**

$$2CH_3CH_2\!-\!OH \underset{excess}{\xrightarrow[413\,K]{H_2SO_4\ (conc.)}} CH_3\!-\!CH_2\!-\!\overset{..}{\underset{..}{O}}\!-\!CH_2\!-\!CH_3 + H_2O$$

Mechanism

I. $CH_3\!-\!CH_2\!-\!\overset{..}{\underset{..}{O}}\!-\!H + H^+ \longrightarrow CH_3CH_2\!-\!\overset{+}{\underset{}{O}}\!-\!H$
$$\xrightarrow[-H_2O]{} CH_3CH_2^+$$

II. $CH_3CH_2\!-\!\overset{..}{\underset{H}{O:}} + CH_3\!-\!CH_2^+ \longrightarrow CH_3CH_2\!-\!\overset{+}{\underset{H}{O}}\!-\!CH_2CH_3$

III. $CH_3CH_2\!-\!\overset{+}{\underset{H}{O}}\!-\!CH_2CH_3 \longrightarrow C_2H_5\!-\!O\!-\!C_2H_5 + H^+$

(ii) **Williamson's synthesis** Only primary alkyl halides when react with sodium alkoxide give ether while tertiary alkyl halides give alkene due to steric hindrance.

$$CH_3CH_2Br + CH_3CH_2\overset{-}{O}\overset{+}{N}a \longrightarrow CH_3CH_2OCH_2CH_3 + NaBr$$

$$\underset{CH_3}{\overset{CH_3}{H_3C\!-\!\overset{|}{\underset{|}{C}}\!-\!\overset{-}{O}\overset{+}{Na}}} + CH_3Br \longrightarrow CH_3\!-\!\overset{..}{\underset{..}{O}}\!-\!\underset{CH_3}{\overset{CH_3}{\overset{|}{\underset{|}{C}}\!-\!CH_3}} + NaBr$$

$$\underset{CH_3}{\overset{CH_3}{H_3C\!-\!\overset{|}{\underset{|}{C}}\!-\!Br}} + N\overset{+}{a}\!-\!\overset{-}{O}C_2H_5 \longrightarrow CH_3\!-\!\underset{CH_3}{\overset{|}{C}}\!=\!CH_2$$

$$+ NaBr + C_2H_5OH$$

alkoxy benzene

Physical Properties of Ethers

(i) Ethers are polar but insoluble in H_2O.

(ii) They have low boiling point than alcohols of comparable molecular masses because ethers do not form hydrogen bonds with water.

(iii) Dimethyl ether and ethyl methyl ether are both gases.

Chemical Reactions of Ether

(i) **Reaction with H*X***

$$R—O—R + HX \longrightarrow RX + R—OH$$

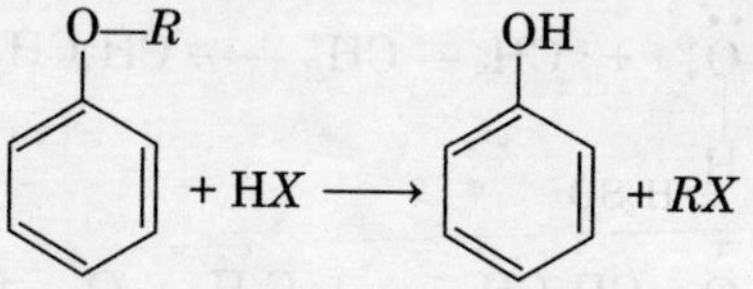

Ethers with two different alkyl groups are also cleaved in the same manner and results in the formation of a primary halide (or smaller and less complex alkyl halide) by S_N2 mechanism.

$$R—O—R' + HX \longrightarrow RX + R'OH$$

The order of reactivity of hydrogen halides is as follows

$$HI > HBr > HCl$$

In ethers if one of the alkyl groups is a tertiary group, the halide formed is a tertiary halide by S_N1 mechanism.

$$CH_3—\underset{CH_3}{\overset{CH_3}{\underset{|}{\overset{|}{C}}}}—O—CH_3 + HI \longrightarrow CH_3—OH + CH_3—\underset{CH_3}{\overset{CH_3}{\underset{|}{\overset{|}{C}}}}—I$$

(ii) **Halogenation**

$$CH_3CH_2OCH_2CH_3 \xrightarrow[\text{Dark}]{Cl_2} \underset{(\alpha\text{-monochloro diethyl ether})}{CH_3CHClOCH_2CH_3}$$

$$C_2H_5OC_2H_5 + \underset{(\text{excess})}{10Cl_2} \xrightarrow[(\text{light})]{h\nu} \underset{(\text{perchlorodiethyl ether})}{C_2Cl_5OC_2Cl_5} + 10HCl$$

(iii) **Reaction with PCl_5**

$$R—O—R + PCl_5 \xrightarrow{\Delta} 2RCl + POCl_3$$

(iv) **Reaction with CO**

$$ROR + CO \xrightarrow[500\text{ atm}]{BF_3/150°C} RCOOR$$

(v) **Electrophilic substitution reactions** In ethers, —OR is *ortho, para* directing group and activates the aromatic ring towards electrophilic substitution reaction.

Ethyl phenyl ester $C_6H_5OC_2H_5$ is also, known as phenetole.

Uses of Ethers

1. Dimethyl ether is used as refrigerant and as a solvent at low temperature.

2. Diethylether is used as an anaesthesia in surgery.

28

Aldehydes, Ketones and Carboxylic Acids

Aldehydes and Ketones

In aldehydes, the **carbonyl group** ($>C=O$) is bonded to carbon and hydrogen, while in the ketones, it is bonded to two carbon atoms.

Nature of Carbonyl Group

The carbon and oxygen of the carbonyl group are sp^2-hybridised and the carbonyl double bond contains one σ-bond and one π-bond.

$$\overset{120°}{>}C=\ddot{\ddot{O}} \longleftrightarrow >\overset{+}{C}-\overset{-}{\ddot{\ddot{O}}} \text{ or } >\overset{\delta+}{C}=\overset{\delta-}{\ddot{O}}$$

The electronegativity of oxygen is much higher than that of the carbon, so their electron cloud is shifted towards the oxygen. Therefore, C—O bond is polar in nature.

Nomenclature

(i) **Nomenclature of aldehydes** In IUPAC system, the suffix 'e' of alkane is replaced by the suffix 'al'. e.g.

Compound	Common name	IUPAC name
HCHO	Formaldehyde	Methanal
CH_3CHO	Acetaldehyde	Ethanal

(ii) **Nomenclature of ketones**   In IUPAC system, the suffix "e" of alkane is replaced by 'one'. e.g.

Compound	Common name	IUPAC name
$H_3C \cdot COCH_3$	Dimethyl ketone (acetone)	Propanone
$H_3C \cdot COC_2H_5$	Ethyl methyl ketone	Butanone

Preparation of Aldehydes and Ketones

(i) **By oxidation of alcohols**   Aldehydes and ketones are generally prepared by oxidation of primary and secondary alcohols, respectively.

$$RCH_2OH \xrightarrow{CrO_3} RCHO$$

$$R{-}\underset{\underset{OH}{|}}{CH}{-}R' \xrightarrow{CrO_3} R{-}\underset{\underset{O}{\|}}{C}{-}R'$$

(ii) **By dehydrogenation of alcohols**   In this method, alcohol vapours are passed over heavy metal catalysts (Ag or Cu). Primary and secondary alcohols give aldehydes and ketones.

$$R{-}CH_2{-}OH \xrightarrow[573\ K]{Cu} RCHO$$

$$R{-}\underset{\underset{OH}{|}}{CH}{-}R' \xrightarrow[573\ K]{Cu} R{-}\underset{\underset{O}{\|}}{C}{-}R'$$

(iii) **By ozonolysis of alkenes**

$$R{-}CH \overset{O\ |\ O}{=\!\!=} CH{-}R \xrightarrow[(ii)\ Zn/H_2O]{(i)\ O_3} 2RCHO$$

benzaldehyde   cyclohexanone

(iv) **By hydration of alkynes**   Acetylene on hydration gives acetaldehyde and other alkynes on hydration give ketones.

$$\underset{\text{acetylene}}{CH{\equiv}CH} + H_2O \xrightarrow[H_2SO_4]{HgSO_4} CH_3{-}\underset{\underset{O}{\|}}{C}{-}H$$

acetaldehyde

$$R-C{\equiv}CH + H_2O \xrightarrow[H_2SO_4]{HgSO_4} \underset{\text{ketone}}{R-\overset{\displaystyle O}{\overset{\displaystyle \|}{C}}-CH_3}$$
$$\underset{\text{alkyne}}{R-C{\equiv}CH + H_2O}$$

(v) By heating Ca salt of acid

$$(RCOO)_2Ca \xrightarrow{\Delta} RCOR + CaCO_3$$

To obtain aldehyde, calcium formate and any other Ca salt of acid are heated.

$$(RCOO)_2Ca + (HCOO)_2Ca \xrightarrow{\Delta} 2RCHO + 2CaCO_3$$

(vi) By decarboxylation and dehydration of aromatic acids

$$C_6H_5COOH + HCOOH \xrightarrow[300°C]{MnO} C_6H_5CHO + H_2O + CO_2$$

$$C_6H_5COOH + CH_3COOH \xrightarrow[100°C]{MnO} C_6H_5COCH_3 + H_2O + CO_2$$

(vii) From *gem*-dihalides

$$CH_3CH\begin{matrix} \diagup Cl \\ \diagdown Cl \end{matrix} + 2KOH\,(aq) \xrightarrow{-2KCl} CH_3CH(OH)_2$$

1, 1-dichloromethane
(*gem*-dihalide)

$$\downarrow -H_2O$$

$$CH_3CHO$$

Preparation of Aldehydes only (Other than Ketones)

(i) Rosenmund reduction

benzoyl chloride   benzaldehyde

$$\xrightarrow[Pd\text{-}BaSO_4]{H_2}$$

Formaldehyde cannot be prepared by this method as HCOCl is highly unstable.

(ii) From nitriles and esters

$$RCN + SnCl_2 + HCl \xrightarrow{dry\ ether} RCH{=}NH \xrightarrow{H_3O^+} RCHO$$

This reaction is called **Stephen reaction**.

Alternatively, nitriles are selectively reduced by diisobutylaluminium hydride, [DiBAL-H] to imines which on hydrolysis give aldehydes.

$$RCN \xrightarrow[\text{(ii) H}_2\text{O}]{\text{(i) AlH(iBu)}_2} RCHO$$

Similarly, esters can also reduced to aldehydes with DiBAL-H.

$$CH_3(CH_2)_9\overset{\overset{\displaystyle O}{\|}}{C}\!-\!OC_2H_5 \xrightarrow[\text{(ii) H}_2\text{O}]{\text{(i) DiBAL-H}} CH_3(CH_2)_9\overset{\overset{\displaystyle O}{\|}}{C}\!-\!H$$

(iii) **Etard reaction**

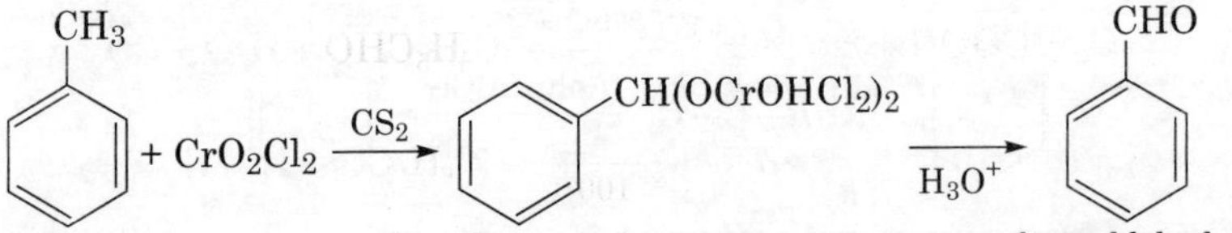

toluene   chromium complex   benzaldehyde

(iv) **Side chain halogenation followed by hydrolysis of toluene**

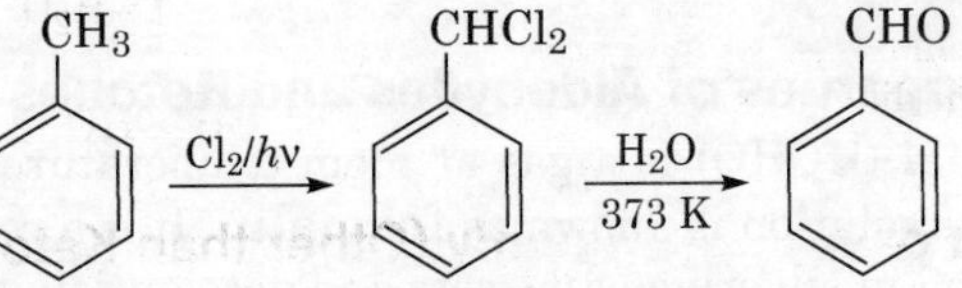

(v) **Gattermann-Koch synthesis**

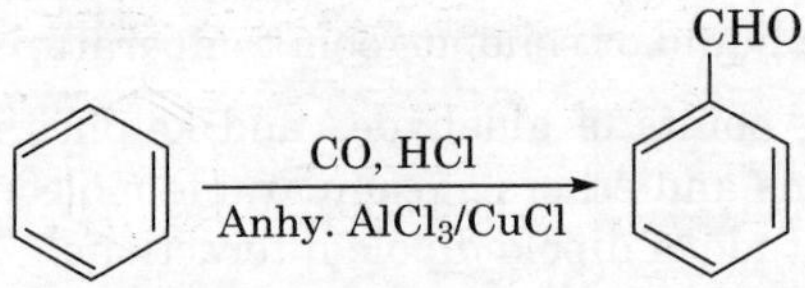

Preparation of Ketones only (Other than Aldehydes)

(i) **From acyl chlorides**

$$2R\!-\!Mg\!-\!X + CdCl_2 \xrightarrow{\text{dry ether}} R_2Cd + 2Mg\!\!\begin{smallmatrix} X \\ \\ Cl \end{smallmatrix}$$

$$2R'\!-\!\overset{\overset{\displaystyle }{\|}}{\underset{\displaystyle O}{C}}\!-\!Cl + R_2Cd \xrightarrow{\text{dry ether}} 2R'\!-\!\overset{\overset{\displaystyle }{\|}}{\underset{\displaystyle O}{C}}\!-\!R + CdCl_2$$

(ii) From nitriles

$$CH_3-CH_2-C\equiv N + C_6H_5MgBr \xrightarrow{\text{ether}} CH_3CH_2-C \overset{NMgBr}{\underset{C_6H_5}{\big<}}$$

$$\xrightarrow[-Mg(OH)Br]{-NH_3} \Big\downarrow H_3O^+$$

$$C_2H_5-C \overset{O}{\underset{C_6H_5}{\big<}}$$
(1-phenylpropanone)

(iii) Friedel-Crafts acylation

(iv) Oppenauer oxidation

$$R_2CHOH + (CH_3)_2C=O \xrightarrow{[(CH_3)_3CO]_3Al} R_2C=O + (CH_3)_2CHOH$$
2° alcohol   ketone   *iso*-propyl
                                    alcohol

Physical Properties of Aldehydes and Ketones

1. Methanal (HCHO) is a gas at room temperature, and its 40% aqueous solution is known as **formalin**. It is a reducing agent, it is used in silvering of mirrors and decolourising vat dyes.

2. Ethanal (CH_3CHO) is a volatile liquid. Other aldehydes and ketones are liquid or solid at room temperature.

3. The boiling points of aldehydes and ketones are higher than hydrocarbons and ethers of comparable molecular mass due to high magnitude of dipole-dipole interactions.

4. Aldehydes and ketones have lower boiling point than those of alcohols of similar molecular masses due to absence of intermolecular hydrogen bonding.

5. The lower members of aldehydes and ketones are miscible with water due to the formation of hydrogen bond with water. However, the solubility decreases with increase in length of alkyl chain.

6. Acetophenone is a hypnotic (sleep producing drug) so used as a medicine under the name hypnone.

Chemical Reactions of Aldehydes and Ketones

1. Nucleophilic addition reactions

$$\overset{\delta+}{\underset{}{\diagdown}}C = \overset{\delta-}{O} + Nu^- \xrightarrow{\text{Slow}} \left[\overset{}{\underset{}{\diagdown}}C \overset{O^-}{\underset{Nu}{\diagup}} \right] \xrightarrow[E^+]{\text{Fast}} \overset{}{\underset{}{\diagdown}}C \overset{OE}{\underset{Nu}{\diagup}}$$

product

Reactivity order is

$$HCHO > CH_3CHO > C_2H_5CHO > CH_3 - \overset{O}{\overset{\|}{C}} - CH_3 >$$

$$C_2H_5 - \overset{O}{\overset{\|}{C}} - CH_3 > C_2H_5 - \overset{O}{\overset{\|}{C}} - C_2H_5 > (CH_3)_3 C - \overset{O}{\overset{\|}{C}} - C(CH_3)_3$$

It is due to $+I$ effect of alkyl groups which decreases the positive charge on carbonyl carbon and steric hinderance (The bulky alkyl group hinder the approach of nucleophile).

(i) Addition of hydrogen cyanide (HCN)

$$H - CN + \overset{\ominus}{O}H \rightleftharpoons :\overset{\ominus}{C}N + H_2O$$

$$\overset{}{\underset{}{\diagdown}}C = O + \overset{\ominus}{C}N \longrightarrow \left[\overset{}{\underset{}{\diagdown}}C = O \overset{O^-}{\underset{CN}{\diagup}} \right] \xrightarrow{H^+} \overset{}{\underset{}{\diagdown}}C \overset{OH}{\underset{CN}{\diagup}}$$

carbonyl   tetrahedral   cyanohydrin
compound   intermediate

(ii) Addition of sodium hydrogen sulphite

$$\overset{}{\underset{}{\diagdown}}C = O + NaHSO_3 \rightleftharpoons \overset{}{\underset{}{\diagdown}}C \overset{OSO_2Na}{\underset{OH}{\diagup}}$$

white crystalline solid

This reaction is used for the separation and purification of aldehydes and ketones. This is because the addition compound formed, is water soluble and can be converted back to the original carbonyl compound by treating with dilute mineral acid or alkali.

(iii) **Addition of Grignard reagent**

$$\diagup \hspace{-0.3em} C{=}O + \overset{\delta-}{R}{-}\overset{\delta+}{Mg}X \xrightarrow[\text{ether}]{\text{dry}} \left[\diagup \hspace{-0.3em} C \diagup \hspace{-0.3em} \begin{matrix} OMgX \\ R \end{matrix} \right]$$

$$\xrightarrow[\text{H}_2\text{O}]{\text{H}^+} \diagup \hspace{-0.3em} C \diagup \hspace{-0.3em} \begin{matrix} OH \\ R \end{matrix} + Mg(OH)X$$

The type of alcohol formed depends upon the aldehyde or ketone used (formaldehyde → 1° alcohols, other aldehydes → 2° alcohols and ketones → 3° alcohols).

(iv) **Addition of lower alcohols**

$$R{-}\underset{\underset{H}{|}}{C}{=}O \xrightarrow{R'\text{OH, HCl gas}} \left[R{-}CH \diagup \hspace{-0.3em} \begin{matrix} OR' \\ OH \end{matrix} \right] \xrightarrow[\text{H}^+]{R'\text{OH}}$$

hemiacetal

$$R{-}CH \diagup \hspace{-0.3em} \begin{matrix} OR' \\ OR' \end{matrix} + H_2O$$

acetal

$$\begin{matrix} R \\ R \end{matrix} \diagdown \hspace{-0.3em} C{=}O + \begin{matrix} CH_2{-}OH \\ | \\ CH_2{-}OH \end{matrix} \xrightarrow[\text{dil. HCl}]{\text{HCl gas}} \begin{matrix} R \\ R \end{matrix} \diagdown \hspace{-0.3em} C \diagup \hspace{-0.3em} \begin{matrix} O{-}CH_2 \\ | \\ O{-}CH_2 \end{matrix} + H_2O$$

ethylene glycol ketal

(v) **Addition of ammonia and its derivatives**

Reaction with ammonia

$$\underset{\text{formaldehyde}}{6HCHO} + 4NH_3 \longrightarrow \underset{\substack{\text{hexamethylene} \\ \text{tetramine (urotropine)}}}{(CH_2)_6N_4} + 6H_2O$$

Urotropine on controlled nitration gives the well known explosive RDX (Research and development explosive).

$$\underset{\text{acetaldehyde}}{CH_3CHO} + NH_3 \longrightarrow \underset{\text{adduct}}{\begin{matrix} H_3C \\ H \end{matrix} \diagdown \hspace{-0.3em} C \diagup \hspace{-0.3em} \begin{matrix} OH \\ NH_2 \end{matrix}} \xrightarrow[-H_2O]{\Delta} \underset{\text{acetaldimine}}{\begin{matrix} H_3C \\ H \end{matrix} \diagdown \hspace{-0.3em} C{=}NH}$$

$$\underset{\text{acetone}}{2CH_3COCH_3} + NH_3 \longrightarrow \underset{\text{diacetonamine}}{\begin{matrix} H_3C \\ H_3C \end{matrix} \diagdown \hspace{-0.3em} C \diagup \hspace{-0.3em} \begin{matrix} NH_2 \\ CH_2COCH_3 \end{matrix}}$$

$$RCHO + RNH_2 \longrightarrow \underset{\text{Schiff's base}}{RCH{=}NR}$$

2. Nucleophilic Addition Eliminaiton Reactions

$$\ce{>C=O + H2N-Z <=> \left[>C< \substack{OH \\ NHZ} \right] -> >C=N-Z + H2O}$$

where, Z = alkyl, aryl, —OH, —NH$_2$, —C$_6$H$_5$NH, —NHCONH$_2$ etc.

Some N-substituted Derivatives of Aldehydes and Ketones

Z	Reagent name	Carbonyl derivative	Product name
—R	Amine	>C=N—R	Substituted imine (Schiff's base)
—OH	Hydroxyl amine	>C=N—OH	Oxime
—NH$_2$	Hydrazine	>C=N—NH$_2$	Hydrazone
—NH—⟨benzene ring⟩	Phenyl-hydrazine	>C=N—NH—⟨benzene ring⟩	Phenylhydrazone
—NH—⟨ring with NO$_2$, NO$_2$⟩	2,4-dinitro-phenyl hydrazine	>C=N—NH—⟨ring with NO$_2$, NO$_2$⟩	2,4-dinitro-phenyl hydrazone
—NH—C(=O)—NH$_2$	Semi-carbazide	>C=N—NH—C(=O)—NH$_2$	Semi-carbazone

3. Reduction

Aldehydes and ketones are reduced to primary and secondary alcohols respectively by sodium borohydride (NaBH$_4$) or lithium aluminium hydride [LiAlH$_4$].

Clemmensen reduction

$$\ce{>C=O ->[Zn\cdot Hg][HCl] >CH2 + H2O}$$

Wolff-Kishner reduction

$$\ce{>C=O ->[H2N NH2][-H2O] >C=N-NH2 ->[KOH/ethylene glycol][\Delta] >CH2 + N2}$$

4. Oxidation

Aldehydes get easily oxidised to carboxylic acids by HNO$_3$, KMnO$_4$, K$_2$Cr$_2$O$_7$, etc., or even by mild oxidising agent.

$$\ce{RCHO ->[[O]] RCOOH}$$

Ketones are generally oxidised under vigorous conditions, i.e. by strong oxidising agents and at elevated temperature.

$$R-\overset{1}{C}H_2-\overset{2}{\underset{\underset{O}{\|}}{C}}-\overset{3}{C}H_2-R' \xrightarrow{[O]} R-COOH + R'CH_2COOH$$
$$\text{(By cleavage of } C_1-C_2 \text{ bond)}$$

$$RCH_2COOH + R'COOH$$
$$\text{(By cleavage of } C_2-C_3 \text{ bond)}$$

During oxidation of unsymmetrical ketones the point of cleavage is such that keto group stays preferentially with the smaller alkyl group **(Popoff's rule).**

(i) **Tollen's test** Aldehydes give bright silver mirror with Tollen's reagent (ammoniacal silver nitrate).

$$RCHO + 2[Ag(NH_3)_2]^+ + 3OH^- \longrightarrow RCOO^- + \underset{\text{silver mirror}}{2Ag\downarrow}$$
$$+ 2H_2O + 4NH_3$$

(ii) **Fehling's test** Fehling solution gives a reddish brown precipitate with aldehydes. (except benzaldehyde)

$$R-CHO + 2Cu^{2+} + 5OH^- \longrightarrow RCOO^- + \underset{\text{red ppt.}}{Cu_2O\downarrow} + 3H_2O$$

[Fehling solution is a mixture of Fehling solution A and Fehling solution B in 1 : 1 ratio. Fehling solution A is aqueous copper sulphate and Fehling solution B is alkaline sodium potassium tartarate which is also called, Rochelle salt.]

(iii) **Benedict solution** With it, aldehydes (except benzaldehyde) also give red ppt. of Cu_2O.

(iv) **Schiff's reagent** It is an aqueous solution of magenta or pink coloured rosaniline hydrochloride which has been decolourised by passing SO_2. Aldehydes give pink colour with this reagent but ketones do not.

5. Haloform reaction Aldehydes and ketones having at least one methyl group [3-α hydrogen] linked to the carbonyl carbon atom (methyl ketones) are oxidised by sodium hypohalite to sodium salts of corresponding carboxylic acids having one carbon atom less than that of carbonyl compound. The methyl group is converted to haloform.

$$R-\overset{\overset{O}{\|}}{C}-CH_3 \xrightarrow{NaOX} R-\overset{\overset{O}{\|}}{C}-O\overset{-}{N}\overset{+}{a} + CHX_3\downarrow$$
$$[X = Cl, Br, I]$$

This oxidation does not affect a carbon-carbon double bond, if present in the molecule.

$$\underset{H_3C}{\overset{H}{>}}C=C\underset{C}{\overset{CH_3}{<}}\underset{O}{\overset{CH_3}{\diagdown}} \xrightarrow{\text{NaOCl}} \underset{H_3C}{\overset{H}{>}}C=C\underset{C}{\overset{CH_3}{<}}\underset{O}{\overset{\overset{-\ +}{ONa}}{\diagdown}} + CHCl_3$$

Iodoform reaction with sodium hypoiodite is also used for the detection of CH_3CO— group or $CH_3CH(OH)$— group by producing yellow solid CHI_3.

6. **Reactions due to α-Hydrogen**

   (i) **Aldol condensation**

$$2\,CH_3-\underset{\text{ethanal}}{CHO} \xrightarrow{\text{dil. NaOH}} CH_3\underset{\underset{OH}{|}}{CH}-CH_2-CHO \xrightarrow[\Delta]{-H_2O}$$

3-hydroxybutanal
(aldol)

$$\longrightarrow CH_3-\underset{\text{but-2-enal}}{CH=CHCHO}$$

$$2CH_3COCH_3 \xrightarrow{\text{dil. Ba(OH)}_2} CH_3-\underset{\underset{OH}{\overset{CH_3}{|}}}{\overset{CH_3}{\underset{|}{C}}}-CH_2COCH_3 \xrightarrow[-H_2O]{\Delta}$$

propanone

ketol

$$\longrightarrow CH_3-\overset{\overset{CH_3}{|}}{C}=CH-COCH_3$$

4-methylpent-3-en-2-one
(mesityl oxide)

Its further condensation gives phorone.

This reaction is exhibited by those aldehydes and ketones which have at least one α-hydrogen.

   (ii) **Cross aldol condensation** It is carried out between the two different aldehydes or ketones. It gives a mixture of four products.

$$CH_3-CHO + CH_3CH_2CHO \xrightarrow[\text{(ii) }\Delta]{\text{(i) NaOH}}$$

$$CH_3CH=CH-CHO + CH_3CH_2CH=\overset{\overset{}{|}}{C}-CHO$$

but-2-enal

$$CH_3$$

2-methylpent-2-enal
(self aldol products)

$$CH_3-CH_2-CH=CH-CHO \ + CH_3-CH=CCHO$$

pent-2-enal

$$\underset{CH_3}{|}$$

2-methylbut-2-enal
(cross aldol product)

Base catalysed crossed aldol condensation between an aromatic aldehyde and an aliphatic aldehyde or ketone is called **Claisen-Schmidt condensation** or **Claisen reaction**

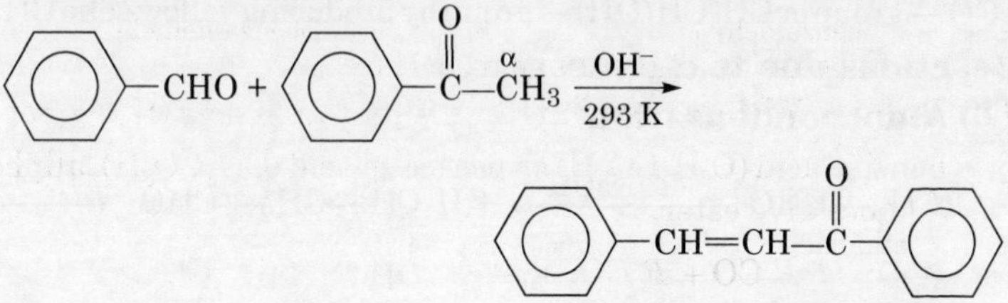

1,3-diphenylprop-2-en-1-one
(benzalacetophenone)
major product

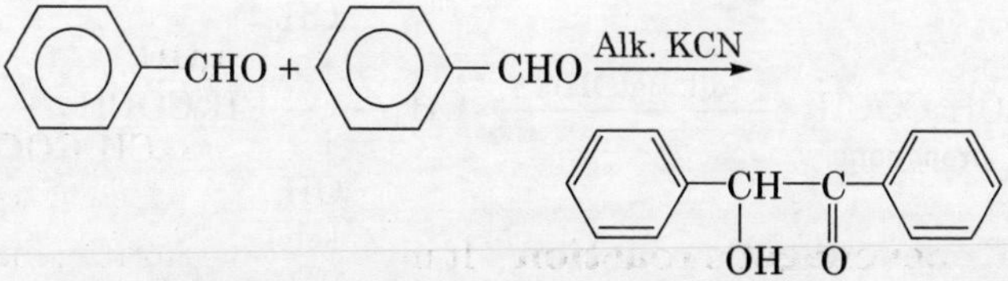

benzoin

The above reaction is called **Benzoin condensation**, not the cross aldol condensation.

7. Other Important Reactions

(i) Cannizzaro reaction

Aldehydes which do not have any α-hydrogen atom, undergo self oxidation and reduction (disproportionation) reaction on treatment with concentrated alkali.

$$2HCHO \xrightarrow{KOH \ (conc.)} CH_3OH + H-\overset{O}{\underset{}{C}}-O^{\ominus}K^{\oplus}$$

methanol   potassium formate

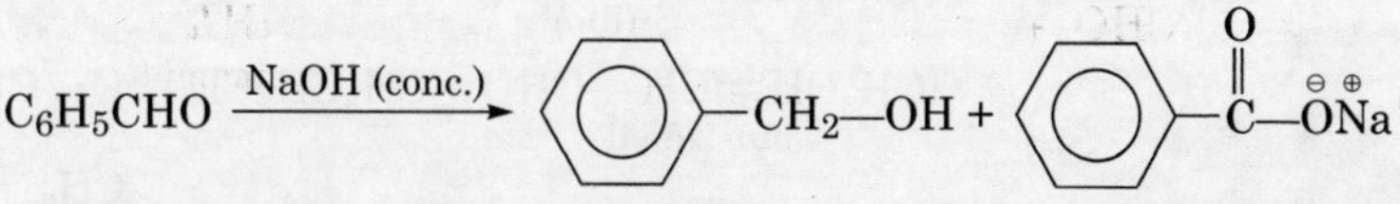

benzyl alcohol   sodium benzoate

(ii) **Electrophilic substitution reaction** Aromatic aldehydes and ketones undergo electrophilic substitution. Carbonyl group shows $+R$ effect, therefore acts as a deactivating and *meta* directing group.

benzaldehyde   *m*-nitrobenzaldehyde

(iii) **Baeyer-Villiger oxidation** With Caro's acid (H_2SO_5) or per benzoic acid ($C_6H_5CO_3H$) or peracetic acid (CH_3CO_3H), aliphatic ketones give ester.

$$R_2CO + R'CO_3H \longrightarrow RCOOR + R'COOH$$
$$\text{per acid}$$

(iv) **Tischenko's reaction** It is a modified form of Cannizzaro reaction.

$$2CH_3CHO \xrightarrow{(C_2H_5O)_3Al} CH_3COOH + C_2H_5OH$$

$$\xrightarrow{H_2SO_4} CH_3COOC_2H_5$$
$$\text{ethyl acetate}$$

(v) **Knoevenagel's reaction** It involves condensation between active methylene group and carbonyl groups in the presence of base.

$$RCH{=}O + H_2C \underset{COOH}{\overset{COOH}{\diagup}} \xrightarrow{-H_2O}$$
$$\text{malonic acid}$$

$$R{-}CH{=}C \underset{COOH}{\overset{COOH}{\diagup}} \xrightarrow[-CO_2]{\Delta} R{-}CH{=}CHCOOH$$
$$(X)$$

If $R = CH_3$, X is crotonic acid and if R is C_6H_5, X is cinnamic acid.

(vi) **Schmidt reaction**

$$RCHO + \underset{\text{hydrazoic acid}}{N_3H} \xrightarrow[\Delta]{\text{Conc. } H_2SO_4} \underset{\text{N-alkyl formamide}}{HCONHR} + N_2$$

(vii) **Reformatsky reaction**

$$R_2C{=}O + \underset{CH_2COOC_2H_5}{\overset{ZnBr}{|}} \longrightarrow R_2\underset{{}^-OZn^+Br}{\overset{|}{C}}CH_2COOC_2H_5$$

$$\overset{H_2O}{\longrightarrow} R_2\underset{OH}{\overset{|}{C}}{-}CH_2COOC_2H_5 \xrightarrow[\Delta]{conc.\ H_2SO_4} R_2C{=}CHCOOC_2H_5$$
$$\underset{\beta\text{-hydroxy ester}}{} \qquad\qquad \underset{\alpha,\,\beta\text{-unsaturated ester}}{}$$

(viii) **Perkin's reaction**

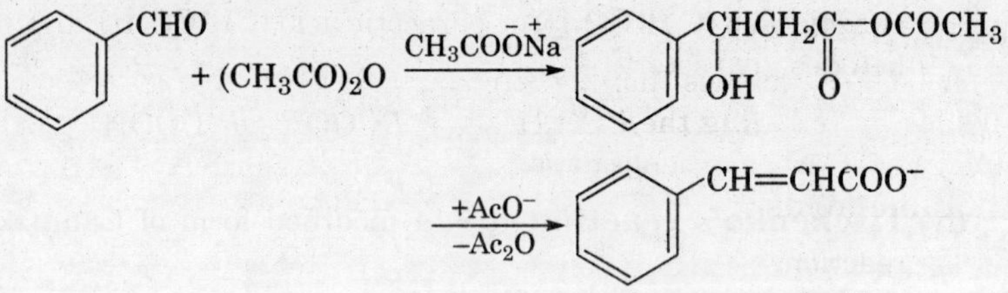

$$\alpha,\beta\text{-unsaturated acid}$$

(ix) **Wittig reaction**

$$\Large{>}C{=}O + PPh_3{=}CH_2 \longrightarrow {>}C{=}CH_2 + Ph_3P{=}O$$

(x) **Polymerisation**

$$nHCHO \rightleftharpoons \underset{paraformaldehyde}{(CH_2O)_n}$$

$$3HCHO \rightleftharpoons \underset{meta\ formaldehyde\ or\ trioxane}{(HCHO)_3}$$

$$3CH_3CHO \rightleftharpoons \underset{paraldehyde\ (hypnotic,\ sleep\ producing)}{(CH_3CHO)_3}$$

$$4CH_3CHO \underset{or\ ionic\ H_2SO_4}{\overset{dryHCl\ gas}{\rightleftharpoons}} \underset{metaldehyde}{(CH_3CHO)_4}$$

Carboxylic Acids

These are the compounds which have $-\overset{\overset{\displaystyle O}{\|}}{C}-OH$ group [carboxyl group]. The word carboxyl is a combination of two words carbonyl ($>C{=}O$) and hydroxyl ($-OH$).

Classification

Depending upon the number of —COOH groups, they are classified as
(i) monocarboxylic acids ; containing one —COOH group
(ii) dicarboxylic acids : containing two —COOH groups.

Sources of carboxylic acids

Formula	Common name	Source
HCOOH	Formic acid	Red ant (formica)
CH_3COOH	Acetic acid	Vineger (acetum)
C_3H_7COOH	Butyric acid	Butter (butyrum)

Nomenclature

Their IUPAC names have been derived from the corresponding
alkanes by replacing the letter '*e*' of the alkane with 'oic' and adding
suffix 'acid' at the end. Thus, monocarboxylic acids are called
alkanoic acids.

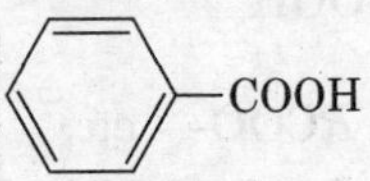

Benzene carboxylic acid
(Benzoic acid)

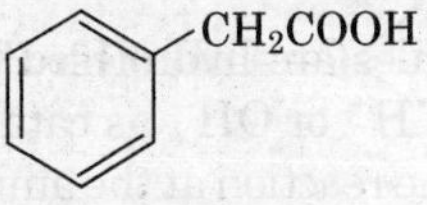

—COOH

2-phenylethanoic acid

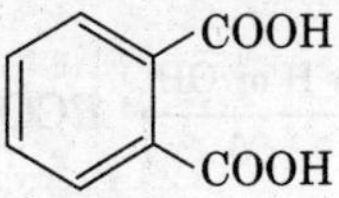

CH₂COOH

COOH
COOH

Benzene-1, 2-dicarboxylic
acid (phthalic acid)

Methods of Preparation of Monocarboxylic Acids

(i) From primary alcohols and aldehydes

$$RCH_2OH \xrightarrow[\text{(ii) } H_3O^+]{\text{(i) Alkaline KMnO}_4} R—COOH$$

$$CH_3(CH_2)_8CH_2OH \xrightarrow{CrO_3 \cdot H_2SO_4} CH_3(CH_2)_8COOH$$
decanoic acid

$$CH_3CHO \xrightarrow[\text{Tollen's reagent}]{[O]} CH_3COOH$$

(ii) **From alkyl benzenes** Alkyl benzene when treated with strong oxidising agent like H_2CrO_4 (chromic acid), acidic or alkaline $KMnO_4$ gives benzoic acid.

(iii) **From acid derivatives** All acid derivatives like amides ($RCONH_2$), acid halides ($RCOCl$), esters ($RCOOR'$), acid anhydrides (RCO—O—COR) on hydrolysis give carboxylic acids. All acid derivatives break from RCO^+.

$$RCOZ \xrightarrow[\text{or dil. NaOH}]{\text{dil. HCl}} RCOOH$$

$Z = $ —NH_2, —$X (X = Cl, Br, I), OR'$, $RCOO$— etc.

Ease of hydrolysis : $RCOCl > (RCO)_2O > RCOOR' > RCONH_2$

(iv) **From nitriles and amides** Nitriles are hydrolysed to amides and then to acids in the presence of H^+ or OH^- as catalyst. Mild reaction conditions are used to stop the reaction at the amide stage.

$$R—CN \xrightarrow[H_2O]{\overset{+}{H} \text{ or } \overset{-}{O}H} R—\overset{\overset{\displaystyle O}{\|}}{C}—NH_2 \xrightarrow[\Delta]{\overset{+}{H} \text{ or } \overset{-}{O}H} RCOOH$$

$$\underset{\text{ethanamide}}{CH_3CONH_2} \xrightarrow[\Delta]{H_3\overset{+}{O}} \underset{\text{ethanoic acid}}{CH_3COOH} + NH_3$$

(v) **From Grignard's reagent** Grignard's reagents react with carbon dioxide (dry ice) to form salts of carboxylic acids which in turn give corresponding carboxylic acids after acidification with mineral acid.

(vi) **By heating *geminal* dicarboxylic acids**

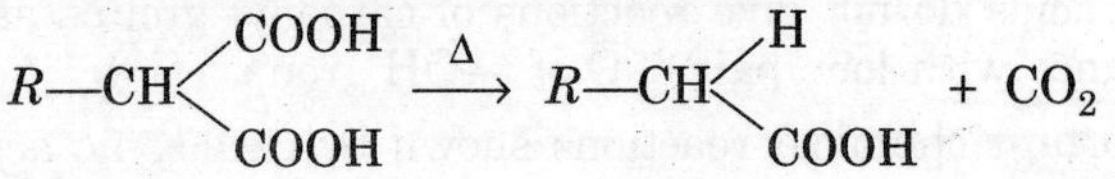

$$R-CH\begin{array}{c} COOH \\ \\ COOH \end{array} \xrightarrow{\Delta} R-CH\begin{array}{c} H \\ \\ COOH \end{array} + CO_2$$

(vii) **From alkynes**

$$R-C\equiv C-R \xrightarrow[KMnO_4/OH^-, \Delta]{(i)\ O_3\ (ii),\ H_2O_2\ or} 2RCOOH$$

Physical Properties of Carboxylic Acids

1. Aliphatic carboxylic acids up to nine carbon atoms are colourless liquids at room temperature with unpleasant odours. The higher acids are wax like solids.

2. The lower carboxylic acids are freely miscible with water due to the presence of intermolecular hydrogen bonding with H_2O molecules. However, the solubility in water decreases gradually due to increase in the size of alkyl group.

3. Monocarboxylic acids have higher boiling points as compared to the alcohols of comparable molecular masses due to the presence of stronger intermolecular hydrogen bonding as shown below.

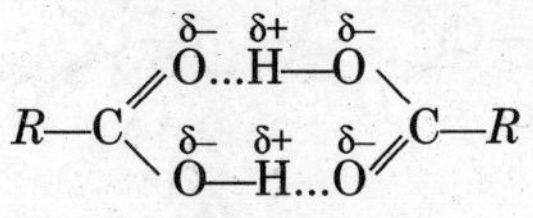

hydrogen bonding in carboxylic acids

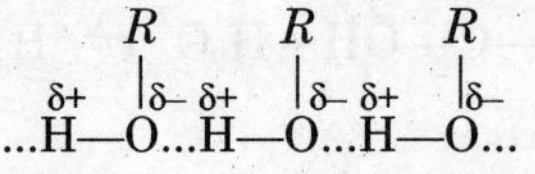

hydrogen bonding in alcohols

4. Melting points of aliphatic monocarboxylic acids shows alternation or oscillation effect, i.e. the m.p. of an acid with even number of carbon atoms is higher than the next lower and next higher homologue containing odd number of carbon atoms. This is because, in case of acids with even number of carbon atoms, the terminal $-CH_3$ and $-COOH$ groups lie on the opposite sides of the *zig-zag* chain. As a result, they get closely packed in the crystal lattice.

5. Glacial acetic acid is completely pure acetic acid and represents the solid state of acetic acid. Below $16.6°C$ temperature pure acetic acid is converted into ice like solid hence, it is called glacial acetic acid.

Chemical Properties of Carboxylic Acids

Carboxylic acids do not give reactions of carbonyl groups as it enters into resonance with lone pair of O of —OH group.

Some important chemical reactions shown by carboxylic acids are as follows :

1. Reaction Involving Cleavage of O—H Bond

$$\boxed{RCOOH}
\begin{cases}
\xrightarrow{\text{Na}} R\overset{\ominus}{C}OO\overset{\oplus}{N}a + \dfrac{1}{2}H_2 \\[2mm]
\xrightarrow{\text{Zn}} (RCOO)_2Zn + H_2 \\[2mm]
\xrightarrow{\text{NaOH}} R\overset{\ominus}{C}OO\overset{\oplus}{N}a + H_2O \\[2mm]
\xrightarrow{\text{NaHCO}_3} R\overset{\ominus}{C}OO\overset{\oplus}{N}a + CO_2 + H_2O \\[2mm]
\xrightarrow{\text{Na}_2\text{CO}_3} 2R\overset{\ominus}{C}OO\overset{\oplus}{N}a + CO_2 + H_2O
\end{cases}$$

Above reactions are used to detect the presence of carboxyl group in an organic compound.

Carboxylic acids dissociate in water to give resonance stabilised carboxylate anions and hydronium ion.

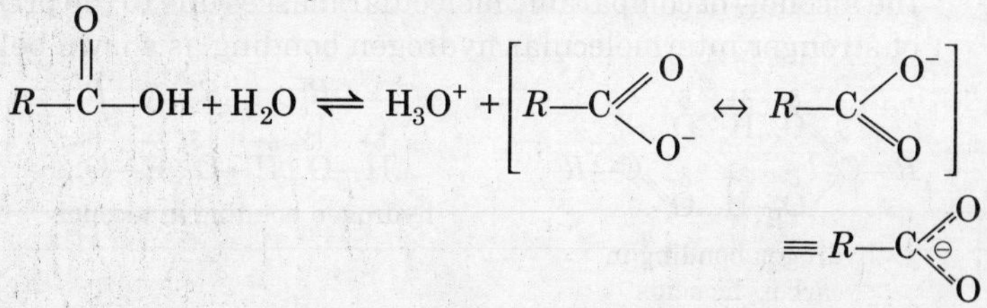

$$R-\overset{\overset{\displaystyle O}{\|}}{C}-OH + H_2O \rightleftharpoons H_3O^+ + \left[R-C\!\!\!\underset{O^-}{\overset{O}{\diagup}} \leftrightarrow R-C\!\!\!\underset{O}{\overset{O^-}{\diagup}} \right]$$

$$\equiv R-C\!\!\!\underset{O}{\overset{O}{\diagup}}{}^{\ominus}$$

The strength of the acid is expressed in terms of the dissociation constant (K_a), also called acidity constant. A stronger acid has higher K_a but lesser pK_a value $(pK_a = -\log K_a)$.

The electron releasing substituents (+I effect) **decrease the acidic strength** of the carboxylic acids by destabilising the carboxylate ion.

Order of + I effect : —H < —CH$_3$ < —C$_2$H$_5$ < —C$_3$H$_7$

Therefore, the order of acidic strength is

HCOOH > CH$_3$COOH > C$_2$H$_5$COOH > C$_3$H$_7$COOH

The electron withdrawing substituents (–I effect) such as halogen atoms (X), nitro (—NO$_2$) group increase the acidic strength by decreasing the magnitude of the negative charge on the carboxylate anion and thus stabilising it. The release of H$^+$ ion becomes easy.

Acidic strength order

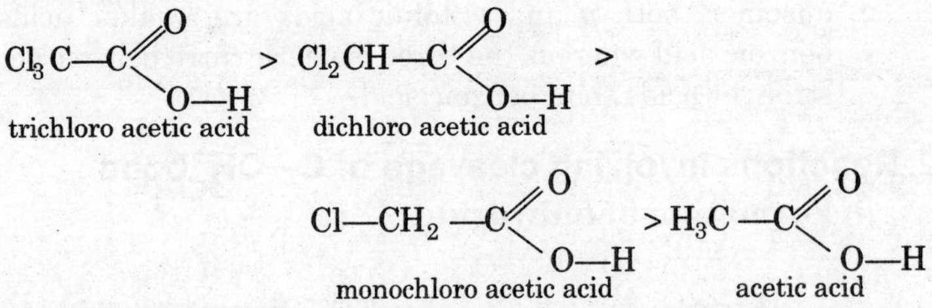

$$Cl_3C—C{\overset{O}{\underset{O—H}{}}} > Cl_2CH—C{\overset{O}{\underset{O—H}{}}} >$$

trichloro acetic acid   dichloro acetic acid

$$Cl—CH_2—C{\overset{O}{\underset{O—H}{}}} > H_3C—C{\overset{O}{\underset{O—H}{}}}$$

monochloro acetic acid   acetic acid

$$FCH_2COOH > ClCH_2COOH > BrCH_2COOH > ICH_2COOH$$

This is because $-I$ effect decreases in the order : F > Cl > Br > I.

$$CH_3—\overset{Cl}{\underset{\alpha}{CH}}—\overset{O}{C}—O—H > Cl—\overset{\beta}{CH_2}—CH_2—\overset{O}{C}—O—H$$

α-chloro propionic acid   β-chloro propionic acid

This is because $-I$ effect decreases with distance.

Per acetic acid (CH_3COOOH) is a weaker acid than acetic acid as acetate ion is stabilised by resonance.

Acidic strength of aromatic acids The parent member of the family is benzoic acid which is a weaker acid ($K_a = 6.3 \times 10^{-5}$) than formic acid ($K_a = 17.7 \times 10^{-5}$) but stronger than acetic acid.

Some important order of acidity of carboxylic acids are

(a)

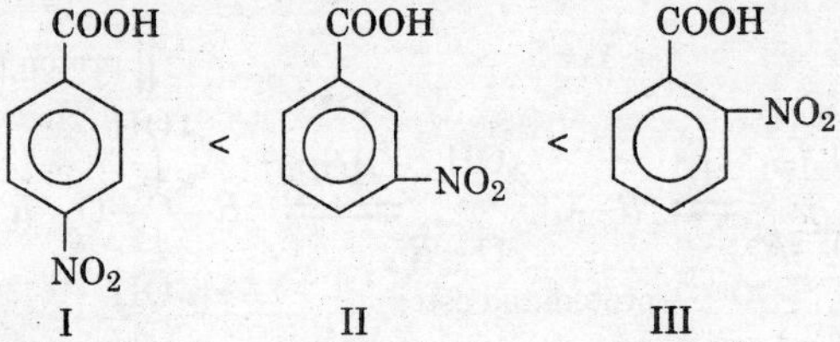

I   II   III
$K_a = 35.0 \times 10^{-5}$ 32.0×10^{-5} 600×10^{-5}

(b) Similarly, K_a values of methyl substituted (toluic acids) at 298 K are as follows :

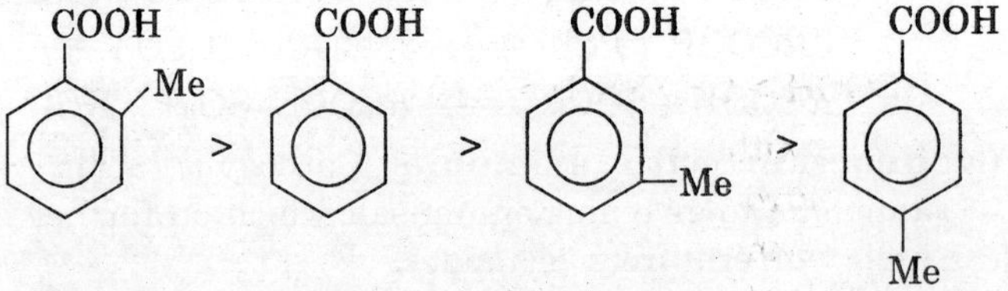

$K_a = 12.5 \times 10^{-5}$ 6.3×10^{-5} 5.5×10^{-5} 4.3×10^{-5}
(*ortho* effect)

From the K_a values, it is evident that with the exception of o-isomer, both p and m-toluic acids are weaker acids than benzoic acid whereas the three isomeric nitro benzoic acids are stronger acids than benzoic acid.

2. Reactions involving cleavage of C—OH bond

(i) Formation of anhydride

(ii) Esterification

$$RCOOH + R'OH \underset{}{\overset{H^+}{\rightleftharpoons}} RCOOR' + H_2O$$

Mechanism

(iii) Reactions with PCl$_5$, PCl$_3$ and SOCl$_2$

$$RCOOH + PCl_5 \longrightarrow RCOCl + POCl_3 + HCl$$
$$3RCOOH + PCl_3 \longrightarrow 3RCOCl + H_3PO_3$$
$$RCOOH + SOCl_2 \longrightarrow RCOCl + SO_2\uparrow + HCl\uparrow$$

(iv) Reaction with ammonia

Carboxylic acids react with ammonia to give ammonium salt which on further heating at high temperature give amides.

$$CH_3COOH + NH_3 \rightleftharpoons \underset{\text{ammonium acetate}}{CH_3CO\overset{-}{O}\overset{+}{N}H_4} \xrightarrow[-H_2O]{\Delta} \underset{\text{acetamide}}{CH_3CONH_2}$$

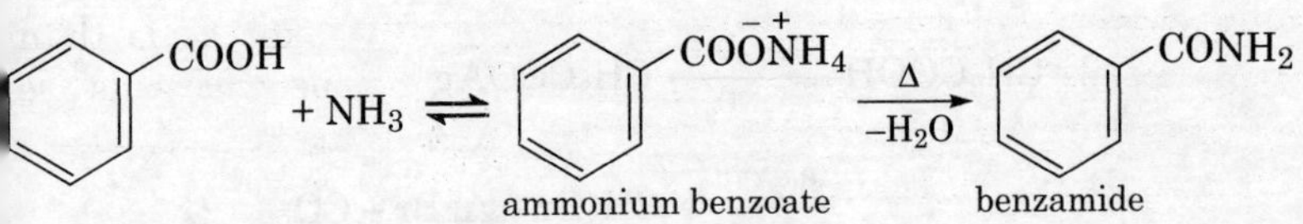
COOH
+ NH3
COONH4
Δ
–H2O
CONH2
ammonium benzoate
benzamide

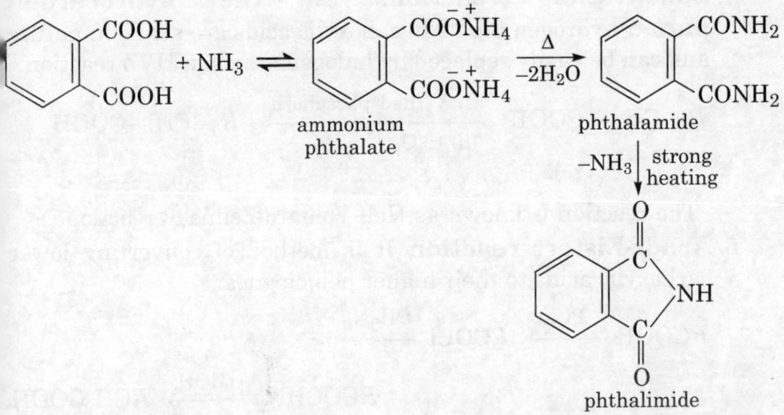
COOH
COOH
+ NH3
COONH4
COONH4
Δ
–2H2O
CONH2
CONH2
ammonium phthalate
phthalamide
–NH3
strong heating
O
C
NH
C
O
phthalimide

3. Chemical reactions involving —COOH group

(i) **Reduction**

$$RCOOH \xrightarrow[\text{or } B_2H_6 \text{ (ii) } H_3O^+]{\text{(i) } LiAlH_4/\text{ether}} R\text{—}CH_2\text{—}OH$$

(ii) **Decarboxylation**

- Using sodalime

$$RCO\overset{\ominus}{O}\overset{\oplus}{N}a \xrightarrow[\Delta]{\text{NaOH, CaO (Ratio 3 : 1)}} R\text{—}H + Na_2CO_3$$

- Electrolytic decarboxylation (Kolbe electrolysis)

$$2RCOONa \longrightarrow 2RCO\bar{O} + 2\overset{+}{Na}$$

$$2H_2O \longrightarrow 2\bar{O}H + 2\overset{+}{H}$$

(iii) Hunsdiecker reaction

$$CH_3COOH \xrightarrow[AgNO_3]{NH_4OH} CH_3COO\bar{O}\overset{+}{A}g$$

$$\xrightarrow{Br_2/CCl_4} CH_3Br + AgBr + CO_2$$

4. **Substitution reactions in the hydrocarbon part** α-hydrogen atoms in caboxylic acids are acidic in nature and can be easily replaced by halogen atoms in HVZ reaction

$$R—CH_2—COOH \xrightarrow[\text{(ii) } H_2O]{\text{(i) } X_2/\text{Red phosphorus}} R—\underset{X}{CH}—COOH$$

The reaction is known as Hell-Volhard-Zelinsky reaction.

5. **Arndt-Eistert reaction** It is method of converting lower carboxylic acids to their higher homologues.

$$RCOOH \xrightarrow{PCl_5} RCOCl \xrightarrow{CH_2N_2}$$

$$\underset{\text{diazo ketone}}{RCOCHN_2} \xrightarrow{HOH} RCH_2COOH$$

5. **Reducing property** Among carboxylic acids, formic acid is the only acid that acts as reducing agent. It reduces, acidified $KMnO_4$ to $MnSO_4$, $HgCl_2$ to Hg, Tollen's reagent to silver mirror and Fehling's solution to red ppt. and itself gets oxidised to CO_2 and H_2O.

$$HCOOH + HgCl_2 \longrightarrow Hg + 2HCl + CO_2$$

7. **Electrophilic substitution reactions of aromatic acids** —COOH group shows $-R$ effect, therefore, acts as a deactivating and *meta*-directing group. Carboxylic acids do not undergo Friedel-Craft's reaction because the carboxylic group is deactivating and the catalyst $AlCl_3$ (anhy.) gets bonded to the carboxyl group.

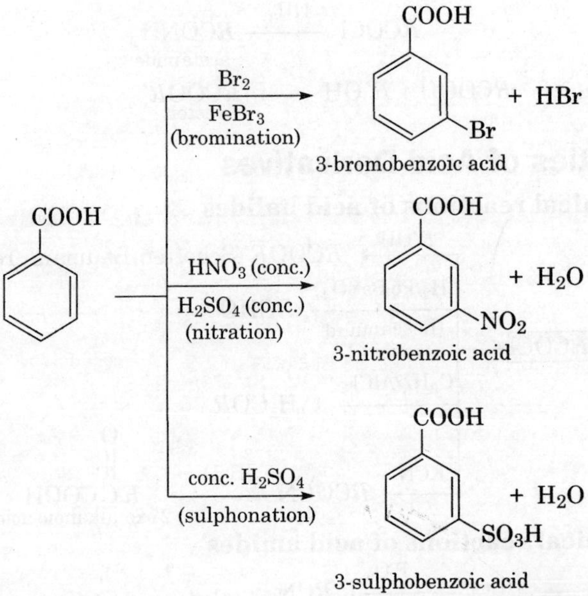

3-bromobenzoic acid

3-nitrobenzoic acid

3-sulphobenzoic acid

Uses

1. Formic acid is used in leather tanning, textile dyeing and finishing.
2. Acetic acid is used in the manufacture of rayon and in plastics, in rubber and silk industries, in cooking and in vinegar (a 8-10% solution of acetic acid).
3. Benzoic acid and its salts are used as urinary antiseptics.
4. Formic acid can act as a reducing agent.

Derivatives of Carboxylic Acids

These are obtained when —OH group of carboxylic acids is replaced by Cl, NH_2, OR' and $OCOR$ and are called respectively acid chloride, acid amide, ester and acid anhydride.

$$RCOCl \xrightarrow{NH_3} \underset{\text{acetamide}}{RCONH_2}$$

$$RCOOH + R'OH \longrightarrow \underset{\text{ester}}{RCOOR'}$$

Properties of Acid Derivatives

1. Chemical reactions of acid halides

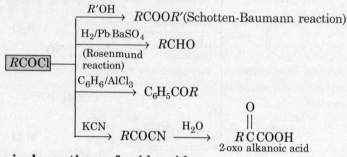

$$RCOCl
\begin{cases}
\xrightarrow{R'OH} RCOOR' \text{(Schotten-Baumann reaction)} \\
\xrightarrow[\substack{\text{(Rosenmund} \\ \text{reaction)}}]{H_2/Pb\cdot BaSO_4} RCHO \\
\xrightarrow{C_6H_6/AlCl_3} C_6H_5COR \\
\xrightarrow{KCN} RCOCN \xrightarrow{H_2O} \underset{\text{2-oxo alkanoic acid}}{R\overset{O}{\overset{||}{C}}COOH}
\end{cases}$$

2. Chemical reactions of acid amides

$$RCONH_2
\begin{cases}
\xrightarrow[\Delta]{P_2O_5} RCN \\
\xrightarrow{NaNO_2 + HCl} RCOOH \\
\xrightarrow[\text{(Hofmann bromamide reaction)}]{Br_2/KOH} RNH_2 \\
\xrightarrow{LiAlH_4} RCH_2NH_2 \\
\xrightarrow{H_3O^+} RCOOH + NH_4^+
\end{cases}$$

3. Chemical reactions of ester

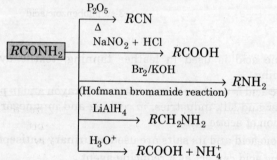

$$RCOOR
\begin{cases}
\xrightarrow{NaOH} RCOO^{\ominus}N^{\oplus}a + R'OH \text{ (saponification)} \\
\xrightarrow{NH_3} RCONH_2 + R'OH \\
\xrightarrow[\text{or Na-C}_2\text{H}_5\text{OH}]{LiAlH_4} RCH_2OH + R'OH
\end{cases}$$

4. Chemical reactions of anhydrides

$$(RCO)_2O
\begin{cases}
\xrightarrow{R'OH} RCOOR' + RCOOH \\
\xrightarrow{C_6H_6/AlCl_3} C_6H_5COR + RCOOH \\
\xrightarrow{C_2H_5NH_2} RCONC_2H_5 + RCOOH
\end{cases}$$

29
Amines

Amines constitute an important class of organic compounds derived by replacing one or more hydrogen atoms of NH_3 molecule by alkyl/aryl group(s).

$$R—NH_2 \qquad R—NH—R \qquad R—N—R \qquad C_6H_5—NH_2$$

primary (1°) secondary (2°) tertiary (3°) aromatic amine

with R below the tertiary nitrogen.

In the IUPAC system, the amines are named as alkanamines, e.g.

$$CH_3—CH_2—NH_2, \quad CH_3CH_2—NH—CH_3, \quad CH_3—CH_2—N\begin{smallmatrix}C_2H_5\\C_2H_5\end{smallmatrix}$$

ethanamine   N-methyl ethanamine   N,N-diethylethanamine

Structure

The nitrogen atom in amine is sp^3-hybridised. The three hybrid orbitals are involved in bond formation and one hybrid atomic orbital contains the lone pair of electrons, giving the pyramidal geometry of amines.

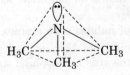

In arylamines, $—NH_2$ group is directly attached to the benzene ring.

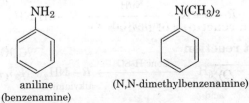

aniline
(benzenamine)

(N,N-dimethylbenzenamine)

Methods of Preparation of Amines

(i) Reduction of nitro compounds

$$R\text{—}NO_2 \xrightarrow[\text{Reduction}]{\text{Raney Ni/Pt}} R\text{—}NH_2 + 2H_2O$$

Reduction can take place by Sn/HCl, Ni/H$_2$, Zn/NaOH, Pd/H$_2$.

The reduction of nitroalkane or nitrobenzene in neutral medium gives hydroxyl amine.

(ii) Ammonolysis of alkyl halides

$$\overset{\bullet\bullet}{N}H_3 + R\text{—}X \longrightarrow R\text{—}\overset{+}{N}H_3X^-$$
$$\text{substituted ammonium salt}$$

$$R\text{—}\overset{+}{N}H_3\bar{X} + NaOH \longrightarrow R\text{—}NH_2 + H_2O + Na^+X^-$$

$$\underset{(1°)}{RNH_2} \xrightarrow{RX} \underset{(2°)}{R_2NH} \xrightarrow{RX} \underset{(3°)}{R_3N} \xrightarrow{RX} \underset{\substack{\text{quaternary} \\ \text{ammonium} \\ \text{salt}}}{R_4N^+X^-}$$

Ammonolysis has the disadvantage of yielding a mixture of primary, secondary and tertiary amines and also a quaternary ammonium salt.

However, primary amine is obtained as a major product by taking excess of NH$_3$.

Order of reactivity of halides with amines is RI > RBr > RCl.

Aromatic amines could not be prepared since aryl halides are much less reactive towards nucleophilic substitution reactions.

(iii) Reduction of nitriles or cyanides

$$R\text{—}C\equiv N \xrightarrow[\text{Na(Hg)/C}_2\text{H}_5\text{OH}]{\text{Ni/H}_2} R\text{—}CH_2NH_2$$

(iv) Schmidt reaction

$$RCOOH + \underset{\substack{\text{hydrazoic} \\ \text{acid}}}{N_3H} \xrightarrow{\text{Conc H}_2\text{SO}_4} \underset{\text{alkylamine}}{R\text{—}NH_2} + N_2\uparrow + CO_2$$

It is a modification of Curtius degradation.

(v) Reduction of amides

$$R-\overset{\overset{\displaystyle O}{\|}}{C}-NH_2 \xrightarrow[\text{(ii) } H_2O]{\text{(i) } LiAlH_4} R-CH_2NH_2$$

(vi) Gabriel's phthalimide reaction

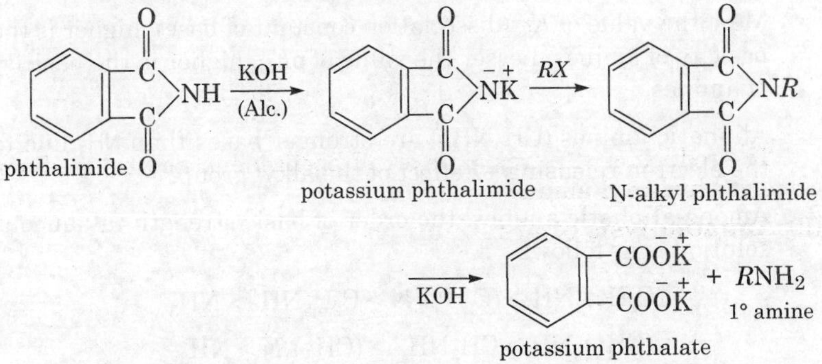

phthalimide

potassium phthalimide

N-alkyl phthalimide

potassium phthalate

1° amine

It only produces 1° amines. This method is not suitable for 1° arylamine because aryl halide does not give nucleophilic substitution reaction.

(viii) Hofmann bromamide degradation reaction

$$R-\overset{\overset{\displaystyle O}{\|}}{C}-NH_2 + Br_2 + 4NaOH \longrightarrow RNH_2 + Na_2CO_3$$
$$+ 2NaBr + 2H_2O$$

In Hofmann degradation reaction, the amine formed has one carbon less than the parent amide. To obtain primary amine with same number of carbon atoms from primary amide, reduction is done with LiAlH$_4$/ether.

Physical Properties of Amines

1. The lower aliphatic amines are gases with fishy smell.

2. Primary amines with three or more carbon atoms are liquid and higher members are all solids.

3. Lower aliphatic amines are water soluble because they can form hydrogen bonds with water molecules, however the solubility decreases with increase of hydrophobic alkyl group/chain.

4. Boiling point order is :

   primary > secondary > tertiary

5. Tertiary amine does not have intermolecular association due to the absence of hydrogen atom available for hydrogen bond formation.

Chemical Properties of Amines

(i) **Basic Strength of Amines** Amines act as Lewis bases due to the presence of lone pair of electrons on the nitrogen atom.

More the value of K_b (dissociation constant of base), higher is the basicity of amines. Lesser the value of pK_b, higher is the basicity of amines.

Aliphatic amines (CH_3NH_2) are stronger bases than NH_3 due to the electron releasing $+I$ effect of the alkyl group.

Among aliphatic amines, the order of basic strength in aqueous solution is as follows

$$(C_2H_5)_2NH > (C_2H_5)_3N > C_2H_5NH_2 > NH_3$$

$$(CH_3)_2NH > CH_3NH_2 > (CH_3)_3N > NH_3$$

Aromatic amines are weaker bases than aliphatic amines and NH_3, due to the fact that the electron pair on the nitrogen atom is involved in resonance with the π-electron pairs of the ring.

Electron releasing groups (e.g $-CH_3, -OCH_3, -NH_2$ etc.) increase the basic strength of aromatic amines while electron withdrawing groups (like $-NO_2, -X, -CN$ etc.) tend to decrease the same.

o-substituted aromatic amines are usually weaker bases than aniline irrespective of the nature of substituent whether electron releasing or electron withdrawing. This is called *ortho* effect and is probably due to steric and electronic factors.

(ii) **Alkylation** All the three types of amines react with alkyl halides to form quaternary ammonium salt as the final product provided alkyl halide is present in excess.

$$C_2H_5NH_2 + C_2H_5Br \xrightarrow{-HBr} (C_2H_5)_2NH \xrightarrow[-HBr]{C_2H_5Br} (C_2H_5)_3\overset{\bullet\bullet}{N}$$

$$\downarrow C_2H_5Br$$

$$(C_2H_5)_4 \overset{+}{N}Br^-$$

Aromatic amines also undergo alkylation as given below :

$$\underset{}{\text{NH}_2}\quad\xrightarrow{\text{C}_2\text{H}_5\text{Cl}}\quad\underset{}{\text{NHC}_2\text{H}_5}\quad\xrightarrow[\text{C}_2\text{H}_5\text{Br}]{-\text{HBr}}\quad\underset{}{\ddot{\text{N}}(\text{C}_2\text{H}_5)_2}\quad\xrightarrow{\text{C}_2\text{H}_5\text{Br}}\quad\underset{\substack{\text{triethylanilinium}\\\text{bromide}}}{\overset{+}{\ddot{\text{N}}}(\text{C}_2\text{H}_5)_3\bar{\text{Br}}}$$

(iii) Acylation

$$\text{C}_2\text{H}_5\text{—NH}_2 + \text{CH}_3\text{COCl} \xrightarrow{\text{Base}} \text{C}_2\text{H}_5\text{—}\underset{\text{H}}{\text{N}}\text{—}\underset{\text{O}}{\text{C}}\text{—CH}_3 + \text{HCl}$$

$$\text{C}_2\text{H}_5\text{—NH}_2 + \text{CH}_3\text{—}\underset{\text{O}}{\text{C}}\text{—O—}\underset{\text{O}}{\text{C}}\text{—CH}_3 \xrightarrow{\text{NaOH}}$$

$$\underset{\substack{\text{H}\quad\text{O}\\\text{acetanilide}}}{\text{C}_2\text{H}_5\text{—}\text{N}\text{—}\text{C}\text{—CH}_3} + \text{CH}_3\text{COOH}$$

(iv) Benzoylation

$$\text{CH}_3\text{NH}_2 + \text{C}_6\text{H}_5\text{COCl} \xrightarrow{\text{Pyridine}} \text{CH}_3\text{NHCOC}_6\text{H}_5 + \text{HCl}$$

Benzoylation of aniline is known as **Schotten Baumann reaction.**

(v) Carbylamine reaction [only by 1° amines]

$$R\text{—NH}_2 + \text{CHCl}_3 + 3\text{KOH} \xrightarrow{\text{Heat}} \underset{\substack{\text{isocyanide}\\\text{(foul smelling)}}}{R\text{—N} \rightleftharpoons \text{C}} + 3\text{KCl} + 3\text{H}_2\text{O}$$

MIC or methyl isocyanate gas ($\text{CH}_3\text{—N=C=O}$) was responsible for Bhopal gas tragedy in December 1984.

(vi) Reaction with nitrous acid

$$R\text{NH}_2 + \text{HNO}_2 \xrightarrow{\text{NaNO}_2 + \text{HCl}} [R\overset{+}{\text{N}}_2\text{Cl}] \xrightarrow{\text{H}_2\text{O}} R\text{OH} + \text{N}_2\uparrow + \text{HCl}$$

Quantitative evolution of nitrogen is used in estimation of amino acids and proteins.

$$\underset{\text{aniline}}{\text{C}_6\text{H}_5\text{—NH}_2} \xrightarrow[\text{273–278 K}]{\text{NaNO}_2 + 2\text{HCl}} \underset{\substack{\text{benzene diazonium}\\\text{chloride}}}{\text{C}_6\text{H}_5\overset{+}{\text{N}}_2\text{Cl}^-} + \text{NaCl} + 2\text{H}_2\text{O}$$

But secondary and tertiary amines react with nitrous acid in different manner. Methyl amine gives dimethyl ether with HNO_2.

(vii) **Reaction with aryl sulphonyl chloride** [Hinsberg reagent]

The reaction of benzenesulphonyl chloride with primary amine yield N-ethyl benzenesulphonamide.

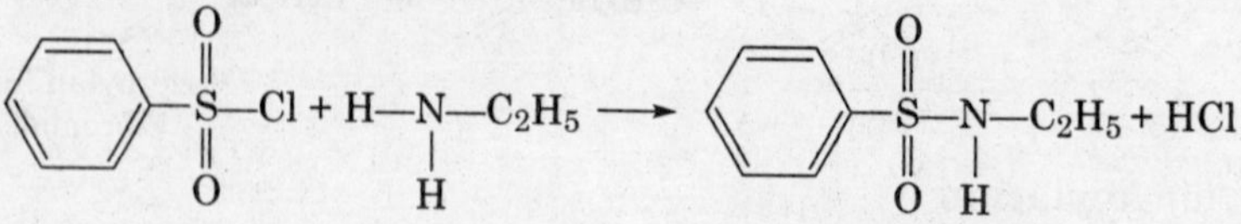

N-ethylbenzene
sulphonamide
(soluble in alkali)

The reaction of benzenesulphonyl chloride with secondary amine yields N,N-diethyl benzene sulphonamide.

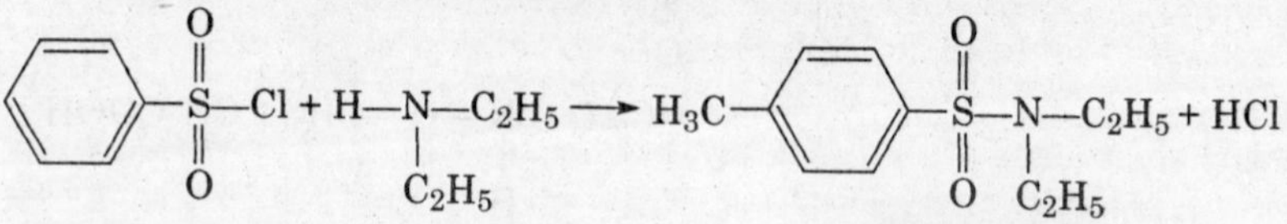

N, N-diethylbenzene
sulphonamide
(insoluble in alkali)

Tertiary amines does not react with benzenesulphonyl chloride.

(viii) **Reaction with aldehydes**   Schiff base is obtained.

$$C_6H_5NH_2 + C_6H_5CHO \xrightarrow[\substack{-H_2O}]{\substack{ZnCl_2 \\ \Delta}} C_6H_5N=CHC_6H_5$$

benzaldehyde   benzylidene aniline
(Schiff base)

(ix) **Electrophilic substitution reactions**   Aniline is *ortho* and *para* directing towards electrophilic substitution reaction due to high electron density at *ortho* and *para*-positions.

(a) **Bromination**

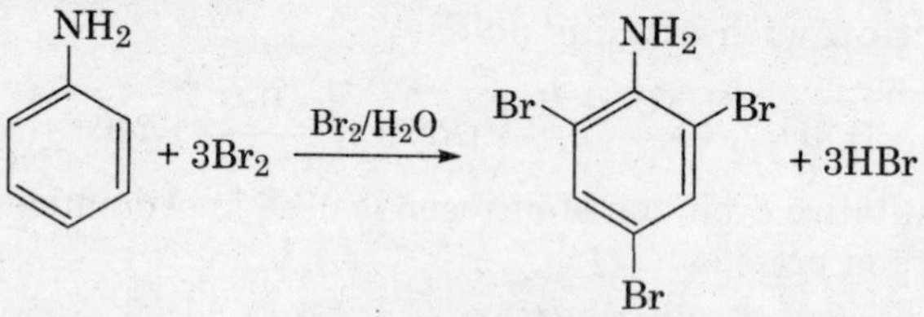

2,4,6-tribromoaniline
(light yellow ppt)

To prepare monosubstituted derivative, activating effect of —NH_2 group must be controlled. It can be done by protecting the —NH_2 group by acetylation with acetic anhydride.

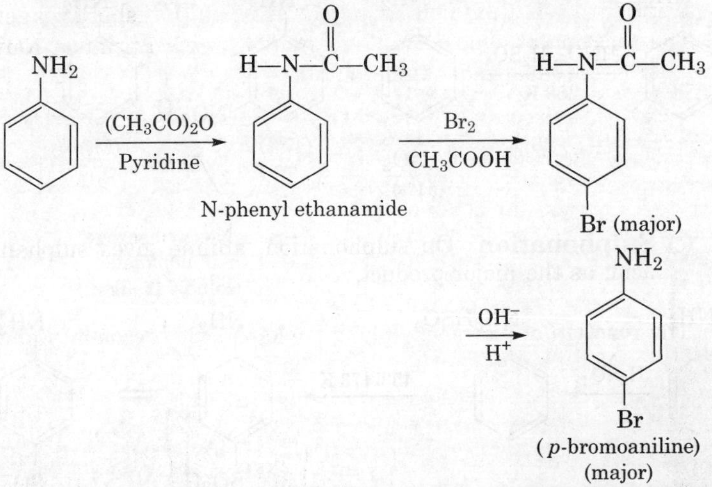

N-phenyl ethanamide

Br (major)

(p-bromoaniline)
(major)

(b) **Nitration** Direct nitration of aniline is not possible as it is susceptible to oxidation, thus amino group is first protected by acetylation.

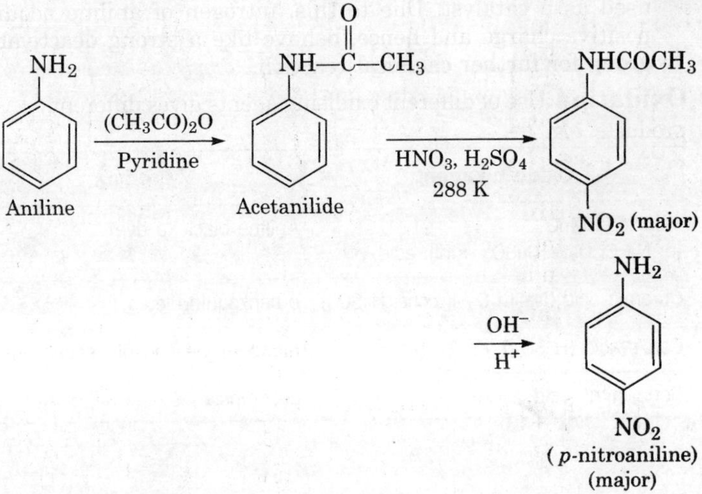

Aniline   Acetanilide NO_2 (major)

(p-nitroaniline)
(major)

In strong acidic medium, aniline is protonated as anilinium ion which is *meta* directing so it gives *meta* product also.

(c) **Sulphonation** On sulphonation, aniline gives sulphanilic acid, as the major product.

(d) Aniline does not undergo **Friedel-Crafts** reaction due to salt formation with aluminium chloride, the Lewis acid, which is used as a catalyst. Due to this, nitrogen of aniline acquires positive charge and hence, behave like a strong deactivating group for further chemical reaction.

(x) **Oxidation** Use of different oxidising agents gives different products. e.g.

Oxidising agent	Product
Acidified $KMnO_4$ (or $Na_2Cr_2O_7$ + $CuSO_4$ + dil. acid)	Aniline black (a dye)
Chromic acid ($Na_2Cr_2O_7$ + conc. H_2SO_4)	*p*-benzoquinone
Caro's acid (H_2SO_5)	nitrobenzene and nitrosobenzene
Conc. nitric acid	decomposes

Separation of Mixture of Amines (1°, 2° and 3°)

(a) **Fractional distillation** This method is based on the boiling points of amines and is used satisfactorily in industry.

(b) **Hofmann's method** Diethyloxalate is called Hofmann's reagent with which mixture of amines is treated.

1° amine forms solid dialkyl oxamide $(CONHR)_2$.

2° amine forms liquid dialkyl oxamic ester $(CONR_2-COOC_2H_5)$

3° amines do not react.

(c) **Hinsberg's method** see chemical reactions on Page 448.

Benzene Diazonium Chloride $(C_6H_5N_2^+Cl^-)$

Preparation (Diazotisation reaction)

$$C_6H_5NH_2 + NaNO_2 + 2HCl \xrightarrow{\text{273-278 K}} C_6H_5 \overset{+}{N} \equiv N - \overset{-}{Cl}$$
$$+ NaCl + 2H_2O$$

The excess acid in diazotisation reaction is necessary to maintain proper acidic medium for the reaction and to prevent combination of diazonium salt formed with the undiazotised amine.

⌐ Diazonium salts are prepared and used in aqueous solutions because in solid state, they explode. ⌐

Physical Properties

It is a colourless crystalline solid, soluble in water. It has tendency to explode when dry.

Stability of Arenediazonium salts

It is relatively more stable than the alkyldiazonium salt. The arenediazonium ion is resonance stabilised as is indicated by the following resonating structures:

Various resonating structures of arenediazonium ion

Chemical Properties

$$\xrightarrow[\text{(Hypophosphorous acid)}]{\text{H}_3\text{PO}_2/\text{H}_2\text{O}} \text{C}_6\text{H}_6 + \text{N}_2\uparrow + \text{H}_3\text{PO}_3 + \text{HCl}$$

$$\xrightarrow[\text{(deamination)}]{\text{CH}_3\text{CH}_2\text{OH}} \text{C}_6\text{H}_6 + \text{N}_2\uparrow + \text{HCl} + \text{CH}_3\text{CHO}$$

$$\xrightarrow{\text{CuBr / HBr}} \underset{\text{(bromobenzene)}}{\text{C}_6\text{H}_5\text{Br}} + \text{N}_2\uparrow$$

$$\xrightarrow{\text{CuCl/HCl}} \text{C}_6\text{H}_5\text{Cl} + \text{N}_2\uparrow \quad \text{(Sandmeyer's reaction)}$$

$$\xrightarrow{\text{Cu/HCl}} \text{C}_6\text{H}_5\text{Cl} + \text{N}_2\uparrow + \text{CuCl (Gattermann's reaction)}$$

$$\xrightarrow{\text{Cu/HBr}} \text{C}_6\text{H}_5\text{Br} + \text{N}_2\uparrow + \text{CuBr}$$

$$\xrightarrow[-\text{N}_2, -\text{KCl}]{\text{KCN / CuCN}} \text{C}_6\text{H}_5\text{CN (benzonitrile)} + \text{N}_2\uparrow$$

$\boxed{\text{C}_6\text{H}_5\text{N}_2^+ \ \text{Cl}^-}$
Diazonium salt

$$\xrightarrow{\text{KI}} \text{C}_6\text{H}_5\text{I} + \text{N}_2\uparrow + \text{KCl}$$

$$\xrightarrow[-\text{HCl}]{\text{HBF}_4} \text{C}_6\text{H}_5\overset{\oplus}{\text{N}}_2(\text{BF}_4)^- \xrightarrow[\substack{\text{(Balz-Schiemann's} \\ \text{reaction)}}]{\Delta} \underset{\text{fluorobenzene}}{\text{C}_6\text{H}_5\text{F}} + \text{BF}_3 + \text{N}_2\uparrow + \text{HCl}$$

$$\xrightarrow[\text{Boiling}]{\text{H}_2\text{O / H}_2\text{SO}_4} \underset{\text{phenol}}{\text{C}_6\text{H}_5\text{OH}} + \text{N}_2\uparrow + \text{HCl}$$

—OH, OH⁻

pH 9–10, cold

p-hydroxyazobenzene
(orange dye)

C₆H₅NH₂

pH 9-10, cold

p-aminoazobenzene
(yellow dye)

Alkyl Cyanides (*R*CN)

These compounds have formula *R*CN. These are the derivatives of HCN.

According to IUPAC system, cyanides are named as 'alkanenitrile', e.g.

$$\underset{\text{butanenitrile}}{C_3H_7CN} \quad , \quad \underset{\text{benzenenitrile}}{C_6H_5CN}$$

Methods of Preparation

(i) **From alkyl halides**

$$RX + KCN(\text{alc.}) \xrightarrow{100°C} \underset{\text{(major)}}{RCN} + \underset{\text{(minor)}}{RNC}$$

(ii) **From acid amides**

$$RCONH_2 \xrightarrow[-H_2O]{P_2O_5, \Delta} RC\equiv N$$

Physical Properties

1. These are neutral compound with pleasant odour, similar to bitter almonds.

2. These are soluble in water as well as organic solvents.

3. These are poisonous but less than HCN.

Chemical Properties

1. **Hydrolysis**

$$RCN \xrightarrow[\substack{\text{alk. } H_2O_2 \\ \text{(partial hydrolysis)}}]{H_2O} \underset{\text{amide}}{RCONH_2} \xrightarrow[H^+]{H_2O} \underset{\text{carboxylic acid}}{RCOOH} + NH_3\uparrow$$

2. **Reduction**

$$RCN + 4\,[H] \xrightarrow{Na + C_2H_5\,OH} RCH_2NH_2$$

$$RCN + 4\,[H] \xrightarrow{LiAlH_4} RCH_2NH_2 \qquad \textbf{(Mendius reduction)}$$

$$RCN \xrightarrow{SnCl_2/HCl} \underset{\text{imine hydrochloride}}{R\,CH{=}NH\cdot HCl} \xrightarrow{H_2O} \underset{\text{aldehyde}}{RCHO} + NH_4Cl$$

3. **Reaction with Grignard's reagent**

$$RCN + R'\,MgX \xrightarrow{\text{Ether}} R{-}\underset{\displaystyle \overset{R'}{|}}{C}{=}NMgX \xrightarrow{2H_2O} R{-}\underset{\displaystyle \overset{R'}{|}}{C}{=}O$$

Alkyl Isocyanides (*R*NC)

According to IUPAC system, these are named as 'alkane isonitrile'.

e.g. CH_3NC methyl isonitrile

C_6H_5NC benzene isonitrile

Methods of Preparation

1. **From alkyl halides**

$$R—X + AgCN \xrightarrow[\Delta]{C_2H_5OH} \underset{\text{(major)}}{RNC} + \underset{\text{(minor)}}{RCN}$$

2. **Carbylamine reaction**

$$RNH_2 + CHCl_3 + 3KOH(alc.) \xrightarrow{\Delta} RNC + 3KCl + 3H_2O$$

3. **From N-alkyl formamide**

$$R—\overset{\displaystyle O}{\overset{\|}{NH—C—H}} \xrightarrow[\text{Pyridine}]{POCl_3} R—N \rightleftharpoons C + H_2O$$

Physical Properties

1. These are colourless unpleasant smelling liquids.

2. These are soluble in organic solvents but insoluble in water.

Chemical Properties

1. **Hydrolysis**

$$R—N \rightleftharpoons C + 2H_2O \xrightarrow{H^+} RNH_2 + HCOOH$$

2. **Reduction**

$$RN \rightleftharpoons C + 4[H] \xrightarrow[\text{or Ni or Pt}]{Na/C_2H_5OH} \underset{2° \text{ amine}}{RNHCH_3}$$

3. **Addition reaction** Due to the presence of unshared pair of electrons on C atom, alkyl isocyanides give addition reaction.

$$RNC + S \longrightarrow RNCS$$
$$RNC + HgO \longrightarrow RNCO + Hg$$
$$RNC + O_3 \longrightarrow RNCO$$

4. **Isomerisation** At 250°C, it isomerises to nitrile.

$$RNC \xrightarrow{\Delta} RCN$$

Nitro Compounds

These are obtained by replacing one H of hydrocarbon by —NO_2 group.

These are named according to IUPAC system as 'nitro alkane'.

Methods of Preparation

1. **From alkyl halides**

$$RX + AgNO_2 \xrightarrow{\Delta} RNO_2 + AgX$$

2. **Nitration** Nitrating mixture is conc. HNO_3 + conc. H_2SO_4.

Benzene + conc.HNO_3 $\xrightarrow{conc.H_2SO_4}$ Nitrobenzene

Physical Properties

1. These are colourless pleasant smelling liquids.

2. Their boiling point are much higher than isomeric alkyl nitriles.

3. These are less soluble in water but readily soluble in organic solvents.

Chemical Properties

1. **Reduction** With Sn/HCl or catalytic hydrogenation, nitroalkanes are reduced to amines.

$$RNO_2 + 6[H] \xrightarrow{Sn/HCl} R{-\!\!-}NH_2 + 2H_2O$$

If neutral reducing agent like Zn dust + NH_4Cl is used, hydroxylamines are obtained as major product.

$$RNO_2 + 4[H] \xrightarrow{Zn + NH_4Cl} \underset{\text{N-alkylhydroxylamine}}{R{-\!\!-}\overset{\displaystyle H}{\overset{|}{N}}{-\!\!-}OH} + H_2O$$

In the presence of $(NH_4)_2S$ or Na_2S, selective reduction takes place.

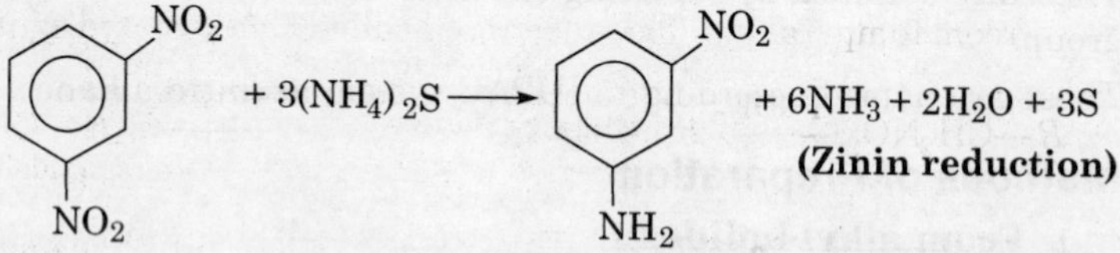

(Zinin reduction)

m-nitro aniline

Nitrobenzene gives different products with different reagents and in different mediums.

Medium	Reagent	Product
Acid	Sn/HCl	aniline
Neutral	Zn/NH₄Cl	N-phenyl hydroxylamine
	Na₃AsO₃/NaOH	azoxybenzene $$\overset{O}{\overset{\uparrow}{(C_6H_5N = NC_6H_5)}}$$
Alkaline	Zn/NaOH, CH₃OH	azobenzene
	Zn/NaOH, C₂H₅OH	hydrazobenzene
Metallic hydride	LiAlH₄	aniline
Electrolytic	dil. H₂SO₄	*p*-aminophenol

2. Action of HNO₂

1° nitroalkane gives nitrolic acid which gives red colour with NaOH.

$$RCH_2NO_2 \xrightarrow[-H_2O]{HNO_2} RC(NO_2) = NOH$$
nitrolic acid

$$\xrightarrow{NaOH} R - \overset{}{\underset{NO}{C}} = \overset{+}{N} \overset{\bar{O}Na^+}{\underset{O^-}{\diagdown}}$$

2° nitroalkanes give pseudo nitrol with HNO₂.

$$R_2CH(NO_2) \xrightarrow[-H_2O]{HNO_2} R_2\underset{N=O}{\overset{}{C}} - NO_2 \xrightarrow{NaOH} Blue$$

3° nitroalkanes does not react with HNO₂.

3. **Nef carbonyl synthesis** Na or K salt of 1° or 2° nitroalkanes give carbonyl compounds on acidification with 50% H_2SO_4 at room temperature. This reaction is called Nef carbonyl synthesis.

$$R\text{—}CH_2NO_2 \xrightarrow{\text{NaOH}} R\text{—}CH\text{=}\overset{+}{N}\diagdown\diagup\!\!\!\overset{O^-Na^+}{O^-} \xrightarrow{50\%\ H_2SO_4} R\text{—}CH\text{=}O$$
aldehyde

4. **Electrophilic substitution** On nitration, nitrobenzene gives *m*-dinitrobenzene (as —NO_2 is a *m*-directing group and strongly deactivating).

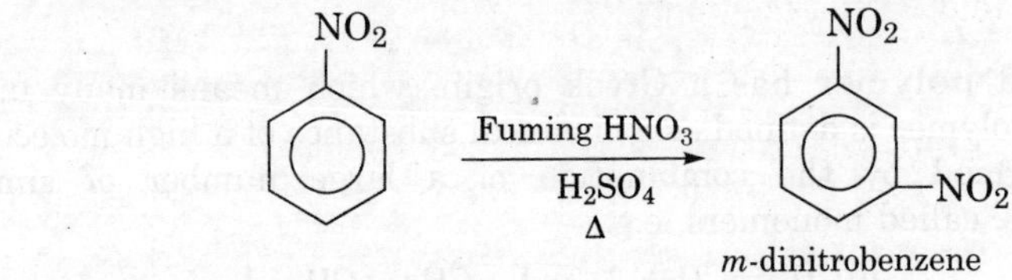

$$\xrightarrow[\substack{H_2SO_4 \\ \Delta}]{\text{Fuming } HNO_3}$$

m-dinitrobenzene

It does not give Friedel-Craft's alkylation.

5. **Nucleophilic substitution reaction** —NO_2 group activates the ring towards nucleophilic substitution.

$$+ OH^- \xrightarrow[\text{Slow}]{\text{NaOH}} \qquad \xrightarrow[-H^+]{\text{Fast}}$$

$$\xrightarrow[\text{NaOH}]{K_3[Fe(CN)_6]} \qquad +$$

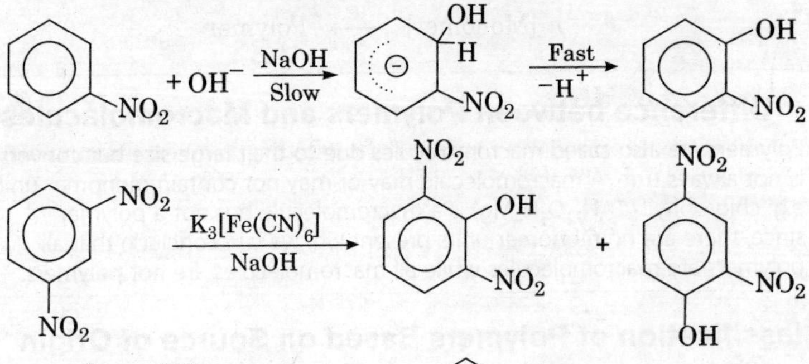

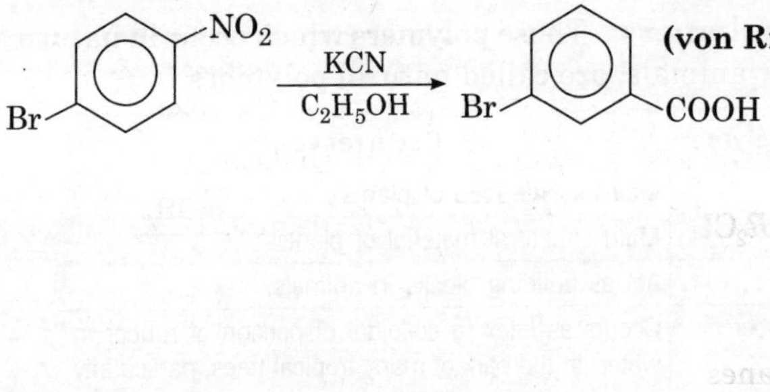

(von Richter reaction)

$$\xrightarrow[C_2H_5OH]{\text{KCN}}$$

30
Polymers

The word **polymer** has a Greek origin, which means many units (parts). Polymer is defined as a chemical substance of a high molecular mass formed by the combination of a large number of simple molecules, called monomers, e.g.

$$n(CH_2{=}CH_2) \longrightarrow +\!\!- CH_2{-}CH_2 -\!\!\!+_n$$

Ethylene   Polyethylene

Polymerisation

The process by which the monomers combine with each other and transform into polymers, is known as **polymerisation**.

$$n \text{ [Monomer]} \longrightarrow \text{Polymer}$$

Difference between Polymers and Macromolecules

Polymers are also called macromolecules due to their large size but converse is not always true. A macromolecule may or may not contain monomer units, e.g. chlorophyll ($C_{55}H_{72}O_5N_4Mg$) is a macromolecule but not a polymer since, there are no monomer units present. So, we can conclude that all polymers are macromolecules while all macromolecules are not polymers.

Classification of Polymers Based on Source of Origin

(i) **Natural polymers** Those polymers which occur in nature, i.e. in plants or animals, are called natural polymers.

Natural polymer	Occurrence
Starch	Main reserve food of plants
Cellulose	Main structural material of plants
Proteins	Act as building blocks in animals.
Natural rubber	Occurs as latex (a colloidal dispersion of rubber in water) in the bark of many tropical trees, particularly from *Hevea Brasiliensis.*

(ii) **Synthetic polymers** The polymers which are prepared in the laboratory are known as synthetic polymers or man-made polymers, e.g. polythene, synthetic rubber, PVC, nylon-6,6, teflon, orlon etc.

(iii) **Semi-synthetic polymers** Polymers obtained by making some modification in natural polymers by artificial means, are known as semisynthetic polymers, e.g. cellulose acetate (rayon), vulcanised rubber etc.

Classification of Polymers Based on Structure

(i) **Linear polymers** These are the polymers in which the monomer units are linked to one another to form long linear chains. These linear chains are closely packed in space. The close

Linear chain polymer

packing results in high densities, tensile strength and high melting and boiling points. e.g. high density polyethene, nylon and polyesters are linear polymers.

(ii) **Branched chain polymers** In such polymers, the monomer units are linked to form long chains with some branched chains of different lengths attached to the main linear chain. As

Branched chain polymer

a result of branching, these polymers are not closely packed in space. Thus, they have low densities, low tensile strength as well as low melting and boiling points. Some common examples of such polymers are low density polyethene, starch, glycogen etc.

(iii) **Cross-linked polymers or network polymers** These are formed from bi functional and tri functional monomers. In such polymers, the monomer units are

Cross linked polymer

linked together to form three dimensional network. These are expected to be quite hard, rigid and brittle. Examples of cross linked polymers are bakelite, glyptal, melamine-formaldehyde polymer etc.

Classification of Polymers Based on Mode of Polymerisation

(i) **Addition polymers** The polymers formed by the polymerisation of monomers containing double or triple bonds (unsaturated compounds) are called addition polymers. Addition polymers have the same empirical formula as their monomers.

Addition polymers can further be classified on the basis of the types of monomers into the following two classes:

Homopolymers The polymers which are obtained by the polymerisation of a single type of monomer are called homopolymers.

$$n(CH_2{=}CH_2) \longrightarrow \ {+}CH_2{-}CH_2{+}_n$$

Ethene   Polythene

Copolymers The polymers which are obtained by the polymerisation of two or more different types of monomers are called copolymers.

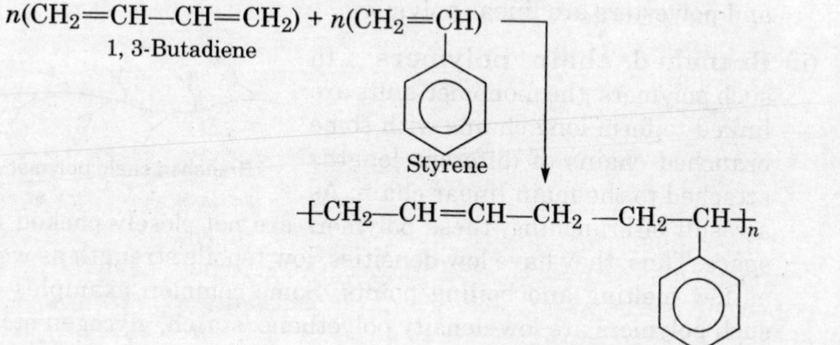

$$n(CH_2{=}CH{-}CH{=}CH_2) + n(CH_2{=}CH)$$

1, 3-Butadiene

Styrene

$${+}CH_2{-}CH{=}CH{-}CH_2\ {-}CH_2{-}CH{+}_n$$

Buna-S (Butadiene styrene copolymer)

(ii) **Condensation polymers** The polymers which are formed by the combination of monomers with the elimination of small molecules such as water, alcohol, hydrogen chloride etc., are known as condensation polymers, e.g. nylon 6,6 is formed by the condensation of hexamethylene diamine with adipic acid and water molecules are eliminated in the process.

$$nH_2N(CH_2)_6NH_2 + nHOOC(CH_2)_4COOH \longrightarrow$$

$${+}NH(CH_2)_6NHCO(CH_2)_4CO{+}_n\ + nH_2O$$

Nylon 6,6

These are generally copolymers. A condensation homopolymer is nylon-6.

Classification of Polymers Based on Molecular Forces

(i) **Elastomers**   These are rubber like solid polymers in which the polymer chains are held together by weakest intermolecular forces, e.g. natural rubber, buna-S, buna-N etc.

The weak binding forces permit the polymers to be stretched. A few 'cross links' are introduced in between the chains, which help the polymer to retract to its original position after the force is released as in case of vulcanised rubber.

(ii) **Fibres**   Fibres belong to a class of polymers which are thread-like and can be woven into fabrics. These are widely used for making clothes, nets, ropes, gauzes, etc. Fibres possess high tensile strength because the chains possess strong intermolecular forces such as hydrogen bonding. The fibres are crystalline in nature and have sharp melting points. A few examples of this class are nylon-6,6, terylene and polyacrylonitrile (PAN).

(iii) **Thermoplastics**   These are linear polymers and have weak van der Waals' forces acting in the various chains. These forces are intermediate of the forces present in the elastomers and in the fibres. When heated, they melt and form a fluid which sets into a hard mass on cooling. Thus, they can be cast into different shapes by using suitable moulds, e.g. polyethene and polystyrene.

⌐ Plasticizers are high boiling esters or haloalkanes. These are added to ⌐
plastics to make them soft like rubber.

(iv) **Thermosetting plastics**   These are normally semifluid substances with low molecular masses. When heated, they become hard and infusible due to the cross-linking between the polymer chains. As a result, they form three dimensional network. A few common thermosetting polymers are bakelite, melamine-formaldehyde resin and urea formaldehyde resin.

Types of Polymerisation Reactions

1. Chain Growth or Addition Polymerisation

It involves formation of reactive intermediate such as free radical, a carbocation or a carbanion. For this polymerisation monomers used are unsaturated compounds like alkenes, alkadienes and their derivatives. Depending upon the nature of the reactive species involved, chain growth polymerisation occurs by the following mechanisms:

   (i) Free radical addition polymerisation
   (ii) Cationic polymerisation
   (iii) Anionic polymerisation

(i) **Free radical addition polymerisation** The monomers used are generally monosubstituted alkenes. The most commonly used catalysts are benzoyl peroxide, hydrogen peroxide or t-butylperoxide etc.

Mechanism The reaction involves the following steps :

Step I Chain initiation step In this step, peroxide undergoes homolytic fission, e.g. benzoyl peroxide on heating produces phenyl free radical which work as initiator.

$$C_6H_5-\overset{\overset{O}{\|}}{C}-O \frown O-\overset{\overset{O}{\|}}{C}-C_6H_5 \longrightarrow$$

$$\left[C_6H_5-\overset{\overset{O}{\|}}{C}-\dot{O} \right] \longrightarrow 2\dot{C}_6H_5 + 2CO_2$$
$$\underset{\text{radical}}{\text{Phenyl}}$$

$$\dot{C}_6H_5 + CH_2=CH_2 \longrightarrow C_6H_5-CH_2-\dot{C}H_2$$

Step II Chain propagation step The new free radical adds to another molecules of monomer to form a larger free radical.

$$C_6H_5CH_2\dot{C}H_2 \xrightarrow{CH_2=CH_2} C_6H_5CH_2CH_2CH_2\dot{C}H_2$$

$$\xrightarrow{nCH_2=CH_2} C_6H_5-(CH_2-CH_2)_{\overline{n}} CH_2-\dot{C}H_2$$

Step III Chain termination step There are three ways of chain termination: Coupling reaction, disproportionation reaction, chain transfer reaction. One mode of termination of chain is shown as under:

$$C_6H_5(CH_2-CH_2)_n CH_2\dot{C}H_2$$
$$C_6H_5(CH_2-\overset{\oplus}{CH_2})_n CH_2\dot{C}H_2 \Big] *$$

$$C_6H_5-(CH_2CH_2)_{\overline{n}} CH_2CH_2CH_2CH_2(CH_2-CH_2)_{\overline{n}} C_6H_5$$
$$\text{Polymer}$$

(ii) **Cationic polymerisation** It involves formation of carbocation which are generated by Lewis acids (like BF_3, $AlCl_3$, $SnCl_4$, etc.) and protonic acids such as H_2SO_4, HF, etc.

Higher the stability of carbocation intermediate, more is the reactivity of monomers towards cationic addition polymerisation.

It involves the following steps:

Step I. **Initiation step**

$$H_2SO_4 \rightleftharpoons H^+ + HSO_4^-$$
$$BF_3 + H_2O \rightleftharpoons H^+ + BF_3(OH^-)$$

$$CH_2{=}C(CH_3)_2 + H^+ \longrightarrow (CH_3)_3C^+$$
$$\text{Carbocation}$$

Step II. **Propagation**

$$(CH_3)_3C^+ + CH_2{=}C(CH_3)_2 \longrightarrow (CH_3)_3{-}C{-}CH_2C^+(CH_3)_2$$

$$\xrightarrow{nCH_2{=}C(CH_3)_2} (CH_3)_3C{-}\!\!\left[\!CH_2{-}C(CH_3)_2\!\right]_{\!n}\!\!CH_2 \cdot C^+(CH_3)_2$$

Step III. **Termination**

$$(CH_3)_3C[CH_2 \cdot C(CH_3)_2]_n CH_2C^+(CH_3)_2$$

$$\xrightarrow{\;-H^+\;} (CH_3)_3C[CH_2 \cdot C(CH_3)_2]_n CH{=}C(CH_3)_2$$

(iii) **Anionic polymerisation** It involves formation of a carbanion. Steps involved in this process are

Step I **Initiation**   Strong bases act as initiator.

$$KNH_2 \longrightarrow K^+ + \overset{\ominus}{N}H_2{}_\square$$

$$CH_2{=}CHCN + \overset{\ominus}{N}H_2 \longrightarrow H_2N{-}CH_2\overset{\ominus}{C}HCN$$
$$\text{Carbanion}$$

Step II **Propagation**

$$H_2N \cdot CH_2\overset{\ominus}{C}HCN + nCH_2{=}CHCN$$

$$\longrightarrow H_2N{-}CH_2{-}CH(CN){-}\!\!\left[\!CH_2\,CH(CN)\!\right]_{\!\overline{n}}\!\!CH_2\overset{\ominus}{C}HCN$$

Step III **Termination**

$$H_2NCH_2CH(CN)[CH_2CHCN]_n {-}CH_2\overset{\ominus}{C}HCN$$

$$\xrightarrow{\;+H^+\;} NH_2CH_2CH(CN){-}\!\!\left[\!CH_2CH(CN)\!\right]_{\!\overline{n}}\!\!CH_2CH_2CN$$

2. **Step Growth on Condensation Polymerisation**

Condensation polymerisation which occurs in a stepwise manner with elimination of some smaller molecules like H_2O, NH_3, HCl, ROH, etc., is concerned with step growth polymerisation, e.g. adipic acid and hexamethylenediamine; phenol and formaldehyde etc., undergo step growth polymerisation.

Distinction Between Chain Growth Polymerisation and Step Growth Polymerisation

S.No.	Chain growth polymerisation	Step growth polymerisation
1.	It proceeds by a chain mechanism characterised by initiation, chain propagation and chain termination.	It proceeds by an equilibrium step mechanism. The step growth process is usually much slower than chain growth polymerisation.
2.	Only one repeating unit is added at a time.	Any two species present can react with elimination of some by product.
3.	Reaction mixture contain only monomers, polymers and the growing chain.	All the molecular species are present at every stage of polymerisation.

Molecular Mass of Polymers

The growth of the polymer chain depends upon the availability of the monomers in the reaction. Thus, the polymer sample contains chain of varying lengths and hence, its molecular mass is always expressed as an average molecular mass.

Number-Average Molecular Mass $(\overline{M}_n)$

If N_1 molecules have molecular mass M_1 each, N_2 molecules have molecular mass M_2 each, N_3 molecules have molecular mass M_3 each and so on,

then, $$\overline{M}_n = \frac{\Sigma N_i M_i}{\Sigma N_i}$$

It is determined by osmotic pressure method.

Mass-Average Molecular Mass $(\overline{M}_w)$

Supposing, as before that N_1, N_2, N_3 etc., molecules have molecular mass M_1, M_2, M_3 etc., respectively,

then, $$\overline{M}_w = \frac{\Sigma N_i M_i^2}{\Sigma N_i M_i}$$

It is determined by light scattering and ultracentrifugation method.

Polydispersity Index

It is the ratio of the mass average molecular mass to the number average molecular mass

$$PDI = \frac{\overline{M}_w}{\overline{M}_n}$$

For natural polymers, PDI is usually equal to one which means that they are monodisperse. In other words, such polymers are more homogeneous. On the contrary, synthetic polymers generally have PDI > 1 which means that they are less homogeneous.

Polyolefins

These are obtained by the addition polymerisation of ethylene and its derivatives.

1. Polythene

Polymer of ethylene or ethene.

(i) Low density polythene (LDP)

$$n(CH_2{=}CH_2) \xrightarrow[\substack{1000 \text{ to } 2000 \text{ atm} \\ (\text{Traces of oxygen} \\ \text{or a peroxide} \\ \text{initiator})}]{350 \text{ K-}570 \text{ K}} \underset{\text{LDP}}{-[CH_2{-}CH_2]_n}$$

It is tough, flexible, transparent, chemically inert as well as poor conductor of electricity. It has moderate tensile strength but good tearing strength.

It is used in the insulation of electricity carrying wires and manufacture of squeeze bottles, toys and flexible pipes.

(ii) High density polyethylene (HDP)

$$n(CH_2{=}CH_2) \xrightarrow[\substack{6\text{-}7 \text{ atm} \\ (\textit{Ziegler Natta} \\ \text{catalyst})}]{333\text{-}343 \text{ K}} \underset{\text{HDP}}{-(CH_2{-}CH_2)_n}$$

It has high density due to close packing. It is also chemically inert and poor conductor of electricity. It is tougher and harder than LDP.

It is used for making containers, house wares, bottles, toys, electric insulation etc.

2. Polystyrene (Styrene)

The monomers are styrene molecules. It is thermoplastic. It is used for making toys, radio and TV cabinets.

$$n\begin{bmatrix} CH{=}CH_2 \\ | \\ C_6H_5 \end{bmatrix} \xrightarrow[\text{Benzoyl peroxide}]{(C_6H_5COO)_2} \left(\begin{array}{c} CH{-}CH_2 \\ | \\ C_6H_5 \end{array}\right)_n$$

$$\underset{\text{Styrene}}{}$$

3. **Polyvinylchloride** (PVC)

$$n\begin{bmatrix} CH_2=CH \\ | \\ Cl \end{bmatrix} \xrightarrow{\text{Dibenzoyl peroxide}} \begin{pmatrix} CH_2-CH \\ | \\ Cl \end{pmatrix}_n$$

Chloroethene
(vinyl chloride)   PVC

It is used for making rain coats, toys, electrical insulation. It is hard and resistant to heat and chemicals.

4. **Polypropylene** (PP)

It is obtained by polymerising propylene in the presence of *Ziegler-Natta* catalyst.

$$n\begin{bmatrix} CH_3 H \\ | \quad | \\ C=C \\ | \quad | \\ H \quad H \end{bmatrix} \xrightarrow{\text{Polymerisation}} \begin{bmatrix} CH_3 H \\ | \quad | \\ C-C \\ | \quad | \\ H \quad H \end{bmatrix}_n$$

propylene   Polypropylene (PP)

It is used for manufacturing of ropes, toys, pipes, fibres, etc.

5. **Polytetrafluoroethene** (Teflon)

$$n(CF_2=CF_2) \xrightarrow[\text{High pressure}]{\text{Catalyst}} \;+CF_2-CF_2\;]_n$$

Tetrafluoroethene   Teflon

It is chemically inert and resistant to attack by corrosive reagent. It is used in making oil seals, gaskets and also for non-stick surface coated utensils.

6. **Polyacrylonitrile** (PAN)

$$n(CH_2=CHCN) \xrightarrow[\text{(Peroxide catalyst)}]{\text{Polymerisation}} \begin{matrix} CN \\ | \\ +CH_2-CH\;]_n \end{matrix}$$

Acrylonitrile   Polyacrylonitrile or orlon

It is used as a substitute for wool in making of commercial fibres known as orlon or acrilan.

Polyamides

The polymers which contain an amide linkage in chain are known as polyamide, e.g. nylon-6,6.

1. Nylon-6,6

It is obtained by the condensation of adipic acid and hexamethylenediamine with the elimination of water molecule.

$$n\text{H}_2\text{N(CH}_2)_6\text{NH}_2 \underset{\text{Hexamethylenediamine}}{} + n\ \text{HO}-\overset{\overset{\text{O}}{\|}}{\text{C}}-(\text{CH}_2)_4-\overset{\overset{\text{O}}{\|}}{\text{C}}-\text{OH} \xrightarrow[-n\text{H}_2\text{O}]{}$$

adipic acid

$$-\!\!\left(\text{N}-(\text{CH}_2)_6-\text{N}-\overset{\overset{\text{O}}{\|}}{\text{C}}-(\text{CH}_2)_4-\overset{\overset{\text{O}}{\|}}{\text{C}}\right)\!\!_{\overline{n}}$$

Nylon-6,6

The polyamides are identified by numbers. These numbers refer to the number of carbon atoms in diamine and in the dibasic acid. As in the above case, the carbon atoms are 6 in each case, therefore the product is described as nylon-6,6.

Properties and Uses

Nylon-6,6 is a linear polymer and has very high tensile strength. It shows good resistance to abrasion. Nylon-6,6 is usually fabricated into sheets. It is used in bristles for brushes and in textile.

2. Nylon-6

Nylon-6 is obtained by heating caprolactum with water at a high temperature.

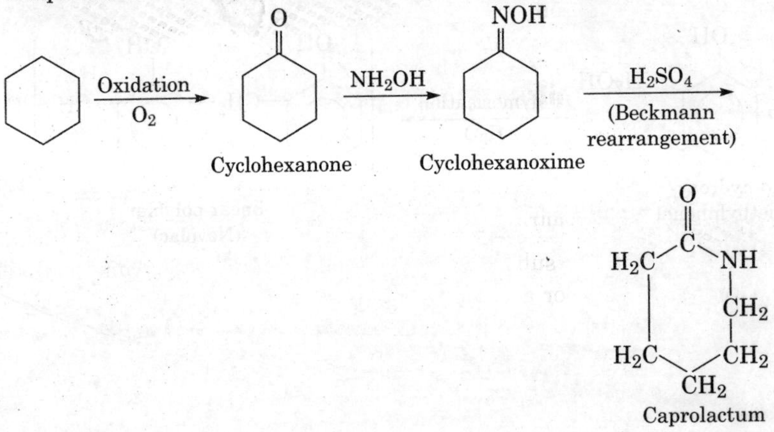

Cyclohexanone   Cyclohexanoxime

Caprolactum

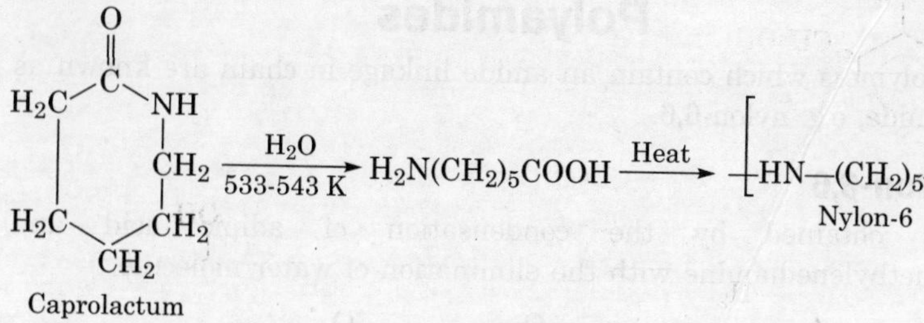

Caprolactum

$$\text{Caprolactum} \xrightarrow[533\text{-}543\ K]{H_2O} H_2N(CH_2)_5COOH \xrightarrow{Heat} \left[HN-(CH_2)_5-\overset{O}{\underset{\|}{C}}\right]_n$$

Nylon-6

Resins

1. Phenol-Formaldehyde Polymer
(Bakelite and Related Polymers)

These polymers are obtained by the condensation reaction of phenol with formaldehyde in the presence of either acid or a base catalyst. The reaction involves the formation of methylene bridge at *ortho*, *para* or both *ortho* and *para* positions. A linear or cross linked material is obtained depending upon the condition of reaction.

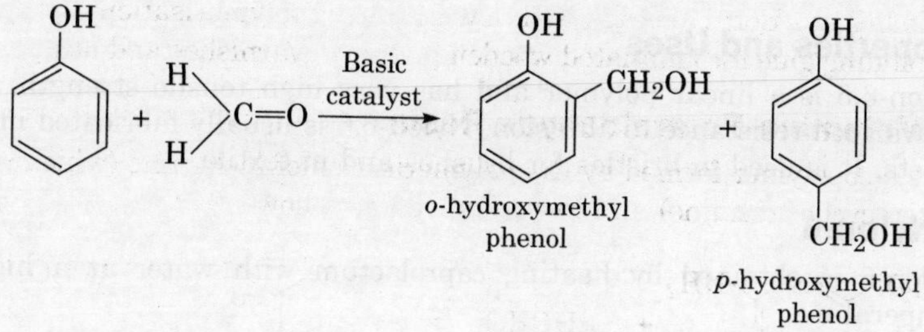

o-hydroxymethyl
phenol

p-hydroxymethyl
phenol

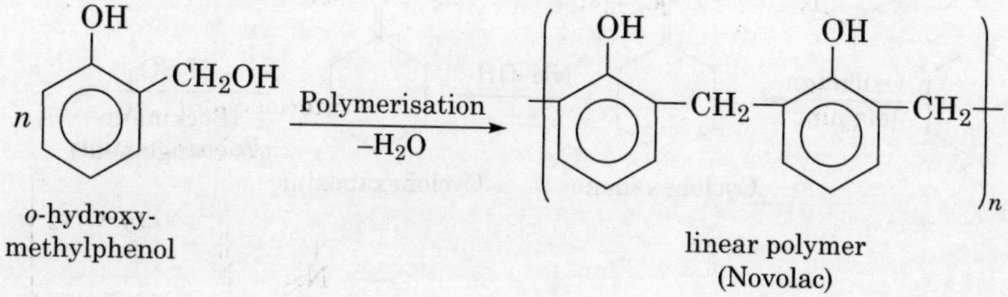

o-hydroxy-
methylphenol

linear polymer
(Novolac)

Cross linked polymer (bakelite)

Uses

Bakelite is used for making combs, phonograph records, electrical switches etc. Soft bakelites with low degree of polymerisation are used as binding glue for laminated wooden plants, in varnishes and lacquers.

2. Melamine-Formaldehyde Resin

It is a copolymer formed by the polymerisation of melamine (which is a heterocyclic triamine) and formaldehyde as follows :

Properties and Uses

It is very hard and tough. It has assumed great importance these days particularly in making of crockery. They do not break even when droped from a height.

3. Urea-Formaldehyde Resin

$$NH_2—\overset{\overset{O}{\|}}{C}—NH_2 + \underset{\text{Formaldehyde}}{2HCHO} \xrightarrow{\text{Heat}}$$

$$\underset{\text{Urea}}{}$$

$$HOCH_2—NH—\overset{\overset{O}{\|}}{C}—NH—CH_2OH$$

$$\downarrow \text{Polymerisation}$$

$$\left(\!\!CH_2—NH—\overset{\overset{O}{\|}}{C}—NH—CH_2\!\!\right)_{\!\!n}$$

$$\text{Urea-formaldehyde resin}$$

4. Natural Rubber

Natural rubber is a coiled linear 1,4-polymer of isoprene.

$$CH_2{=}\underset{\text{Isoprene}}{\overset{\overset{\displaystyle CH_3}{|}}{C}}{-}CH{=}CH_2$$

In the polymer chain of natural rubber, the residual double bonds are located between C_2 and C_3 of the isoprene unit. All these double bonds have *cis* configuration, and thus natural rubber is *cis*-1,4-polyisoprene.

A section of the polymeric chain of natural rubber

In the natural rubber, there is no polar substituent. The only intermolecular forces are van der Waals' forces. The *cis*-configuration gives the polymeric chain of natural rubber a coiled structure. As a result, it can be stretched by the application of a force. When the force is removed, the chain returns back to its original coiled shape.

Natural rubber is soft and sticky. It can be used only in the temperature range 10°C–50°C. At higher temperature, it becomes soft and at low temperature, it becomes brittle. It has high water absorption capacity. It is attacked by oxidising agents and organic solvents. As such, it cannot be used very extensively for commercial purposes.

Vulcanisation of Rubber

The properties of natural rubber can be modified by introducing —S—S— polysulphide crosslinks in its structure. This process of introducing —S—S— crosslinks in the structure of natural rubber by heating with sulphur at 110°C is called **vulcanisation of rubber**.

Vulcanisation is carried out by adding sulphur (3-5%) and zinc oxide to the rubber, and then heating the object at about 110°C for about 20–30 minutes. **Zinc oxide accelerates the rate of vulcanisation**. Vulcanisation introduces polysulphide (—S—S—) bonds between the adjacent chains. These crosslinks tend to limit the motion of chains relative to each other.

---

5. Neoprene

Polymer formed by polymerisation of chloroprene is called neoprene or synthetic rubber.

$$n(CH_2{=}\overset{\overset{\displaystyle Cl}{|}}{C}{-}CH{=}CH_2) \xrightarrow{\text{Polymerisation}} {+}CH_2{-}\overset{\overset{\displaystyle Cl}{|}}{C}{=}CH{-}CH_2{\xrightarrow{}}_n$$

Chloroprene   Neoprene

It is used for the manufacturing conveyers belts, gasket and hoses.

6. Buna-N

It is a copolymer of buta-1,3-diene and acrylonitrile. It is formed as follows

$$n\,CH_2{=}CH{-}CH{=}CH_2 + n\,CH{=}CH_2$$

buta-1,3- diene $\overset{\displaystyle |}{CN}$

                             Acrylonitrile

$$\downarrow \text{Polymerisation}$$

$$+CH_2{-}CH{=}CH{-}CH_2{-}CH_2{-}\overset{\overset{\displaystyle CN}{|}}{CH}{\rightarrow}_n$$

Buna-N

Properties and Uses

It act as insulator in nature and is used for making conveyor belts and printing rollers.

Polyesters

The polymers which contain an ester linkage are known as polyester, e.g. dacron.

1. Polymethylmethacrylate (PMMA)

It is prepared by the polymerisation of methylmethacrylate in the presence of suitable organic peroxide.

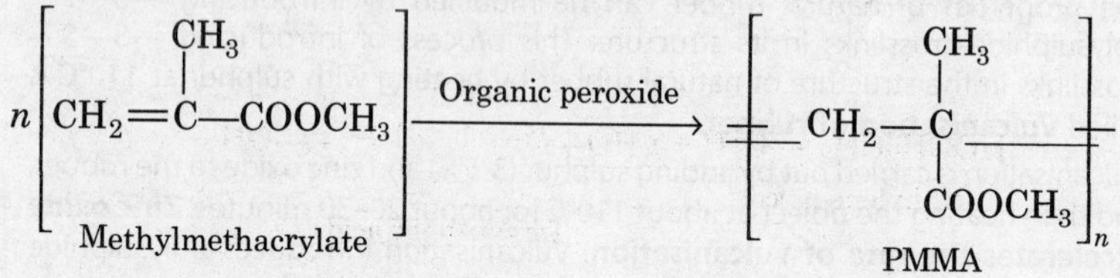

$$n\left[CH_2=\underset{\underset{Methylmethacrylate}{}}{\overset{\overset{CH_3}{|}}{C}}-COOCH_3\right] \xrightarrow{\text{Organic peroxide}} \left[CH_2-\underset{\underset{COOCH_3}{|}}{\overset{\overset{CH_3}{|}}{C}}\right]_n$$

PMMA

The polymer is known by several commercial names such as lucite, acrylite, plexiglass and perspex.

Properties and Uses

It is a hard and transparent polymer and is quite resistant to the effect of light, heat and ageing. It is used, in the manufacture of unbreakable lights, protective coatings, dentures, and in making windows for aircrafts.

2. Glyptal

It is a polyester having crosslinks. It is a thermosetting plastic. It is obtained by condensation of ethylene glycol or glycerol and phthalic acid.

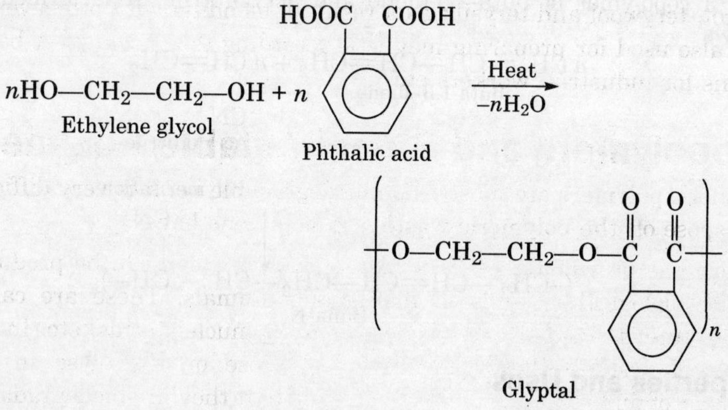

$$nHO-CH_2-CH_2-OH + n\;\underset{\text{Phthalic acid}}{\overset{\text{HOOC}\quad\text{COOH}}{\bigcirc}} \xrightarrow[-nH_2O]{\text{Heat}}$$

Ethylene glycol

$$\left[O-CH_2-CH_2-O-\overset{\overset{O}{\|}}{C}\;\overset{\overset{O}{\|}}{C}\right]_n$$

Glyptal

When its solution in a suitable solvent is evaporated, it leaves a tough but non-flexible film. It is, therefore, used in the manufacture of paints and lacquers.

3. Terylene (Dacron)

It is a condensation product of ethylene glycol and terephthalic acid. Polymerisation is carried out at 420 to 460 K in the presence of catalyst mixture of zinc acetate and antimony trioxide.

Ethylene glycol

Terephthalic acid

Polymerisation

Terylene or dacron

Properties and Uses

Terylene is highly resistant to the action of chemical and biological agents. Its fibres are quite strong and durable. It can also be blended with wool or cotton to obtain fabrics of desired composition.

Terylene is used in the manufacture of a variety of clothes such as terycot, terywool and terysilk as a result of blending with other yerns. It is also used for preparing magnetic recording tapes, conveyer belts, aprons for industrial workers etc.

Biopolymers and Biodegradable Polymers

Synthetic polymers are mostly non-biodegradable i.e. it is very difficult to dispose off the polymeric waste, e.g. polythene bags.

Nature has provided us a variety of polymers which can be produced by the biological systems in plants and animals. These are called **biopolymers,** e.g. polysaccharides, proteins, nucleic acids, etc. In the biological system, these polymers decompose or hydrolyse in the presence of different enzymes. This means that they are biodegradable. Aliphatic polyesters are the common examples of biodegradable polymers.

1. PHBV (poly-β-hydroxybutyrate-co-β-hydroxyvalerate)

It is a copolymer of 3-hydroxybutanoic acid and 3-hydroxypentanoic acid.

3-hydroxybutanoic acid   3-hydroxypentanoic acid

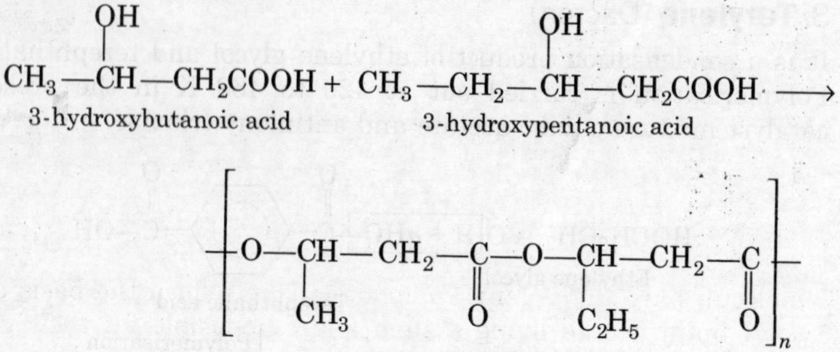

(PHBV)

2. Nylon-2-Nylon-6

It is an alternating polyamide copolymer of glycine (H_2N-CH_2-COOH) and amino caproic acid [$H_2N(CH_2)_5COOH$] and is biodegradable.

Few More Important Polymers

1. Saran is a copolymer of vinyldene chloride and other monomers and is used for wrapping food materials.

2. ABS rubber is a copolymer of acrylonitrile, buta-1,3-diene and styrene.

3. Bubble gum contains styrene butadiene (Buna-S) rubber.

4. Epoxy resins are used in making adhesives such as araldite, etc. These are the copolymer of epichlorohydrin and bisphenol-A.

5. Thikol is another variety of synthetic rubber which is a copolymer of ethylene chloride and sodium tetrasulphide (Na_2S_4).

6. Dynel is a copolymer of vinyl chloride and acrylonitrile and is used for making human hair wigs.

7. Silk is a thread like natural polymer which is obtained from cocoons of silk worms. It is a natural polyamide fibre.

8. Thermocol is a foamed plastic obtained by blowing air through molten polystyrene or polyurethane.

9. Superglue is a polymer of methyl α-cyanoacrylate and is obtained by anionic polymerisation of the monomer.

31

Biomolecules

Biomolecules are the organic compounds which form the basis of life, i.e. they build up the living system and responsible for their growth and maintenance.

The sequence that relates biomolecules to living organism is

Biomolecules → Organelles → Cells → Tissues → Organs → Organ systems → Living organism.

Carbohydrates

Optically active polyhydroxy aldehydes (aldoses) or ketones (ketoses) or the compounds which produce these units on hydrolysis are known as carbohydrates. They are also called **saccharides**.

Classification of Carbohydrates

(i) Reducing and Non-reducing Sugars

Based upon reducing and non-reducing properties, carbohydrates are classified as reducing and non-reducing sugars. Carbohydrates that reduces Fehling's reagent or Tollen's reagent are termed as reducing carbohydrates. e.g. All monosaccharides and disaccharides (except sucrose). But carbohydrates which do not reduce such reagents are known as non-reducing carbohydrates. e.g. sucrose and polysaccharides.

(ii) Sugars and Non-sugars

On the basis of taste, carbohydrates are classified as sugars and non-sugars. The monosaccharides and oligosaccharides having sweet taste are collectively known as **sugars**. Polysaccharides which are insoluble in water and not sweet in taste, are known as **non-sugars.** (Latin *Saccharum* = sugar) due to sweet taste of simpler members.

(iii) Monosaccharides, Oligosaccharides and Polysaccharides

Depending upon the number of simple molecules produced upon hydrolysis, carbohydrates are classified as, monsaccharides, oligosaccharides and polysaccharides :

I. Monosaccharides

These cannot be hydrolysed further to simpler molecules and subdivided into tetroses, pentoses or hexoses depending upon the number of carbon atoms. These are also called **homopolysaccharides.**

Aldotetroses	e.g Erythrose, Threose
Aldopentoses	e.g Xylose, Ribose
Aldohexoses	e.g Glucose, Galactose
Ketohexoses	e.g Fructose

All naturally occurring monosaccharides belong to D-series.

Killiani synthesis is used to convert an aldose into next higher aldose.

1. Glucose

It is also known as Dextrose. It is present in grape sugar, corn sugar, blood sugar ($C_6H_{12}O_6$).

Manufacture

By hydrolysis of starch with hot dil mineral acids and by hydrolysis of sucrose.

$$\underset{\text{sucrose}}{C_{12}H_{22}O_{11}} + H_2O \xrightarrow{\quad H^+ \quad} \underset{\text{glucose}}{C_6H_{12}O_6} + \underset{\text{fructose}}{C_6H_{12}O_6}$$

$$\underset{\text{starch or cellulose}}{(C_6H_{10}O_5)_n} + nH_2O \xrightarrow[\text{393 K; 2-3 bar}]{H^+} \underset{\text{glucose}}{n\,C_6H_{12}O_6}$$

Extra glucose is stored in liver as glycogen.

α and β-glucose

In intermolecular hemiacetal formation (cyclic structure), —CHO is converted into —CHOH which can have two configurations as shown below

$$\left. \begin{array}{c} H-C_1-OH \\ | \end{array} \right| \qquad \left. \begin{array}{c} HO-C_1-H \\ | \end{array} \right|$$

α-form (i)   β-form (ii)

Glucose having (i) configuration about C_1 is the α-glucose and having (ii) configuration about C_1 is β-glucose. The carbon C_1 is known as **anomeric** carbon and these compounds are called **anomers**. Both the forms are optically active. α-D-glucose has specific rotation +111.5° and β-D-glucose has specific rotation + 19.5°.

Mutarotation

When either of the two forms of glucose is dissolved in water, there is a spontaneous change in specific rotation till the equilibrium value of +52.5°. This is known as mutarotation.

$$\alpha\text{-D(+) Glucose} \rightleftharpoons \text{Equilibrium mixture} \rightleftharpoons \beta\text{-D-(+) Glucose}$$
$$+111.5° \qquad\qquad +52.5° \qquad\qquad +19.5°$$

Properties of Glucose

Glucose has one aldehyde group, one primary hydroxyl ($—CH_2OH$) and four secondary hydroxyl ($—CHOH$) groups and gives the following reactions:

(i) Glucose on acetylation with acetic anhydride gives a pentaacetate confirming the presence of five hydroxyl groups in glucose.

$$\begin{array}{c} CHO \\ | \\ (CHOH)_4 \\ | \\ CH_2OH \\ \text{glucose} \end{array} + 5(CH_3CO)_2O \longrightarrow \begin{array}{c} CHO \\ | \\ (CHOCOCH_3)_4 \\ | \\ CH_2OCOCH_3 \\ \text{pentacetyl glucose} \end{array} + 5CH_3COOH$$

(ii) Glucose reacts with hydroxylamine to give monoxime and adds with a molecule of hydrogen cyanide to give a cyanohydrin.

$$CH_2OH(CHOH)_4CHO \xrightarrow{HCN} CH_2OH(CHOH)_4CH{\Large\langle}{\begin{array}{l}OH\\CN\end{array}}$$
$$\text{glucose} \qquad\qquad\qquad\qquad \text{glucose cyanohydrin}$$

$$\xrightarrow[-H_2O]{NH_2OH} CH_2OH(CHOH)_4 CH{=}NOH$$
$$\text{glucose oxime}$$

These reactions confirm the presence of carbonyl group in glucose.

(iii) Glucose reduces ammoniacal silver nitrate solution (Tollen's reagent) to metallic silver and also Fehling's solution or Benedict solution to reddish brown cuprous oxide (Cu_2O) and itself gets oxidised to gluconic acid. This confirms the presence of an aldehydic group in glucose.

(iv) With mild oxidising agent like bromine water, glucose is oxidised to gluconic acid. Glucose on oxidation with nitric acid gives saccharic acid.

$$HOOC—(CHOH)_4—COOH \xleftarrow{HNO_3} HOCH_2(CHOH)_4CHO$$
$$\text{saccharic acid} \qquad\qquad\qquad\qquad \text{glucose}$$

$$\Big\downarrow Br_2/H_2O$$

$$HOCH_2—(CHOH)_4—COOH$$
$$\text{gluconic acid}$$

(v) Glucose on prolonged heating with HI forms *n*-hexane, suggesting that all the 6 carbon atoms in glucose are linked linearly.

$$HOCH_2—(CHOH)_4—CHO \xrightarrow{HI, \Delta}$$

$$H_3C—CH_2—CH_2—CH_2—CH_2—CH_3$$

However, with Na/Hg and water, glucose is reduced to sorbitol $HOH_2C(CHOH)_4CH_2OH$.

(vi) D-glucose reacts with three molecules of phenyl hydrazine to give osazone (glucosazone).

$$
\begin{array}{c}
CHO \\
| \\
CHOH \\
| \\
(CHOH)_3 \\
| \\
CH_2OH
\end{array}
\quad \xrightarrow[-2H_2O]{3C_6H_5NHNH_2} \quad
\begin{array}{c}
CH{=}NNHC_6H_5 \\
| \\
C{=}N\cdot NHC_6H_5 \\
| \\
(CHOH)_3 \\
| \\
CH_2OH
\end{array}
$$

glucose   glucosazone

(vii) Glucose on reaction with methyl alcohol in the presence of dry HCl(*g*) forms α and β-methyl glycosides. The reaction occurs only at the OH of hemiacetylic carbon.

α-methyl glucoside   β-methyl glucoside

Cyclic structure of glucose Given by Haworth and Hirst.

α-D (+) glucose   β-D (+) glucose

Glucose is sometimes illustrated as a chair form :

α-anomer   β-anomer

2. Fructose [Fruit Sugar ($C_6H_{12}O_6$)]

Manufacture

By hydrolysis of inulin.

$$(C_6H_{10}O_5)_n + nH_2O \xrightarrow{H^+} nC_6H_{12}O_6$$

inulin   fructose

Structure

Fructose has furanose structure, i.e. ring structure consisting of four C-atoms and one O atom.

α-D (–)   β-D (–)
fructofuranose   fructofuranose

α and β-fructose

The two forms have different configuration about C_2.

α-fructose   β-fructose

Fructose does not reduce Br_2 water.

Epimers

Monosaccharides differing in configuration at a carbon other than anomeric carbon are called epimers, e.g. glucose and galactose differ in configuration at C_4, hence called epimers.

Osazones

Monosaccharides and reducing disaccharides react with excess of phenyl hydrazine to form crystalline substances of the structure

$$CH\!=\!NNHC_6H_5$$
$$|$$
$$C\!=\!NNHC_6H_5$$
$$|$$
$$(CHOH)_x$$
$$|$$
$$CH_2OH$$

It is known as **osazones** and glucose and fructose give same osazone.

II. Oligosaccharides

(Greek *oligos* = few). On hydrolysis, they generally give two to nine monosaccharides (same or different) and are further classified as disaccharides, e.g. sucrose, maltose, lactose, trisaccharides and so on. $C_{12}H_{22}O_{11}$ is a disaccharide because it gives two monosaccharides.

$$\underset{\text{sucrose}}{C_{12}H_{22}O_{11}} + H_2O \longrightarrow \underset{\text{glucose}}{C_6H_{12}O_6} + \underset{\text{fructose}}{C_6H_{12}O_6}$$

The bond formed between two monosaccharides is called a **glycosidic bond** and normally it is (1, 4) bond.

1. Sucrose, $(C_{12}H_{22}O_{11})$

Sucrose is most abundant in plants and known as **cane sugar** or **table sugar** or **invert sugar** as equimolar mixture of glucose and fructose is obtained by hydrolysis of sucrose.

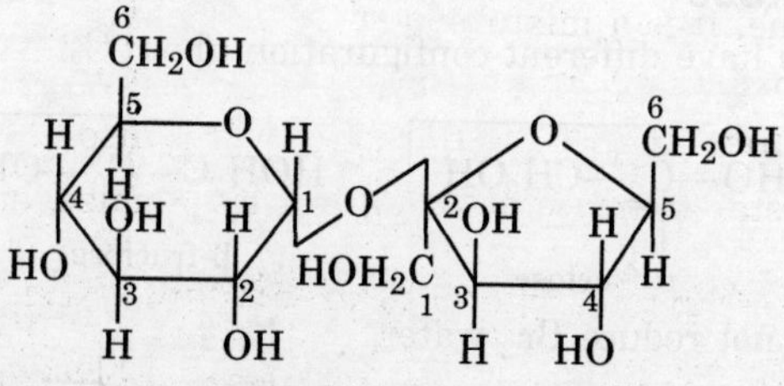

Structure of sucrose

2. Lactose or Milk sugar

It is present in milk of mammals and made up of **one glucose** and **one galactose** units. It is reducing sugar. Souring of milk is due to the conversion of lactose to lactic acid.

3. **Maltose or Malt sugar**

It is named because of its occurrence in malted grain of Barley. Mostly found in germinating seeds and tissue where starch is broken down. It is a reducing sugar and formed by condensation of 2 glucose units.

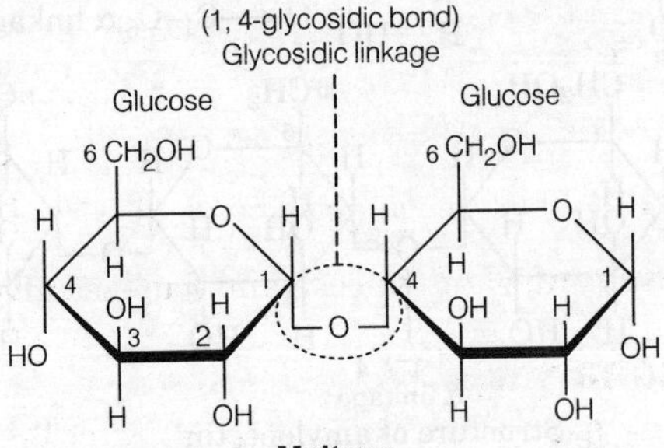

Maltose

Trisaccharides

Carbohydrate that yield three monosaccharide units on hydrolysis are called trisaccharide e.g; Raffinose ($C_{18}H_{32}O_{16}$).

$$(C_{18}H_{32}O_{16}) + 2H_2O \xrightarrow{H^+} \text{Glucose + Fructose + Galactose}$$

III. Polysaccharides

These are polymers of monosaccharides. Examples are starch, cellulose, glycogen, etc.

1. **Starch,** $(C_6H_{10}O_5)_n$

It is a polymer of α-glucose and a major reserve food in plants. It turns blue with iodine. It is a mixture of two components:

(i) **Amylose** (20%), an unbranched water soluble polymer.

(ii) **Amylopectin** (80%), a branched water insoluble polymer.

Sources of starch are potatoes, wheat, rice, maize, etc.

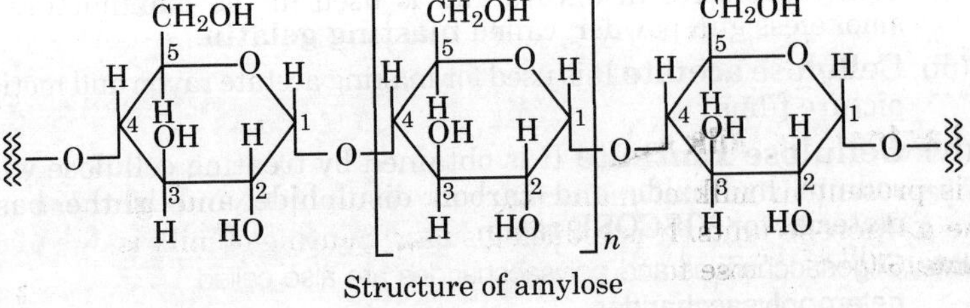

Structure of amylose

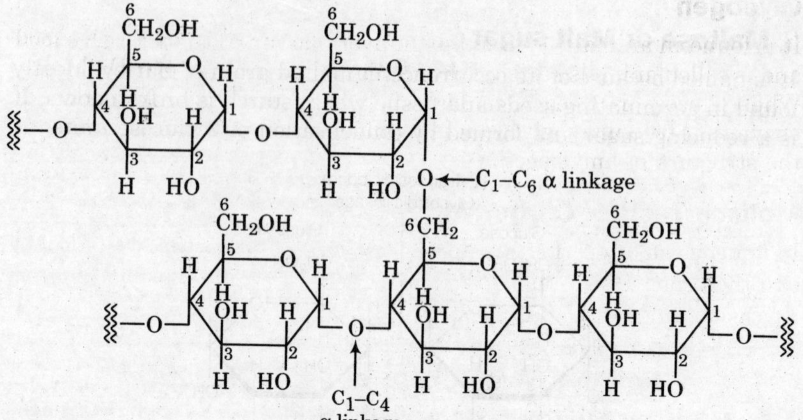

Structure of amylopectin

2. Cellulose, $(C_6H_{10}O_5)_n$

It is the most abundant and structural polysaccharide of plants. It is important food source of some animals. It is a polymer of $D(+)\beta$-glucose. The chief sources of cellulose are wood (contains 50% cellulose rest being lignin, resins, etc) and cotton (contains 90% cellulose rest being fats and waxes).

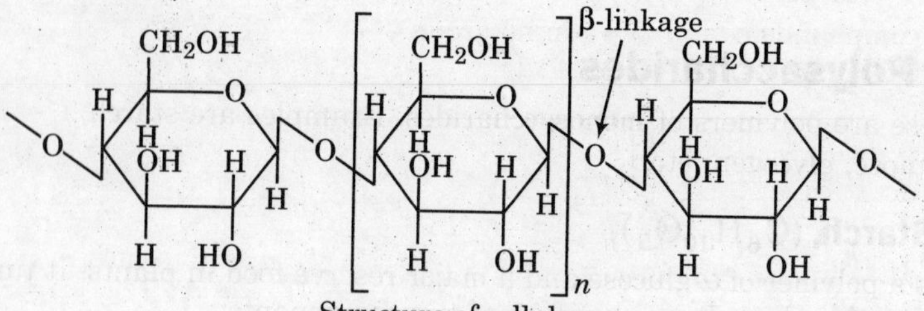

Structure of cellulose

Several materials are obtained from cellulose:

(i) **Mercerised cotton** Cellulose treated with conc. sodium hydroxide solution acquire silky lustre. It is called mercerised cotton.

(ii) **Gun cotton** It is completely nitrated cellulose (cellulose nitrate), highly explosive in nature and is used in the manufacture of smokeless gun powder, called **blasting gelatin**.

(iii) **Cellulose acetate** It is used for making acetate rayon and motion picture films.

(iv) **Cellulose xanthate** It is obtained by treating cellulose with sodium hydroxide and carbon disulphide and is the basic material for VISCOSE rayon.

Note Oligosaccharides and polysaccharides are also called **heteropolysaccharides**.

Glycogen

It is found in animal body (mainly in liver and muscles) as reserve food and is called animals starch. Like starch, it is a polymer of α-D-glucose. When glucose is needed in body it breaks down by the action of enzymes. Structurily, glycogen is highly branched and resemble with the structure of amylopectin.

Molisch Test for Carbohydrates

In aqueous solution of compound add solution of α-naphthol in alcohol and then conc. H_2SO_4 along the walls of the test tube. Purple coloured ring is obtained at the junction.

Relative Sweetness of Some Sugars

Cane sugar is assumed to have a sweetness of 10. The relative sweetness of other sugars is

Lactose	: 1.6	Invert sugar : 12.6
Fructose	: 17.3	Maltose : 3.2
Saccharin	: 300 (an artificial sweetener)	
Glucose	: 7.4	

Amino Acids

The compounds containing amino group ($—NH_2$) and carboxylic group ($—COOH$) are called amino acids.

$$\overset{\displaystyle NH_2}{\underset{}{R—CH—COOH}}$$

General formula $R—\underset{\alpha\text{-amino acid }(R \,=\, \text{side chain})}{\overset{NH_2}{|}{CH}}—COOH$

R = H, alkyl or aryl group. Except glycine ($H_2N \cdot CH_2COOH$), others are optically active in nature.

Classification of Amino Acids

(a) **α, β, γ-amino acids** Depending upon the position of $—NH_2$ on the carbon chain *wrt* $—COOH$ group.

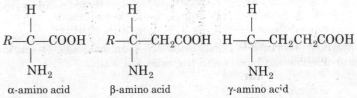

| α-amino acid | β-amino acid | γ-amino acid |

(b) **Neutral** Having one —NH_2 and one —COOH,
e.g. $NH_2 \cdot CH_2 \cdot COOH$ (glycine).

(c) **Acidic** Having one —NH_2 and two —COOH,

$$\overset{\displaystyle NH_2}{\underset{\displaystyle |}{}}$$

e.g. $HOOC \cdot CH_2 \cdot CH—COOH$ (aspartic acid)

(d) **Basic** Having two or more —NH_2 and one —COOH,
e.g.

$$\overset{\displaystyle NH_2}{\underset{\displaystyle |}{}}$$

$H_2N(CH_2)_4—CH—COOH$ (lysine).

Essential and Non-essential Amino Acids

Human body can synthesise ten out of twenty amino acids, called non-essential amino acids. The remaining ten amino acids required for protein synthesis are not synthesised by body and are called essential amino acids. They are

1. Phenylalanine
2. Histidine
3. Tryptophan
4. Valine
5. Methionine
6. Threonine
7. Arginine
8. Leucine
9. Isoleucine
10. Lysine

Nomenclature

They are known by their common names and abbreviated by first three letters of their common names e.g. glycine as 'gly' and alanine as 'ala'.

Configuration of α-Amino Acids

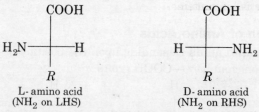

L- amino acid
(NH₂ on LHS)

D- amino acid
(NH₂ on RHS)

Naturally occurring α-amino acids are L-amino acids. D-amino acids occur in some antibiotics and bacterial cell walls.

Structure of Amino Acids

$$\underset{\text{as anion (high pH)}}{\overset{\overset{\displaystyle ..}{NH_2}}{NH_2}-\overset{\overset{\displaystyle R}{|}}{CH}-CO\bar{O}} \rightleftharpoons \underset{\substack{\text{Zwitter ion, (isoelectric} \\ \text{point)}}}{\overset{\overset{\displaystyle +}{H_3N}}{H_3N}-\overset{\overset{\displaystyle R}{|}}{CH}-CO\bar{O}} \overset{\overset{\displaystyle +}{H}}{\rightleftharpoons} \underset{\text{as cation (low pH)}}{\overset{+}{H_3N}-\overset{\overset{\displaystyle R}{|}}{CH}-COOH}$$

Peptides

Peptides are condensation products of two or more amino acids.

$$H_2N-\overset{\overset{\displaystyle R}{|}}{CH}-COOH + H_2N-\overset{\overset{\displaystyle R}{|}}{CH}-COOH \xrightarrow{-H_2O}$$

$$H_2N-\overset{\overset{\displaystyle R}{|}}{CH}-\overset{\overset{\displaystyle O}{\|}}{C}-NH-\overset{\overset{\displaystyle R}{|}}{CH}-COOH$$
dipeptide

$\overset{\overset{\displaystyle O}{\|}}{-C}-NH-$ is known as peptide linkage and C—N as a peptide bond.

Two molecules of different amino acids can form two dipeptides. Three molecules of different amino acids can give six tripeptides.

> Dipeptide has only one peptide bond, tripeptide has two peptide bonds and so on. Thus, a polypeptide made up of n-amino acids has $(n-1)$ peptide bonds.

Polypeptides

Condensation products of many amino acids (≈ 10000) is known as polypeptide and those polypeptides which have molecular mass above than 10000 are called proteins.

Proteins

They are linear polymers of α-amino acids.

Structure of Proteins

(a) **Primary structure** It simply reveals the sequence of amino acids.

(b) **Secondary structure** α-helix structure maintained by hydrogen bonds or β-pleated sheet structure when R is small group.

(c) **Tertiary structure** The folding and superimposition of polypeptide chains forms a compact globular shape, termed as tertiary structure. It is stabilised by covalent, ionic, hydrogen and disulphide bonds.

The precise arrangement constitutes the quaternary structure.

Classification on the Basis of Molecular Shape

1. **Fibrous proteins** When the polypeptide chains run parallel and are held together by hydrogen and disulphide bonds, then fibre like structure is formed. Such proteins are insoluble in water. e.g. Keratin (present in hair, wool) etc.

2. **Globular proteins** This structure results when the chains of polypeptides coil around to give a spherical shape. These are usually soluble in water e.g. insulin, albumins.

Classification on the Basis of Hydrolysis Products

(i) **Simple proteins** These yield only α-amino acids upon hydrolysis. e.g. albumin.

(ii) **Conjugated proteins** These yield α-amino acids and non-protein part, called prosthetic group.

Protein	Prosthetic group
Nucleoproteins	Nucleic acid
Phosphoproteins	Phosphoric acid
Glycoproteins	Carbohydrates
Metalloproteins	Metals
Lipoproteins	Lipids

(iii) **Derived proteins** These are obtained by partial hydrolysis of simple or conjugated proteins.

Proteins → Proteoses → Peptones → Polypeptides

Classification on the Basis Functions

(i) **Structural proteins** Fibrous proteins and globular proteins.

(ii) **Enzymes** Serve as biological catalyst e.g. pepsin, trypsin etc.

(iii) **Hormones** e.g. Insulin

(iv) **Contractile proteins** Found in muscles, e.g. myosin, actin.

(v) **Antibodies** Gamma globulins present in blood.

(vi) **Blood protein** Albumins, haemoglobin and fibrinogen.

Haemoglobin is a globular protein. Its prosthetic group is heme. It contains 574 amino acid units distributed in four polypeptide chains. Two chains containing 141 amino acid residues each are called α-chains and the two chains containing 146 amino acid residues are called β-chains.

⌐ Sickle cell anaemia is caused by defective haemoglobin obtained by replacing only one amino acid, i.e. glutamic acid by valine. ⌐

Denaturation of Proteins

The process that changes the three dimensional structure of native proteins is called denaturation of proteins. It can be caused by change in pH, addition of electrolyte, heating or addition of solvent like water, alcohol or acetone.

Tests of Proteins

(i) **Biuret Test**

Protein solution + NaOH + dil. $CuSO_4 \rightarrow$ pink or violet colour.

(ii) **Millon's Test**

Protein solution + Millon's reagent $\rightarrow$ red colour

Millon's reagent is solution of mercuric nitrate and traces of sodium nitrate solution.

(iii) **Iodine reaction**

Protein solution + iodine in potassium iodide solution $\rightarrow$ yellow colour.

(iv) **Xanthoprotein test**

Protein solution + conc. $HNO_3 \rightarrow$ yellow colour $\xrightarrow{\text{NaOH}}$ orange colour.

Enzymes

Enzymes constitute a group of complex proteinoid organic compounds, produced by living organisms which catalyse the chemical reaction.

Non-proteinous components enhance the activity of certain enzymes and are known as **co-enzymes**. These include metal ions like $Mn^{2+}, Mg^{2+}, K^+, Na^+, Zn^{2+}, Co^{2+}$ etc., heterocyclic ring systems (pyrrole, purine, pyridine, etc.), a sugar residue, phosphoric acid and residue of vitamins like thiamine, riboflavin etc.

Endoenzyme acts in the same cell in which it is synthesised, while **exo-enzyme** acts outside the cell in which it is synthesised.

Nomenclature

They are usually named by adding the suffix 'ase' to the root name of the substrate e.g. urease, maltase, diastase, invertase, etc.

Oxidative Enzymes

They catalyse oxidation-reduction reaction and are mostly conjugated proteins.

Some Common Enzymes

Name	Substrate	Products
Urease	Urea	$CO_2 + NH_3$
Maltase	Maltose	Glucose
Invertase	Sucrose	Glucose + fructose
Amylase	Starch	Maltose
Trypsin	Proteins	Amino acids
Ascorbic acid oxidase	Ascorbic acid	Dehydroascorbic acid

Characteristic Features of Enzymes

(i) **Rate of reaction** They increase the rate of reaction up to 10^6 to 10^7 times.

(ii) **Specific nature** Urease catalyse the hydrolysis of urea and not methyl urea, so these are specific in nature.

(iii) **Optimum temperature** It is active at 20-30°C.

(iv) **pH of medium** It is about 7 but for pepsin, it is 1.8-2.2 and for trypsin, it is 7.5-8.3.

(v) **Concentration** Dilute solutions are more effective.

(vi) **Amount of enzyme** Very small amount can accelerate the reaction.

(vii) **Enzyme inhibitors** These compounds inhibit the enzyme action. With the help of such compounds, the reaction can be controlled.

Mechanism of Enzyme Action

Enzyme + Substrate → [Enzyme substrate] →

Product + Enzyme Activated complex

Applications of Enzymes

(i) **Treatment of diseases** The congenital disease phenyl ketonuria caused by phenylalanine hyroxylase can be cured by diet of low phenylalanine content. Enzyme streptokinase is used for blood clotting to prevent heart disease.

(ii) **In industry** Tanning of leather, fermentation process etc.

Vitamins

The organic compounds other than carbohydrates, proteins and fats which are required by body to maintain normal health, growth and nutrition are called vitamins.

The vitamins are complex organic molecules. They are represented by letters such as A, B, C, D, E, K.

Vitamins are broadly classified into two types,

(i) Water soluble vitamins and

(ii) Fat soluble vitamins.

Vitamins A, D, E and K are fat soluble whereas vitamins B and C are water soluble. Vitamin H is neither fat soluble nor water soluble.

Vitamins and the Diseases Caused by their Deficiency

Vitamin	Chemical nature	Deficiency diseases
Vitamin A (Carotenoids or Axerophytol or retinol)	Soluble in oils and fats, but insoluble in water.	Night blindness, Xerophthalmia (cornea becomes opaque), drying of skin.
Vitamin B_1 (Thiamine)	Soluble in water, destroyed by heat.	Beriberi, loss of appetite.
Vitamin B_2 (Riboflavin)	Soluble in water, stable to heat, destroyed by light.	Cracked lips, sore tongue and skin disorders.
Vitamin B_6 (Pyridoxine)		Nervous disturbances and convulsions
Vitamin B_{12} (Cyano cobalamin)	Soluble in water and contains cobalt, red crystalline.	A serious type of anaemia. (pernicious anaemia)
Vitamin C (Ascorbic Acid, $C_6H_8O_6$)	Soluble in water, destroyed by cooking and exposure to air.	Scurvy, dental caries, pyorrhea, anaemia.
Vitamin D (Ergo calciferol)	Mixture of four complex compounds containing C,H and O. Soluble in fats and oils but insoluble in water. Stable towards heat and oxidation. This vitamin regulates the absorption of calcium and phosphate in intestine.	Infantile rickets, deformation of bones and teeth.
Vitamin E (Tocopherol)	Mixture of 3 complex substances containing C, H and O. Soluble in fats and oils but insoluble in water. Stable to heat and oxidation.	Loss of sexual power and degeneration of muscle fibres in animals.
Vitamin K (phylloquinone)	Mixture of two complex substances containing C, H and O. Soluble in fats but insoluble in water. Stable to heat and oxidation.	Tendency to haemorrhage and impaired clotting of blood.

Nucleic Acids

Important Terms of Nucleic Acids

(i) **Nitrogenous base** Derived from purines having two rings in their structure. e.g. Adenine (A) and Guanine (G) and derived from pyrimidines having one ring in their structure e.g. Thymine (T), Uracil (U) and Cytosine (C).

Two H–bonds are present between A and T (A = T) while three H-bonds are present between C and G (C $\equiv$ G).

(ii) **Pentose sugar** It is either ribose or deoxy ribose (not having oxygen at C_2).

(iii) **Nucleoside** Ribose–/deoxyribose + one base unit from A, G, C, T or U.

(iv) **Nucleotides** Nucleotides consist of 5-carbon sugar + nitrogenous base +1,3-phosphate groups.

(v) **Ribonucleotide** Phosphate unit + Ribose + one base unit from A, G, C, or U.

(vi) **Deoxyribo nucleotide** Phosphate unit + Deoxyribose + one base from A, G, C or T.

DNA and RNA

Nucleic acid is polynucleotide, present in the living cells or bacterial cells having no nucleus and in viruses having no cells. These are of two types:

(i) **DNA** Deoxyribonucleic acid.

DNA + $H_2O \rightarrow$ Phosphoric acid + deoxyribose + A, G, C, T

(ii) **RNA** Ribonucleic acid.

RNA + $H_2O \rightarrow$ Phosphoric acid + Ribose + A, G, C, U

Structure of DNA

It consists of two polynucleotide chains, each chain form a right handed helical spiral with ten bases in one turn of the spiral. The two chains coil to double helix and run in opposite direction. These are held together by hydrogen bonding.

Structure of RNA

It is usually a single strand of ribonucleotides and take up right handed helical conformation. Up to 12000 nucleotides constitute an RNA.

It can base pair with complementary strands of DNA or RNA. According to standard base pairing rules-G pairs with C, A pairs with U or T. The paired strands in RNA–RNA or RNA–DNA are anti parallel as in DNA.

In both DNA and RNA, heterocyclic base and phosphate ester linkages are at C_1 and C_5' respectively of the sugar molecule.

Types of RNA

(i) **Messanger RNA** (*m*-RNA) It is produced in the nucleus and carries information for the synthesis of proteins.

(ii) **Transfer RNA** (Soluble or Adoptive RNA) (*s*-RNA, *t*-RNA)   It is found in cytoplasm. Its function is to collect amino acids from cytoplasm for protein synthesis.

Functions of Nucleic Acids

1. Direct the synthesis of proteins.
2. Transfer the genetic information (hereditary characters).

IMPORTANT TERMS

Replication

It is a process in which a molecule of DNA can duplicate itself.

Template   It means pattern. In the process of replication of DNA, the parent strand serves as template.

Gene   The portion of DNA carrying information about a specific protein is called gene.

Genetic code   The relation between the amino acid and the nucleotide triplet is called genetic code.

Codons   The nucleotide bases in RNA function in groups of three (triplet) in coding amino acids. These base triplets are called codons.

The word code is used with reference to DNA, codon with reference to *m*-RNA and anticodon with reference to *t*-RNA.

Lipids

The constituents of animals and plants soluble in organic solvents (ether, chloroform, carbon tetrachloride), but insoluble in water are called lipids. (Greek *lipose* = fat)

Types of Lipids

(i) **Simple lipids**

(a) **Fats and oils** on hydrolysis give long chain fatty acids + glycerol.

(b) **Waxes** Long chain fatty acids + long chain alcohols.

Vegetable and animal oils and fats have similar chemical structure and are triesters of glycerol, called glycerides.

Simple glycerides contain one type of fatty acids. Mixed glycerides contain two or three types of fatty acids.

Common saturated fatty acids CH_3—$(CH_2)_n$ COOH.

When $n = 4$ caproic acid; $n = 6$ caprylic acid; $n = 8$ capric acid, $n = 10$ lauric acid $n = 12$ myristic acid; $n = 14$ palmitic acid, $n = 16$ stearic acid.

Common unsaturated fatty acids

$C_{17}H_{33}COOH$ oleic acid; $C_{17}H_{33}COOH$ linoleic acid.

Difference between oils and fats Oils are liquids at ordinary temperature (below 20°) and contain lower fatty acids or unsaturated fatty acids.

Fats are solids or semisolids above 20°C and contain higher saturated fatty acids. Oils and fats act as "energy reservoirs" for the cells.

(ii) **Phospholipids** Phosphate + glycerol + fatty acids + a nitrogen containing base.

Function of phospholipids are

1. As emulsifying agents since they carry hydrophilic polar groups and hydrophobic non-polar groups.

2. They absorb fatty acids from the intestine and transport to blood cells.

(iii) **Glycolipids** They contain one or more simple sugars and are important components of cell membranes and chloroplast membranes.

(iv) **Terpenes** Menthol, camphor are common plant terpenes. Carotenoids and pigments are also terpenes.

(a) **Essential oils** The volatile, sweet smelling liquids obtained from flowers, leaves, stems, etc. Example of terpenes are esters of lower fatty acid, e.g. clove oil, rose oil, lemon oil.

(b) **Drying oils** The oils which are converted into tough, transparent mass when exposed to air by oxidation polymerisation process are called drying oils. e.g. Linseed oil, perilla, poppy seed oils.

Cotton seed oil and til oil are semidrying oils.

Acid Value
It is the number of milligrams of KOH required to neutralise the free acid present in 1 g of oil or fat.

Saponification Value
It is the number of milligrams of KOH required to saponify 1 g of oil or fat or the number of milligrams of KOH required to neutralise the free acid resulting from the hydrolysis of 1 g of an oil or fat.

Iodine Value
It is the number of grams of iodine absorbed by 100 g of oil or fat.

Reichert–Meissel Value (R/M Value)
It is the number of cc of N/10 KOH required to neutralise the distillate of 5 g of hydrolysed fat.

Hormones

These are the chemical substances which are produced by endocrine (ductless) glands in the body. Hormones acts as **chemical messengers.**

Some examples of ductless (endocrine) glands are thyroid, pitutary, adrenal, pancreas, testes and ovaries.

Hormones are divided into three types :

(i) steroids

(ii) proteins or polypeptides

(iii) amines.

Some Typical Hormones and their Functions

	Hormone	Source	Chemical name	Function
1.	Thyroxin	Thyroid	Amino acid	Stimulates metabolism.
2.	Adrenaline	Adrenal	Amine	Increases pulse rate and blood pressure, release glucose from glycogen and fatty acids from fats.
3.	Insulin	Pancreas	Peptide	Decreases blood glucose.
4.	Glucagon	Pancreas	Peptide	Increases blood glucose.
5.	Testosterone	Testes	Steroid	Controls normal functioning of male sex organs.
6.	Estrone and Estradiol	Ovary	Steroid	Controls normal functioning of female sex organs.
7.	Progesterone	Ovary	Steroid	Prepare uterus for pregnancy, controls menstrual cycle.
8.	Cortisone	Adrenal cortex	Steroid	Metabolism of water, mineral salts, fats, proteins and carbohydrates.

Insulin is a protein hormone which is secreted by β-cells of the pancreas. Insulin was the first polypeptide in which the amino acid sequence was experimentally determined. Its deficiency leads to diabetes mellitus.

32

Chemistry in Everyday Life

The branch of science which makes use of chemicals for the treatment of diseases [therapeutic effect] is called **chemotherapy**.

Medicines or Drugs

Chemicals which may be used for the treatment of diseases and for reducing the suffering from pain are called medicines or drugs.

Some important classes of drugs are :

1. Antacids

The chemical substances which neutralize the excess acid in gastric juice and raise the pH to an appropriate level in stomach are called antacids.

The most commonly used antacids are weak bases such as sodium bicarbonate [sodium hydrogencarbonate, $NaHCO_3$], magnesium hydroxide [$Mg(OH)_2$] and aluminium hydroxide [$Al(OH)_3$].

Generally liquid antacids are more effective than tablets because they have more surface area available for interaction and neutralisation of acid.

Milk is a weak antacid.

Histamine stimulates the secretion of pepsin and hydrochloric acid. The drug cimetidine [Tegamet] was designed to prevent the interaction of histamine with the receptors present in the stomach wall. Cimetidine binds to the receptors that triggers the release of acid into the stomach. This result in release of lesser amount of acid. Now **ranitidine (zantac), omeprazole** and **lansoprazole** are used for hyperacidity.

2. Tranquilizers (Psychotherapeutic Drugs)

Chemical substances used for the treatment of stress, anxiety, irritability and mild or even severe mental diseases, are known as tranquilizers. These affect the central nervous system and induce sleep for the patients as well as eliminate the symptoms of emotional distress. They are the common constituents of sleeping pills.

Noradrenaline is one of the neurotransmitter that plays a role in mood changes. If the level of noradrenaline is low, the signal sending activity becomes low, and the person suffers from depression. In such situations antidepressant drugs are required. These drugs inhibit the enzymes which catalyse the degradation of noradrenaline. If the enzyme is inhibited, this important neurotransmitter is slowly metabolized and can activate its receptor for longer periods of time, thus counteracting the effect of depression. Iproniazid and phenelzine are two such drugs.

Barbituric acid and its derivatives *viz.* veronal, amytal, nembutal, luminal, seconal are known as barbiturates. Barbiturates are hypnotic, i.e. sleep producing agents.

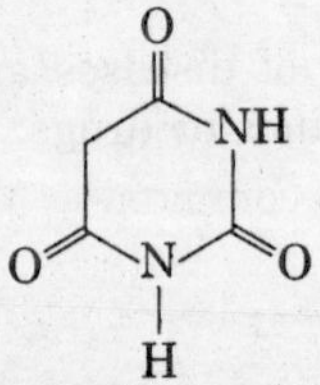

barbituric acid 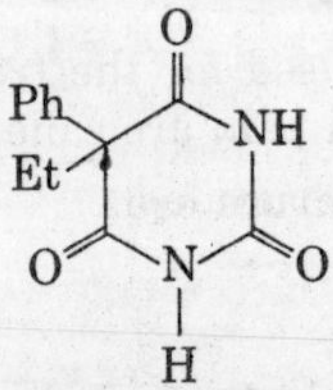   luminal 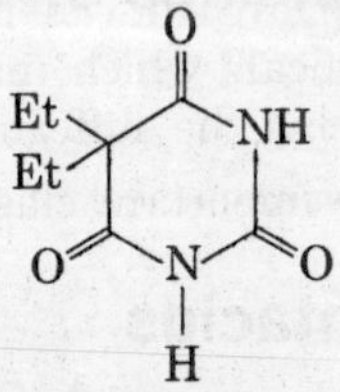   veronal

Equanil is used to control depression and hypertension.

Non-hypnotic chlorodiazepoxide and meprobamate are relatively mild tranquilizers suitable for relieving tension.

3. Analgesics

Medicines used for getting relief from pain without causing impairment of consciousness are called analgesics. These are of two types :

(i) Narcotics

Drugs which produce sleep and unconsciousness are called narcotics. These are habit forming drugs. For example, morphine and codeine. Morphine diacetate is commonly known as heroin.

(ii) Non-narcotics

These are non-habit forming chemicals which reduce mild to moderate pain such as headache, toothache, muscle and joint pain, etc. These are also termed as **non-addictive**. These drugs do not produce sleep and unconsciousness. Aspirin (2-acetoxybenzoic acid) is most commonly used analgesic with antipyretic properties. Now these days because of its anti-blood clotting action, aspirin is widely used to prevent heart-attacks.

(Acetylsalicyclic acid)
aspirin

Aspirin is toxic for liver and sometimes also causes bleeding from stomach. So, naproxen, ibuprofen, paracetamol,diclofenac sodium are other widely used analgesics.

4. Antipyretics

These are the chemical substance which reduce body temperature during high fever. Paracetamol, aspirin, phenacetin (4-hydroxy acetanilide), analgin and novalgin, etc., are common antipyretics. Out of these, paracetamol (4-acetamidophenol) is most common.

paracetamol

5. Antimicrobials

An antimicrobial tends to kill or prevent development of microbes or inhibit the pathogenic action of microbes such as bacteria, fungi and virus selectively.

Sulpha drugs constitute a group of drugs which are derivatives of sulphanilamide and have great antimicrobial capacity, thus, these are widely used against diseases such as dyptheria, dysentry, tuberculosis, etc.

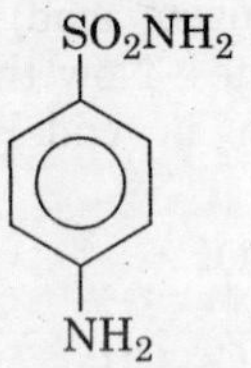

sulphanilamide

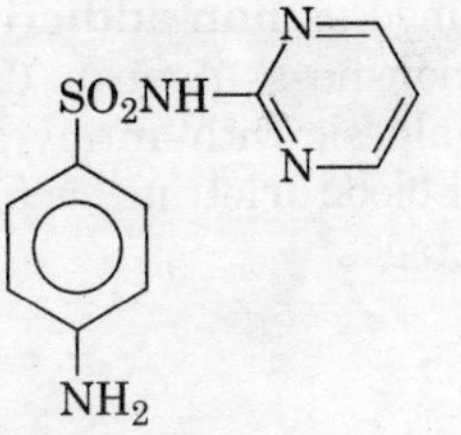

sulphadiazine

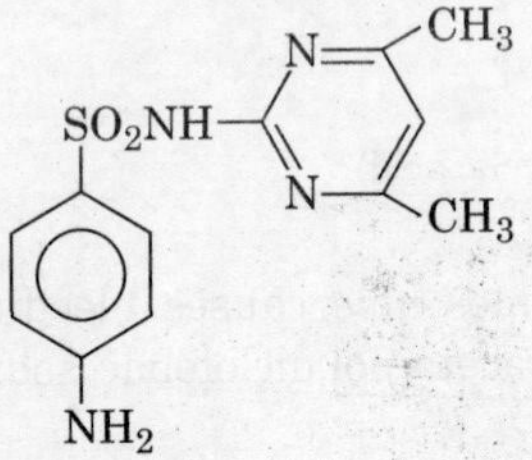

sulphadimidine

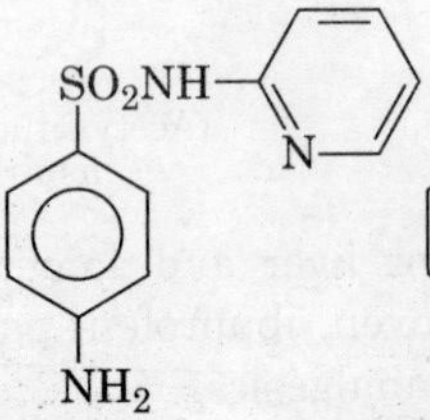

sulphapyridine

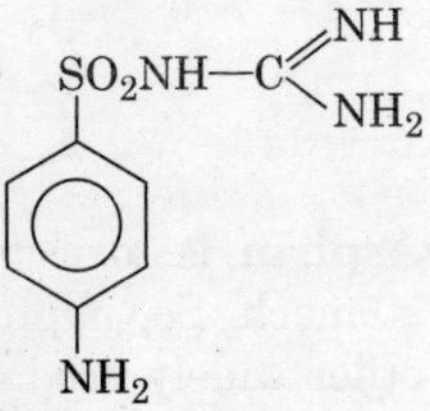

sulphaguanidine

In these structure, drugs are analogues of *p*-amino benzoic acid. Different types of antimicrobial drugs are as follows :

(i) Antibiotics

These are the substances (produced wholly or partially by chemical synthesis) which in low concentrations inhibit the growth of microorganisms or destroy them by intervening in their metabolic processes.

Antibiotics are products of microbial growth and thus, antibiotic therapy has been likened to 'setting one thief against another'.

Antibiotics are of two types :

(a) **Bactericidal antibiotics** have cidal (killing) effect on microbes. For example, penicillin, ofloxacin, amino glycosides, etc.

(b) **Bacteriostatic antibiotics** have a static (inhibitory) effect on microbes. For example, erythromycin, tetracycline, chloramphenicol, etc.

Penicillin was the first antibiotic discovered (by Alexander Fleming) in 1929. It is a narrow-spectrum antibiotic. Ampicillin and amoxicillin are semi-synthetic modifications of penicillin. Penicillin is not suitable to all persons and some persons are allergic to it. Consequently, it is essential to test the patients for sensitivity (or allergy) to penicillin, before it is administered.

In India, penicillin is manufactured at Pimpri and Rishikesh (Uttarakhand).

Broad-spectrum antibiotics also called wide-spectrum antibiotics, which are effective against several different types of harmful microorganisms. These antibiotics can kill or inhibit a wide range of gram positive or gram negative bacteria. e.g. Tetracycline, chloramphenicol (given in case of typhoid, dysentery, fever etc.) ofloxacin, etc.

(ii) **Antiseptics**

These are the chemicals which either kill or prevent the growth of microorganisms. Antiseptics are applied to the living tissues such as wounds, cuts, ulcers and skin diseases in the form of antiseptic creams like furacin and soframycin. Some important examples of antiseptics are

(a) **Dettol** is a mixture of chloroxylenol and terpineol.

chloroxylenol

terpineol

(b) **Bithional** is added to soaps to impart antiseptic properties to reduce the odour produced by bacterial decomposition of organic matter on the skin.

bithional

(c) **Tincture of iodine** is a 2-3% solution of iodine in alcohol, which is a powerful antiseptic for wounds.

(d) **Iodoform** (CHI_3) is also used as an antiseptic for wounds.

(e) **Boric acid** in dilute aqueous solution is a weak antiseptic for eyes.

(iii) **Disinfectants**

These are the chemical substances which kill microorganisms but are not safe to be applied to the living tissues. They are generally used to kill the microorganisms present on inanimate objects such as floors, drainage system, instruments, etc.

Some common examples of disinfectants are as follows :
(a) **1% phenol solution** is disinfectant while in lower concentration 0.2% solution of phenol is antiseptic.
(b) **0.2-0.4 ppm aqueous solution of chlorine** is used for sterilisation of water to make it fit for drinking purpose.
(c) **SO_2 at very low concentrations** behaves like disinfectant.
(d) **Formaldehyde (HCHO) in the gaseous forms** is used for disinfecting rooms and operation theatres in hospitals.

6. Antifertility Drugs

These are the chemical substances used to control the pregnancy. These are also called **oral contraceptives**. They belong to the class of natural products, known as **steroids**.

Birth control pills essentially contain a mixture of synthetic estrogen and progesterone derivatives. Norethindrone is widely used as antifertility drug.

Chemicals in Food

1. Artificial Sweetening Agents

Sucrose (table sugar) and fructose are the most widely used natural sweeteners. But they add calories to our intake and promote tooth decay. To avoid these problems many people take artificial sweeteners.

Organic substances which have been synthesized in lab are known to be many times sweeter than cane sugar. Such compounds are known as artificial sweetening agents or artificial sweeteners.

Some important artificial sweeteners are given below :

(i) Saccharin (o-sulphobenzimide)

Discovered by while he constant in Fahlberg was working at Hopkins university in 1879.

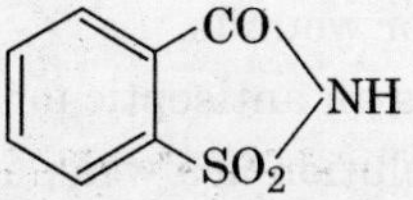

saccharin 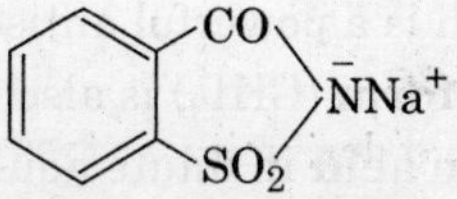   sodium salt of saccharin
                   soluble in water

It is the most popular artificial sweetener. It is 550 times as sweet as cane sugar, since it is insoluble in water, so it is sold in the market, its soluble form are its sodium or calcium salts.

It is non-biodegradable so excreted from the body in urine (unchanged). It's use is of great value for diabetic persons and people who need to control intake of calories.

(ii) **Aspartame**

It is the methyl ester of the dipeptide derived from phenylalanine and aspartic acid. It is also known as 'Nutra sweet'.

It decomposes at baking or cooking temperatures and hence, can be used only in cold food and soft drinks.

Aspartame has the same amount of calories as sugar (4 cal per gram).

Aspartame should not be used by people suffering from the genetic disease known as PKU (phenyl ketone urea). Because in such people decomposition of aspartame gives phenylpyruvic acid. Accumulation of phenylpyruvic acid is harmful especially to infants that causes brain damage and mental retardation.

(iii) **Alitame**

It is quite similar to aspartame but more stable than aspartame. It is 2000 times as sweet as sucrose. The main problem for such sweetener is the control of sweetness of the substance to which it is added because it is high potency sweetener.

(iv) **Sucralose**

It is a trichloro derivative of sucrose. It's appearance and taste are like sugar. It is stable at cooking temperature. It is almost 600 times as sweet as sucrose. However, it neither provide calories nor causes tooth decay.

(v) **Cyclamate**

It is N-cyclohexylsulphamate. It is only 20 times sweeter than cane sugar.

$$\text{—NHSO}_3^{\ominus}\overset{\oplus}{\text{Na}}$$

cyclamate

2. **Food Preservatives**

These are the chemical substances added to food to prevent their spoilage due to microbial growth (bacteria, yeasts and moulds) and to retain their nutritive value for longer periods .

The most commonly used preservatives include table salt, sugar, vegetable oil, vinegar, citric acid, spices and sodium benzoate ($C_6H_5COO^-\overset{+}{N}$a). Salts of sorbic acid and propanoic acid are also used as preservatives for cheese, baked food, pickles, meat and fish products.

(i) **Sodium benzoate** is metabolised by conversion into hippuric acid ($C_6H_5CONHCH_2COOH$), which is ultimately excreted in urine. It is used in soft drinks and acidic foods.

(ii) **Antioxidants** like BHT (butylated hydroxy toluene) and BHA (butylated hydroxy anisole) retard the action of oxygen on the food and help in the preservation of food materials.

(BHT)   (BHA)

Cleansing Agents

The word detergent means cleansing agent. Actually detergent word is derived from Latin word **'detergere'** means **"to wipe off"**.

Cleansing agents are the substances which remove dirt and have cleansing action in water. These are also called **surfactants**.

Detergents can be classified into two types.

(i) Soapy detergents or soaps, and

(ii) Non-soapy detergents or soapless soap.

1. Soaps

Soaps are sodium or potassium salts of higher fatty acids (containing large number of carbon atoms) e.g. stearic acid, oleic acid and palmitic acid. Sodium salts of fatty acids are known as **hard soaps** while the potassium salts of fatty acids are known as **soft soaps**.

Hard soaps are prepared by cheaper oil and NaOH while soft soaps are prepared by oil of good quality and KOH. The soft soaps do not contain free alkali, produce more lather and are used as toilet soaps, shaving soaps and shampoos.

Preparation of soaps

Soaps containing sodium salts are formed by heating fat (glyceryl ester of fatty acid) with aqueous sodium hydroxide solution. This reaction is known as **saponification**.

$$
\begin{array}{c}
\text{CH}_2\text{—O—}\overset{\overset{\displaystyle O}{\|}}{\text{C}}\text{—C}_{17}\text{H}_{35} \\
| \qquad \overset{\displaystyle O}{\|} \\
\text{CH—O—}\overset{\overset{\displaystyle O}{\|}}{\text{C}}\text{—C}_{17}\text{H}_{35} \quad + 3\text{NaOH} \xrightarrow{\Delta} 3\text{C}_{17}\text{H}_{35}\text{COO}^-\text{Na}^+ \;+\;
\begin{array}{c}
\text{CH}_2\text{—OH} \\
| \\
\text{CH—OH} \\
| \\
\text{CH}_2\text{—OH}
\end{array} \\
| \qquad \overset{\displaystyle O}{\|} \\
\text{CH}_2\text{—O—}\overset{\overset{\displaystyle O}{\|}}{\text{C}}\text{—C}_{17}\text{H}_{35}
\end{array}
$$

fat
(Glyceryl ester of stearic acid)
(soap) sodium stearate   glycerol

$$\text{Oil/Fat} + \text{NaOH} \xrightarrow{\Delta} \text{Soap} + \text{Glycerol}$$

The solution left after removing the soap contains glycerol, which can be recovered by fractional distillation. To improve the quality of soaps desired colours, perfumes and medicinal chemical substances, are added.

Types of Soaps

Different types of soaps are made by using different raw materials.

    (i) **Toilet soaps** These are prepared by using better grade of fat or oil and care is taken to remove excess alkali. Colour and perfumes are added to make these more attractive.

    (ii) **Floating soaps** These can be prepared by beating tiny air bubbles into the product before it hardens.

    (iii) **Transparent soaps** These are made by dissolving the soap in ethanol and then evaporating the excess solvent.

    (iv) **Medicated soaps** Medicated soaps are prepared by adding some antiseptics like dettol or bithional.

(v) **Shaving soaps** These contain glycerol to prevent rapid drying. A gum called rosin is added while making them. It forms sodium rosinate which lather well.

(vi) **Laundry soaps** These contain fillers like sodium rosinate, sodium silicate, borax and sodium carbonate.

(vii) **Soap chips** These are made by running a thin sheet of melted soap on a cool cylinder and scraping off the soaps in small broken pieces.

(viii) **Soap granules** These are dried miniature soap bubbles.

(ix) **Soap powder and scouring soaps** These contain a scouring agent (abrasive) such as powdered pumice or finely divided sand and builders like sodium carbonate and trisodium phosphate. Builders increases the cleansing action of soaps by making them to act more quickly.

Disadvantages of Soaps

Soap is good cleansing agent and is 100% biodegradable, i.e. microorganisms present in sewage water can completely oxidise soap to CO_2. As a result, it does not create any pollution problem. However, soaps have two disadvantages:

(i) Soaps cannot be used in hard water since calcium and magnesium ions present in hard water produce curdy white precipitates of calcium and magnesium soaps.

$$2C_{17}H_{35}CO\overset{-}{O}\overset{+}{N}a + CaCl_2 \longrightarrow \underset{\text{insoluble}}{(C_{17}H_{35}CO\overset{-}{O})_2\overset{2+}{Ca}} + 2NaCl$$

$$2C_{17}H_{35}CO\overset{-}{O}\overset{+}{N}a + MgSO_4 \longrightarrow \underset{\text{insoluble}}{(C_{17}H_{35}COO)_2\overset{2+}{Mg}} + Na_2SO_4$$

These insoluble soaps separate as scum in water and causes hindrance to washing because the precipitate adheres onto the fibre of the cloth as gummy mass. Thus, a lot of soap is wasted if water is hard.

(ii) Soaps cannot be used in acidic solutions since acids precipitate the insoluble free fatty acids which adhere to the fabrics and thus, reduce the ability of soaps to remove oil and grease from fabrics.

$$\underset{\text{soap}}{R CO\overset{-}{O}\overset{+}{N}a} + H^+ \longrightarrow \underset{\substack{\text{free fatty acid} \\ \text{precipitate out}}}{R COOH} + Na^+$$

Soapless Soap/Synthetic Detergents

Synthetic detergents have all the properties of soaps but actually does not contain any soap, so they are known as 'soapless soaps'.

Straight chain alkyl group containing detergents are biodegradable whereas branched chain alkyl group containing detergents are non-biodegradable.

Unlike soaps, synthetic detergents can be used in both soft and hard water. This is due to the reason that calcium and magnesium salts of water are soluble in detergents. Synthetic detergents are mainly classified into three categories:

1. Anionic Detergents

These are sodium salts of sulphonated long chain alcohols or hydrocarbons.

    (i) Alkyl hydrogen sulphates are formed by treating long chain alcohols with concentrated sulphuric acid are neutralised with alkali to form anionic detergents.

$$CH_3(CH_2)_{10}CH_2\!-\!OH \xrightarrow[H_2SO_4]{Conc.} CH_3(CH_2)_{10}CH_2\!-\!OSO_3H$$

      lauryl alcohol   lauryl hydrogen sulphate

$$\downarrow aq.\ NaOH$$

$$CH_3(CH_2)_{10}CH_2OSO_3^-Na^+$$

                    sodium lauryl sulphate
                    (anionic detergent)

   (ii) Alkyl benzene sulphonates are obtained by neutralising alkyl benzene sulphonic acids with alkali.

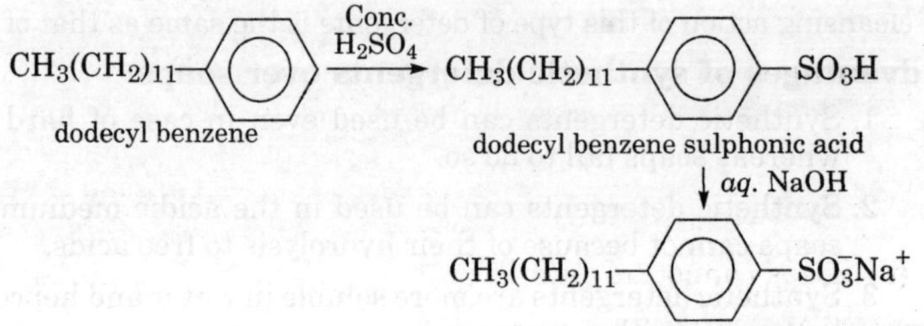

$$CH_3(CH_2)_{11}\!\!-\!\!\bigcirc \xrightarrow[H_2SO_4]{Conc.} CH_3(CH_2)_{11}\!\!-\!\!\bigcirc\!\!-\!SO_3H$$

    dodecyl benzene   dodecyl benzene sulphonic acid

$$\downarrow aq.\ NaOH$$

$$CH_3(CH_2)_{11}\!\!-\!\!\bigcirc\!\!-\!SO_3^-Na^+$$

            sodium dodecyl benzene sulphonate (SDS)
                      or
        sod-4-(1-dodecyl) benzene sulphonate
              (Anionic detergent)

In such detergents, the anionic part of the molecule is involved in the cleansing action.

They are mostly used for household work and **in tooth paste**.

2. **Cationic Detergents**

These are quaternary ammonium salts of amines with acetates, chlorides or bromides as anion. For example,

$$\left[CH_3(CH_2)_{15} - \overset{\overset{\displaystyle CH_3}{|}}{\underset{\underset{\displaystyle CH_3}{|}}{N^+}} - CH_3 \right] Br^-$$

cetyltrimethyl ammonium
bromide

Cationic detergents are used in hair conditioner. They have germicidal properties but are expensive therefore, these are of limited use.

3. **Non-ionic Detergents**

Such detergents does not contain any ion in their constitution. One such detergent can be obtained by reaction of stearic acid and polyethylene glycol.

$$HO-CH_2-CH_2-OH + n\ CH_2-CH_2 \longrightarrow$$
ethylene glycol

$$\underset{\text{ethylene oxide}}{\overset{O}{\diagup}}$$

$$HO-(CH_2CH_2O)_n-CH_2CH_2OH$$
polyethylene glycol

$$CH_3(CH_2)_{16}COOH \text{ (stearic acid)} \downarrow H_2O$$

$$CH_3(CH_2)_{16}COO(CH_2CH_2O)_n CH_2CH_2-OH$$
polyethylene glycol stearate

Liquid dish washing detergents are non-ionic type. Mechanism of cleansing action of this type of detergents is the same as that of soaps.

Advantages of synthetic detergents over soaps

1. Synthetic detergents can be used even in case of hard water whereas soaps fail to do so.

2. Synthetic detergents can be used in the acidic medium while soaps cannot because of their hydrolysis to free acids.

3. Synthetic detergents are more soluble in water and hence, form better lather than soaps.

4. Synthetic detergents have a stronger cleansing action than soaps.

Chemistry in Colouring Matter

The natural or synthetic colouring matter which are used in solution to stain materials especially fabrics are called **dyes**.

All colouring substances are not dyes, e.g. azobenzene, a coloured substance does not act as dye.

A dye have following characteristics :

1. It must have a suitable colour.
2. It can be fixed on the fabric either directly or with the help of mordant.
3. It must be resistant to the action of water, acid and alkalies.

The groups, responsible for colour, are called **chromophore**, e.g.

$$-N{=}N-, \quad -\overset{\overset{\displaystyle O}{\|}}{N}{\rightarrow}O, \quad {>}C{=}O, \quad {>}C{=}S \text{ etc.}$$

The substance which do not given colour itself but intensify the colour of chromophore, are called **auxochrome**.

e.g. $-OH$, $-SO_3H$, $-COOH$, $-NH_2$, $-NHR-$, $-NR_2$.

Classification of Dyes on the Basis of Constitution

(i) **Nitro or nitroso dye** Chromophore NO_2 or NO group, Auxochrome = $-OH$ group, e.g. picric acid, martius yellow, Gambine, naphthol yellow-S.

(ii) **Azo dye**, e.g. bismark brown, methyl orange, methyl red, congo red, etc.

(iii) **Anthraquinone dye** e.g. alizarin

(iv) **Indigo** is the oldest known dye. Other examples are tyrian purple, indigosol.

(v) **Phthalein dye** e.g. phenolphthalein, fluorescein, eosin, mercurochrome.

(vi) **Triarylmethane dye**, e.g. malachite green, rosaniline.

Classification of Dyes on the Basis of Application

(i) **Direct dyes** These dyes applied directly to fibre and are more useful to the fabrics containing H-bonding like cotton, rayon, wool, silk and nylon, e.g. martius yellow, congo red, etc.

(ii) **Acid dyes** These are water soluble and contain polar acidic groups which interact with the basic group of fabric, e.g. Orange-1, congo red, methyl orange, etc. These dyes does not have affinity for cotton but are used for silk, wool, etc.

(iii) **Basic dyes** These dyes contain basic group (like NH_2 group) and react with anionic sites present on the fabric. These are used to dye nylons and polyester, e.g. butter yellow, magenta (rosaniline), aniline yellow, etc.

(iv) **Vat dyes** Being water insoluble, these cannot be applied directly. These are first reduced to a colourless soluble form by a reducing agent in large vats and then, applied to fabrics. After applying, these are oxidised to insoluble coloured form by exposure to air or some oxidising agents, e.g. Indigo, tyrian purple, etc.

(v) **Mordant dyes** These are applied with the help of a binding material (e.g. metal ion, tannic acid or metal hydroxide) called mordant. Depending upon the metal ion used, the same dye can give different colours. Alizarin is an important example of such dyes.

(vi) **Ingrain dye** These dyes are synthesised directly on the fabric. These are water insoluble and particularly suitable for cotton fibres. Azo dyes belong to this group of dye.

(vii) **Disperse dye** These are applied to the fabric in the form of their dispersion in a soap solution in the presence of a stabilising agent like cresol, phenol, benzoic acid, etc. These are used to colour synthetic fabrics like nylon, orlon, polyesters and cellulose acetate. Anthraquinone dyes and monoazo dye are the examples of dispersed dye.

Chemistry in Cosmetics

Cosmetics are used for decorating, beautifying or improving complexion of skin. Some of the cosmetics of daily use are as

Creams

These are stable emulsions of oils or fats in water and contain emmollients (to prevent water loss) and humectants (to attract water) as two fundamental components.

Perfumes

These solutions have pleasant odour and invariably consist of three ingredients: a vehicle (ethanol + H_2O), fixative e.g. sandalwood oil, benzoin, glyceryl diacetate etc.) and odour producing substance, (e.g. terpenoids like linalool, anisaldehyde (p-methoxy- benzaldehyde etc.)

Talcum Powder

It is used to reduce irritation of skin. Talc ($Mg_3(OH)_2Si_4O_{10}$), chalk, ZnO, zinc sterate and a suitable perfume are the constituents of talcum powder.

Deodorants

These are applied to mask the body odour. These possess antibacterial properties. Aluminium salts, ZnO, ZnO_2, $(C_{17}H_{35}COO)_2Zn$ can be used in deodorant preparation.

Rocket Propellants

Substances used for launching rockets are called **rocket propellants**. These are the combination of an oxidiser and a fuel.

Depending upon the physical states of oxidiser and fuels, rocket propellants are classified as

(i) Solid Propellants

These are further divided into two classes :

(a) **Composite propellants** In these propellants, fuel is polymeric binder such as polyurethane or polybutadiene and oxidiser is ammonium per chlorate or potassium perchlorate.

(b) **Double base propellants** These mainly use nitroglycerine (liquid) and nitrocellulose (solid). The nitrocellulose gels in nitroglycerine sets in as a solid mass.

(ii) Liquid Propellants

Oxidiser = N_2O_4, liquid O_2, HNO_3 and Fuel = kerosene, alcohol, hydrazine or liquid hydrogen.

There are of two types :

(a) **Monopropellants** In such propellants, the substance act an fuel as well as oxidiser. e.g. CH_3NO_2, H_2O_2, CH_3ONO_2 etc.

(b) **Bi-liquid propellants** Fuels = kerosene, alcohol etc., and oxidiser = liquid O_2, liquid N_2O_4 or HNO_3.

(iii) Hybrid Propellants

In these, solid fuel and liquid oxidiser is used, e.g. acrylic rubber (solid fuel) and liquid N_2O_4 (liquid oxidiser).

SLV-3 (space launch vehicle-3) and ASLV (Augmented space launch vehicle) the Indian satellites used composite solid propellants.

In space shuttle, liquid O_2 + liquid H_2 is used.

33

Nuclear Chemistry

The branch of chemistry which deals with the study of composition of atomic nucleus, nuclear forces, nuclear reactions and radioactive materials, is called nuclear chemistry.

Nucleons and Nuclear Forces

Protons and neutrons which reside in the nucleus, are called **nucleons** and forces binding them in the nucleus, are called **nuclear forces.**

These are short range forces operating over very small distances (1 fermi = 10^{-15} cm).

These forces are 10^{21} times stronger than the electrostatic forces.

n^0 and p^+ are held together by very rapid exchange of nuclear particles, called (π^-) **mesons** (discovered by Yukawa). Its mass is 273 times more than the mass of the electron and it may be positively charged (π^+), negatively charged (π^-) or neutral (π^0).

$$_1H^1 + _{-1}\pi^0 \longrightarrow _0n^1$$

$$_0n^1 + _{+1}\pi^0 \longrightarrow _1H^1$$

Parameter of Nucleus

(i) **Radius of nucleus** It is proportional to the cube root of the mass number of element.

$$R = R_0 \times A^{1/3}$$

where, A = mass number, R = radius of nucleus

R_0 = proportionality constant = 1.4×10^{-13} m = 1.4×10^{-15} cm

Radius of the nucleus = $10^{-13} - 10^{-12}$ cm

(ii) **Nuclear density**   It is calculated as, $d = \dfrac{3 \times \text{mass}}{4\pi R_0^3}$

density of all nuclei is constant.

It is very large ($\approx 10^{17}$ kg/m^3) compared to atomic density ($\approx 10^3$ kg/m^3).

(iii) **Volume of nucleus**   Volume of nucleus = $\dfrac{4}{3}\pi R^3 = 10^{-36}$ cm^3

(Volume of atom = 10^{-24} cm^3)

Factors Affecting Stability of Nucleus

Stability of nucleus is affected by following factors :

1. Neutron-proton Ratio or *n/p* Ratio

It is the main factor for determining the stability of nucleus.

The nuclei located in the **zone of stability** or **belt of stability** are stable.

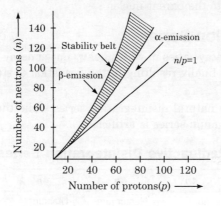

Nuclei lying above this zone, have higher n/p ratio and undergo β-emission to get the zone of stability.

Here, a n^0 is transformed into p^+ and give β and antineutrino. Thus, emission of β-particles increases the number of proton and decreases the number of neutrons.

$$_0n^1 \rightarrow {_1}H^1 + {_{-1}}e^0 + \text{antineutrino}$$

Nuclei lying below this zone, have low n/p ratio and undergo positron emission or K-electron capture, to get the zone of stability.

During *K*-electron capture, p^+ is converted into n^0 and X-rays are emitted. e.g.

$$_{26}\text{Fe}^{55} + _{-1}e^0 \longrightarrow _{25}\text{Mn}^{55}\,(K - e^- \text{ capture})$$

Generally nuclei with n/p ratio higher than 1.56 undergo spontaneous fission.

2. Magic Numbers

Nuclei having 2, 8, 20, 28, 50, 82 and 126 protons or neutrons are stable, hence these numbers are called magic numbers.

Nuclei with even numbers of both p^+ and n^0 are generally more stable than those with their odd numbers.

Group Displacement Law

This law was given by Soddy, Russel and Fajans in 1913 to decide the position of element, obtained after radioactive disintegration, in the Periodic Table.

According to this law, 'In an α-emission, the daughter nuclei will occupy a position which is two places left to the position of parent nuclei and in a β-emission, the daughter nuclei will occupy a position one place right to the parent nuclei.

Disintegration Series

These are the decay series in which heavy nuclei decay by a series of α and β-emissions finally resulting in the formation of stable isotopes of lead.

There are three natural disintegration series while the fourth series, called the neptunium series is artificial.

Radioactive Disintegration Series

Series	4n	4n + 1	4n + 2	4n + 3
Name	Thorium	Neptunium	Uranium	Actinium
Parent element	$_{90}\text{Th}^{232}$	$_{94}\text{Pu}^{241}$	$_{92}\text{U}^{238}$	$_{92}\text{U}^{235}$
Prominent element	$_{90}\text{Th}^{232}$	$_{93}\text{Np}^{237}$	$_{92}\text{U}^{238}$	$_{89}\text{Ac}^{227}$
End product	$_{82}\text{Pb}^{208}$	$_{83}\text{Bi}^{209}$	$_{82}\text{Pb}^{206}$	$_{82}\text{Pb}^{207}$
Number of particles lost	α = 6 β = 4	α = 8 β = 5	α = 8 β = 6	α = 7 β = 4

To find a series, mass number is divided by 4.

Artificial Radioactivity

The phenomenon of conversion of a stable nuclei into a radioactive nuclei by bombarding it with a high speed projectile is called artificial radioactivity or induced radioactivity (given by Curie and Joliot).

The element with atomic number greater than 92 (after U) are obtained by this process. These are called **transuranium elements.** These all are synthetic and radioactive.

e.g. $\underset{\text{projectile}}{_{13}Al^{27}} + _0n^1 \longrightarrow \underset{\substack{\text{radioactive} \\ \text{stable}}}{_{11}Na^{24}} + _2He^4 \longrightarrow _{12}Mg^{24} + _{-1}e^0$

n^0, p^+, deuteron ($_1H^2$) and α-particles ($_2He^4$) are used as projectile.

Artificial Transmutation

The conversion of a non-radioactive element into another non-radioactive elements by artificial means, i.e. by bombarding with some fundamental particles, is called artificial transmutation. e.g.

$$_7N^{14} + _2He^4 \longrightarrow _8O^{17} + _1H^1$$

Nuclear Reactions

In these reactions, the nuclei of atoms interact with other nuclei or elementary particles such as α, β, p, d, n etc., and results in the formation of a new nucleus and one or more elementary particles.

A nuclear reaction can be represented as

parent nuclei (projectile, obtained particle) daughter nuclei.

e.g. the reaction,

$$\underset{\alpha\text{-particle}}{_4Be^9 + _2He^4} \longrightarrow \underset{\text{neutron}}{_6C^{12} + _0n^1} \text{ is represented as}$$

$$_4Be^9 (\alpha, n) \, _6C^{12}.$$

Energy of a nuclear reaction, Q
 = (total mass of products − total mass of reactants) × 931.5 MeV.

For **exoergic reactions**, Q is negative and for **endoergic reactions**, Q is positive.

Types of Nuclear Reactions

(i) **Projectile capture reactions** In these reactions, the projectile is absorbed with or without the emission of γ-radiations. e.g.

$$_{92}U^{238} + _0n^1 \longrightarrow _{92}U^{239} + \gamma$$

(ii) **Particle-particle reactions** In these reactions, an elementary particle is also obtained along with the product e.g.

$$_{11}Na^{23} + _1H^1 \longrightarrow _{12}Mg^{23} + \underset{\substack{\text{elementary}\\\text{particle}}}{_0n^1}$$

(iii) **Spallation reactions** In these reactions, high speed projectiles with energies approximately 40 MeV chip fragments from a heavy nucleus, leaving a small nucleus, e.g.

$$_{29}Cu^{63} + _2He^4 + (400 \text{ MeV}) \longrightarrow _{17}Cl^{37} + 14_1H^1 + 16_0n^1$$

(iv) **Fission reactions** In these reactions, a heavy nucleus is broken down into two or more medium heavy fragments with the emission of a large amount of energy, e.g.

$$_{92}U^{235} + _0n^1 \longrightarrow _{56}Ba^{141} + _{36}Kr^{92} + 3_0n^1 + 200 \text{ MeV}$$

(v) **Fusion reactions** In these reactions, lighter nuclei fuse together to give comparatively heavier nuclei. e.g.

$$_1H^2 + _1H^3 \longrightarrow _2He^4 + _0n^1 + 17.6 \text{ MeV}$$

These reactions are the source of tremendous amount of energy.

Applications of Radioactivity

1. Estimation of Age (Dating Technique)

(i) **Carbon dating technique** It is used to determine the age of wood, animal fossils etc. It is based upon the ratio of C^{14} to C^{12} which remains constant in living organisms but decreases in dead sample. By comparing these two, the age is determined.

The age is calculated by using the formula,

$$t = \frac{2.303}{k} \log_{10} \frac{N_0}{N}$$

N_0 = ratio of C^{14} / C^{12} in atmosphere, N = ratio of C^{14} / C^{12} in dead matter.

(ii) **Uranium dating technique** The age of earth, minerals, rocks etc., is determined by this technique. It is based upon the U^{238} / Pb^{206} ratio.

$$\text{Age, } t = \frac{2.303}{k} \log_{10} \left[1 + \frac{Pb^{206}}{U^{238}} \right]$$

2. **Medicinal Use**

Radioisotopes are used to diagnose and cure many diseases. These can be used in three ways.

(i) **In vivo studies** ^{51}Cr is used for such technique.

(ii) **In therapeutic procedure** (to cure diseases)   Co - 60 is used for the treatment of cancer, Na-24 is injected to trace the flow of blood, I-131 is used for the treatment of thyroid and P-32 is used for leukemia.

(iii) **Imaging procedure**   I-131 is used to study the structure and activity of thyroid gland. I-123 is used in brain imaging and Tc-99 M is used in bone scans.

Radioisotopes are also widely used to find the reaction mechanism, in industry and in agriculture.

34

Analytical Chemistry

Introduction

The branch of chemistry which deals with the identification of constituents of a substance and calculation of their amounts is called analytical chemistry.

Branches of Analytical Chemistry

The branches of analytical chemistry are

(a) **Qualitative analysis** It deals with the identification of various constituents present in a given material. It further be classified as

1. Qualitative analysis of inorganic compounds
2. Qualitative analysis of organic compounds

(b) **Quantitative analysis** It deals with the measurement of amounts/volume/strength of a substance/solution.

Qualitative Analysis of Inorganic Compounds

It involves the following steps :

1. Preliminary tests
2. Dry tests
3. Wet tests for anions
4. Wet tests for cations

Preliminary Tests

(i) **Solubility** Compounds that dissolve in water to the extent of approximately 0.02 mol per litre (0.02M) are usually classified as 'soluble' compounds, while those that are less soluble are classified as "insoluble" compounds. No gaseous or solid substances are infinitely soluble in water.

1. All common inorganic acids are soluble in water. Low molecular weight organic acids are soluble.

2. All common compounds of the group IA metal (Na, K, etc) and the ammonium ion, NH_4^+, are soluble in water.

3. All common nitrates NO_3^-, acetates, CH_3COO^-, and perchlorates, ClO_4^-, are soluble in water.

4. (a) All common chlorides, Cl^-, are soluble in water except AgCl, Hg_2Cl_2 and $PbCl_2$.

   (b) The common bromides Br^-, and iodides I^-, show approximately the same solubility behaviour as chlorides, but there are some exceptions. As the halide ions (Cl^-, Br^-, I^-) increase in size, the solubilities of their slightly soluble compounds decrease. Although $HgCl_2$ is readily soluble in water, $HgBr_2$ is only slightly soluble and HgI_2 is even less soluble.

   (c) The solubilities of the pseudo-halide ions, CN^- (cyanide) and SCN^- (thiocyanate), are quite similar to those of the corresponding iodides. Additionally, both CN^- and SCN^- show strong tendencies to form soluble complex compounds.

5. All common sulphates, SO_4^{2-}, are soluble in water except $PbSO_4$, Hg_2SO_4 and $BaSO_4$. $CaSO_4$ and Ag_2SO_4 are sparingly soluble.

6. All common metal hydroxides are insoluble in water except those of the group IA metals and the lower members of the group IIA metals, beginning with $Ca(OH)_2$.

7. All common carbonates CO_3^{2-}, phosphates, PO_4^{3-}, and arsenates AsO_4^{3-}, are insoluble in water except those of the group IA metals and $NH_4^+ \cdot MgCO_3$ is fairly soluble.

8 All common sulphides, S^{2-} are insoluble in water except those of the group IA and group IIA metals and the ammonium ion.

(ii) **Colour change on heating** Certain oxides change colour on heating and this fact can be used to identify salt.

Oxides	Colour	
	In cold	**On heating**
ZnO	white	yellow
Fe_2O_3	brown	black/red
PbO	red	yellow

Observation	Inference
Sublimate formed with smell of NH_3	NH_4^+ salts
Sublimate formed without smell of NH_3	Hg^{2+} salts
Brown fumes	Some nitrates

Dry Tests

(a) **Borax bead test** If borax, $Na_2B_4O_7 \cdot 10H_2O$ is heated on the platinum loop, a transparent colourless glass like bead of sodium metaborate ($NaBO_2$) and boric anhydride (B_2O_3) is formed.

$$Na_2B_4O_7 \xrightarrow{\Delta} 2NaBO_2 + B_2O_3$$

Characteristics coloured beads are produced with salts of copper, iron.

$$CuO + B_2O_3 \longrightarrow \underset{\text{copper (II) metaborate}}{Cu(BO_2)_2}$$

Results have been summarised in table.

Colour in Oxidising and Reducing Flames in Borax-Bead Test

Oxidising flame		Reducing flame		Metal
Hot	**Cold**	**Hot**	**Cold**	
Green	Blue	Colourless	Opaque red-brown	Copper
Yellowish-brown	Yellow	Green	Green	Iron
Violet	Reddish-brown	Grey	Grey	Nickel
Yellow	Colourless	Brown	Brown	Molybdenum
Rose-violet	Rose-violet	Red	Violet	Gold
Yellow	Colourless	Yellow	Yellowish-brown	Tungsten

Oxidising flame		Reducing flame		Metal
Hot	Cold	Hot	Cold	
Yellow	Pale yellow	Green	Bottle-green	Uranium
Yellow	Greenish -yellow	Brownish	Emerald -green	Vanadium
Yellow	Colourless	Grey	Pale violet	Titanium
Orange-red	Colourless	Colourless	Colourless	Cerium

(b) **Microcosmic salt bead test** A test similar to borax bead test is used for identification of coloured cations if microcosmic salt, $Na(NH_4)HPO_4 \cdot 4H_2O$, is used.

$$Na(NH_4)HPO_4 \xrightarrow{\Delta} \underset{\substack{\text{transparent} \\ \text{bead}}}{NaPO_3} + H_2O \uparrow + NH_3 \uparrow$$

$$NaPO_3 + CoO \longrightarrow \underset{\text{(blue bead)}}{NaCoPO_4}$$

Results have been summarised in the following table.

Microcosmic Salt Bead Test

Oxidising flame	Reducing flame	Metal
Green when hot, blue when cold	Colourless when hot, red when cold	Copper
Yellowish-or reddish-brown when hot, yellow when cold	Yellow when hot, colourless to green when cold	Iron
Green, hot and cold	Green, hot and cold	Chromium
Violet, hot and cold	Colourless, hot and cold	Manganese
Blue, hot and cold	Blue, hot and cold	Cobalt
Brown, hot and cold	Grey when cold	Nickel
Yellow, hot and cold	Green when cold	Vanadium
Yellow when hot, yellow-green when cold	Green, hot and cold	Uranium
Pale yellow when hot, colourless when cold	Green when hot, blue when cold	Tungsten
Colourless, hot and cold	Yellow when hot, violet when cold	Titanium

(c) **Sodium carbonate bead test** The sodium carbonate bead is prepared by fusing a small quantity of sodium carbonate on a platinum wire loop in the Bunsen flame; a white, opaque bead is produced. If this is moistened, dipped into a little KNO_3 and then into a small quantity of a manganese salt (for example) and the whole mixture is heated in the oxidising flame, a green bead of sodium manganate (Na_2MnO_4) is formed.

$$MnO + Na_2CO_3 + O_2 \xrightarrow{\Delta} Na_2MnO_4 + CO_2$$

A yellow bead is obtained with chromium salt due to formation of sodium chromate (Na_2CrO_4).

$$2Cr_2O_3 + 4Na_2CO_3 + 3O_2 \longrightarrow 4Na_2CrO_4 + 4CO_2$$

(d) **Flame test** Paste of salt and conc. HCl is taken into the lower oxidising zone and colour imparted to the flame by salts is observed. Salts, particularly of group V (Ba^{2+}, Ca^{2+}, Sr^{2+}) are identified by colours of the flame and summarised in Table

Flame Tests

Colour	Cation
Golden yellow	Na^+
Violet	K^+
Carmine-red	Li^+
Brick-red	Ca^{2+}
Apple-green	Ba^{2+}, Mo^{2+}
Green	Cu^{2+}, (BO_3^{3-}), Tl^{3+}
Crimson-red	Sr^{2+}

The yellow colouration due to sodium masks is that of potassium. In such cases view the flame through cobalt glass, the yellow sodium colour is absorbed and the potassium flame appears crimson.

Wet Tests for Anions

Salt or mixture is treated with dil. H_2SO_4 and also with conc. H_2SO_4 separately and by observing the types of gases evolved, confirmatory tests of anions are performed.

Observation with Dilute H_2SO_4

S. No.	Observation	Acid radical	Confirmatory test*
1.	Brisk effervescence with evolution of colourless and odourless gas	CO_3^{2-} (carbonate)	Gas turns lime water (or baryta water) milky but milkyness disappears on passing gas in excess (A)*
2.	Brown fumes	NO_2^- (nitrite)	Add KI and starch solution—blue colour (B)*
3.	Smell of rotten eggs (H_2S smell) on heating	S^{2-} (sulphide)	Gas turns lead acetate paper black (C) Sodium carbonate extract (SE) + sodium nitroprusside solution $\rightarrow$ purple colour (D)

(i) **Carbonate**

$$Na_2CO_3 + H_2SO_4 \longrightarrow Na_2SO_4 + H_2O + CO_2$$

$$\underset{\text{lime water}}{Ca(OH)_2} + CO_2 \longrightarrow \underset{\text{milky}}{CaCO_3 \downarrow} + H_2O$$

(ii) **Nitrite**

$$2NaNO_2 + H_2SO_4 \longrightarrow Na_2SO_4 + 2HNO_2$$

$$3HNO_2 \longrightarrow HNO_3 + 2NO \uparrow + H_2O$$

$$2NO + O_2(air) \longrightarrow 2NO_2 \text{ (brown)}$$

$$2KI + H_2SO_4 + 2HNO_2 \longrightarrow K_2SO_4 + 2H_2O + 2NO + I_2$$

$$I_2 + starch \longrightarrow \text{(blue colour) starch iodide}$$

(iii) **Sulphide**

$$Na_2S + H_2SO_4 \longrightarrow H_2S + Na_2SO_4$$

$$H_2S + (CH_3COO)_2Pb \longrightarrow \underset{\text{(black)}}{PbS} + 2CH_3COOH$$

$$Na_2S + \underset{\substack{\text{sodium} \\ \text{nitroprusside}}}{Na_2[Fe(CN)_5NO]} \longrightarrow \underset{\text{(purple)}}{Na_4[Fe(CN)_5NOS]}$$

Observation with Concentrated H$_2$SO$_4$

S.No.	Observation	Acid radical	Confirmatory test
1.	Colourless pungent gas giving white fumes with *aq* NH$_4$OH	Cl$^-$ (chloride)	Add MnO$_2$ in the same test tube and heat — pale green Cl$_2$ gas (*A*), SE + HNO$_3$ + AgNO$_3$ solution $\longrightarrow$ white ppt soluble in *aq* NH$_3$ (*B*) **Chromyl chloride test**
2.	Reddish brown fumes	Br$^-$ (bromide)	Add MnO$_2$ and heat — yellowish brown Br$_2$ gas. SE + HNO$_3$ + AgNO$_3$ solution — pale yellow ppt partially soluble in *aq* NH$_3$ **Layer test**
3.	Violet pungent vapours turning starch paper blue	I$^-$ (iodide)	SE + HNO$_3$ + AgNO$_3$ $\longrightarrow$ yellow ppt insoluble in *aq* NH$_3$ **Layer test**
4.	Brown pungent fumes intensified by the addition of Cu-turnings	NO$_3^-$ (nitrate)	**Ring test** (I)

(i) Chloride

$$KCl + H_2SO_4 \underset{\text{(conc.)}}{\longrightarrow} KHSO_4 + HCl$$

$$HCl + NH_3\,(aq) \longrightarrow \underset{\text{(white fumes)}}{NH_4Cl}$$

$$4HCl + MnO_2 \xrightarrow{\Delta} MnCl_2 + Cl_2\uparrow + 2H_2O$$

$$KCl + AgNO_3 \longrightarrow \underset{\text{white ppt}}{AgCl\downarrow} + KNO_3$$

$$AgCl + 2NH_3\,(aq) \longrightarrow \underset{\text{soluble}}{[Ag(NH_3)_2]Cl}$$

Chromyl-chloride test

Chloride + $K_2Cr_2O_7$ (solid) + conc. $H_2SO_4 \xrightarrow{\text{heat}}$ reddish brown vapours of chromyl-chloride (CrO_2Cl_2). Pass these vapours into NaOH solution, yellow Na_2CrO_4 solution is formed. On adding CH_3COOH and $(CH_3COO)_2Pb$, yellow ppt of lead chromate ($PbCrO_4$) is formed.

$$KCl + H_2SO_4 \xrightarrow[\text{conc.}]{\Delta} KHSO_4 + HCl$$

$$K_2Cr_2O_7 + 2H_2SO_4 \xrightarrow[\text{conc.}]{\Delta} 2KHSO_4 + 2CrO_3 + H_2O$$

$$CrO_3 + 2HCl \longrightarrow CrO_2Cl_2 + H_2O$$

$$CrO_2Cl_2 + 4NaOH \longrightarrow Na_2CrO_4 + 2NaCl + 2H_2O$$

$$Na_2CrO_4 + (CH_3COO)_2Pb \longrightarrow \underset{\text{yellow ppt}}{PbCrO_4\downarrow} + 2CH_3COONa$$

(ii) Bromide

$$KBr + H_2SO_4 \xrightarrow[\text{conc.}]{\Delta} KHSO_4 + HBr$$

$$4HBr + MnO_2 \xrightarrow{\Delta} Br_2 + 2H_2O + MnBr_2$$

$$NaBr + AgNO_3 \longrightarrow \underset{\text{pale yellow ppt}}{AgBr\downarrow} + NaNO_3$$

$$AgBr + 2NH_3\,(aq) \longrightarrow \underset{\text{partially soluble}}{[Ag(NH_3)_2]Br}$$

Layer test

$SE + Cl_2$ water $\xrightarrow{\text{shake}}$ yellowish orange colour in $CHCl_3$ layer (CS_2 or CCl_4 can be taken instead of $CHCl_3$).

$$2NaBr + Cl_2 \longrightarrow 2NaCl + \underset{\substack{\text{orange yellow}\\\text{soluble in } CHCl_3}}{Br_2}$$

In case of I^-, violet colour of I_2 in $CHCl_3$ layer

$$2NaI + Cl_2 \longrightarrow 2NaCl + I_2 \text{ (violet)}$$

(iii) **Iodide**

$$\underset{\text{conc.}}{KI + H_2SO_4} \xrightarrow{\Delta} KHSO_4 + HI$$

$$2HI + H_2SO_4 \longrightarrow I_2(\text{violet}) + 2H_2O + SO_2$$

Layer test See Layer test (above).

(iv) **Nitrate**

$$\underset{\text{conc.}}{NaNO_3 + H_2SO_4} \longrightarrow NaHSO_4 + HNO_3$$

$$4HNO_3 \longrightarrow \underset{\text{brown fumes}}{4NO_2} + O_2 + 2H_2O$$

$$Cu + 4HNO_3 \longrightarrow Cu(NO_3)_2 + 2NO_2 + 2H_2O$$

Ring test To water extract (all NO_3^- are water soluble) add freshly prepared $FeSO_4$ solution and then conc. H_2SO_4 carefully by the side of the test-tube. A dark brown ring of $[Fe(H_2O)_5NO]^{2+}SO_4^{2-}$ at the interface between the two liquids is formed.

$$2NaNO_3 + 2H_2SO_4 \longrightarrow 2NaHSO_4 + 2HNO_3$$
$$2HNO_3 + 6FeSO_4 + 3H_2SO_4 \longrightarrow 3Fe_2(SO_4)_3 + 2NO + 4H_2O$$
$$[Fe(H_2O)_6]SO_4 + NO \longrightarrow [Fe(H_2O)_5NO]^{2+}SO_4^{2-} + H_2O$$

Wet Tests for Cations

Different basic radicals have different solubility products and precipitated by different reagents. Thus, on the basis of solubility products and reagent used, basic radicals are classified into following groups.

Classification of Basic Radicals into Groups Based on K_{sp} Values

Group	Basic radicals	Group reagent	Precipitate as	Explanation
I	Pb^{2+}	dil. HCl	chloride ($PbCl_2$)	K_{sp} values of chlorides are low, hence precipitated. Others have higher K_{sp} values hence not precipitated.
II	Cu^{2+}	H_2S gas in the presence of dil. HCl	sulphides (CuS)	K_{sp} values of II group sulphides are low hence precipitated by low $[S^{2-}]$ ion. HCl (with common H^+ ion) decreases ionisation of H_2S which gives low $[S^{2-}]$. Hence, II group sulphides are precipitated. Others with higher K_{sp} values are not precipitated.
III	Al^{3+}, Fe^{3+}	NH_4OH in the presence of NH_4Cl	hydroxide, $Al(OH)_3$ etc.	K_{sp} values of III group hydroxides are low. NH_4Cl (with common NH_4^+ ion) decrease ionisation of NH_4OH giving low $[OH^-]$. Hence, group III is precipitated.
IV	Zn^{2+}, Ni^{2+}	H_2S in ammoniacal medium	sulphides (ZnS etc.)	K_{sp} values of sulphides of group IV are high hence precipitation takes place in higher $[S^{2-}]$. Basic medium increases ionisation of H_2S, thus increasing $[S^{2-}]$ hence group IV is precipitated.
V	Ca^{2+}, Ba^{2+}	$(NH_4)_2CO_3$ + NH_4Cl	carbonates ($CaCO_3$ etc.)	K_{sp} values of carbonates are less than that of group VI (Mg^{2+}) hence precipitation before Mg^{2+}.
VI	Mg^{2+}	NH_4OH + Na_2HPO_4 (only for Mg^{2+})	white ppt ($MgHPO_4$)	—
0 (zero)	NH_4^+	—	—	tested independently from original solution.

(a) **Group I** Pb^{2+} is precipitated as insoluble chlorides on adding dil. HCl to aqueous solution. If no precipitate is formed, this group is absent.

$$Pb^{2+} + 2Cl^- \longrightarrow PbCl_2 \downarrow$$

Precipitates are separated. Filtrate is for group II.

(b) **Group II** Filtrate of group I + dil. HCl + H_2O. Pass H_2S gas $\longrightarrow$

- black ppt — CuS (salt is blue)
- Cu^{2+} — (salt is blue)
- $3CuS$ (black) $+ 8HNO_3 \longrightarrow 3Cu(NO_3)_2 + 2NO + 3S + 4H_2O$
  soluble (blue)
  (C)

$(C) + CH_3COOH + K_4[Fe(CN)_6] \longrightarrow$ reddish brown ppt
$$Cu(NO_3)_2 + 2CH_3COOH \longrightarrow (CH_3COO)_2Cu + 2HNO_3$$

$$2(CH_3COO)_2Cu + K_4[Fe(CN)_6] \longrightarrow Cu_2[Fe(CN)_6]$$
reddish brown ppt
$$+ 4CH_3COOK$$

$$Bi(NO_3)_3 + 3NH_4OH \longrightarrow Bi(OH)_3 + 3NH_4NO_3$$

(c) **Group III** Boil off H_2S gas from the filtrate of group II. Add NH_4Cl and one drop of dil. HNO_3; heat, cool and add $NH_4OH \longrightarrow$ ppt

- Reddish brown ppt of $Fe(OH)_3$ if Fe^{3+} is present (salt is brown).
- White ppt of $Al(OH)_3$ if Al^{3+} is present (salt is colourless).

  (i) Al^{3+} white ppt of $Al(OH)_3$ (salt is colourless) + NaOH solution (excess) $\longrightarrow$ ppt dissolves forming $NaAlO_2$.

$$Al(OH)_3 + NaOH \longrightarrow Na[AlO_2] + 2H_2O$$
sodium meta-aluminate
(A) (soluble)

White ppt reappears if NH_4Cl is added into soluble meta-aluminate and boiled.

$$Na[AlO_2] + NH_4Cl + H_2O \xrightarrow{\Delta} NaCl + Al(OH)_3 + NH_3$$

  (ii) Fe^{3+} $Fe(OH)_3$ ppt are insoluble in NaOH but soluble in conc. HCl.

$$Fe(OH)_3 + 3HCl \longrightarrow FeCl_3 + 3H_2O$$
soluble (B)

- (B) + CH_3COOH + $K_4[Fe(CN)_6]$ $\longrightarrow$ blue ppt
  potassium
  ferrocyanide

$$4FeCl_3 + 3K_4[Fe(CN)_6] \longrightarrow Fe_4[Fe(CN)_6]_3 + 12KCl$$
ferric ferrocyanide
(Prussian blue)

$$FeCl_3 + \underset{\substack{\text{potassium} \\ \text{sulphocyanide}}}{KCNS} \longrightarrow \underset{\substack{\text{blood red} \\ \text{colour}}}{[Fe(CNS)]Cl_2} + KCl$$

- Fe^{2+} does not give these tests, hence at the start of this group, HNO_3 is added to convert Fe^{2+} into Fe^{3+}.

(d) **Group IV** Filtrate of group III + NH_4OH + $NH_4Cl \xrightarrow{\Delta}$ pass H_2S gas $\longrightarrow$

- white ppt (salt colourless) of ZnS
- black ppt (salt green) of NiS

(i) $\mathbf{Zn^{2+}}$ ZnS ppt (white) are soluble in dil. HCl.

$$\underset{(A)}{ZnS + 2HCl \longrightarrow ZnCl_2 + H_2S}$$

- (A) + NaOH $\longrightarrow$ white ppt soluble in excess of NaOH.

$$\underset{(A)}{ZnCl_2} + 2NaOH \longrightarrow \underset{\text{white ppt.}}{Zn(OH)_2\downarrow} + 2NaCl$$

$$Zn(OH)_2 + 2NaOH \longrightarrow \underset{\substack{\text{sodium zincate} \\ \text{(soluble)}}}{Na_2ZnO_2} + 2H_2O$$

White ppt of ZnS reappears on passing H_2S into soluble Na_2ZnO_2 solution.

$$Na_2ZnO_2 + H_2S \longrightarrow 2NaOH + \underset{\text{White ppt.}}{ZnS\downarrow}$$

(iii) $\mathbf{Ni^{2+}}$ NiS (black ppt) is soluble in conc. HCl in the presence of oxidising agent like $KClO_3$.

$$\underset{\text{conc.}}{NiS + 2HCl + O} \longrightarrow \underset{\substack{\text{soluble }(C) \\ \text{(green)}}}{NiCl_2} + H_2O + S$$

$(C) + NH_4OH + $ dimethyl glyoxime $\longrightarrow$ cherry red ppt

$$NiCl_2 \ + \ 2CH_3\!\!-\!\!C\!\!=\!\!NOH$$
$$\underset{in \ NH_4OH}{(C)} \qquad \underset{\substack{| \\ CH_3\!\!-\!\!C\!\!=\!\!NOH}}{}$$
$$\underset{\text{dimethyl glyoxime}}{} \qquad \longrightarrow$$

cherry red ppt
(dimethyl glyoximate)

(e) **Group V**

Filtrate of group IV $\xrightarrow[\text{(ii) } NH_4OH, (NH_4)_2CO_3]{\text{(i) boil off } H_2S}$ white ppt

- $BaCO_3, CaCO_3$ appear as white ppt.
- **Flame test** Perform flame test with these group ppt.

  Green flame $\quad - \quad Ba^{2+}$

  Brick red $\quad\quad - \quad Ca^{2+}$

- Dissolve the ppt in CH_3COOH.

$$(CH_3COO)_2Ba + K_2CrO_4 \longrightarrow \underset{\text{(yellow ppt.)}}{BaCrO_4 \downarrow} + 2CH_3COOK$$

$$(CH_3COO)_2Ca + (NH_4)_2C_2O_4 \longrightarrow \underset{\text{white ppt.}}{CaC_2O_4 \downarrow} + 2CH_3COONH_4$$

(f) **Group VI (Mg^{2+})** Filtrate of group V $+ \ NH_4OH + Na_2HPO_4$

$\longrightarrow$ a fine crystalline ppt on scratching the side of the test tube.

$$MgCl_2 + NH_4OH + Na_2HPO_4 \longrightarrow \underset{\text{white ppt}}{Mg(NH_4)PO_4 \downarrow}$$
$$+ 2NaCl + H_2O$$

(g) **Group Zero $(NH)_4^+$**

- Salt $+ NaOH \xrightarrow{\Delta}$ gas giving white fumes with HCl

$$NH_4Cl + NaOH \xrightarrow{\Delta} NH_3(g) + NaCl + H_2O$$

$$NH_3 \ (g) + HCl \longrightarrow \underset{\text{white fumes}}{NH_4Cl}$$

- Salt + NaOH $\xrightarrow{\Delta}$ gas $\xrightarrow{\text{add Nessler's reagent}}$ brown ppt or brown or yellow colouration (oxydimercuri ammonium iodide) called iodide of Millon's base (A). A is also called basic mercury (II) amido iodine.

$$NH_4Cl + NaOH \xrightarrow{\Delta} NH_3 + NaCl + H_2O$$

$$NH_3 + 3NaOH + 2K_2HgI_4 \longrightarrow O\Big\langle{\!\!\!\!\begin{array}{c} Hg \\ Hg \end{array}\!\!\!\!}\Big\rangle NH_2I$$

Nessler's reagent

(A)

$$+ 4KI + 3NaI + 2H_2O$$

Above reaction can also be written as

$$NH_4^+ + 2[HgI_4]^{2-} + 4OH^- \longrightarrow HgO \cdot Hg(NH_2)I\downarrow + 7I^- + 3H_2O$$

Qualitative Analysis of Organic Compounds

It also involves following steps :

1. Preliminary test   2. Element detection   3. Test of functional group.

1. Preliminary Tests

(a) **Heat test** The compound is heated in flame. If it burns with smoky flame, it is an aromatic compound and if it burns with non-smoky flame, it is an aliphatic compound.

(b) **Colour**

Colour	Substance
Yellow	Iodoform, nitro compounds and quinones
Orange	o-nitroaniline
Brown-red	Azo compounds, diamines, aromatic amines, amino-phenol
Pink	Naphthols
Colourless	Simple phenols, carbohydrates, alcohols, aldehydes, ketones, lower aliphatic acid and their anhydrides

(c) **Odour**

Odour	Substance
Fishy smell	Aliphatic and aromatic amines
Carbolic smell	Phenols, cresols, naphthols
Ammoniacal smell	Tertiary amines
Sweet smell	Chloroform
Oil of winter green	Methyl salicylate
Characteristic aromatic smell	Benzene, toluene

Odour	Substance
Mousy	Acetamide, acetonitrile
Fruity	Esters
Penetrating smell	$HCHO$, CH_3CHO and $HCOOH$
Pleasant	Ketones (aliphatic and aromatic)
Smell of bitter almonds	C_6H_5CHO, nitrobenzene, nitrotoluene
Vinegar smell	CH_3COOH
Garlic smell	Thiophenol, thioalcohol
Wine like	Alcohol

Element Detection

See chapter purification and characterisation of organic compounds.

Tests of Functional Groups

1. **Tests for Carboxylic** (—COOH) **Group**

   (i) **Litmus paper test** Dip blue litmus paper in the aqueous solution or suspension of the compound, it turns red.

   (ii) **Sodium bicarbonate test** In a test tube take a little quantity of the compound and then, add a saturated solution of sodium bicarbonate. Formation of brisk effervescence shows the presence of —COOH group.

   benzoic acid   sodium benzoate

   (iii) **Ester formation** Heat a small quantity of organic compound with ethyl alcohol and a few drops of conc H_2SO_4. Cool the solution and pour in a tube containing water. A fruity smell, due to formation of an ester, indicates the presence of carboxylic group.

   $$R\text{—COOH} + C_2H_5OH \xrightarrow{\text{conc. } H_2SO_4} \underset{\substack{\text{ester} \\ \text{(fruity smell)}}}{RCOOC_2H_5} + H_2O$$

2. **Tests for Alcoholic** (—OH) **Group**

   (i) **Ceric ammonium nitrate test** To small amount of organic compound or its aqueous solution, add a few drops of ceric ammonium nitrate solution. A red colour indicates the presence of alcoholic hydroxy group.

   $$2ROH + (NH_4)_2Ce(NO_3)_6 \longrightarrow \underset{\text{red colour}}{Ce(NO_3)_4 \cdot (ROH)_2} + 2NH_4NO_3$$

(ii) **Lucas test** This test is used to distinguish between primary, secondary and tertiary alcohols. In this test, treat 2 mL of organic compound with about 8 mL of Lucas reagent (for preparing Lucas reagent dissolve 32 g of anhy $ZnCl_2$ in 20 mL of conc HCl and shake.)

(a) Immediate formation of turbidity indicates the presence of **tertiary alcohol.**

(b) Formation of turbidity after 4-5 min shows the presence of **secondary alcohols.**

(c) If solution remains clear, then **primary alcohol** is present.

3. **Tests for Phenolic** (Ph—OH) **Group**

(i) **Ferric chloride test** To aqueous or alcoholic solution of compound, add few drops of ferric chloride ($FeCl_3$) solution. Formation of green, red or violet colour shows the presence of phenol.

$$6C_6H_5OH + FeCl_3 \longrightarrow 3H^+ + [Fe(OC_6H_5)_6]^{3-} + 3HCl$$
$$\underset{\text{violet}}{}$$

(ii) **Liebermann's nitroso reaction** Fuse a little amount of compound with a crystal of $NaNO_2$ in a test tube. Cool the mixture and add 1 mL conc H_2SO_4. A deep green to blue solution is formed which turns red when poured in a large excess of water. The red aqueous solution becomes again deep green or blue if made alkaline with NaOH. It shows the presence of phenol.

Note *Nitrophenol does not respond to* $FeCl_3$ *test as well as Liebermann's nitroso reaction.*

4. **Test for Carbonyl group**

2,4-dinitro phenyl hydrazine test In a dry test tube add few drops of the organic compound (if liquid) or its alcoholic solution (if solid) to about 2 mL of the reagent and one drop of conc H_2SO_4. Shake vigorously, heat (if necessary) and allow to stand for about 5 min. A yellow or orange ppt separates out in case of a compound containing carbonyl group due to formation of respective hydrazones.

$$>C=O + H_2N \cdot HN-\!\!\!\!\bigcirc\!\!\!\!-NO_2$$

carbonyl
compound

NO_2

2,4-dinitro phenyl hydrazine

$$>C=N \cdot HN-\!\!\!\!\bigcirc\!\!\!\!-NO_2 \downarrow + H_2O$$

NO_2

yellow or orange red coloured crystalline
derivative of 2,4-dinitrophenyl hydrazine
of carbonyl compound

Differentiating tests for Aldehyde (—CHO) **Group**

(i) **Tollen's reagent test** Take a little quantity of the compound in a test tube and add 2 mL of freshly prepared reagent. Shake, warm and allow the contents to stand for 2–3 min. Formation of silver mirror or a grey ppt indicates the presence of an aldehydic group.

$$2Ag(NH_3)_2OH + R \cdot CHO \longrightarrow \quad 2Ag \downarrow \quad + \quad RCOONH_4$$

Silver mirror
or grey ppt

$$+ 3NH_3 + H_2O$$

(ii) **Fehling's solution test** Take a mixture of equal amounts of Fehling's solution A and B, and a few drops of organic compound and boil the contents. Formation of a red ppt shows the presence of an aldehyde.

$$2CuO + R \cdot CHO \longrightarrow Cu_2O \downarrow + RCOOH$$

Red ppt.

Note *Both the above tests are also given by reducing sugars.*

(iii) **Schiff 's reagent test** Add 5–6 drops of organic compound to 2 mL of the reagent. Shake vigorously. After some time formation of a deep pink colour indicates the presence of an aldehydic group.

Schiff's reagent (colourless)

violet colour

(iv) **Benedict's solution test** Boil the compound with 2–3 mL of Benedict's solution for few minutes. Appearance of a red-yellow ppt confirms the presence of aliphatic aldehydes.

Note *This test is usually given by only aliphatic aldehydes, thus used to differentiate between aliphatic and aromatic aldehydes.*

5. **Tests for Ketone** $\left(\dfrac{R}{R} \!\!>\!\! C\!=\!O \right)$ **Group**

Sodium nitroprusside test Add 0.1 g of solid or 0.2 cc of liquid compound to 2 cc of sodium nitroprusside solution and then, make it alkaline with 2–3 drops of sodium hydroxide. A red or purple colour indicates the presence of ketone (benzophenone does not give this test).

6. **Tests for Primary Amine** $(-NH_2)$ **Group**

(i) **Carbylamine test** Warm a little quantity of the compound with 2 drops of chloroform and 2 mL of alcoholic caustic potash. An intolerable offensive odour of carbylamine indicates the presence of primary amine.

$$\underset{\substack{\text{primary} \\ \text{amine}}}{R\!-\!NH_2} + CHCl_3 + 3KOH \longrightarrow \underset{\text{carbylamine}}{R\cdot NC\!\uparrow} + 3KCl + 3H_2O$$

(ii) **Dye test** Dissolve about 0.2 g of the compound in dil HCl and cool. Now, add cold solution of 10% aq $NaNO_2$ solution. Pour all this content into a beaker containing alkaline β-naphthol solution. Formation of a red or orange dye indicates the presence of aromatic primary amino group.

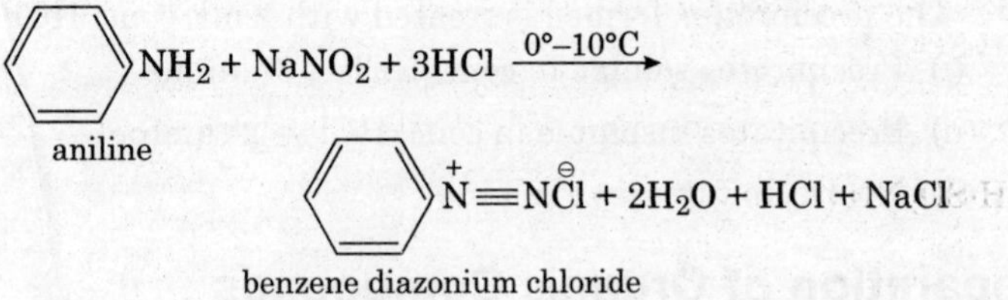
NH2 + NaNO2 + 3HCl
0°–10°C
aniline
N≡NCl + 2H2O + HCl + NaCl
benzene diazonium chloride

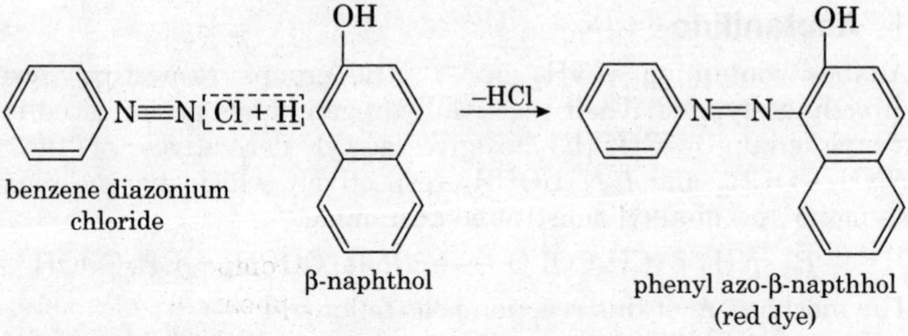
N≡N Cl + H
OH
–HCl
N=N
OH
benzene diazonium chloride
β-naphthol
phenyl azo-β-napthhol (red dye)

Note *Dye test is given only by aromatic amines*

7. **Tests to Distinguish between Primary, Secondary and Tertiary Amines**

(i) **Nitrous acid test** Prepare a solution of nitrous acid by adding ice cold dil HCl to a solution of 1% aq $NaNO_2$. Add gradually this solution to 0.2 g of the organic compound in 10 mL dil HCl.

(a) Formation of brisk effervescence shows the presence of **aliphatic primary amine**.

$$R\text{—}NH_2 + HNO_2 \longrightarrow ROH + H_2O + N_2\uparrow$$

(b) Formation of an oily dark coloured liquid indicates the presence of **secondary amine.**

$$\underset{\text{secondary amine}}{R_2NH} + HNO_2 \longrightarrow \underset{\text{nitroso compound (oily)}}{R_2N\cdot NO} + H_2O$$

(c) No reaction indicates the presence of **aliphatic tertiary amine** while production of green or brown colour indicates the presence of **aromatic tertiary amines.**

(ii) **Hinsberg's test** Take about 0.2 g of the compound, add 1 mL of 5% NaOH and 3 mL pyridine. Shake well and add few drops of benzene sulphonyl chloride with continuous shaking and cool it.

The precipitates formed is treated with 2 mL conc. HCl

(i) Precipitates soluble in conc. HCl — 3° amine

(ii) Precipitates insoluble in conc. HCl — 2° amine

(iii) No precipitates — 1° amine

Preparation of Organic Compounds

1. Acetanilide

Amines containing —NH$_2$ and NH groups respectively can be directly acetylated. Their reactive hydrogen atoms get replaced by the acetyl group (—COCH$_3$) to give acetyl derivatives of the type RNH · COCH$_3$ and R_2N · COCH$_3$ respectively which may be regarded as mono and di-alkyl substituted acetamide.

$$R—NH_2 + (CH_3CO)_2O \longrightarrow R NH · COCH_3 + CH_3COOH$$

The mechanism of this reaction is as follows

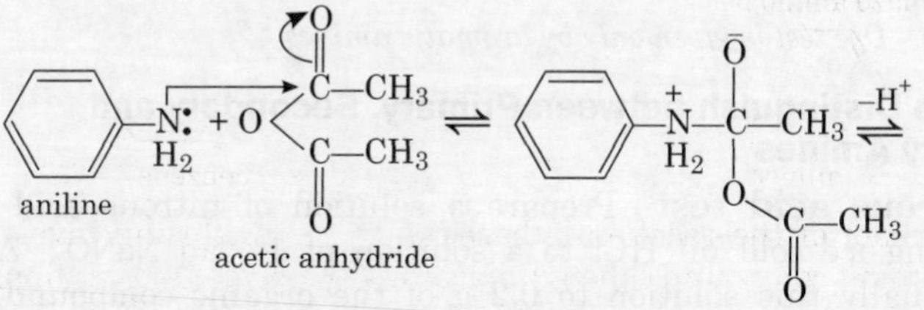

aniline

acetic anhydride

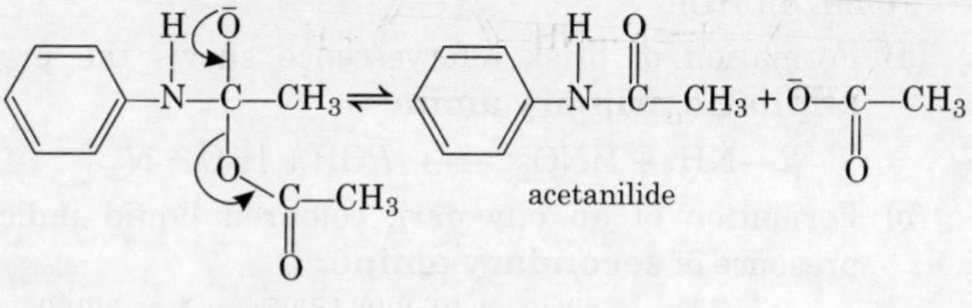

acetanilide

2. *p*-nitro Acetanilide

When acetanilide is treated with a mixture of conc HNO$_3$ and conc H$_2$SO$_4$, it gives *p*-nitro acetanilide alongwith a little amount of *o*-isomer. In this process fuming HNO$_3$ in the presence of conc H$_2$SO$_4$, gives nitronium ion (NO$_2^+$) which attack on acetanilide to form *p*-nitro acetanilide through the cyclopentadienyl cation (intermediate) formation.

$$HNO_3 + H_2SO_4 \longrightarrow \underset{\text{Nitronium ion}}{NO_2^+} + H_2O + HSO_4^-$$

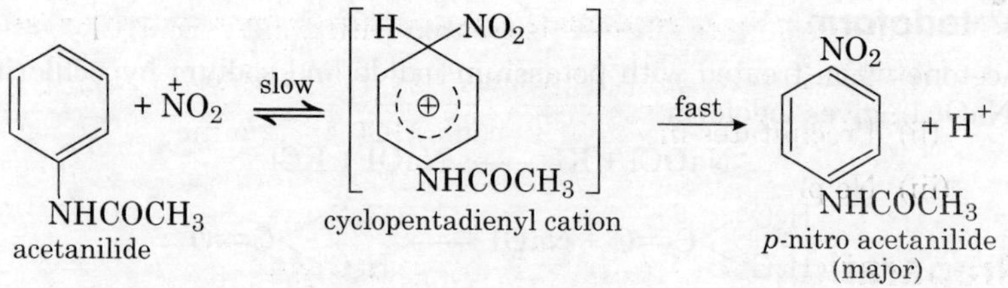

acetanilide — cyclopentadienyl cation — *p*-nitro acetanilide (major)

$$\overset{+}{H} + \overset{-}{H}SO_4 \longrightarrow H_2SO_4$$

3. **Aniline Yellow**

When diazo amino benzene is heated with dil. HCl at 40°C, for a short time, aniline hydrochloride and aniline formed which further reacts with HCl gives *p*-amino azo benzene.

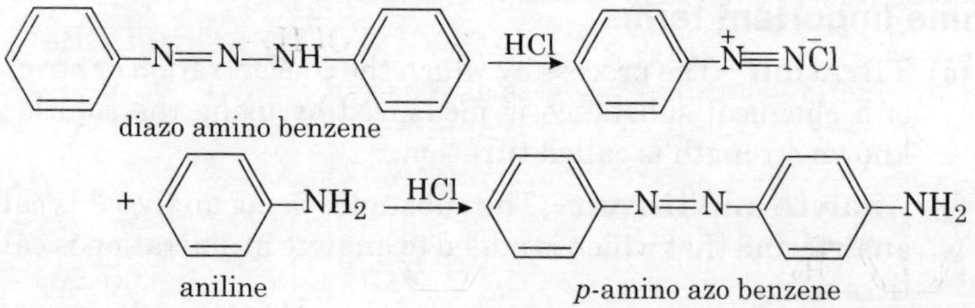

diazo amino benzene

aniline — *p*-amino azo benzene

The mechanism of the reaction is based on the equilibrium involving the diazo amino compound, phenyl diazonium chloride and aniline.

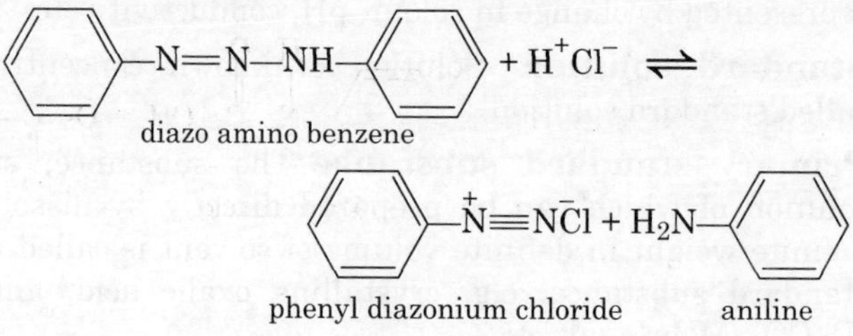

diazo amino benzene

phenyl diazonium chloride — aniline

The reaction takes place between the two later compounds under weakly acidic conditions.

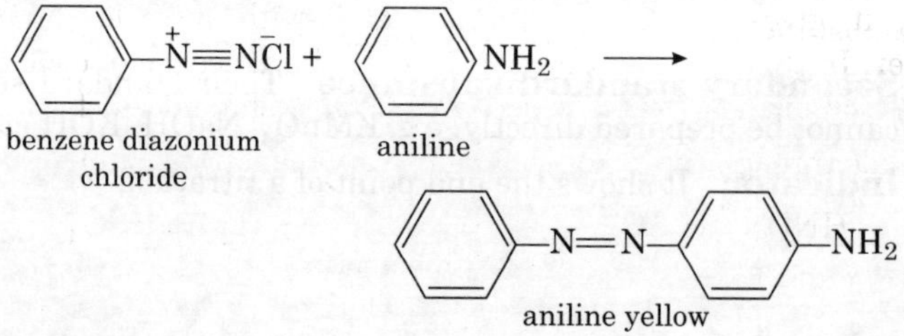

benzene diazonium chloride — aniline

aniline yellow

4. Iodoform

Acetone when treated with potassium iodide and sodium hypochlorite (NaOCl), gives iodoform.

$$NaOCl + KI \longrightarrow NaOI + KCl$$

$$\underset{H_3C}{\overset{H_3C}{>}}C=O + NaOI \longrightarrow \underset{H_3C}{\overset{I_3C}{>}}C=O$$

$$\xrightarrow{NaOH} CH_3COO\overset{-}{N}\overset{+}{a} + \underset{\substack{\text{Iodoform} \\ \text{(yellow ppt.)}}}{CHI_3} \downarrow$$

Titrimetric Exercises

Some Important terms

(a) **Titration** The process by which the concentration or strength of a chemical substance is measured by using the solution of known strength is called titration.

(b) **Analyte and titrant** The substance being analysed is called analyte and that which is added to analyte in a titration is called titrant.

(c) **Equivalence point or end point** It is point at which the reaction between two solutions is just complete. It is generally represented by change in colour, pH, conductivity etc.

(d) **Standard solution** Solution of known concentration is called standard solution.

(e) **Primary standard substance** The substance, standard solution of which can be prepared directly by dissolving its definite weight in definite volume of solvent is called primary standard substance, e.g. crystalline oxalic acid, anhydrous Na_2CO_3, Mohr's salt etc.

The substance, which occur in pure state, are non-hydroscopic, non-deliquescent, generally behave as primary standard substance.

(f) **Secondary standard substance** Their standard solution cannot be prepared directly. e.g. $KMnO_4$, NaOH, KOH etc.

(g) **Indicator** It shows the end point of a titration.

(i) In acidimetry and alkalimetry, the choice of indicators mainly depends upon the nature of the acids and alkalies used. Methyl orange, phenolphthalein are some of the important indicators used in these titrations.

(ii) As no indicator gives correct results in the titration of weak acids against weak bases, such titrations are to be avoided.

Oxalic Acid *vs* KMnO$_4$ Titration

This is an example of redox titrations, in which a reducing agent (as oxalic acid) is estimated by titrating it with a standard solution of oxidising agent (as KMnO$_4$). Such reactions are accompanied by the change in valency of ions. In these titrations oxidation and reduction takes place simultaneously i.e. while one substance is being oxidised, the other one is being reduced.

$$2KMnO_4 + 3H_2SO_4 \longrightarrow K_2SO_4 + 2MnSO_4 + 3H_2O + 5[O]$$

oxidising
agent

$$5 \begin{matrix} COOH \\ | \\ COOH \end{matrix} + 5[O] \longrightarrow 5H_2O + 10CO_2\uparrow$$

reducing agent

The last drop of KMnO$_4$ itself acts as an indicator **(self indicator).**

In this titration, first the standard solution of oxalic acid is prepared which is then titrated with the KMnO$_4$ solution in the presence of dil. H$_2$SO$_4$. The procedure is repeated to obtain a set of concurrent readings.

Calculations

(i) Weight of oxalic acid dissolved in 250 mL measuring flask,

$= z$ .... g

Weight of oxalic acid in 1000 mL $= \dfrac{.... \times 1000}{250} = ...$ g/L

Normality of oxalic acid (prepared)

$$= \dfrac{\text{Strength (g) L}}{\text{Eq. wt. of oxalic acid}} = \dfrac{.........}{63.04} \text{ N}$$

(ii) **For the titrations using standard oxalic acid solution**

$$N_1V_1 = N_2V_2$$

Oxalic acid   KMnO$_4$
(Known)

$$\dfrac{.........}{63.04} \text{ N} \times 20 \text{ mL} = N_2 \times ....$$

$$N_2 = ... \text{ N}$$

(iii) **For the titration using supplied oxalic acid solution**

$$N_3 V_3 = N_4 V_4$$

Oxalic acid   KMnO$_4$ [$\because N_4 = N_2$]
(unknown)

$$N_3 = \ldots\ldots\ldots N$$

Strength of oxalic acid in g/L = $N_3 \times$ Eq. wt. of oxalic acid

$$= \ldots\ldots\ldots \text{ g/L}$$

The oxalic acid solution with dil H$_2$SO$_4$ is heated to near about 70°– 80°C.

Sulphuric acid should be in excess otherwise a brown ppt due to formation of MnO$_2$ will be formed.

This titration cannot be carried out in presence of acid like HNO$_3$ and HCl, because HNO$_3$ itself is an oxidising agent, so it will interfere with the oxidising action of KMnO$_4$ and HCl reacts chemically with KMnO$_4$ solution.

Mohr's Salt *vs* KMnO$_4$ Titration

This titration is also an example of redox titrations and work on the same principle as oxalic acid *vs* KMnO$_4$ titration. In this titration the active constituent of ferrous ammonium sulphate (Mohr's salt) is ferrous sulphate, which is oxidised to ferric sulphate by acidified potassium permanganate as follows.

$$2KMnO_4 + 3H_2SO_4 \longrightarrow K_2SO_4 + 2MnSO_4 + 3H_2O + 5[O]$$

$$[2FeSO_4 + H_2SO_4 + [O] \longrightarrow Fe_2(SO_4)_3 + H_2O] \times 5$$

$$\overline{2KMnO_4 + 8H_2SO_4 + 10FeSO_4 \longrightarrow K_2SO_4 + 2MnSO_4}$$

$$+ 5Fe_2(SO_4)_3 + 8H_2O$$

Calculations

(i) Weight of ferrous ammonium sulphate dissolved in 250 mL measuring flask = $z \ldots$ g

weight of ferrous ammonium sulphate in 1000 mL

$$= \frac{\ldots \times 1000}{250}$$

$$= \ldots \text{ g/L}$$

Normality of ferrous ammonium sulphate (prepared)

$$= \frac{\text{Strength(g / L)}}{\text{Eq. wt. of ferrous ammonium sulphate}}$$

$$= \frac{\cdots}{63.04} \text{N}$$

(ii) **For the titrations using standard ferrous ammonium sulphate solution**

$$N_1 V_1 = N_2 V_2$$

Mohr's salt $KMnO_4$
(Known)

$$\frac{\cdots}{63.04} \text{N} \times 20 \text{ mL} = N_2 \times \ldots$$

$$N_2 = \ldots \text{N}$$

(iii) **For the titration using supplied ferrous ammonium sulphate solution**

$$N_3 V_3 = N_4 V_4$$

ferrous ammonium sulphate $KMnO_4$ $[\because N_4 = N_2]$ (unknown)

$$N_3 = \ldots \text{N}$$

Strength of ferrous ammonium sulphate in $g/L = N_3 \times$ Eq. wt. of ferrous ammonium sulphate

$$= \ldots g/L$$

Appendix 1

Greek Letters & Their Names

α	alpha
β	beta
γ	gamma
δ	delta
ζ	zeta
η	eta
θ	theta
ι	iota
κ	kappa
λ	lambda
μ	mu
υ	nu
π	pi
ρ	rho
σ	sigma
τ	tau
φ	phi
χ	chi
ψ	psi
ω	omega

Appendix 2

Fundamental Physical Constants

S. No.	Physical constant	Symbol	Value
1.	Acceleration due to gravity	g	$9.81 \ ms^{-2}$
2.	Atomic mass unit	amu (u)	$1.660453 \times 10^{-27} \ kg$
3.	Avogadro constant	N_A	$6.02217 \times 10^{23} \ mol^{-1}$
4.	Boltzmann constant	K	$1.38062 \times 10^{-23} \ JK^{-1}$
5.	Electronic charge	e	$1.602192 \times 10^{-19} \ C$
6.	Faraday constant	F	$9.64867 \times 10^4 \ C \ mol^{-1}$
7.	Gas constant	R	$8.314 \ JK^{-1} mol^{-1}$
8.	Molar volume of ideal gas at (STP)	V_m	$2.24136 \times 10^{-2} \ m^3 \ mol^{-1}$
9.	Planck constant	h	$6.62620 \times 10^{-34} \ Js$
10.	Rydberg constant	R_H	$1.973731 \times 10^7 \ m^{-1}$
11.	Standard pressure (atmosphere)	p	$101325 \ Nm^{-2}$
12.	Velocity of light of vacuum	c	$2.997925 \times 10^8 \ ms^{-1}$

Additional Constants

$$\pi = 3.1416, \ \ln X = 2.303 \log_{10} X$$

Appendix 3

Periodic Table

Modern Periodic Table

Appendix 4

Important Conversion Factors

Common Unit of Mass and Weight

1 pound = 453.59 gram = 0.45359 kilogram

1 kilogram = 1000 gram = 2.205 pound

1 gram = 10 decigram = 100 centigram

= 1000 milligram

atomic mass unit = 1.6606×10^{-24} gram

1 metric tonne = 1000 kilogram = 2205 pound

Common Units of Volume

1 quart = 0.9463 litre

1 litre = 1.056 quart

1 litre = 1 cubic decimetre = 1000 cubic

centimetre = 0.001 cubic metre

1 millilitre = 1 cubic centimetre

= 0.001 litre = 1.056×10^{-3} quart

1 cubic foot = 28.316 litre = 29.902 quart

= 7.475 gallon

Common Units of Energy

1 Joule = 1×10^7 erg

1 thermochemical calorie = 4.184 joule

The amount of heat required to the temperature of one gram of water from 14.5°C to

15.5°C = 4.184×10^7 erg

= 4.129×10^{-2} litre-atmosphere

= 2.612×10^{19} electron volt

1 erg = 1×10^{-7} joule

= 2.3901×10^{-8} calorie

1 electron volt = 1.6022×10^{-19} joule

= 1.6022×10^{-12} erg

1 litre-atmosphere = 24.217 calorie

= 101.32 joule

= 1.0132×10^9 erg

Common Units of Length

1 inch = 2.54 centimetre (exactly)

1 mile = 5280 feet

= 1.609 kilometre

1 yard = 36 inches

= 0.9144 metre

1 metre = 100 centimetre

= 39.37 inches

= 3.281 feet

= 1.094 yard

1 kilometre = 1000 metre

= 1094 yard

= 0.6215 mile

1 Angstrom = 1.0×10^{-8} centimetre

= 0.10 nanometre

= 1.0×10^{-10} metre

= 3.937×10^{-9} inch

Common Units of Pressure

1 atmosphere = 760 millimetre

of mercury

= 1.013×10^5 pascal

= 14.70 pound per square inch

1 bar = 10^5 pascal

1 torr = 1 millimetre of mercury

1 pascal = $1 \ kg/ms^2$ = $1 \ N/m^2$

Common Units of Temperature

SI Base Unit : Kelvin (K)

K = – 273.15°C

K = °C + 273.15

°F = 1.8 (°C) + 32

°C = $\dfrac{°F - 32}{1.8}$

Appendix 5
Popular Scientist & Their Work

1. **Angstrom, Anders Jonas** He worked mainly with emission spectra Fraunhofer absorption lines wavelengths. Since 1905, spectral wavelengths have been expressed in Å.
$$1Å = 10^{-10} \text{ m or } 1Å = 10^{-8} \text{ cm}$$

2. **Arrhenius, Svante** (August) He demonstrated that electroytes are conductors due to the movement of ions. He gave the following equation to show the effect of temperature at rate constant.
$$k = Ae^{-E_a/RT}$$
This equation is known by the name Arrhenius equation.

3. **Aston, Francis William** He designed the mass spectrograph and discovered the isotopes of neon.

4. **Avogadro , Amedeo** He proposed a method for computing molecular weights from vapour densities. He also proposed that equal volumes of all gases contain equal numbers of molecule under similar temperature and pressure condition. [Avogadro's law].

5. **Bartlett, Neil** Bartlett synthesize first compound of a noble gas in 1962, *i.e.*, xenon hexachloroplatin.

6. **Becquerel, Antoine Henri** He discovered radioactivity in fluorescent salts of uranium.

7. **Berzelius, Jons Jacob** He discovered several elements, *i.e.*, Ce, Se, Li, Th and V. He proposed vital force theory of organic compounds.

8. **Bohr, Niels Henrik David** He proposed atomic model in 1913 to explain line spectrum of hydrogen.

9. **Boltzmann, Ludwig Eduard** He worked on the kinetic theory of gases and on thermodynamics.

10. **Boyle, Robert** He worked on gases, flame tests and acid base indicators. He was the first to give a definition of a chemical element.

11. **Bragg, Sir William Henry** He worked on X-ray crystallography analysis.

12. **Bronsted, Johannes Nicolaus** He proposed acid base theory as Lowry-Bronsted theory.

13. **Bunsen, Robert Wilhelm** He popularized the use of Bunsen burner and developed the Bunsen cell.

14. **Cavendish, Henry** He correctly distinguished between hydrogen and carbon dioxide.

15. **Charles, Jacques Alexandre Cesar** He proposed Charles law. He became the first person to make an ascent in a hydrogen balloon.

16. **Crookes, Sir William** He discovered cathode rays and developed an improved vacuum tube.

17. **Curie, Marie** She had discovered radium and polonium.

18. **Dalton, John** He is best remembered for Dalton's atomic theory.

19. **de-Broglie, Louis-Victor Pierre Raymond** He is the best known for wave particle duality of light. He gave the following relation $\lambda = \dfrac{h}{p}$.
This is called de-Brogile equation.

20. **Debye, Peter Joseph William** He introduced the idea of electric dipole moments in molecules.

21. **Dumas, Jean Baptiste Andre** He devised a method of measuring vapour density.

22. **Einstein, Albert** He proposed theory of relativity.

23. **Fahrenheit, Gabriel Daniel** He developed the mercury in glass thermometer and devised a temperature scale to go with it *i.e.,* Fahrenheit scale.

24. **Faraday, Michael** He proposed laws of electrolysis.

25. **Fleming, Sir Alexander** He discovered the antibiotic penicillin.

26. **Frankland, Sir Edward** He produced organometallic compounds (zinc dialkyls) firstly.

27. **Gay-Lussac, Joseph** He gives the laws of chemical combination in gases helped to establish the atomic theory.

28. **Gibbs Josiah Willard** He developed the theory of chemical thermodynamics and function free energy as $G = H - TS$.

29. **Graham, Thomas** He was associated with diffusion of gases and colloids.

30. **Haber, Fritz** He proposed industrial method for production of NH_3.

31. **Heisenberg, Werner Karl** He is the best known for his Uncertainty principle.

32. **Huckel, Erich** He proposed Huckel rule for aromaticity.

33. **Kekule, Friedrich August Von Stradonitz** He proposed structure of benzene.

34. **Kelvin, Lord** He introduced the concept of absolute zero and developed Kelvin temperature scales.

35. **Lavoisier, Antoine Laurent** He discovered oxygen and nitrogen in air. He also devised a rational nomenclature for chemical compounds.

36. **Le- Chatelier** He proposed the principle for chemical equilibrium, known as the Le-Chatelier's principle.

37. **Lewis, Gilbert Newton** He introduced the concept of Lewis acids and bases. He also introduced the concept of a stable octet of electrons.

38. **Maxwell, James Clark** He was one of the founders of the kinetic theory of gases.

39. **Mary Hordgkin** She was a British chemist who used the technique of X-ray crystallography to educidate the structures of biomolecules.

40. **Mendeleef, Dmitri Ivanovich** He framed the Periodic Table of the elements based on atomic masses.

41. **Nernst, (Hermann) Walther** He mainly worked on electrochemistry and thermochemistry.

42. **Ostwald, Friedrich Wilhelm** He worked on hydrolysis, viscosity, ionization and catalysis.

43. **Pauli, Wolfgang Ernst** He proposed Pauli's exclusion principle which explained the electronic make up of atoms.

44. **Planck, Max Karl Ernst Ludwig** He formulated the quantum theory.

45. **Ramsay Sir William** He discovered the noble gases [Ne, Ar, Kr Xe and Rn].

46. **Soddy, Frederick** He proposed the existence of isotopes.

47. **Thomson, Sir Joseph John** He is the best known for the discovery of electron and atomic model.

48. **Urey Harold Clayton** He is the best known for the discovery of deuterium ($_1^2D$) [Heavy hydrogen].

49. **Wohlder, Friedrich** He synthesised the first organic compound urea (NH_2CONH_2) in 1828.

Appendix 6

Some Important Ores/Minerals and Their Chemical Formulae

S.No.	Name	Formula
1.	Alumina	Al_2O_3
2.	Argentite	Ag_2S
3.	Asbestos	$CaMg_3(SiO_3)_4$
4.	Bauxite	$Al_2O_3 \cdot 2H_2O$
5.	Borax (tincal)	$Na_2B_4O_7 \cdot 10H_2O$
6.	Calcite	$CaCO_3$
7.	Calamine	$ZnCO_3$
8.	Carnallite	$KCl \cdot MgCl_2 \cdot 6H_2O$
9.	Cassiterite	SnO_2
10.	Cerussite	$PbCO_3$
11.	Chalk (aragonite, marble, limestone)	$CaCO_3$
12.	Chile salt petre	$NaNO_3$
13.	Cinnabar	HgS
14.	Clay	$Al_2O_3 \cdot 2SiO_2 \cdot 2H_2O$
15.	Copper pyrites	$CuFeS_2$
16.	Corrundum	Al_2O_3
17.	Cryolite	Na_3AlF_6
18.	Cuprite (ruby copper)	Cu_2O
19.	Dolomite	$MgCO_3 \cdot CaCO_3$
20.	Epsomite (epsom salt)	$MgSO_4 \cdot 7H_2O$
21.	Fluorapatite	$3Ca_3(PO_4)_2 \cdot CeF_2$
22.	Fluorspar	CaF_2
23.	Galena	PbS
24.	Gypsum	$CaSO_4 \cdot 2H_2O$
25.	Haematite (red)	Fe_2O_3
26.	Horn silver	$AgCl$
27.	Iron pyrites	FeS_2
28.	Kieserite	$MgSO_4 \cdot H_2O$
29.	Limonite (brown)	$Fe_2O_3 \cdot 3H_2O$
30.	Magnesite	$MgCO_3$
31.	Magnetite	Fe_3O_4
32.	Malachite	$Cu(OH)_2 \cdot CuCO_3$
33.	Pyrolusite	MnO_2
34.	Siderite	$FeCO_3$
35.	Sylvine	KCl
36.	Talc	$Mg_3(Si_4O_{10}(OH)_2$
37.	Zinc blende	ZnS
38.	Zincite	ZnO

Appendix 7

Important Compounds and Their Formulae

S.No.	Compound	Formula
1.	Absolute alcohol	C_2H_5OH
2.	Alum	$M_2^I SO_4 \cdot M_2^{III}(SO_4)_3 \cdot 24H_2O$ ($M^I = Na^+, K^+, NH_4^+; M^{III} = Al^{3+}, Cr^{3+}, Fe^{3+}$)
3.	Aspirin	$o\text{-}CH_3OCO - C_6H_4 - COOH$
4.	Baking soda	$NaHCO_3$
5.	Baryta water	A solution of $Ba(OH)_2$
6.	Black oxide	MnO_2
7.	Bleaching powder	$CaOCl_2$
8.	Blue vitriol	$CuSO_4 \cdot 5H_2O$
9.	Borax (tincal)	$Na_2B_4O_7 \cdot 10H_2O$
10.	Borazole (inorganic benzene)	$B_3N_3H_6$
11.	Calgon	$Na_2[Na_4(PO_3)_6]$
12.	Calomel	Hg_2Cl_2
13.	Carbolic acid	C_6H_5OH
14.	Carborundum	SiC
15.	Caustic potash	KOH
16.	Chloropicrin (tear gas)	$CCl_3 - NO_2$
17.	Chrome yellow	$PbCrO_4$
18.	Chromyl chloride	CrO_2Cl_2
19.	DDT	Dichlorodiphenyltrichloroethane
20.	Dry ice	Solid CO_2
21.	Ferric alum	$K_2SO_4 \cdot Fe_2(SO_4)_3 \cdot 24H_2O$
22.	Freon	CCl_2F_2
23.	Gammexane (BHC)	$C_6H_6Cl_6$
24.	Glauber salt	$Na_2SO_4 \cdot 10H_2O$
25.	Grape sugar	$C_6H_{12}O_6$ (fructose)
26.	Gun powder	KNO_3 (70%) + S (12%) + charcoal (13%)
27.	Gypsum salt (gypsum)	$CaSO_4 \cdot 2H_2O$
28.	Inorganic rubber	$(PNCl_2)_n$
29.	Hydrolith	CaH_2
30.	Hypo	$Na_2S_2O_3 \cdot 5H_2O$
31.	King of chemicals (oil of vitriol)	H_2SO_4
32.	Laughing gas	N_2O
33.	Litharge	PbO

S.No.	Compound	Formula
34.	Lunar caustic	$AgNO_3$
35.	Marshall's acid	$H_2S_2O_8$ (perdisulphuric acid)
36.	Marsh gas	CH_4
37.	Milk of lime (slaked lime or lime water)	$Ca(OH)_2$
38.	Milk of magnesia	$Mg(OH)_2$
39.	Mohr salt	$FeSO_4 \cdot (NH_4)_2SO_4 \cdot 6H_2O$
40.	Muriatic acid	HCl
41.	Mustard gas	$ClCH_2CH_2SCH_2CH_2Cl$
42.	Oleum	$H_2S_2O_7$
43.	Oil of winter green (methysalicylate)	o-$HOC_6H_4COOCH_3$
44.	Pearl ash	K_2CO_3
45.	Perhydrol	30% H_2O_2
46.	Permutit (zeolite)	$Na_2O \cdot Al_2O_3 \cdot 2SiO_2 \cdot 6H_2O$
47.	Philosopher's wool	ZnO
48.	Phosgene	$COCl_2$
49.	Plaster of Paris	$CaSO_4 \cdot \frac{1}{2}H_2O$
50.	Prussian blue	$Fe_4[Fe(CN)_6]_3$
51.	Prussic acid	HCN
52.	Quick lime (lime)	CaO
53.	Red oxide	Pb_3O_4
54.	Rochelle salt	$KNaC_4H_4O_6 \cdot 4H_2O$
55.	Rust	$Fe_2O_3 \cdot xH_2O$
56.	Smelling salt	$(NH_4)_2CO_3$
57.	Soda ash	Na_2CO_3 (anhydrous)
58.	Spirit of wine (grain alcohol)	C_2H_5OH
59.	Talc	$3MgO \cdot 4SiO_2 \cdot H_2O$
60.	Teflon	$(C_2F_4)_n$
61.	TEL	$(C_2H_5)_4Pb$
62.	TNT	Trinitrotoluene (an explosive)
63.	Turnbull's blue	$KFe(F(CN)_6)$
64.	Vinegar	CH_3COOH (7–8%)
65.	Washing soda	$Na_2CO_3 \cdot 10H_2O$
66.	Water glass	Na_2SiO_3
67.	White vitriol	$ZnSO_4 \cdot 7H_2O$
68.	Wood spirit	CH_3OH

Appendix 8

Important Facts

S. No.	Property	Element/Ion
1.	Smallest cation	H^+
2.	Largest cation	Cs^+
3.	Solid with highest density	Iridium (Ir)
4.	Liquid with highest density	Mercury (Hg)
5.	Elements named in honour of the countries	Ru, Ge, Po, Am
6.	Most electronegative elements	Fluorine (F)
7.	Most abundant elements on earth	Oxygen (O)
8.	Most abundant metal in earth crust	Aluminium (Al)
9.	Liquid metal	Mercury (Hg)
10.	Lustrous non-metal	Iodine (I_2)
11.	Hardest among non-metals	Diamond
12.	Soft metals	Na, K
13.	Best ductile metals	Au, Ag
14.	Best conductor metal	Silver (Ag)
15.	Most poisonous element	Pu
16.	Element with maximum number of isotopes	Ag
17.	Most electropositive metal	Caesium (Cs)
18.	Liquid non-metal	Br
19.	Metal kept in paraffin wax	Li
20.	Coinage metals	Ag, Au, Cu, Al

Appendix 9

Composition and Uses of Different Alloys

S. No.	Alloy	Composition	Uses
1.	Stainless steel	Fe = 73%, Cr = 18% Ni = 8% and cabon	For making cutlery, ornamental, pieces and automobile parts.
2.	Invar	Fe = 64%, Ni = 36%	For making measuring instruments and clock pendulums.
3.	Alinco	Fe = 63%, Ni = 20% Al = 12%, Co = 5%	For making permanent magnets.
4.	Tungsten steel	Fe = 83%, Tungsten (W) = 14% and carbon	For making cutting tools for high speed lathes.
5.	Manganese steel	Fe = 85%, Mn = 13% and carbon	For making rock drills, rail lines, burglar proof safes and crushing machinery
6.	Nickel steel	Ni = 4.2%	For making electromagnets and ocean cables.
7.	Permalloy	Fe = 21%, Ni = 78% and carbon	For making shafts and ocean cables.
8.	Silicon steel	Fe = 85%, Si = 15%	Pumps and pipes for carrying acids.
9.	Brass	Cu = 60 – 80% Zn = 40 – 20%	Utensils, condenser tubes and cartridges. Utensils, coins, statues.
10.	Bronze	Cu = 75 – 90% Sn = 25 – 10%	
11.	Monel metal	Cu = 30%, Ni = 67%, Fe + Mn = 3%	For acid containers, acid pumps etc.
12.	Bell metal	Cu = 80%, Sn = 20%	Bells, Gongs
13.	Gun metal	Cu = 87%, Sn = 10%, Zn = 3%	Guns, casting, gears.
14.	German silver	Cu = 50%, Zn = 25%, Ni = 25%	Utensils, ornaments.
15.	Constantan	Cu = 60%, Ni = 40%	For making resistance boxes, thermocouples.
16.	Phosphor bronze	Cu = 95%, Sn = 4.8% P = 0.2%	Springs electrical equipments.
17.	Aluminium bronze	Cu = 90%, Al = 10%	Coins, picture frames, cheap jewellery.
18.	Coinage silver	Ag = 90%, Cu = 10%	Silver coins.
19.	Dental alloy	Ag = 33%, Hg = 52%, Sn = 15%	For filling teeth cavities.
20.	Palladium silver	Ag = 40%, Pd = 60%	Potentiometer wires and winding of some special instruments.
21.	Silver solder	Ag = 63%, Cu = 30%, Zn = 7%	Soldering and for jointing metals.
22.	Sterling silver	Ag = 80%, Cu = 20%	A standard quality of silver used in jewellery.

Preparation of Common Laboratory Reagents

I. Concentrate Acids

S.No.	Name	Approximate concentration	Specific gravity	Percentage by weight
1.	Acetic acid (glacial)	17.6 M (17.6 N)	1.06	99.5%
2.	Conc. hydrochloric acid	11.7 M (11.7 N)	1.19	36.0%
3.	Conc. nitric acid	15.6 M (15.6 N)	1.42	69.5%
4.	Conc. sulphuric acid	18 M (36.0 N)	1.84	98.0%

II. Dilute Acids

S. No.	Name	Concentration	Method of preparation
1.	Dil. acetic acid	5 M (5 N)	Dilute 285 mL of glacial acetic acid with distilled water and make up the volume of 1 L.
2.	Dil. hydrochloric acid	5 M (5 N)	Add 430 mL of conc. HCl in the distilled water and make up the volume to 1 L.
3.	Dil. nitric acid	5 M (5 N)	Add 320 mL of conc. nitric acid to distilled water and make up the volume to 1 L.
4.	Dil. sulphuric acid	2.5 M (5 N)	Pour 140 mL of conc. sulphuric acid slowly and with constant stirring in 500 mL of distilled water. Cool and make up the volume to 1 L.

III. Bases

1.	Ammonia solution (Liquor ammonia)	15 M (15 N)	As supplied
2.	Dil. ammonia solution (Ammonium hydroxide)	2 M (2 N)	Pour 266.6 mL of the conc. ammonia solution in distilled water and make up the volume of 1 L.
3.	Sodium hydroxide	5 M (5 N)	Dissolve 200 g sodium hydroxide pellets in 1 L of distilled water.

IV. Other Important Reagents

S. No.	Name	Concentration	Molar mass	Method of preparation
1.	Ammonium acetate	2 M (2 N)	77	Dissolve 154 g of the salt in distilled water and dilute to 1 L.
2.	Ammonium chloride	5 M (5 N)	53.5	Dissolve 267.5 g of the salt in distilled water and dilute to 1 L.
3.	Ammonium carbonate	1.7 M (3.5 N)	96	Dissolve 160 g of ammonium carbonate in 140 mL liquor ammonia and make up the solution 1 L with distilled water.
4.	Ammonium molybdate			Dissolve 100 g of the salt in a mixture of 100 mL of liquor ammonia solution and add 250 g of ammonium nitrate and dilute it to 1L with distilled water.
5.	Ammonium oxalate	0.5 M (1 N)	142	Dissolve 71 g of the salt in distilled water and dilute to 1L.
6.	Ammonium sulphate	1 M (2 N)	132	Dissolve 132 g of the salt in distilled water and dilute to 1L.
7.	Barium chloride ($BaCl_2 \cdot 2H_2O$)	0.5 M (0.5 N)	244	Dissolve 61 g of the salt in distilled water and dillute to 1L.
8.	Bromine water	Approx. saturated	160	Add 2 mL of bromine in 100 mL of distilled water shake the mixture well. Keep it in a dark bottle.
9.	Calcium chloride	0.5 M (0.5 N)	219	Dissolve 55 g of the salt in distilled water and make up the volume to 1L.
10.	Chlorine water		71	Prepare chlorine by treating solid $KMnO_4$ with conc. HCl. Saturate 1 L of distilled water with chlorine gas and keep the solution in a dark coloured bottle.
11.	Copper sulphate	14%	249.5	Dissolve 14 g of the salt in distilled water and make up the volume to 100 mL.
12.	Cobalt nitrate	0.15 M (0.075 N)	291	Dissolve 43.65 g of the salt in distilled water and make up the volume to 1L.
13.	Dimethyl glyoxime	1%		Dissolve 1.0 g of the solid in 100 mL ethyl alcohol.
14.	Diphenylamine	0.5%		Dissolve 0.5 g of the solid in 85 mL of conc. sulphuric acid and dilute it with care with distilled water to 100 mL.
15.	Disodium hydrogen phosphate $Na_2HPO_4 \cdot 12H_2O$	0.3 M (N)	358	Dissolve 120.0 g of the salt in distilled water and make up the volume to 1L.

S. No.	Name	Concentration	Molar mass	Method of preparation
16.	Ferric chloride $FeCl_3 \cdot 6H_2O$	0.33 M (1 N)	270	Dissolve 90 g of the salt in distilled water containing 10 mL of conc. hydrochloric acid and make up the volume of 1 L.
17.	Iodine solution		254	Dissolve 1.0 g of iodine crystals in a solution of 2 g potassium iodide in minimum amount of water and dilute the solution to 100 mL.
18.	Lead acetate $(CH_3COO)_2Pb$	0.5 M (N)		Dissolve 200 g of solid salt in 500 mL of distilled water containing 15 mL acetic acid and make up the volume to 1 L with distilled water.
19.	Lime water $Ca(OH)_2$	0.02 M (0.04 N)	74	Shake 2–3 g of calcium hydroxide with 1 L distilled water, filter the solution after sometimes and keep it in a reagent bottle. Bottle should be securely stoppered in order to protect the reagent from CO_2 of atmosphere.
20.	Litmus solution (blue)			Dissolve 10 g of litmus in distilled water and make the volume to 1 L.
21.	Litmus solution (red)			To the blue litmus solution add about 10 drops of dilute hydrochloric acid.
22.	Methyl orange			Dissolve 1 g of the solid in 1L of distilled water.
23.	Mercuric chloride	0.25 M (0.5 N)	272	Dissolve 70 g of the salt in small amount of distilled water and make up the volume to 1 L with distilled water.
24.	Nessler's reagent $K_2[HgI_4]$			Dissolve 23 g of mercuric iodide and 16 g of potassium iodide in distilled water and make up the volume to 100 mL. Add 150 mL of 4 M NaOH solution. Allow it to stand for 24 h and decant the solution. Solution should be stored in a dark coloured bottle.
25.	Potassium chromate K_2CrO_4	0.25 M (0.5 N)	194	Dissolve 49 g of the salt in distilled water and make up the volume to 1L.
26.	Potassium dichromate $(K_2Cr_2O_7)$	0.15 M (1 N)	294	Dissolve 49.0 g of the salt in distilled water and make up the volume to 1L.
27.	Potassium ferrocyanide	0.15 M (0.5 N)	368	Dissolve 46.l0 g of the salt in distilled water and dilute to 1L.

S. No.	Name	Concentration	Molar mass	Method of preparation
28.	Potassium ferricyanide	0.2 M (0.5 N)	329	Dissolve 55.0 g of the salt in distilled water and dilute to 1L.
29.	Potassium iodide KI	0.5M (0.5 N)	166	Dissolve 83.0 g of the salt in distilled water and make up the volume to 1L.
30.	Potassium permanganate $KMnO_4$	0.06 M (0.3 N)	158	Dissolve 10.0 g of the salt in 1L distilled water. Heat the solution and filter it through glass wool.
31.	Potassium thiocyanate	0.5 M (0.5 N)	97	Dissolve 49.0 g of the salt in distilled water and make up the volume to 1L.
32.	Phenolphthalein	1%		Dissolve 1.0 g of the solid in 100 mL of ethyl alcohol.
33.	Silver nitrate $AgNO_3$	0.1 M	170	Dissolve 17 g of the salt in 250 mL of distilled water and store it in a brown coloured bottle.
34.	Sodium acetate	5 M (5 N)	82	Dissolve 410 g of salt in distilled water and dilute to 1L.
35.	Sodium nitroprusside			Dissolve 4 g of the solid in 100 mL of distilled water.
36.	Starch			Prepare a paste of about 1.0 g of soluble starch in cold water and pour it gradually in 100 mL of boiling water with constant stirring. Boil it for 10 min and cool.
37.	Yellow ammonium sulphide $(NH_4)_2 S_x$	6 N		Take about 200 mL of conc. ammonia solution in a bottle and saturate it with H_2S gas. Add 10 g of flower of sulphur and 200 mL of conc. NH_4OH. Warm gently and shake well until sulphur is completely dissolved. Dilute the solution to 1L with distilled water.

Appendix 11

Important Name Reactions

1. Aldol condensation

$$2CH_3-CHO \underset{}{\overset{\text{Dil. NaOH}}{\rightleftharpoons}} CH_3-\underset{\underset{OH}{|}}{CH}-CH_2-CHO \xrightarrow[-H_2O]{\Delta}$$

3-hydroxy butanal

(Aldol)

$$CH_3-CH=CHCHO$$
But$-2-$enal

2. Cannizzaro reaction

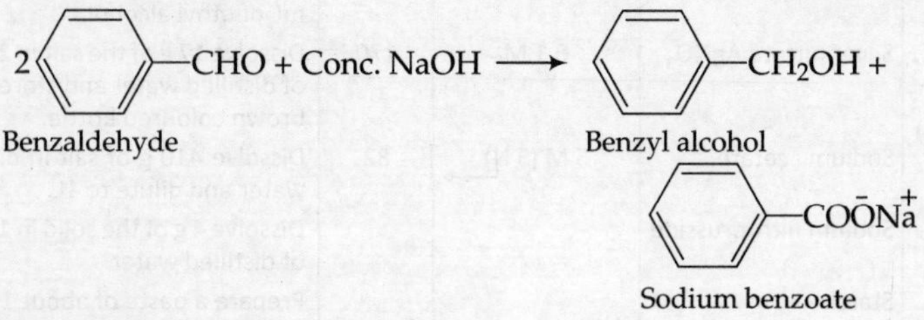

Benzaldehyde

Benzyl alcohol

Sodium benzoate

3. Carbylamine reaction

$$R-NH_2 + CHCl_3 + 3KOH \xrightarrow{\Delta} RNC + 3KCl + 3H_2O$$

4. Clemmensen reduction

$$\underset{}{>}C=O \xrightarrow[HCl]{Zn-Hg} >CH_2 + H_2O$$

5. Coupling reaction

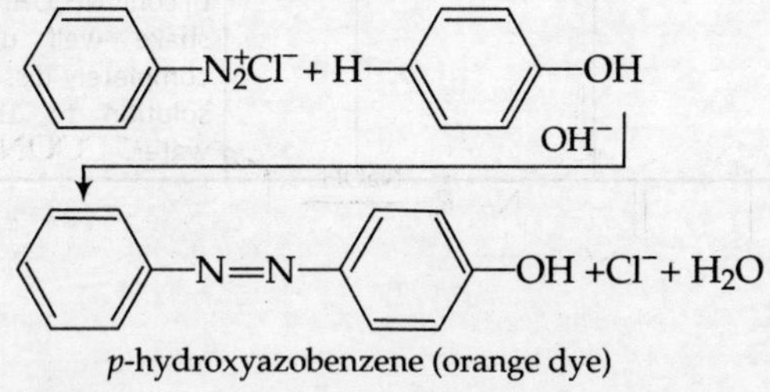

p-hydroxyazobenzene (orange dye)

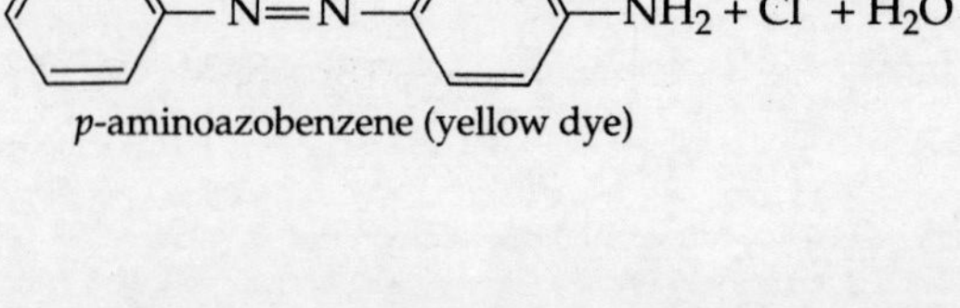

p-aminoazobenzene (yellow dye)

6. Etard reaction

7. Friedel Crafts acylation reaction

8. Gabriel phthalimide synthesis

9. Gattermann's reaction

10. Gattermann's-Koch reaction

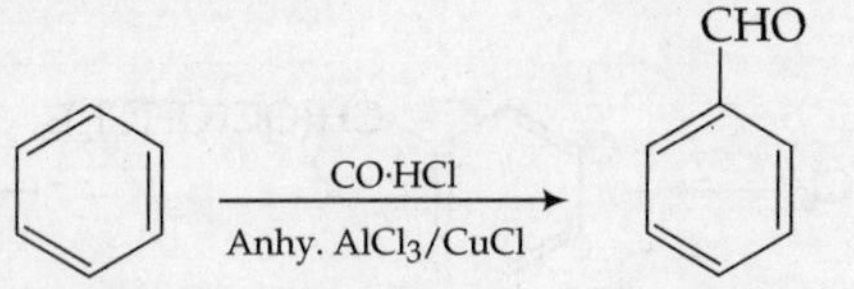

Benzene — Benzaldehyde

11. Haloform reaction

$$R-\overset{\overset{\displaystyle O}{\|}}{C}-CH_3 \xrightarrow{NaOX} R-\overset{\overset{\displaystyle O}{\|}}{C}-ONa + CHX_3$$

[X = Cl, Br, I]

12. Hell-Volhard-Zelinsky reaction

$$CH_2COOH \xrightarrow[\text{(ii) } H_2O]{\text{(i) } X_2 / \text{Red phosphorus}} R-\underset{\alpha}{\overset{\overset{\displaystyle X}{|}}{C}H}-COOH$$

(X = Cl, Br)
[α-halocarboxylic acid]

13. Hofmann bromamide degradation reaction

$$R-\overset{\overset{\displaystyle O}{\|}}{C}-NH_2 + Br_2 + 4NaOH \longrightarrow R-NH_2 + Na_2CO_3 + 2NaBr + 2H_2O$$

14. Kolbe reaction

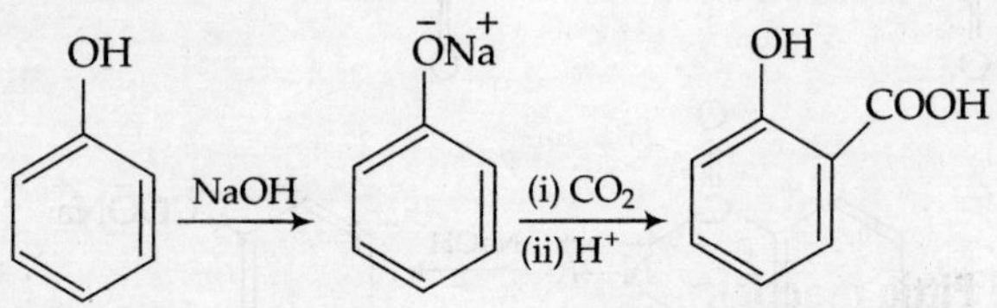

2-hydroxybenzene

15. Reimer-Tiemann reaction

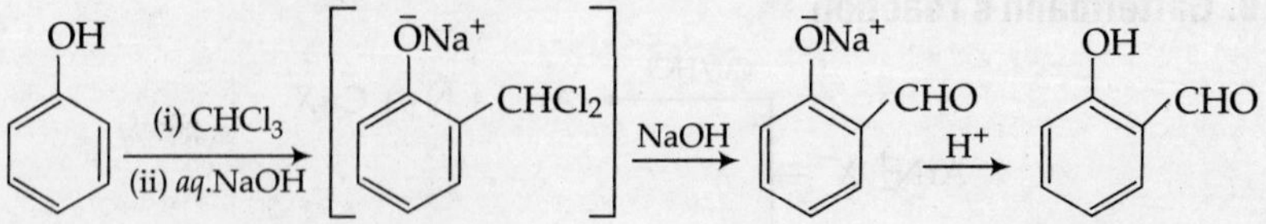

Salicyladehyde

16. Rosenmund reduction

Benzoyl chloride $\xrightarrow[\text{H}_2]{\text{Pd-H}_2\text{SO}_4}$ Benzaldehyde

17. Stephen reaction

$$RCN + SnCl_2 + HCl \longrightarrow RCH = NH \xrightarrow{H_3O^+} RCHO$$

18. Swarts reaction

$$H_3C-Br + AgF \longrightarrow H_3C-F + AgBr$$

19. Williamson synthesis

$$RX + RONa \longrightarrow R-O-R + NaX$$

20. Wolff-Kishner reduction

$$\text{\Large$>$}C=O \xrightarrow[-H_2O]{H_2N-NH_2} \text{\Large$>$}C=NNH_2 \xrightarrow[\Delta]{KOH / \text{ethylene glycol}} \text{\Large$>$}CH_2 + N_2$$

21. Wurtz reaction

$$CH_3Br + 2Na + BrCH_3 \xrightarrow[\text{ethane}]{\text{Dry ether}} CH_3-CH_3 + 2NaBr$$

22. Wurtz Fittig reaction

Appendix 12

Nobel Laureates in Chemistry

Year	Laureate	Country	Rationale
2018	George Smith	United states	"For the phagedisplay of peptides and antibodies"
	Gregory Winter	United Kingdom	
2017	Jacques Dubochet	Switzland	"For developing cryo-electron microscopy for the high resolution structure determination of bimolecules in solution"
	Joachim Frank	United states	
	Richard Henderson	United Kingdom	
2016	Fraser stoddart	United states	"For the design and synthesis of molecular machines"
	Ben Feringa	Netherlands	
	Jean pierre Sauvage	France	
2015	Thomas Lindahl	Sweden	"For mechanistic studies of DNA repair"
	Paul L. Modrich	United states	
	Aziz Sancar	United state	
2014	Eric Betzig	United State	"for the development of super-resolved fluorescence microscopy"
	Stefan W. Hell	Germany	
	William E. Moerner	United State	
2013	Martin Karplus	United State, Austria	"for the development of multiscale models"
	Michael Levitt	United State/ Bretain	"for complex chemical systems"
	Arich Warshel	United State/Israeli	
2012	Brian Kobilka	United States	"for studies of G-protein-coupled receptors"
	Robert	United states	
2011	Dan Shechtman	Israel	"for the discovery of quasicrystals"
	Robert Lefkowitz	United States	
2010	Ei-ichi Negishi	United States	"for palladium-catalyzed cross couplings in organic synthesis"
	Akira Suzuki	Japan	
	Richard F. Heck	United States	
2009	Thomas A. Steitz	United States	"for studies of the structure and function of the ribosome"
	Ada E. Yonath	Israel	
	Venkatraman Ramakrishnan	India	
2008	Martin Chalfie	United States	"for the discovery and development of the green fluorescent protein, GFP"
	Roger Y. Tsien	United States	
	Osamu Shimomura	Japan[108]	

Year	Laureate	Country	Rationale
2007	Gerhard Ertl	Germany	"for his studies of chemical processes on solid surfaces"
2006	Roger D. Kornberg	United States	"for his studies of the molecular basis of eukaryotic transcription"
2005	Robert H. Grubbs	United States	"for the development of the metathesis method in organic synthesis"
	Richard R. Schrock	United States	
	Yves Chauvin	France	
2004	Avram Hershko	Israel	"for the discovery of ubiquitin-mediated protein degradation"
	Irwin Rose	United States	
	Aaron Ciechanover	Israel	
2003	Roderick MacKinnon	United States	"for discoveries concerning channels in cell membranes [...] for structural and mechanistic studies of ion channels"
	Peter Agre	United States	
2002	John B. Fenn	United States	"for the development of methods for identification and structure analyses of biological macromolecules [...] for their development of soft desorption"
	Koichi Tanaka	Japan	"for then development of soft desorption ionisation methods for mass spectrometric analyses of biological macromolecules"
	Kurt Wüthrich	Switzerland	"for the development of methods for identification and structure analyses of biological macromolecules [...] for his development of nuclear magnetic resonance spectroscopy for determining the three dimensional structure of biological macromolecules in solution"
			"for discoveries concerning channels in cell membranes [...] for the discovery of water channels"
2001	Ryoji Noyori	Japan	"for their work on chirally catalysed hydrogenation reactions"
	K. Barry Sharpless	United States	"for his work on chirally catalysed oxidation reactions"
	William S. Knowles	United States	
2000	Alan J. Heeger	United States	
	Alan G. MacDiarmid	United States	"for their discovery and development of conductive polymers"
		New Zealand	
	Hideki Shirakawa	Japan	
1999	Ahmed Zewail	Egypt	"for his studies of the transition states of chemical reactions using femtosecond spectroscopy"
		United States	
1998	Walter Kohn	United States	"for his development of the density-functional theory"
	John A. Pople	United Kingdom	"for his development of computational methods in quantum chemistry"

Year	Laureate	Country	Rationale
1997	Paul D. Boyer	United States	"for their elucidation of the enzymatic mechanism underlying the synthesis of adenosine triphosphate (ATP)"
	John E. Walker	United Kingdom	
	Jens C. Skou	Denmark	"for the first discovery of an ion-transporting enzyme, Na^+, K^+-ATPase"
	Robert F. Curl Jr	Unitedx States	
1996	Sir Harold W. Kroto	United Kingdom	"for their discovery of fullerenes"
	Richard E. Smalley	United States	
1995	Mario J. Molina	United States	"for their work in atmospheric chemistry, particularly concerning the formation and decomposition of ozone"
	F. Sherwood Rowland	United States	
	Paul J. Crutzen	Netherlands	
1994	George A. Olah	United States / Hungary	"for his contribution to carbocation chemistry"
1993	Kary B. Mullis	United States	"for contributions to the developments of methods within DNA-based chemistry [...] for his invention of the polymerase chain reaction (PCR) method"
	Michael Smith	Canada	"for contributions to the developments of methods within DNA-based chemistry [...] for his fundamental contributions to the establishment of oligonucleotide-based, site-directed mutagenesis and its development for protein studies"
1992	Rudolph A. Marcus	United States	"for his contributions to the theory of electron transfer reactions in chemical systems"
1991	Richard R. Ernst	Switzerland	"for his contributions to the development of the methodology of high resolution nuclear magnetic resonance (NMR) spectroscopy"
1990	Elias James Corey	United States	"for his development of the theory and methodology of organic synthesis"
1989	Sidney Altman	Canada United States	"for their discovery of catalytic properties of RNA"
	Thomas Cech	United States	
1988	Johann Deisenhofer	Federal Republic of Germany	"for their determination of the three-dimensional structure of a photosynthetic reaction centre"
	Robert Huber	Federal Republic of Germany	
	Hartmut Michel	Federal Republic of Germany	
1987	Jean-Marie Lehn	France	"for their development and use of molecules with structure-specific interactions of high selectivity"
	Donald J. Gram	United States	
	Charles J. Pedersen	United States	